STATISTICAL METHODS FOR ENGINEERS AND SCIENTISTS

A SERIES OF PROGRAMMES ON MATHEMATICS
FOR
SCIENTISTS AND TECHNOLOGISTS

CONSULTANT EDITOR:

A.C. BAJPAI

PROFESSOR OF MATHEMATICAL EDUCATION AND DIRECTOR OF CAMET

Titles available in this series:

FORTRAN AND ALGOL	A.C. Bajpai, H.W. Pakes, R.J. Clarke, J.M. Doubleday and T.J. Stevens
MATHEMATICS FOR ENGINEERS AND SCIENTISTS - *Volume 1*	A.C. Bajpai, I.M. Calus, J.A. Fairley
MATHEMATICS FOR ENGINEERS AND SCIENTISTS - *Volume 2*	A.C. Bajpai, I.M. Calus, J.A. Fairley, D. Walker
NUMERICAL METHODS FOR ENGINEERS AND SCIENTISTS	A.C. Bajpai, I.M. Calus, J.A. Fairley
STATISTICAL METHODS FOR ENGINEERS AND SCIENTISTS	A.C. Bajpai, I.M. Calus, J.A. Fairley

CAMET

(CENTRE FOR ADVANCEMENT OF MATHEMATICAL EDUCATION IN TECHNOLOGY)

LOUGHBOROUGH UNIVERSITY OF TECHNOLOGY

STATISTICAL METHODS FOR ENGINEERS AND SCIENTISTS

A STUDENTS' COURSE BOOK

A.C. BAJPAI

I.M. CALUS

J.A. FAIRLEY

LOUGHBOROUGH UNIVERSITY OF TECHNOLOGY

JOHN WILEY & SONS

CHICHESTER · NEW YORK · BRISBANE · TORONTO

Library of Congress Cataloging in Publication Data:

Bajpai, Avi C.
　　Statistical methods for engineers and scientists.

　　(A Series of programmes on mathematics for scientists
and technologists)
　　Bibliography: p.
　　Includes index.
　　1. Mathematical statistics—Programmed instructions.
2. Engineering—Statistical methods—Programmed
instructions. 3. Science—Statistical methods—Programmed
instruction. I. Calus, Irene M., joint author. II. Fairley, J.
Alex, joint author. III. Title. IV. Series.
QA276.B245　　　　　519.5'07'7　　　　78-2481

ISBN 0 471 99644 0

Printed in Great Britain

PREFACE

This is a volume of programmes on statistical methods which is part of a course
written for undergraduate science and engineering students in universities,
polytechnics and other colleges in all parts of the world.   Statistical methods
are now included in the syllabuses for all such students and this book covers
most of the work that these students are likely to require.   The emphasis is on
the practical side of the subject, but this is not to say that this is a manual
of instructions to be carried out without any understanding of the why or
wherefore.   The aim is to convey sufficient information about the basis of the
various statistical methods to enable the student to use them sensibly and
appropriately.

In preparing examples for illustration and practice, much time and effort has
been expended in seeking out, by personal contact and by searches of technical
literature, the uses to which statistical techniques are actually being put by
today's engineers and scientists.   In this way it is hoped to remedy the
undergraduate's lack of experience of situations demanding a statistical
approach.   Sometimes, in the interests of realism, the original data is quoted,
but usually some adaptation has been made to keep the numbers simple.   When
learning the subject there is nothing, in general, to be gained by a lot of
complicated arithmetic and it can be very off-putting.   Of course, the student
is made aware of the availability of computers for dealing with larger scale
calculations but doing relatively simple examples manually does help to give,
at the learning stage, a better understanding of the principles and methods that
are being studied.   A pocket calculator (there is no need for a very elaborate
model) will speed calculations and relieve any tedium.

The volume comprises three Units in which are grouped programmes on allied
topics.   For the student who is going to follow the course in its entirety, it
is best to work through the programmes in the order in which they appear.   To
meet individual requirements, programmes, or parts of programmes, may be omitted.
Sometimes suggestions are made about this at the appropriate place or it may be
done under the guidance of the student's tutor.   The guiding rule is that,
before reading a programme, the student should be familiar with the items listed
under the heading of Prerequisites at the beginning of each Unit.

The programmed method of presentation has been used throughout and has many
advantages.   The development of the subject proceeds in carefully sequenced
steps, the student working through these at his own pace.   The active
participation of the student is required in many places where he or she is asked
to answer a question or to solve, either partially or completely, a problem.
The answers to these are always given so that the student can check his attempt
and thus obtain a continuous assessment of his understanding of the subject.
Explanation of the material covered is given in greater detail than is often to
be found in conventional style textbooks, especially at those points where
difficulties are most likely to occur.

In places where units are involved, the S.I. system has been used.   The
standard practice of using italic letters for quantities, e.g., C for
capacitance, has not, however, been followed as italic lettering is used for the
answer frames.   Where natural logarithms occur, the notation ln is used.

Where references are made to frames in the same programme, only the frame
numbers are given.   Where page numbers are quoted as well, this indicates that
references are to frames in another programme.

Several references are made to the companion volumes in this series.   The
details of these books are:

Mathematics for Engineers and Scientists, Volume 1
A.C. Bajpai, I.M. Calus, J.A. Fairley   Wiley, 1973

Mathematics for Engineers and Scientists, Volume 2
A.C. Bajpai, I.M. Calus, J.A. Fairley, D. Walker   Wiley, 1973

Numerical Methods for Engineers and Scientists
A.C. Bajpai, I.M. Calus, J.A. Fairley   Wiley, 1977

Fortran and Algol
A.C. Bajpai, H.W. Pakes, R.J. Clarke,
J.M. Doubleday, T.J. Stevens   Wiley, 1972

In making these references we seek to knit together the various mathematical
topics in a student's course.

In spite of careful checking by the authors, it is possible that the
occasional error has crept through.   They would appreciate receiving
information about any such mistakes which might be discovered.

A debt of gratitude to the following is acknowledged with pleasure:

Loughborough University of Technology for supporting this venture.

Staff and students of the university and other institutions who have
participated in the testing of programmes or given advice on applications in
their specialist fields.

Our colleague, Dr. P.E. Lewis of the Department of Engineering Mathematics,
and *Mr. C. Scott of Swinburne College of Technology, Melbourne, Australia*
for their helpful comments.

Mr. J.J. Leeming, and the publishers *Blackie and Son Ltd.,* for permission to
make use of a road traffic problem described in "Statistical Methods for
Engineers".

Dr. G.W. Hoffler, of NASA Johnson Space Flight Center, for permission to make
use of biomedical data recorded on Apollo space flightcrews.

Aberdeen Grammar School and *Wychwood School, Oxford* for so generously lending
copies of the project reports which led their teams into the finals of the
BBC TV Young Scientists of the Year contest in 1975 and 1976 respectively.

Mrs. Barbara Bell and *Mrs. G. Anthony* for their work in the preparation of the
final manuscript.

John Wiley & Sons Ltd for their help and cooperation.

The *University of London* and the *Council of Engineering Institutions* for
permission to use questions from their past examination papers.   These are
denoted by L.U. and C.E.I. respectively.

INSTRUCTIONS

Each programme is divided up into a number of FRAMES
which are to be worked *in the order given*.   You will
be required to participate in many of these frames and
in such cases the answers are provided in ANSWER
FRAMES, designated by the letter A following the
frame number.   Steps in the working are given where
this is considered helpful.   The answer frame is
separated from the main frame by a line of asterisks:
********.   Keep the answers covered until you have
written your own response.   If your answer is wrong,
go back and try to see why.   Do not proceed to the
next frame until you have corrected any mistakes in
your attempt and are satisfied that you understand
the contents up to this point.

You will find it useful to make a summary of the main
results and formulae as you go along.   This could be
done at the end of each programme, after you have
finished the miscellaneous examples.   By that time
you should be able to pinpoint the salient features of
the material that has been presented to you.   The
summary will then be handy for future reference.

As far as possible, examples have been structured to
avoid complicated arithmetic, but obviously a pocket
calculator (there is no need for a very elaborate
model) will speed calculations and relieve any tedium.

CONTENTS

UNIT 1 - Probability Distributions -
Elementary Ideas and Standard Models

UNIT 3 - Variance Analysis, Correlation and Regression

ANALYSIS OF VARIANCE

CORRELATION

REGRESSION

UNIT 1
PROBABILITY DISTRIBUTIONS—
Elementary Ideas and Standard Models

This Unit comprises five programmes:

(a) Descriptive Methods

(b) Probability

(c) Probability Distributions for Discrete Variates (1)

(d) Probability Distributions for Discrete Variates (2)

(e) Probability Distributions for Continuous Variates

Before reading these programmes, it is necessary that you are familiar with the following

Prerequisites

For (a): The Σ notation for sums.

For (b): No special requirements.

For (c): The contents of the previous programmes.
          The binomial series.

For (d): The contents of the previous programmes.
          The exponential function.

For (e): The contents of the previous programmes.
          Simple integration, including integration by parts.

Note: These are the prerequisites if the Unit is to be followed in its entirety
       but a variety of options are open for an abbreviated course of study.
       Some are indicated at the time – e.g. the evaluation of some integrals in
       (e) is shown as optional, thus dispensing with the need to know about
       integration by parts. Also an instruction for skipping FRAMES 15-21 on
       the exponential distribution is given in (e). If this is done, and
       FRAMES 46-47 also omitted, the contents of (d) would no longer be a
       prerequisite for (e). Other possibilities for adapting the course to
       individual needs exist and are best done with advice from a tutor.

Descriptive Methods

Variates - Discrete and Continuous

Some examples are given below of situations which would give rise to numerical data affected by chance variation.   In such variation, which statisticians call RANDOM VARIATION, no pattern or regularity is shown by the sequence of values taken by the variable.   The variation may be due, wholly or in part, to errors of measurement or it may simply be inherent in the nature of the variable under consideration.

   (i)   When a die is thrown, the result, given by the number of dots on the face which falls uppermost, will be 1, 2, 3, 4, 5 or 6.   No errors of measurement are involved in this case, just the combination of many factors which vary from throw to throw, producing differing results.

  (ii)   When estimating the strength of a radioactive source the number of disintegrations in, say, one-minute intervals might be counted.   Errors could arise from the malfunctioning of the counting equipment but even if it is functioning perfectly there will still be variation between counts recorded during successive intervals because of the way in which radioactive decay occurs.

 (iii)   When electric light bulbs which have been made to the same specification are subjected to life-tests, there may be some error in measuring the length of life but it will be negligible compared with the variation in durability from one bulb to another.

  (iv)   Titration is a technique used by analytical chemists.   When a chemist titrates 5 ml of 0·1M HCl (a certain strength of hydrochloric acid) with a solution of NaOH (sodium hydroxide, an alkali) he is finding experimentally what volume of the alkali is required to neutralise the given volume of acid.   From this he can calculate the strength of the NaOH solution.   If you are not familiar with the technique, this is what happens:

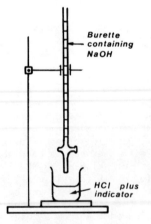

Burette
containing
NaOH

HCl plus
indicator

5 ml of the HCl is measured* out into a beaker. Some of the NaOH is placed in a burette and a reading taken* of the level of liquid in the tube.   The tap is opened and NaOH allowed to flow into the beaker until it is observed* that neutralisation has taken place (this is shown by an "indicator", such as methyl red which is red in an acid solution and yellow in an alkaline one).   The tap is then closed and a second reading of the level of NaOH in the burette is taken*.

Now at each stage, at the point marked *, an error can creep in, so that the value of the required volume of NaOH, obtained by subtracting the two readings, will be subject to error and repeat titrations may yield different answers.

In each of the situations just described you will see that there is a degree of
uncertainty in the result and in each you have an example of a RANDOM VARIABLE,
also termed a VARIATE.   In (i) the variate is the number of dots on the
uppermost face of the die, in (ii) it is the number of disintegrations in a
one-minute interval, in (iii) it is the length of life of a light bulb and in
(iv) it is the volume of NaOH.

A closer look at these examples will reveal that variates are of two kinds.   In
(i) and (ii) the value taken by the variate on a particular occasion is obtained
by counting and is therefore essentially an integer.   When a die is thrown the
result may be 2 or 3, but never $2\frac{1}{2}$ or 2·7.   A variate like this, which can
only take particular values and not intermediate ones, is said to be DISCRETE.

On the other hand, where measuring is involved, as with lengths, areas, volumes,
times, weights etc., the variate is regarded as being CONTINUOUS.   In both (iii)
and (iv) you have an example of a continuous variate.   When you look at this
kind of data you might get the impression that you are dealing with a discrete
variate.   For instance, if you glance forward to FRAME 7 you will see that in
the set of data given there the lengths of life of the lamps take only integer
values.   However, that is only because they were recorded to the nearest hour,
e.g. as 1356 or 1357, but that is not saying that a life of between 1356 and
1357 hours cannot exist.   The lamp can burn out at any point on the time scale
including times between 1356 hours and 1357 hours.

Statistical methods are needed if one is to arrive at the best interpretation of
numerical data which has been affected by chance variation.   In this programme
we shall be looking at ways of presenting and summarising quantitative data of
either kind, discrete or continuous, so as to bring out the salient points.

The Use of Computers

As you might expect, the treatment of quantitative data can involve large-scale
manipulations and calculations.   This would be the case when there is a huge
mass of data or in multivariate analysis, where it is not just one variate that
is being investigated but the relationship between two or more (e.g. in a
chemical manufacturing process these could be the % impurity in the product, the
feedrate and the inlet temperature).   In such situations the electronic digital
computer has given a boost to the use of statistical methods.   In research,
however, the number of experimental results obtained is often severely restricted
(by available time, labour, equipment etc.) so there is then only a small amount
of data to be processed and a pocket calculator can give the answer more quickly
than a less accessible computer.

In this text we shall give some indications of where a computer can be used to
advantage, but computer programs will not in general be given because of the
variety of languages in existence.   Instead just one will be shown, for readers
who have not seen a computer program before, and flow diagrams will serve to
demonstrate the approach to use when programming for a computer.   The next frame
explains briefly what flow diagrams are, for those of you who haven't met them
before or need your memories refreshing.

Flow Diagrams

A FLOW DIAGRAM (or FLOW CHART) shows diagrammatically the sequence of steps to be

carried out in the solution of a problem.   The different steps are represented
by "blocks" which are joined by lines, with arrows to indicate the direction of
"flow" of the sequence.   Different block shapes are used for different types of
step, but there is no universally accepted convention about which shape should
correspond to which type of step.   We shall follow the convention laid down in
"Fortran and Algol" where a fuller description of flow diagrams may be found.

The following flow diagram is for finding the magnitude x (i.e. absolute value)
of a real number A.   It is not the only way in which this simple problem can be
flowcharted, but it does illustrate all the shapes of block, and other features,
that will be standard in this text.

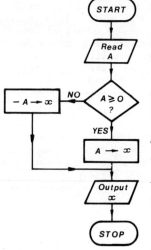

Obviously the value of A must be known before its
magnitude can be found.

This is a decision-making step, giving rise in this case
to a two-way branch.   If A = 0 were to be considered
separately, there would be a three-way branch.

This means the value of the LHS (in this case A) is
assigned to the variable named x.

Whichever path was taken, the number stored in the
computer as "x" is now the answer required.

Tabular Representation of Data

Viewers of the annual Miss World contest are dazzled by the figures that they see
before them.   So, also, will you find yourself dazzled when looking at figures
of another kind - a mass of numerical data such as that shown below:

As a preliminary to a full-scale traffic survey, it was necessary to have some
information about the number of occupants of cars entering a certain town on
Saturday afternoons, and an occupancy count was made on each of 40 cars.   The
results were:

1	3	2	2	3	1	1	2	2	1
1	4	3	1	3	2	3	2	2	2
1	2	5	1	3	1	2	1	3	1
4	1	1	3	4	2	2	1	1	4

Is the variate here discrete or continuous?

****

5A

Discrete

A simpler picture of the occupancy of the cars is obtained if the data is given
in the form of a table, showing the number of cars with 1 occupant, the number
with 2 occupants, and so on.   To tabulate the data in this way, you will
probably find it easiest to work your way systematically through the 40 counts
assigning each to the appropriate category using a tally mark as shown and
working with blocks of five to facilitate the final totalling.   In fact, the
observer might well record this particular data in this way in the first place.

Number of occupants		Number of cars
1	++++ ++++ ++++	15
2	++++ ++++ | |	12
3	++++ | | |	8
4	| | | |	4
5	|	1
		——
		40

This is a simple example of a FREQUENCY TABLE.   The variate (which will
henceforth be denoted by x) is, in this case, "number of occupants".   The
number of cars with x occupants shows the FREQUENCY with which that value of x
occurred.   We shall use f for frequency.   Sometimes, it may be more helpful
if the frequencies are shown as a proportion of the total, i.e. if the RELATIVE
FREQUENCY is shown.   For 1 occupant this would be 15/40 or 0·375, for 2
occupants 12/40 or 0·3 and so on.   For x occupants the relative frequency is
obviously f/N, where N is the total number of observations.

What is the sum of the relative frequencies in (i) this table, (ii) any
frequency table?

                 ****

(i) 1   (ii) 1

___

As a second example, we shall now consider the formation of a frequency table
for the results of life-testing 80 tungsten filament electric lamps.   The life
of each lamp is given in hours, to the nearest hour:

854	1284	1001	911	1168	963	1279	1494	798	1599
1357	1090	1082	1494	1684	1281	590	960	1310	1571
1355	1502	1251	1666	778	1200	849	1454	919	1484
1550	628	1325	1073	1273	1710	1734	1928	1416	1465
1608	1367	1152	1393	1339	1026	1299	1242	1508	705
1199	1155	822	1448	1623	1084	1220	1650	1091	210
1058	1930	1365	1291	683	1399	1198	518	1199	2074
811	1137	1185	892	937	945	1215	905	1810	1265

Is the length of life of a lamp a continuous or a discrete variate?

                 ****

*Continuous.   As was mentioned in an earlier frame, you might get the impression,
from looking at the data, that we are dealing with a discrete variate but that
is only how it appears and it is a case of appearances being deceptive.   A lamp*

could burn out at any instant in time, so its life is measured along a continuous scale.

FRAME 8

Obviously, to obtain a frequency table of a reasonable size, it will be necessary to condense the results by grouping values together.   The choice of grouping is a matter of striking a balance between too small a number of groups, with consequent loss of useful information, and too many groups, with consequent retention of irrelevant detail.   As a first step towards making this choice, you must see what range of values of the variate has to be covered.   Look at the lamp data and find the smallest value recorded and the largest.

$$**$$

8A

The smallest value recorded was 210 and the largest 2074.

FRAME 9

Suppose values from 201 up to and including 400 formed the first group, then values from 401 up to and including 600 the next group, and so on, continuing with groups of the same width.   How many groups will be required to cover all the values in this set of data?

$$**$$

9A

10

FRAME 10

This size of frequency table would meet our requirements.   The grouping having been decided on, the 80 values can now be classified by working systematically through them and allocating each one to the appropriate category, using tally marks as previously described.   Thus, starting at the top left-hand corner with 854, this would be allocated to the group 801-1000, then 1357 to the group 1201-1400, and so on.   It would be a useful exercise for you to continue with this procedure and obtain the frequency table.   Then state the relative frequency of lamps with recorded lives in the 1201-1400 group.

$$**$$

10A

Life (hours)		Number of lamps
201- 400	|	1
401- 600	||	2
601- 800	++++	5
801-1000	++++ ++++ ||	12
1001-1200	++++ ++++ ++++ ||	17
1201-1400	++++ ++++ ++++ ++++	20
1401-1600	++++ ++++ ||	12
1601-1800	++++ ||	7
1801-2000	|||	3
2001-2200	|	$\frac{1}{80}$

Check that this total does equal the number of observations.

<u>10A</u>   (continued)

For group 1201-1400, relative frequency = 20/80 = 0·25.

<u>FRAME 11</u>

You will notice that, with the groups for this table defined in the way shown, there is always a gap between the right-hand end point of one group and the left-hand end point of the next one (i.e. between 400 and 401, 600 and 601 etc.).   This may appear to contradict our previous decision that we were dealing with a continuous variate.   However, when you remember that a life recorded as 400 hours would in reality have been between 399·5 and 400·5 hours and similarly 401 covers true values between 400·5 and 401·5, you will see that this contradiction is more apparent than real.   Thus the true end points of the groups are as now shown, with continuous coverage along the time scale.

End points given as values as measured	End points given as true values
201-400	200·5-400·5
401-600	400·5-600·5
601-800	600·5-800·5
⋮	⋮

You will therefore see that the real boundaries of the groups are at 200·5, 400·5, 600·5 etc.   What difficulty would have arisen in forming the frequency table from the data if boundaries had been chosen at 200, 400, 600 etc., i.e. if the groups had been defined as 200-400, 400-600, 600-800, ... ?

$$***$$

<u>11A</u>

The question would arise: To which group should values like 200, 400, 600 etc. be allocated?   This can be resolved by allocating a frequency of ½ to each of the groups for which the value is a boundary, but it is better to avoid the problem by choosing groups whose actual end points are not values which can occur in the data.

<u>FRAME 12</u>

You were given the task of classifying the lamp data because you would then gain experience at first hand of what is involved in the construction of a frequency table, but if you were asked to do many more exercises of this kind you would, no doubt, find them boring and repetitive.   It is to just such boring and repetitive jobs that the computer is suited, though it should be remembered that the data will still have to be punched on to cards or paper tape or typed in at a terminal.

When programming this problem there is more than one approach that can be adopted. The one shown here considers each group as being numbered - 1st group, 2nd group and so on - and a formula is used to find the number of the group to which each value belongs.   The flow diagram overleaf and accompanying explanatory notes describe the method in more detail.   The corresponding program was written in 1900 FORTRAN and run on Loughborough University's ICL 1904S computer.   The print-out (see page 9) shows both the program (which is just a list of instructions) and the resulting frequency table when applied to the lamp data.

Notice that the group mid-points are stated instead of the group boundaries, a practice sometimes adopted in frequency tables.   You should have no difficulty in seeing that the group whose boundaries are 200·5 and 400·5 has its mid-point at 300·5, the next group has its mid-point at 500·5 and so on.

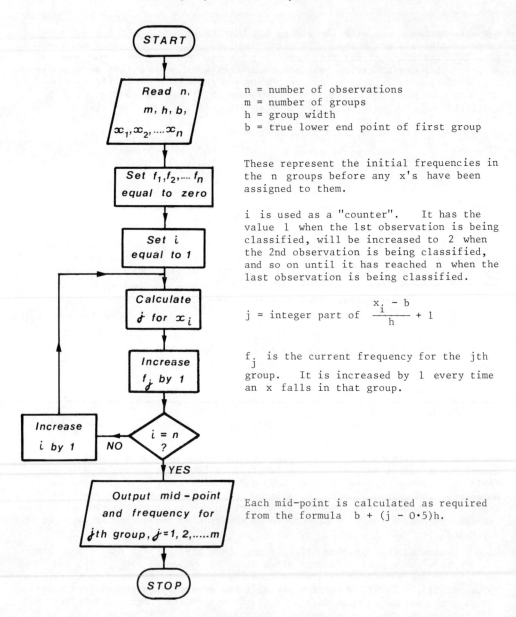

n = number of observations
m = number of groups
h = group width
b = true lower end point of first group

These represent the initial frequencies in the n groups before any x's have been assigned to them.

i is used as a "counter". It has the value 1 when the 1st observation is being classified, will be increased to 2 when the 2nd observation is being classified, and so on until it has reached n when the last observation is being classified.

$$j = \text{integer part of } \frac{x_i - b}{h} + 1$$

f_j is the current frequency for the jth group. It is increased by 1 every time an x falls in that group.

Each mid-point is calculated as required from the formula $b + (j - 0·5)h$.

To test your understanding of the flow diagram, answer the following:

For the lamp data, what values would you use for n, m, h, b? If x_1 is taken as 854 and x_2 as 1357, what will be the two corresponding values of j?

FRAME 12   (continued)

LOUGHBOROUGH UNIVERSITY COMPUTER CENTRE GEORG. 2L MK3J STREAM Q RUN ON 15/11/76

JOB IMCFRE,AM,IMC2084
CARDLIST
HPFORTRAN
****
 80 10 200. 200.5
   854.   1284.   1001.   911.   1168,   9&3.   1279.   1494.   798.   1599.
  1357.   1090.   1082.   1494.   1084,   1251.   590.   960.   1310.   1571.
  1355.   1502.   1251.   1666.   778,   1200.   849.   1454.   919.   1484.
  1550.   628.   1325.   1073.   16/3,   1710.   1734.   1928.   1416.   1465.
  1608.   1367.   1152.   1393.   1359,   1026.   1299.   1242.   1508.   705.
  1199.   1155.   822.   1448.   1623,   1084.   1220.   1650.   1091.   210.
  1058.   1930.   1365.   1291.   685,   1309.   1198.   518.   1199.   2074.
   811.   1137.   1185.   892.   937,   945.   1215.   905.   1810.   1265.

       SOFOR COMPILATION SYSTEM MARK 54A

       MASTER FREQUENCY
C THIS PROGRAM CLASSIFIES DATA INTO A FREQUENCY TABLE
       DIMENSION X(100),NF(15)
       READ(1,1)N,M,H,B
     1 FORMAT(I4,I3,F5.0,F7.1)
C THE VALUES OF N,M,H,B HAVE NOW BEEN READ
       READ(1,2)(X(I),I=1,N)
     2 FORMAT(10F8.0)
C THE VALUES OF X HAVE NOW BEEN READ
       DO 3 J=1,M
     3 NF(J)=0
C NF(J) IS THE FREQUENCY IN THE JTH GROUP. EVERY NF(J) HAS NOW BEEN SET TO ZERO
       DO 4 I=1,N
       J=(X(I)-B)/H+1
     4 NF(J)=NF(J)+1
C THE FREQUENCIES HAVE NOW BEEN FOUND AND ARE STORED AS THE ARRAY NF
C THE NEXT AND FINAL STEP IS TO PRINT OUT THE FREQUENCY TABLE
       WRITE(2,5)
     5 FORMAT(11X,5HGROUP,7X,9HFREQUENCY/9X,9HMID-POINT)
       DO 6 J=1,M
       CVX=B+(J-0.5)*H
C THE MID-POINT OF THE JTH GROUP HAS NOW BEEN CALCULATED
     6 WRITE(2,7)CVX,NF(J)
     7 FORMAT(10X,F7.1,9X,I3)
       STOP
       END

       FINISH

           GROUP   FREQUENCY
          MID-POINT
            300.5   1
            500.5   2
            700.5   5
            900.5   12
           1100.5   17
           1300.5   20
           1500.5   12
           1700.5   7
           1900.5   3
           2100.5   1

       ****

$n = 80 \qquad m = 10 \qquad h = 200 \qquad b = 200 \cdot 5$
$(x_1 - b)/h + 1 = (854 - 200 \cdot 5)/200 + 1 = 4 \cdot 2675 \qquad j = 4$
$(x_2 - b)/h + 1 = 6 \cdot 7825 \qquad j = 6$

FRAME 13

It may sometimes be more useful to know how many observations were below or
above a certain value, rather than how many occurred in a certain group.   This
is given by the appropriate CUMULATIVE FREQUENCY for that value.   For instance,
if you refer to the frequency table in 9A you will see that there were
$8(= 1 + 2 + 5)$ lamps whose recorded length of life was less than $800 \cdot 5$ hours.
How many had a recorded life of more than $1600 \cdot 5$ hours?

****

13A

$11(= 1 + 3 + 7)$

FRAME 14

In the following table we have started filling in the cumulative frequencies for
the lamp data.   The "less than" cumulative frequency, associated in each case
with the upper boundary of the group, is shown on the left.   On the right you
can see the "more than" cumulative frequency associated with the lower
boundary of the group.   Both are also shown expressed as percentages of the
total frequency, being often more readily interpreted in this form.

		"Less than"		"More than"	
Group boundaries	Frequency	Cumulative frequency	% cumulative frequency	Cumulative frequency	% cumulative frequency
$- 200 \cdot 5$	0	0	0		
$200 \cdot 5 - 400 \cdot 5$	1	1	$1 \cdot 25$		
$400 \cdot 5 - 600 \cdot 5$	2	3	$3 \cdot 75$		
$600 \cdot 5 - 800 \cdot 5$	5	8	10		
$800 \cdot 5 - 1000 \cdot 5$	12				
$1000 \cdot 5 - 1200 \cdot 5$	17				
$1200 \cdot 5 - 1400 \cdot 5$	20				
$1400 \cdot 5 - 1600 \cdot 5$	12				
$1600 \cdot 5 - 1800 \cdot 5$	7			11	$13 \cdot 75$
$1800 \cdot 5 - 2000 \cdot 5$	3			4	5
$2000 \cdot 5 - 2200 \cdot 5$	1			1	$1 \cdot 25$
$2200 \cdot 5 -$	0			0	0

Finish filling in the four right-hand columns.

****

Group boundaries	Frequency	"Less than"		"More than"	
		Cumulative frequency	% cumulative frequency	Cumulative frequency	% cumulative frequency
− 200·5	0	0	0		
200·5− 400·5	1	1	1·25	80	100
400·5− 600·5	2	3	3·75	79	98·75
600·5− 800·5	5	8	10	77	96·25
800·5−1000·5	12	20	25	72	90
1000·5−1200·5	17	37	46·25	60	75
1200·5−1400·5	20	57	71·25	43	53·75
1400·5−1600·5	12	69	86·25	23	28·75
1600·5−1800·5	7	76	95	11	13·75
1800·5−2000·5	3	79	98·75	4	5
2000·5−2200·5	1	80	100	1	1·25
2200·5−	0			0	0

FRAME 15

Saying, for example, that 11 lamps lasted more than 1600·5 h is, of course, only another way of saying that 69 lasted less than that, so obviously the "more than" frequency values are just another way of looking at the "less than" ones. Both have been included here in order that you can fully appreciate their meaning, but in practice you would choose which of the two alternatives better suited your purpose. The "less than" one is more commonly used, and is what is usually meant by the term cumulative frequency. In this book, when the term cumulative frequency is used you should assume that the "less than" interpretation is meant unless otherwise stated.

FRAME 16

Graphical Representation of Data

Some people prefer to see the distribution of frequencies shown diagrammatically instead of in the form of a table.

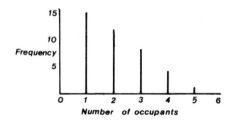

When the variate is discrete, a LINE DIAGRAM (or BAR CHART) is appropriate. In this, each frequency is represented by the length of a line (or bar, if the line is widened to make it show up more), as is illustrated here for the car occupancy data which was tabulated in FRAME 6.

FRAME 17

When the variate is continuous, one kind of frequency diagram which is appropriate is the HISTOGRAM, in which each frequency is represented by the <u>area</u> of a rectangle. This is illustrated here for the lamp data as classified in 10A.

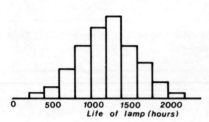

Life of lamp (hours)

The base of each rectangle extends from the lower group boundary to the upper, on a scale representing the variate, in this case the length of life in hours. It is not possible to show this exactly on a small diagram, so part of the histogram is now given on an enlarged scale, to make it quite clear.

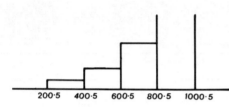

Notice that the true group boundaries must be used, so that the horizontal scale representing length of life is covered continuously, with no breaks between the rectangles (except where the frequency is zero, of course).

FRAME 18

Because the rectangles are all of equal width, then, if their areas are proportional to the frequencies, so also are their heights. Thus, in the actual construction, a suitable vertical scale is chosen and a height of 3 units would then be measured off for a rectangle which is to represent a frequency of 3, and so on. There may be a tendency, therefore, to think of the height as representing the frequency. Does it matter, anyway, you may ask? In a later programme the concept of the histogram will be used in developing a "mathematical model" for the frequency distribution of a continuous variate, and the idea of the area of the rectangle representing the frequency in the group is basic to that development. The vertical scale on the histogram should be thought of as representing frequency density i.e. frequency per unit of interval on the horizontal axis. This is illustrated by the diagram.

$\dfrac{3}{200}$ [3]
←200→

FRAME 19

Of less importance than the histogram, but perhaps worth mentioning, is the FREQUENCY POLYGON, in which each frequency is plotted against the mid-point of the group, as is shown here for the lamp data.

Mid-point of group	Frequency
300·5	1
500·5	2
700·5	5
900·5	12
1100·5	17
1300·5	20
1500·5	12
1700·5	7
1900·5	3
2100·5	1

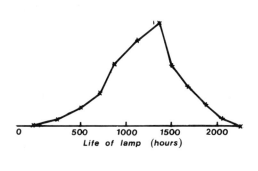

To be consistent with what was said about the histogram at the end of the last frame, the vertical scale for the frequency polygon should be considered as representing frequency density, rather than frequency itself.   You can then imagine the frequency polygon being superimposed on the histogram.   Does that suggest to you anything about the area under the frequency polygon and the total area of the rectangles in the histogram?

****

19A

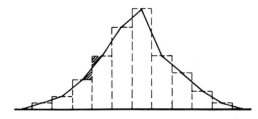

The frequency polygon can be obtained by joining up the mid-points of the tops of the rectangles.   Because of the equality of such areas as the two shaded, the area under the frequency polygon is equal to the total area of the rectangles in the histogram.   Both, in fact, represent the total frequency, 80 in this case.

FRAME 20

Just as a frequency distribution can be described diagrammatically by a frequency polygon, so can a cumulative frequency distribution be represented by a curve called an OGIVE.   This is illustrated on the next page for the lamp data, using the % "less than" cumulative frequencies obtained in FRAME 14 and plotting them against the upper end point of the group.

The shape of this curve (like an elongated S) is typical of ogives for frequency distributions which, like that for the lamp data, show approximate symmetry about a central peak.   (More about this in a later programme.)

Length of life (hours)	% cumulative frequency
< 200·5	0
< 400·5	1·25
< 600·5	3·75
< 800·5	10
< 1000·5	25
< 1200·5	46·25
< 1400·5	71·25
< 1600·5	86·25
< 1800·5	95
< 2000·5	98·75
< 2200·5	100

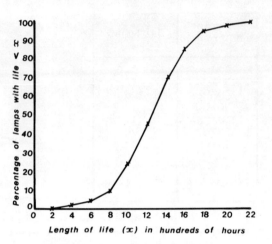

Length of life (x) in hundreds of hours

Arithmetical Description of a Distribution

Some aspects of a distribution can be described in quantitative terms by calculating certain values from it.   First we shall deal with

Measures of Location (or Position or Central Tendency)

When buying electric lamp bulbs you can pay a little extra to get the "longer-life" type.   When tested, the lives (in hours) of 5 "standard" bulbs and 5 "longer-life" bulbs were as follows:

| "Standard": | 1357, | 1090, | 1666, | 1494, | 1623 |
| "Longer-life": | 2181, | 2741, | 3212, | 3264, | 2897 |

Here it would be useful to have a measure which, for each type of bulb, would give a general indication of the time lasted.   This is sometimes termed a "measure of location", as its aim is to indicate whereabouts the observations are located (in this case, on the time scale).   The measure most often used to meet this need is

The Arithmetic Mean

Probably you are already familiar with this and know that

$$\text{Arithmetic Mean} = \frac{\text{Sum of all the observations}}{\text{Total number of observations}} \qquad (21.1)$$

Other types of mean exist (e.g. the geometric mean) but they are not widely used and it is invariably the arithmetic mean which is referred to if the word 'mean' is used.

Applying (21.1) to the data for the 5 "Standard" electric lamp bulbs gives their mean length of life as

$$\frac{1357 + 1090 + 1666 + 1494 + 1623}{5} = \frac{7230}{5} = 1446 \text{ hours}$$

What is the mean length of life of the "Longer-life" bulbs?

                    ****

$\dfrac{14\ 295}{5} = 2859\ hours$

More generally, if x_1, x_2, ... x_n are n values of a variate x, then their arithmetic mean $\overline{x}$ is given by

$$\overline{x} = \frac{x_1 + x_2 + \ldots\ldots + x_n}{n}$$

$$= \frac{1}{n} \sum_{i=1}^{n} x_i,$$ which can be written in the more abbreviated form $\dfrac{1}{n} \Sigma x$.

Properties of the Arithmetic Mean

This is a convenient point at which to notice two properties of the arithmetic mean.   The first concerns the values of $x - \overline{x}$, i.e. the deviations of the individual observations from the arithmetic mean.   Some of these deviations will be positive and some negative.   Write down their values for each of the sets of lamp data in FRAME 21.   What do you notice about their sum in each case?

****

"Standard":   *−89,   −356,   +220,   +48,   +177*
           Sum = −445 + 445 = 0

"Longer−life":   *−678,   −118,   353,   405,   38*
           Sum = −796 + 796 = 0

The fact that in each case the positive and negative deviations have exactly cancelled each other out in the summation does not imply that there was anything special about the data.   A little simple algebra will show that it must always happen, as a consequence of the definition of $\overline{x}$.   For any n observations x_1, x_2, ... x_n:

$$\Sigma(x - \overline{x}) = (x_1 - \overline{x}) + (x_2 - \overline{x}) + \ldots + (x_n - \overline{x})$$

$$= (x_1 + x_2 + \ldots + x_n) - n\overline{x}$$

$$= n\overline{x} - n\overline{x} = 0$$

i.e. the sum of the deviations from the arithmetic mean is always zero.

The second property concerns the squares of the deviations.   This can be illustrated by a few simple calculations.

If the values taken by a variate x are:

$$8, \quad -2, \quad 6, \quad 0, \quad 3, \quad 9$$

the mean $\bar{x} = 4$ and the values of $x - \bar{x}$ are

$$+4, \quad -6, \quad 2, \quad -4, \quad -1, \quad 5 \qquad \text{(CHECK: Sum = 0)}$$

Then the sum of the squares of these deviations i.e. $\Sigma(x - \bar{x})^2$ is

$$4^2 + (-6)^2 + 2^2 + (-4)^2 + (-1)^2 + 5^2 = 16 + 36 + 4 + 16 + 1 + 25 = 98$$

Now write down the deviations of the x-values from <u>any</u> number <u>other than</u> $\bar{x}$ and calculate the sum of the squares of these deviations.   In <u>other words</u>, find $\Sigma(x - a)^2$ for any a, where $a \neq \bar{x}$.   Is this sum greater than, less than or equal to the value found for $\Sigma(x - \bar{x})^2$?

$$**$$

25A

Greater than.   If your answer disagrees, check your arithmetic!

FRAME 26

As you were invited to choose your own value for a, it looks as if a general property of $\Sigma(x - \bar{x})^2$ is involved.   If you think that there was something special about the values of x which were used, try another set (not necessarily 6 in number, either).   In fact only elementary algebra is required to settle the matter once and for all, as will now be shown.

$$\Sigma(x - a)^2 = \Sigma\{(x - \bar{x}) + (\bar{x} - a)\}^2$$

$$= \Sigma\{(x - \bar{x})^2 + 2(x - \bar{x})(\bar{x} - a) + (\bar{x} - a)^2\}$$

$$= \Sigma(x - \bar{x})^2 + 2(\bar{x} - a)\Sigma(x - \bar{x}) + \Sigma(\bar{x} - a)^2 \qquad (26.1)$$

If you have difficulty in following manipulations involving Σ notation, write out the expressions in full.   For example, rewrite $\Sigma\{(x - \bar{x}) + (\bar{x} - a)\}^2$ as

$$\{(x_1 - \bar{x}) + (\bar{x} - a)\}^2 + \{(x_2 - \bar{x}) + (\bar{x} - a)\}^2 + \ldots + \{(x_n - \bar{x}) + (\bar{x} - a)\}^2$$

This should help you to understand what is going on when the more abbreviated Σ form is being used.

Now, remembering that there are n values of x and that $\bar{x}$ is their mean, can you simplify the second and third terms on the R.H.S. of (26.1)?

$$**$$

26A

2nd term = 0 as $\Sigma(x - \bar{x}) = 0$ 3rd term = $n(\bar{x} - a)^2$

FRAME 27

Thus, $\Sigma(x - a)^2 = \Sigma(x - \bar{x})^2 + n(\bar{x} - a)^2$ (27.1)

As $(\bar{x} - a)^2$ is always positive if $a \neq \bar{x}$, you will see that $\Sigma(x - a)^2$ must then always be greater than $\Sigma(x - \bar{x})^2$.   Furthermore $\Sigma(x - a)^2$ will have its minimum value when $a = \bar{x}$.   In other words, <u>the sum of the squares of the</u> <u>deviations is a minimum when the deviations are taken from the arithmetic mean</u>.

An alternative way of establishing this result is to consider $\Sigma(x - a)^2$ as a function of a and then use differentiation to show that a minimum occurs when $a = \bar{x}$.   This approach, showing that the definition of the arithmetic mean $\bar{x}$ follows from the application of the least squares criterion, is used in the "Least Squares" programme in Unit 2 of our book "Numerical Methods for Engineers and Scientists".

FRAME 27   (continued)

Do you know anything about moments of inertia?   If the answer is "No" proceed
directly to the next frame.   If the answer is "Yes", look again at (27.1) and
see whether it reminds you of a property of moments of inertia (or other forms
of second moment).

****

27A

*The Parallel Axes Theorem, which relates the moment of inertia about an axis
with the moment of inertia about a parallel axis through the centre of gravity.
That theorem shows, of course, that the moment of inertia is least when taken
about an axis through the centre of gravity.*

FRAME 28

Calculation of the Mean from a Frequency Table

So far we have only dealt with the calculation of the mean when the data is in
the form of the individual observations but, as you have already seen, when the
number of observations is large it is convenient to condense them into a
frequency table.   The problem now is how to find the mean when the data is in
this form.

In FRAMES 5 and 6 the data on the occupancy of 40 cars was given in both forms.
Working from the original 40 observations, to find the mean number of occupants
per car you would add up all the observations (getting the total number of
occupants) and divide by the total number of cars.   Do this now - it may seem
a trivial exercise but it will help you to understand what follows.

****

28A

Total number of occupants = 84   Mean number of occupants per car = $\frac{84}{40}$ = 2·1

FRAME 29

Now, reference to the frequency table in FRAME 6 shows that in adding up the 40
figures in this data you were actually adding together fifteen 1's, twelve 2's,
eight 3's, four 4's and one 5.   That is to say, the total of 84 could have
been found from $15 \times 1 + 12 \times 2 + 8 \times 3 + 4 \times 4 + 1 \times 5$.

The calculation of the mean from the frequency table can be set out like this:

Number of occupants x	Frequency f	fx
1	15	15
2	12	24
3	8	24
4	4	16
5	1	5
	—	—
	40	84

Mean = $\frac{84}{40}$ = 2·1

NOTE: This lay-out shows how the result
is arrived at, but, if a calculator is
being used, it is not necessary to write
down the values of fx.   They can just
be accumulated in the memory until the
end of the table is reached.

From this you will easily see that for a frequency table with n groups

$$\overline{x} = \frac{\sum\limits_{i=1}^{n} f_i x_i}{\sum\limits_{i=1}^{n} f_i} \qquad \text{which, in the more abbreviated form, is} \quad \frac{\Sigma fx}{\Sigma f}$$

This is not really a different formula from that given in FRAME 22, just a different version of it, for use when the data has been classified into a frequency table.

Test your understanding of this frame with the following problem:

Another part of the traffic survey involved recording the number of motorised vehicles which passed an observation point during a 30 - second interval. This was done for 120 such intervals and the results are summarised in the frequency table below.

Number of vehicles (x)	0	1	2	3	4	5	6	7	8
Number of intervals in which x vehicles were observed	7	21	25	31	19	11	3	1	2

What was the total number of vehicles observed?   What was the mean number of vehicles passing in a 30 - second interval?

****

336   336/120 = 2·8

Notice that, for the data on car occupancy, <u>exactly</u> the same result is obtained for the mean value, whether it is based on the original 40 observations or on the frequency table.   That is because exactly the same information is available in both forms of the data.   In our case, we started with the 40 observations and then tabulated them, but it would be possible to reverse the process, i.e. to deduce from the frequency table what the original 40 values were.   Can you say the same of the frequency table for the lamp data?

****

No.   Once the data had been classified a certain amount of information had been lost.   For instance, the table tells us that 2 lamps had lives which were from 201 to 400 hours in length but it does not tell us what their actual lengths of life were.

To find the mean length of life of the 80 lamps from the frequency table it is necessary to make an approximation.   All the observed values falling in a particular group are taken as having the value at the mid-point of the group. In reality, some will have been larger and some smaller, but one assumes that these differences will roughly cancel each other out.   The group mid-points were used in FRAME 19 in drawing the frequency polygon.   Using the table shown

FRAME 31   (continued)

there, the calculation of the mean length of life is as follows:

Group mid-point x	Frequency f	fx
300·5	1	300·5
500·5	2	1001·0
700·5	5	3502·5
900·5	12	10806·0
1100·5	17	18708·5
1300·5	20	26010·0
1500·5	12	18006·0
1700·5	7	11903·5
1900·5	3	5701·5
2100·5	1	2100·5
—	80	98040·0

Mean $= \dfrac{98\,040}{80} = 1225 \cdot 5$

NOTE: If the original 80 values of x are added together, they give $\Sigma x = 98\,288$, whence $\bar{x} = 1228 \cdot 6$. This shows you how near, in this example, to the true value of $\bar{x}$ is the approximation using the mid-points in the frequency table.

(You will see later how you can reduce the size of numbers in a calculation such as this.)

FRAME 32

The Mode

One unfortunate feature of the arithmetic mean has already become apparent.   In the case of the car occupancy data, the mean number of occupants per car was 2·1. But have you ever seen a car with 2·1 occupants???   When the variate is discrete it often happens that the mean turns out to have a value that cannot actually be taken by the variate.   Also, it may be more useful to know the value of the variate which occurs most frequently.   For instance, the designer of an electric car for use in towns might wish to know what seating capacity is most often required.   The most frequently occurring value of the variate is called the MODE (from the French word for fashion).   Thus, a glance at the frequency distribution for the car occupancy data shows the mode to be 1 as that is the value of the variate for which the frequency is highest.

The use of the mode is most often associated with discrete variates.   In the case of continuous variates the mode is the value where the frequency density is highest.   In a frequency table it is only possible to identify the group where this occurs, it being the interval containing the largest number of observations.   In the histogram this modal group would be the one corresponding to the highest rectangle.

Now look back to the frequency table for the lamp data in answer frame 10A and decide which is the modal group.

                    ****

32A

The one covering recorded lives of 1201-1400 hours,   i.e. actual lives between 1200·5 and 1400·5 h.

FRAME 33

The Median

Another disadvantage of the arithmetic mean is that it can sometimes give a false impression as a result of being influenced by extreme observations.

Consider, for instance, 10 households in a small rural community whose incomes (in £) for the fiscal year 1974-1975 were as follows:

1550	1400	1250	1050	940
960	720	1030	23 000	1600

The mean income for these households is £3350 but this is clearly not a representative value and does not give a true indication of the standard of living enjoyed by the people as a whole in that area.   Nine of the households have incomes well below the mean.   In the area there were two cottages inhabited by agricultural workers, also some bungalows for old people living on small pensions, but there was also a large house occupied by a comparatively wealthy man.

In such situations there is some merit in the MEDIAN as a measure of central tendency.   This is obtained by arranging the observations in order of magnitude. Then, if there is an odd number of them, the middle value is the median.   For example, if the data for the "Standard" type of lamp given in FRAME 21 is rearranged in this way the result is

$$1090 \qquad 1357 \qquad 1494 \qquad 1623 \qquad 1666$$

and the median is 1494 hours.   If the number of observations is even, it is usual to take the median as the mean of the two middle values.   The 10 household incomes rearranged in order of magnitude are:

$$720, \quad 940, \quad 960, \quad 1030, \quad 1050, \quad 1250, \quad 1400, \quad 1550, \quad 1600, \quad 23\,000$$

The two middle values are 1050 and 1250 so the median would be taken as 1150. Now rearrange the data on "Longer-life" bulbs in FRAME 21 and deduce their median life.

```
****************************************************
```

33A

2897 hours

FRAME 34

In each of these examples the median was easily obtained as there were only a few observations to be re-ordered, but finding it for a larger number of observations would be more tedious and time-consuming.   Rearranging data in order of magnitude is a problem that occurs not only in finding the median, and computer programs for it are quite common.   For instance, examination marks may be treated in this way so that students can be listed in order of attainment.

The flow diagram in this frame takes n values of x, rearranges them in order of magnitude (from lowest to highest) and then finds the median.   Applying it to the data on "Longer-life" lamps for which you have just found the median yourself, the value of n would be 5 and x_1, x_2, x_3, x_4, x_5 would be read in as 2181, 2741, 3212, 3264 and 2897 respectively.   After the set of operations for i = 2 to 5 have been carried out for the first time, the values of x_4 and x_5 will have been interchanged, causing the value of j to be altered to 1.   This, in turn, will cause the same set of operations to be repeated, leading to an interchange of the values of x_3 and x_4.   As j will again be 1, the set of operations will be repeated once more but no interchanges will be required and the zero value of j will indicate that the re-ordering has been accomplished.   To help clarify this for you, the table on the next page gives the values of x_1, ... x_5 in store at the start of each set of operations (i.e. when j has been set to zero).

x_1	x_2	x_3	x_4	x_5
2181	2741	3212	3264	2897
2181	2741	3212	2897	3264
2181	2741	2897	3212	3264

(i)   Suppose that, instead, the data on "Standard" bulbs, i.e. 1357, 1090, 1666, 1494, 1623 had been read in as the starting values for x_1, x_2, x_3, x_4, x_5 respectively.   Form the table, corresponding to that above, showing the values of x_1, ... x_5 in store at the start of each stage.

(ii) What alteration would you make to the flow diagram for it to put the x's into order from highest to lowest, instead of the reverse order used here?

From the point of view of finding the median, does it matter which order is used?

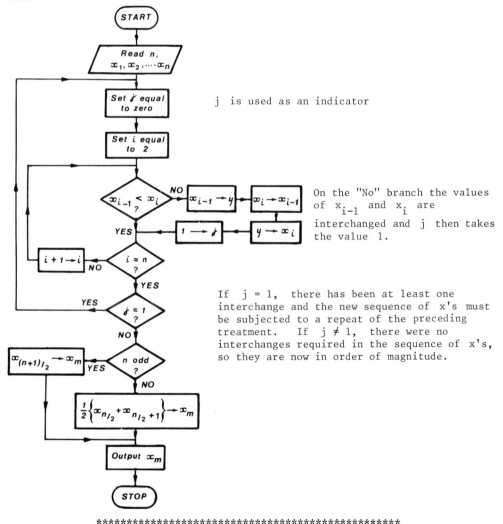

j is used as an indicator

On the "No" branch the values of x_{i-1} and x_i are interchanged and j then takes the value 1.

If j = 1,   there has been at least one interchange and the new sequence of x's must be subjected to a repeat of the preceding treatment.   If j ≠ 1,   there were no interchanges required in the sequence of x's, so they are now in order of magnitude.

****

34A

(i)	x_1	x_2	x_3	x_4	x_5
	1357	*1090*	*1666*	*1494*	*1623*
	1090	*1357*	*1494*	*1623*	*1666*

(ii) Change $x_{i-1} < x_i$ *into* $x_i < x_{i-1}$ *(or* $x_{i-1} > x_i$, *of course).*
No, it doesn't matter. The method of finding the median is the same, whether the values of the variate are ordered from lowest to highest or highest to lowest.

FRAME 35

Notice that, in the case of the lamp data (either "Standard" or "Longer-life"), if the 5 bulbs were being tested simultaneously the value of the median would become apparent as soon as the 3rd failure occurred. This illustrates another advantage of the median over the arithmetic mean, an advantage which has led to the use of "half-life" as a measure of the activity of a radioactive element. It is the time at which half the atoms present have disintegrated i.e. it is the median value of the time at which individual atoms disintegrate. Since the time for complete disintegration is infinite the median has the practical advantage that it is based on only half the atoms – those which are the first to disintegrate.

The median is used for similar reasons in measuring the toxicity of insecticides. If a batch of insects is exposed to the test material they do not all die at the same time, and some may survive the treatment altogether. The median life is the time taken for half of them to die, low values of the median indicating high toxicity of the insecticide.

FRAME 36

The median is sometimes described as the "50% point" because 50% of observations are below it and 50% above. With this in mind, we now turn to the problem of finding the median when the data has been grouped in a frequency table. Taking the test results for 80 electric lamps which you were asked to classify in this way in FRAME 10, the median life will be such that 40 lamps had lives which were of lesser duration and 40 had lives which were greater in length. As a first step, look at the table in answer frame 14A, which also shows cumulative frequencies, and state the interval in which the median occurs.

****

36A

There were 37 observations less than 1200·5 and 57 observations less than 1400·5 so the median must be between 1200·5 and 1400·5.

FRAME 37

The position of the median within the interval can only be estimated. For it to be such that the area of the histogram is bisected it must be such that the rectangle representing the frequency in the interval 1200·5 – 1400·5 is divided in the ratio 3:17.

FRAME 37   (continued)

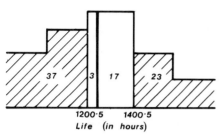

Life (in hours)

By simple proportion,

Median = $1200 \cdot 5 + \dfrac{3}{20} \times 200 = 1230 \cdot 5$ hours

For comparison you may be interested to know that if the original 80 observations (as given in FRAME 7) are arranged in order of magnitude, the two middle values (i.e. the 40th and 41st) are 1242 and 1251, giving the median as 1246·5 hours.

The median could also be estimated from the ogive, shown in FRAME 20.   How would this be done?

****

37A

Read off the value of x *corresponding to a value of 50% on the vertical axis.*

FRAME 38

Measures of Dispersion (or Spread or Variability)

Another feature of data which may be important is the amount of scatter of the observations.   Where the quality of a product is involved the consumer may, in fact, be as much concerned with the consistency of the quality as with its general level.   This could be so with the length of life of electric lamps where they are installed in large numbers and labour costs are reduced if the bulbs are replaced collectively rather than individually as they fail.   Where errors of measurement are the cause of variation among the observations, a measure of this variation would be relevant in comparing one analytical technique with another, or one measuring instrument with another.

In experimentation generally, the existence of errors cannot be ignored.   This is a convenient point at which to distinguish between the terms "accuracy" and "precision" which tend to be used synonymously in everyday language but which are usually interpreted differently in error analysis.   An illustration of this difference is given in "The Experimental Method" (ed. R.K. Penny, Longman, London 1974).   It recounts the experience of a householder who decided to check the functioning of the electricity meter installed by the local Electricity Board by running a 1 kW appliance for 1 hour when all other appliances had been switched off.   Theoretically the meter should have then recorded a consumption of 1 kWh, but the reading (taken very meticulously by the householder) was 1·37 kWh and repeat experiments gave very much the same result.   The meter was replaced and the householder carried out 5 tests which gave a mean reading of exactly 1 kWh, but there was now considerable variation between the readings. The first meter was exhibiting good precision but poor accuracy, the second poor precision but good accuracy.   The householder gave up at this point lest a further replacement should result in a meter combining poor precision with poor accuracy!

FRAME 39

Continuing with the same theme, an illustration from analytical chemistry may help in consolidating your understanding of what we are trying to get across to you.

To determine the percentage of an element in a compound, analyst A tried two
different methods (1 and 2) and analyst B just used method 1.   Now, in fact,
the percentage was already known, so we can get an indication of how good are
the methods and the analysts by looking at the results (10 replicates in each
case).   These are shown in the dot diagrams (each result represented by a dot •)
and both the true value and the mean $\bar{x}$ of the 10 experimental results are
marked on the scale representing % element in the compound.

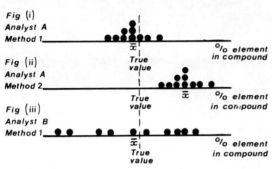

You will notice that, using method
1, both analysts obtain a value
of $\bar{x}$ very close to the true value.
(The data used was fictitious.   In
reality it would be unusual for
both $\bar{x}$'s to be the same but we
have chosen this situation to
emphasise our point.)   However,
whereas A's results show fairly
close agreement, B's are much more
widely scattered.   This suggests
that A's precision is good, but
B's poor.   When using method 2,
analyst A maintains his consistency
(again, for emphasis, the data has been "manufactured" so that the pattern of
variation in his results remains <u>exactly</u> the same) but the difference between $\bar{x}$
and the true value is now much greater.

Where results are, on average, too high or too low, there is a systematic error
or bias in the measurements, and the greater the extent to which this happens,
the poorer the accuracy.   Thus:

Fig. (i) can be said to represent good precision combined with good accuracy.
Fig.(ii) can be said to represent good precision combined with poor accuracy.

How would you describe Fig.(iii) in such terms?

                    ****

                                                                             39A

Poor precision combined with good accuracy.

To sum up:

A measuring instrument or technique is absolutely accurate if it has no
systematic error or bias.   The mean of an infinitely large number of repeated
measurements would then coincide with the true value of what is being measured.
The further away this mean is from the true value, the less accurate is the
measuring device.

A measuring instrument or technique is absolutely precise if it gives the same
result in repeated measurements.   The more repeated measurements vary among
themselves, the less precise is the measuring device.

As yet in this programme you have not seen how the dispersion of data can be
described in quantitative terms, but you are now about to do so and will then
know how precision can be assessed.

Having looked at scatter in the context of experimental error, we now consider
the question of how it can be measured.   As with the choice of a measure of
location to give a representative value, there are various possibilities.

Without doubt, the measure of dispersion which is easiest to understand and
easiest to calculate is the RANGE.   The formula for this is simply:

              Range = Largest observation - Smallest observation

For the results of life-testing 80 electric lamps, given in FRAME 7, it was
noted that the shortest life was 210 hours and the longest 2074 hours.   Thus,
for that set of data, the range is   2074 - 210   i.e.   1864 hours.

Now, find the range for the data on the incomes of 10 households given in
FRAME 33.   Then omit the highest income and find the range for the remaining 9.

              ****

41A

£22 280,   £880.

The advantage of the range lies in its simplicity.   This has led to its use in
quality control where, in a mass production situation, there is regular
monitoring of the standard of the product by testing a few items from the
production line.   The variation in quality from one product to another is one
of the things that must be looked at.   Early detection of something amiss with
the process is important, and as no special skills or computing facilities are
required for the calculation of the range its value is available as soon as the
tests have been made.

Although the range meets a need in the kind of situation just described, its
very simplicity is also its disadvantage.   As you have seen with the data on
household incomes, it can be influenced unduly by one exceptional observation.
It is only a crude measure of spread, based on just two of the observations with
the values of the others ignored apart from the fact that they are between these
two extremes.   Thus although the two sets of data

	576	642	763	856	947	1023	1136	1248
and	576	962	987	1001	1014	1016	1020	1248

have the same range, the observations between the two extremes vary much more
among themselves in the first set than in the second.

The INTERQUARTILE RANGE cuts out the more extreme values in a distribution.
It is the range which covers the middle 50% of the observations and is the
difference between the LOWER and UPPER QUARTILES.   These are such that, of all
the observations, 25% are less than the lower quartile and 25% are greater
than the upper quartile.   The histogram and cumulative frequency curve on the
next page should make this clear.

You will see that, just as the median divided the distribution into two halves,
so, with the introduction of the quartiles, the distribution is now divided
into four quarters.   In a similar way, DECILES divide the distribution into
tenths and PERCENTILES into hundredths.   Thus, for instance, the lower quartile
can be regarded as the 25th percentile.

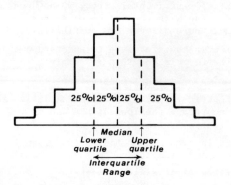 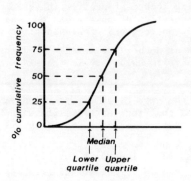

You have already seen how the median life for the 80 lamps tested could be estimated when the data had been classified into a frequency table.   Now have a go at finding the lower quartile, upper quartile and interquartile range.   (The frequency table is in answer frame 14A.)

****

43A

Lower quartile = 1000·5 hours.   There are 57 lives < 1400·5 and hence the upper quartile can be estimated as $1400·5 + \frac{3}{12} \times 200 = 1450·5$ hours. Interquartile range = 450 hours.

FRAME 44

The other measures of dispersion that will be considered here are connected with the variation about the mean.   Obviously the values of the deviations $x_1 - \bar{x}$, $x_2 - \bar{x}$,   etc. will give some indication of this variation and we might first have the idea of using the mean of these deviations as an overall measure. However, if you think back to a previous result you will realise that this would be quite useless.   Why?

****

44A

The sum of the deviations is always zero, so their mean would always be zero and would convey no information at all.

FRAME 45

One way of getting round this difficulty is to treat all deviations as positive i.e. to use the mean of their absolute values.   This is called the MEAN DEVIATION (or, more strictly, the MEAN ABSOLUTE DEVIATION) and for n observations x_1, x_2, ... x_n it would be

$$\frac{|x_1 - \bar{x}| + |x_2 - \bar{x}| + \dots + |x_n - \bar{x}|}{n}$$

which can be abbreviated to $\frac{1}{n} \Sigma |x - \bar{x}|$.

In 23A you found the values of $x - \bar{x}$ for the 5 lives of "Standard" type lamps to be:

FRAME 45   (continued)

$$-89, \ -356, \ +220, \ +48, \ +177$$

The mean deviation for that set of data would therefore be

$$\frac{89 + 356 + 220 + 48 + 177}{5} = \frac{890}{5} = 178 \ \text{hours}$$

Now find the mean deviation for the corresponding data for the "Longer-life" lamp bulbs.   (See 23A again for the values of $x - \bar{x}$.)

****

45A

(678 + 118 + 353 + 405 + 38)/5 = 1592/5 = 318·4 hours

FRAME 46

Taking the absolute values may have found a way round the problem of the positive and negative deviations cancelling each other out, but it is not the most satisfactory way.   You have seen that there are no difficulties from the computational standpoint, but statistical methods have their basis in mathematical theory and it is there that the absolute (or modulus) function is an awkward one.   As $|x - \bar{x}|$ means $x - \bar{x}$ if $x > \bar{x}$ and $\bar{x} - x$ if $x < \bar{x}$, these two subdivisions of the whole range of values of x have to be considered separately as far as the function is concerned.   This complication does not arise when $(x - \bar{x})^2$ is used as another way of preventing the positive values of $x - \bar{x}$ being offset by the negative ones.   The mean of the squares of the deviations is called the VARIANCE.   For n observations $x_1, x_2, \ldots x_n$ this would be

$$\frac{(x_1 - \bar{x})^2 + (x_2 - \bar{x})^2 + \ldots + (x_n - \bar{x})^2}{n} \qquad \text{i.e.} \qquad \frac{1}{n} \Sigma(x - \bar{x})^2$$

Although this is the variance of these n observations, you will find, when you have progressed further in your study of this subject, that that may not be quite what is wanted.   Take the case of the 5 "Standard" type lamps which were life-tested.   One would usually want to know, not how variable was the length of life among those 5 lamps but how variable was the length of life among all the lamps of that type.   In that situation an adjustment factor of $\frac{n}{n-1}$ is applied to get an unbiased variance estimate, but you need not concern yourself with this for the present.   It is only mentioned in case you have seen a variance formula used elsewhere with $n - 1$ in the denominator instead of n. (It only makes an appreciable difference, anyway, if n is small.)

FRAME 47

Returning to the definition of variance, let us think about the units in which it would be measured.   If x were the diameter in millimetres of rivet heads being manufactured by a mass-production process, in what units would the variance of x be?   Is variance in the same units as the other measures of dispersion so far considered, i.e. range, interquartile range and mean deviation?

****

47A

The variance of x would be in mm^2.
Range, interquartile range and mean deviation are all in the same units as the

variate itself, but variance will be in those units squared.

To get a measure of dispersion which is in the same units as the variate itself,
the square root of the variance is taken, giving the STANDARD DEVIATION.   Thus:

$$\text{Standard deviation} = \sqrt{\text{Variance}}$$

$$= \sqrt{\text{Mean of squares of deviations from mean}}$$

Maybe you have met root-mean-square values before.   In the "Applications of
Integration" programme in Unit 2 of our Mathematics for Engineers and Scientists
Volume 1 they were introduced in relation to alternating currents.   Such a
current i can be represented by $I_M \sin \omega t$, where t is time, and for any

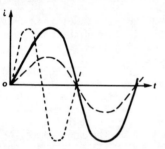

sinusoidal oscillation the mean value over one cycle
is zero.   The situation is the same as it was with
the values of $x - \bar{x}$ in that the "positives" and the
"negatives" always cancel each other out.   Just as
the mean value of $x - \bar{x}$ will tell us nothing about
the spread of the x's, so the mean value of i over
one cycle tells us nothing about an alternating
current.

If you are on familiar ground here, you will
probably have recognised variance as being a
"mean-square" value and standard deviation as being
a "root-mean-square" value.

An error of 0·5 mm is more serious in measuring a length of 1 cm than in
measuring a length of 1 m, as 0·5 mm is a much larger percentage of 1 cm than
it is of 1 m.   On the other hand, an error may depend on the size of what is
being measured so that if a length is increased a hundredfold so is the error in
measuring it.   Experimentalists often therefore think in terms of the relative
error rather than the actual error.   For similar reasons it is sometimes
useful to describe variability by expressing the standard deviation as a
proportion of the mean, usually as a percentage.   This measure is called the
COEFFICIENT OF VARIATION.   The formula for it as a percentage is simply

$$\text{Coefficient of variation} = \frac{\text{Standard deviation}}{\text{Mean}} \times 100 \qquad (49.1)$$

You have already seen that the standard deviation is in the same units as the
mean.   For the diameters of rivet heads, referred to in FRAME 47, whose mean
and standard deviation are both in mm, will the coefficient of variation be in
(i) mm, (ii) mm² or (iii) dimensionless?   (Remember that the 100 in
(49.1) is to convert the proportion to a percentage.)

$$***$$

(iii) dimensionless, like the relative error.

The mean and standard deviation both being in the same units as the variate, the coefficient of variation is, then, always independent of the unit of measurement.   Thus if the rivet head diameter measurements were recorded in cm instead of mm, the coefficient of variation would be unaltered.   However, the coefficient of variation is not independent of the origin from which measurements are made.   (You will understand the reason for this when coding of data is dealt with at the end of the programme.)   Thus, if, for example, the variate were temperature, recorded in $^{\circ}$C, converting these values to $^{\circ}$F would alter the coefficient of variation as the zeros on the two scales are at different points.   Looking at another example, if temperature fluctuations in a continuous chemical process are shown by a trace on a chart recorder, the coefficient of variation of trace heights will be the same as that of the temperatures provided that the base line on the chart corresponds to 0° on the temperature scale being used.

Form of $\Sigma(x - \overline{x})^2$ suitable for computational purposes

With some electronic calculators, the calculation of a standard deviation is just a matter of entering the data and pressing the appropriate key;   but such aids are not always readily available and there is, in any case, some advantage to you, at this stage, in going through the steps of the calculation yourself. The major part of the computation is in finding the sum of the squares of the deviations from the mean, i.e. in finding $\Sigma(x - \overline{x})^2$.   After that it is only a matter of a division to get the variance, and then taking the square root if the standard deviation is required.

In fact, one example of calculating such a sum of squares has already occurred, in FRAME 25.   That is now set out here in the column lay-out appropriate to computational procedures.

x	x - $\overline{x}$	(x - $\overline{x}$)^2
8	4	16
-2	-6	36
6	2	4
0	-4	16
3	-1	1
9	5	25
24		98
$\overline{x}$ = 4		

It is possible to cut out one step in this procedure by using an alternative form of $\Sigma(x - \overline{x})^2$.   In FRAME 27, an equation relating $\Sigma(x - a)^2$ and $\Sigma(x - \overline{x})^2$ was given, in which a could take any value.

Now put a = 0 in (27.1) and rearrange the result to give a formula for $\Sigma(x - \overline{x})^2$.

****

$$\Sigma(x - \overline{x})^2 = \Sigma x^2 - n\overline{x}^2 \qquad (51A.1)$$

As $n\overline{x} = \Sigma x$,   (51A.1) can also be written as

$$\Sigma(x - \overline{x})^2 = \Sigma x^2 - \overline{x}\Sigma x \qquad \text{or} \qquad \Sigma(x - \overline{x})^2 = \Sigma x^2 - \frac{1}{n}(\Sigma x)^2 \quad (52.1)$$

The calculation of the R.H.S. of (52.1) for the same data as in the previous frame would be as follows:

x	x^2
8	64
-2	4
6	36
0	0
3	9
9	81
—	—
24	194

$\Sigma x = 24$ $(\Sigma x)^2 = 24^2$ $\Sigma x^2 = 194$

Note the difference in meaning between $(\Sigma x)^2$ and Σx^2. Whereas $(\Sigma x)^2$ tells you to add up the x's and then square their sum, Σx^2 tells you to square the x's and then add up the squares.

$$\Sigma x^2 - \frac{1}{n}(\Sigma x)^2 = 194 - 24^2/6 = 194 - 96 = 98$$

This way, one step in the computation has been eliminated, that of finding the deviations $x - \bar{x}$. This is an economy, even when a calculator or computer is being used, as it means less pressing of keys or less statements in the program. In fact, with some calculators and in a computer program, the sums Σx and Σx^2 can be accumulated simultaneously making (52.1) a particularly convenient formula to use. Try it out for yourself by calculating Σu, Σu^2 and hence $\Sigma(u - \bar{u})^2$ for the following six values of a variate u: 6, -4, 4, -2, 1, 7.

****

52A

$\Sigma u = 12$ $\Sigma u^2 = 122$ $\Sigma(u - \bar{u})^2 = 122 - 12^2/6 = 122 - 24 = 98$

FRAME 53

Calculation of the Variance and Standard Deviation from a Frequency Table

Now let us look at the calculation of the variance and standard deviation when the data has been grouped into a frequency table. As with the arithmetic mean, it is just a matter of interpreting the previous formulae. You saw that $\frac{\Sigma x}{n}$ became $\frac{\Sigma fx}{\Sigma f}$, the "x" for each group being "weighted" according to its frequency f. In calculating the variance, the values of $(x - \bar{x})^2$ will also have to be given the appropriate weighting f and the frequency table version of the basic formula is therefore $\frac{\Sigma f(x - \bar{x})^2}{\Sigma f}$.

Can you write down the formula for the computation of $\Sigma f(x - \bar{x})^2$ corresponding to (52.1)?

****

53A

$\Sigma f(x - \bar{x})^2 = \Sigma fx^2 - (\Sigma fx)^2/\Sigma f$ (53A.1)

FRAME 54

The car occupancy data will now be used as an illustration. In the table overleaf, the columns on the L.H.S. show how cumbersome the computation can be when working from the actual definition in terms of deviations from the mean. The columns on the R.H.S. use the alternative form given by (53A.1) with the consequent economy of steps in the working.

x	f	fx	$x - \bar{x}$	$(x - \bar{x})^2$	$f(x - \bar{x})^2$	x	f	fx	fx^2
1	15	15	-1·1	1·21	18·15	1	15	15	15
2	12	24	-0·1	0·01	0·12	2	12	24	48
3	8	24	0·9	0·81	6·48	3	8	24	72
4	4	16	1·9	3·61	14·44	4	4	16	64
5	1	5	2·9	8·41	8·41	5	1	5	25
	40	84			47·6		40	84	224

$$\bar{x} = \frac{84}{40} = 2 \cdot 1$$

$$\Sigma f(x - \bar{x})^2 = 224 - 84^2/40$$
$$= 224 - 176 \cdot 4$$
$$= 47 \cdot 6$$

Either method then gives

Variance = 47·6/40 = 1·19

Standard deviation = $\sqrt{1 \cdot 19}$ = 1·091

Before proceeding further, it would be a good idea to consolidate some of the ground already covered so you should now answer the following:

In an investigation into the brittleness of nylon bars, each of 250 test bars was subjected to a test at five places along its length to see whether it would break under a certain applied force.   The number of breaks which occurred was recorded for each bar and the results are given in the following table:

Number of breaks	0	1	2	3	4	5
Number of bars	141	62	31	14	1	1

(i)   At how many of the 1250 test points did a break occur?
(ii) At what proportion of these test points did a break occur?
(iii) Calculate the mean number of breaks per bar.
(iv) State the mode of the distribution.
(v)   Calculate the variance and standard deviation of the distribution.

****

x	f	fx	fx^2
0	141	0	0
1	62	62	62
2	31	62	124
3	14	42	126
4	1	4	16
5	1	5	25
	250	175	353

(i) Σfx here represents the total number of breaks, which was therefore 175.

(ii) Proportion $= \dfrac{175}{1250} = \dfrac{7}{50}$ or 14%

(iii) $\bar{x} = \dfrac{175}{250} = 0 \cdot 7$

(iv) 0

(v)   Variance $= (353 - 175^2/250)/250$
$= (353 - 175 \times 0 \cdot 7)/250$
$= 230 \cdot 5/250 = 0 \cdot 922$

Standard deviation $= 0 \cdot 960$

The flow diagram sets out the computation of the mean and standard deviation of
a frequency distribution along lines suitable for a computer program.   It
assumes that groups are of equal width.   The values of the frequencies are all
read in at the outset and put into store, but they could alternatively be read
in one at a time, as required, thus removing the necessity to use a subscripted
variable.

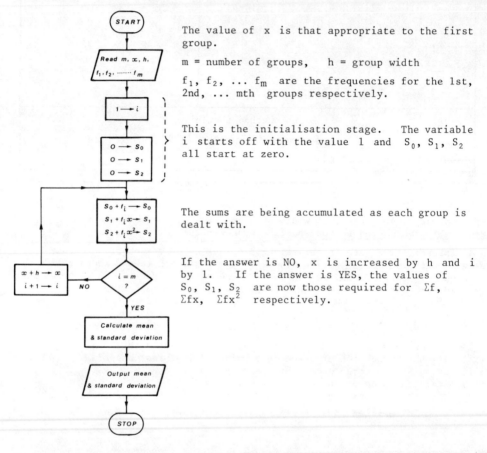

The value of x is that appropriate to the first
group.

m = number of groups,   h = group width

f_1, f_2, ... f_m are the frequencies for the 1st,
2nd, ... mth groups respectively.

This is the initialisation stage.   The variable
i starts off with the value 1 and S_0, S_1, S_2
all start at zero.

The sums are being accumulated as each group is
dealt with.

If the answer is NO, x is increased by h and i
by 1.   If the answer is YES, the values of
S_0, S_1, S_2 are now those required for Σf,
Σfx, Σfx^2 respectively.

To test your understanding of this flow diagram, see whether you can write down
the values of m, x, h, f_1 and f_m which would be read in as data

 (i)   for the nylon bars frequency table which we have just been working with,
(ii)   for the lives of lamps frequency table given in FRAME 19.

        ****

56A

(i) m = 6,   x = 0,   h = 1, f_1 = 141, f_m = 1

(ii) m = 10,   x = 300·5,   h = 200, f_1 = 1, f_m = 1

Coding of data

Arithmetic is always simpler if there are fewer digits in the working.
Obviously you would be more concerned about this if you were having to do the
calculations yourself, but it is still worth considering even when a calculator
or computer is being used.   After all, it is easier to enter 2 in a calculator
than 1500·5 and anyway the registers have only a limited capacity (true even of
computers).   In particular, when the number of observations is large and values
of x involve several figures, applying (52.1) can result in considerable loss
of significance.   (You will already have been alerted to such dangers if you
have read the first programme in Unit 1 of our "Numerical Methods for Engineers
and Scientists".)   The following example will give you an idea of what can
happen, even with comparatively few observations:

104·3,   104·2,   104·9,   104·1,   104·0   are 5 values of a variate x, giving

$$\Sigma x = 521 \cdot 5, \quad \Sigma x^2 = 54\,392 \cdot 95 \quad \text{and} \quad \Sigma x^2 - (\Sigma x)^2/n = 54\,392 \cdot 95 - 54\,392 \cdot 45 = 0 \cdot 50.$$

Notice that 7 figures have to be carried in the working to yield 2 sig. figs.
in the answer.   If Σx^2 and $(\Sigma x)^2/n$ were rounded to 5 sig. figs., their
difference would then be 1 i.e. <u>double</u> the correct value.

The number of figures required in calculations can be reduced by a change of
origin and/or unit.   This is known as CODING.

Let us look first at the use of a change of <u>origin</u>.   You would probably make
such a change intuitively, anyway, if, for instance, you were given the 5 values
of x quoted in the previous frame and asked to find their mean.   Instead of
adding them up, getting the total 521·5 and then dividing by 5 to get 104·3,
you would see that it is easier to just find the mean of 0·3, 0·2, 0·9, 0·1
and 0·0, i.e. 0·3, and add it on to 104.   In effect you would temporarily
be working with values of x', where x' = x - 104.   That is, a temporary
origin, where x' = 0, is chosen at x = 104.   As x = x' + 104, it is obvious
that $\bar{x} = \bar{x}' + 104$, thus justifying algebraically what is arrived at by
intuition.

The values of u given in FRAME 52 were, in fact, obtained from the values of x
given there, by a change of origin.   A quick glance at the figures should now
reveal to you what new origin was chosen.   Write down the equation relating
(i) x and u,   (ii) $\bar{x}$ and $\bar{u}$.   Find $\bar{x}$ and $\bar{u}$ from Σx and Σu respectively,
and check that the values you obtain satisfy the relationship in your answer to
(ii).

****

(i) $u = x - 2$ *or* $x = u + 2$ *(ii)* $\bar{u} = \bar{x} - 2$ *or* $\bar{x} = \bar{u} + 2$

   $\bar{x} = 24/6 = 4$ *and* $\bar{u} = 12/6 = 2$, *thus satisfying (ii)*

When you found $\Sigma(u - \bar{u})^2$ in 52A you may have noticed that its value, 98, was
the same as that of $\Sigma(x - \bar{x})^2$, given in FRAME 52.   The reason for this
equality can now be established.   Look at the answers you have just written
down in response to the last frame and deduce a relationship between every value
of $u - \bar{u}$ and the corresponding value of $x - \bar{x}$.

****

$u - \overline{u} = x - \overline{x}$

This obviously leads to $\Sigma(u - \overline{u})^2 = \Sigma(x - \overline{x})^2$ and, in consequence, to var(u) = var(x). (var(u) is an abbreviation for the variance of u.)

Now to describe a change of origin in more general terms. When starting with values of a variate x, changing the origin to x = k will give values of x' where

$$x' = x - k \qquad \text{i.e.} \qquad x = x' + k$$

If follows that $\overline{x}' = \overline{x} - k \qquad \text{i.e.} \qquad \overline{x} = \overline{x}' + k$

whence $x' - \overline{x}' = x - \overline{x}$ and $\Sigma(x' - \overline{x}')^2 = \Sigma(x - \overline{x})^2$

$$\therefore \ \ \text{var}(x') = \text{var}(x)$$

Thus, if obtaining a variance is your sole aim, you can reduce the size of the numbers in the calculations by subtracting a suitable constant from all the observations. As the variance of the new values is the same as the variance of the original ones, you can then forget all about the subtraction which has taken place.

We shall now look at how a change of unit can reduce the number of digits required in the working. Like the change of origin it is an idea you would find springing to mind quite naturally. For instance, if the salaries of 4 people were £2800, £3100, £2100 and £4400 and you were asked to find their mean salary you would probably, for the moment, disregard the 0's and calculate the mean of 28, 31, 21 and 44. Having found that to be 31 you would then put the 0's back again and give the answer as £3100. What you would really be doing is making a temporary change of unit from £'s to £100's. If x denotes the original salaries and x' the working values, the relation between them is seen to be

$$x' = \frac{x}{100} \qquad \text{or} \qquad x = 100x' \qquad (61.1)$$

$$\text{whence} \qquad \overline{x} = 100\overline{x}' \qquad (61.2)$$

What are the values of $\overline{x}'$ and $\overline{x}$ respectively?

****

$\overline{x}' = 31 \qquad \overline{x} = 3100$

Now look at (61.1) and (61.2), write down the equation which connects every value of $x - \overline{x}$ with the corresponding value of $x' - \overline{x}'$ and deduce the relation between var(x) and var(x').

****

$x - \overline{x} = 100(x' - \overline{x}') \qquad \Sigma(x - \overline{x})^2 = 10\,000\Sigma(x' - \overline{x}')^2$
$var(x) = 10\,000\ var(x')$

Notice that, while in the case of the mean it is a matter of multiplying by 100 when changing back to the original units, as stated in (61.2), in the case of $\Sigma(x - \overline{x})^2$ or the variance a factor of 100^2 is required.

What will be the relationship here between the standard deviations of x and x'?

****

63A

s.d.(x) = 100 s.d.(x')
(s.d.(x) is an abbreviation for the standard deviation of x.)

FRAME 64

In the example of the salaries the use of a larger working unit, i.e. £100 instead of £1, avoided a lot of zeros (only 2 per value of x, but 4 per value of x^2, remember). For the following data it would be advantageous to choose a smaller working unit and thus avoid decimals.

The percentage of KCN (potassium cyanide) in a fire-metal extraction liquor was estimated at 5 different times during a production run. The results were: 0·30, 0·33, 0·26, 0·29, 0·32.

Using x for values of % KCN, the change to a unit of 0·01% KCN would give values of x' where $x' = \dfrac{x}{0\cdot01} = 100x$.

See if you can write down the equations giving (i) $\overline{x}$ in terms of $\overline{x}'$, (ii) $\Sigma(x - \overline{x})^2$ in terms of $\Sigma(x' - \overline{x}')^2$, (iii) var(x) in terms of var(x'), (iv) s.d.(x) in terms of s.d.(x').

****

64A

(i) $\overline{x} = 0\cdot01\overline{x}'$ *(ii) $\Sigma(x - \overline{x})^2 = 0\cdot0001\Sigma(x' - \overline{x}')^2$*
(iii) var(x) = 0·0001 var(x')   *(iv)   s.d.(x) = 0·01 s.d.(x')*

FRAME 65

Generalising, if a temporary change of unit is effected by the substitution $x' = \dfrac{x}{h}$, then x = hx' and $\overline{x} = h\overline{x}'$

whence $x - \overline{x} = h(x' - \overline{x}')$ and $\Sigma(x - \overline{x})^2 = h^2\Sigma(x' - \overline{x}')^2$

$\therefore$ $var(x) = h^2 var(x')$ and   s.d.(x) = h s.d.(x')

FRAME 66

So far, the illustrations of coding shown have used <u>either</u> a working origin <u>or</u> a working unit. We shall now turn to examples where <u>both</u> are used.

In FRAME 58 the change of origin made by x' = x - 104 was applied to the values of x given in FRAME 57. The values of x' thus obtained were 0·3, 0·2, 0·9, 0·1 and 0·0. A change of unit as well as change of origin would make things even simpler by getting rid of the decimals. Which of the following do you think would achieve this?

(i) $x' = \dfrac{x - 104}{0\cdot1}$ (ii) $x' = 0\cdot1(x - 104)$ (iii) $x' = 10(x - 104)$

****

(i) or (iii).   Both represent the same transformation.

The values of x' thus obtained would be: 3, 2, 9, 1 and 0 giving $\Sigma x' = 15$,
$\Sigma x'^2 = 95$ and $\Sigma(x' - \overline{x}')^2 = \Sigma x'^2 - (\Sigma x')^2/5 = 95 - 15^2/5 = 50$.   Notice the
reduction in the number of figures required in the working, as compared with
that with the x's in FRAME 57.

The calculations are not finished, however, as it is necessary to change back to
the original origin and unit.   For this we require x in terms of x', and so
rewrite $x' = \dfrac{x - 104}{0 \cdot 1}$ as $x = 0 \cdot 1x' + 104$.   Now write down $\overline{x}$ in terms of $\overline{x}'$
and $\Sigma(x - \overline{x})^2$ in terms of $\Sigma(x' - \overline{x}')^2$, and use these relationships to deduce
the values of $\overline{x}$ and $\Sigma(x - \overline{x})^2$ from the values of $\Sigma x'$, $\Sigma x'^2$ etc. given at the
beginning of this frame.

****

$\overline{x} = 0 \cdot 1\overline{x}' + 104$ *and* $\Sigma(x - \overline{x})^2 = 0 \cdot 01\Sigma(x' - \overline{x}')^2$
$\overline{x}' = \dfrac{15}{5} = 3$ *leads to* $\overline{x} = 0 \cdot 1 \times 3 + 104 = 104 \cdot 3$ *(which agrees with the value*
found from Σx in FRAME 58)
$\Sigma(x - \overline{x})^2 = 0 \cdot 01 \times 50 = 0 \cdot 50$ *(which agrees with the value found in FRAME 57)*

To sum up,

$$x' = \frac{x - k}{h} \qquad (68.1)$$

represents a change of origin and a change of unit.

You then have

$$\overline{x} = h\overline{x}' + k \qquad (68.2)$$
$$\Sigma(x - \overline{x})^2 = h^2\Sigma(x' - \overline{x}')^2$$
$$var(x) = h^2\ var(x')$$
$$s.d.(x) = h\ s.d.(x') \qquad (68.3)$$

What were the values of h and k used in the preceding frame?   What values
of h and k would give   0, 3, -4, -1 and 2 for the coded form of the % KCN
data in FRAME 64?

****

$h = 0 \cdot 1$ $k = 104$
$h = 0 \cdot 01$ $k = 0 \cdot 30$ *i.e.* $x' = \dfrac{x - 0 \cdot 30}{0 \cdot 01}$ *or* $x' = 100x - 30$

We shall now look at the use of coding in calculating the mean and standard
deviation for a frequency table.   In the case of the calculations in FRAMES 54
and 55 the values of the variate x (number of occupants in the first example,
number of breaks in the second) could not be made any simpler by coding but the

same cannot be said of the frequency table showing the lives of 80 electric
lamps.   In FRAME 31 the mean was calculated from this table, the arithmetic
was already beginning to look rather nasty and we purposely avoided this set of
data when later demonstrating variance and standard deviation calculations.
Just think of the size of numbers that would occur in the column fx^2!   A
change of origin and unit will reduce the number of figures required in the
working as you will now see.

The choice of a working origin can make some allowance for personal preference.
If you prefer to avoid working with negative numbers, move the origin to
x = 300·5 i.e. take k = 300·5, but the greatest reduction in the size of
numbers would be achieved by taking k = 1100·5 or 1300·5.   We'll use 1100·5.
On its own, this change of origin, represented by x' = x - 1100·5, will lead
to values of x' which are all (i) positive, (ii) negative, (iii) multiples of
the group width.   Which of (i), (ii) and (iii) is correct?

****

69A

*(iii) x' will take values -800, -600, -400, -200, 0, 200 etc. which are all
    multiples of 200, the group width.*

FRAME 70

You will now see that it would be a good idea to choose 200 hours as a working
unit - the group width is always a convenient choice when coding for frequency
tables, for reasons which should now be obvious.

Substituting k = 1100·5 and h = 200 in (68.1) gives $x' = \dfrac{x - 1100·5}{200}$

Using this formula, write down the values of x' corresponding to
x = 300·5, 500·5, 700·5, ..., 2100·5.

****

70A

-4,   -3,   -2,   -1,   0,   1,   2,   3,   4,   5

FRAME 71

The calculation of the mean and standard deviation of this frequency
distribution is set out in the following table:

x	f	x'	fx'	fx'^{2}
300·5	1	-4	-4	16
500·5	2	-3	-6	18
700·5	5	-2	-10	20
900·5	12	-1	-12	12
1100·5	17	0	0	0
1300·5	20	1	20	20
1500·5	12	2	24	48
1700·5	7	3	21	63
1900·5	3	4	12	48
2100·5	1	5	5	25
			50	270

$\bar{x}' = \dfrac{50}{80}$

Substituting in (68.2) gives

$\bar{x} = 200 \times \dfrac{50}{80} + 1100·5 = 1225·5$

$\Sigma f(x' - \bar{x}')^2 = 270 - 50^2/80 = 238·75$

$\mathrm{var}(x') = 238·75/80 \qquad = 2·9844$

$\mathrm{s.d.}(x') = 1·728$

$\mathrm{s.d.}(x) = 200 \times 1·728$ from (68.3)

$\qquad\qquad = 346$

Mean length of life = 1225·5 hours
Standard deviation = 346 hours

Now, an example to give you a chance to try out these ideas for yourself.

One of the factors considered when determining the susceptibility to liquefaction, during earthquake motions, of sands below a foundation is their penetration resistance as measured by blow counts (number of blows per unit length of penetration). At a site under investigation, blow count tests were made at different depths and locations in the soil layer. The results are classified in the table below:

Class interval (blows/unit length)	1-10	11-20	21-30	31-40	41-50	51-60
Number of tests	11	29	18	4	5	3

The mean, variance and standard deviation of this distribution are required and the calculations are to be done using a change of unit and origin.

As a preliminary, decide what the working unit should be and suggest a working origin. Then write down the formula giving the coded values x' in terms of x (blows/unit length).

****

The interval width is 10 and this should be used as the working unit.

Any of the interval mid-points i.e. 5·5, 15·5, 25·5, ..., 55·5 can be used as a working origin. Whichever one you chose should be substituted for k, with h = 10, in (68.1) to give the formula asked for. Thus, if 25·5 is your working origin, the formula should be $x' = \dfrac{x - 25·5}{10}$.

Having ensured that you are on the correct path, all is now ready for you to go ahead with the calculations. The solution in the answer frame will use 25·5 as a temporary origin so you will find it easier to check your working if you do the same.

****

x	f	x'	fx'	fx'^2
5·5	11	-2	-22	44
15·5	29	-1	-29	29
25·5	18	0	0	0
35·5	4	1	4	4
45·5	5	2	10	20
55·5	3	3	9	27
			-28	124

$\overline{x}' = \dfrac{-28}{70} = -0·4$

$\overline{x} = -10 \times 0·4 + 25·5 = 21·5$

$var(x') = \{124 - (-0·4)(-28)\}/70$
$\qquad = 1·611$

$var(x) = 1·611 \times 10^2 = 161$
$s.d.(x) = \sqrt{1·611} \times 10 = 12·7$ } *to 3 sig.figs.*

Quiz

Before proceeding to the miscellaneous examples, a quick quiz may help to reinforce your assimilation of the ideas which have been presented in this programme.

FRAME 74   (continued)

FILL IN THE GAPS IN THE FOLLOWING SENTENCES:

1. In a histogram, frequencies are represented by ....

2. The variate in Question ...... of the examples in FRAME 75 is discrete.

3. For the frequency table in Question 6 in FRAME 75:
    (i)   The interval width is .... and the interval mid-points are ....
    (ii) When drawing a histogram for this distribution, the bases of the
          rectangles would have their end points at ....
    (iii) The cumulative frequency table would show that there are
          0 observations < ....
          3 observations < ....
          .. observations < 49·5
    (iv) When the ogive is drawn, the vertical scale will represent ....
          and the horizontal scale ....

4. (i)   The 25th percentile is called the ....
    (ii) The 50th percentile is called the ....
    (iii) ......% of observations exceed the 75th percentile, which is called
          the ....

5. If $\overline{x}$ is the mean of n values of x, then $\sum\limits_{i=1}^{n} (x_i - \overline{x})$ is always equal to

    .... If a has any value other than $\overline{x}$, then $\sum\limits_{i=1}^{n} (x_i - \overline{x})^2$ is

    .... than $\sum\limits_{i=1}^{n} (x_i - a)^2$.

6. Coefficient of variation = $\dfrac{\text{........}}{\text{Mean}} \times 100$

7. For a discrete variate the mode is the value corresponding to the highest
    ....

8. When using coding for calculating the mean and standard deviation from a
    frequency table, a suitable choice of working unit is ....

    ****

74A

1. *the areas of rectangles.*

2. *2*

3. *(i)   10;   34·5, 44·5, ... 124·5*
    (ii)   29·5, 39·5, 49·5 etc.
    (iii) 29·5, 39·5, 9
    (iv)   % cumulative frequency, speed in km/h

4. *(i)   lower quartile   (ii) median   (iii) 25, upper quartile*

5. *zero, less*

6. *standard deviation*

7. *frequency (NOTE: For a continuous variate, the mode occurs where the
    frequency density is highest.)*

8. *the interval width.*

Miscellaneous Examples

In this frame a collection of miscellaneous examples is given for you to try. Answers are supplied in FRAME 76, together with such working as is considered helpful.

1. A team of three geologists, investigating the composition of river pebbles, collected basalt pebbles from a selected stream and measured their intermediate diameters.

    One member of the team collected 50 such pebbles and found their intermediate diameters to have a mean of 26 mm, another member collected 25, giving a mean of 30 mm, and the third obtained a mean value of 20 mm from his collection of 35 pebbles.

    Find the mean intermediate diameter of all the pebbles collected by the team.

    (The intermediate diameter is a measurement used by geologists in assessing pebble size.)

2. A standard method for counting bacteria in liquids (such as milk and drinking water) entails, first of all, the dilution with sterile water of the liquid under examination. Next, 1 ml of the diluted liquid is placed in a nutrient medium in a dish and incubated for 24 hours. The colonies of bacteria which have formed by that time are then counted, it being assumed that each colony has arisen from a single organism in the original 1 ml sample.

    The following table shows the counts obtained when 40 samples from the diluted liquid had been incubated.

Number of colonies	0	1	2	3	4
Number of dishes	8	13	12	5	2

    Find the mean, variance and standard deviation of the number of bacteria in 1 ml of diluted liquid.

3. Ten observations of a variate x were made, giving the following values:

    129·6 128·9 129·0 129·1 128·8 129·5 129·4 128·9 129·2 129·3

    The data was "coded" by changing the origin (by subtracting 129 from each of these values) and also changing the unit. The corresponding values of the new variate u were then:

    6   -1   0   1   -2   5   4   -1   2   3

    State the formula for u in terms of x, and for x in terms of u. Then, given that $\Sigma u = 17$ and $\Sigma u^2 = 97$, find $\bar{u}$, $\bar{x}$, $\Sigma(u - \bar{u})^2$ and $\Sigma(x - \bar{x})^2$.

4. The mean and standard deviation of some temperature data, recorded in $^{\circ}$C, are 30 and 5 respectively. If the data were converted into $^{\circ}$F, what would the mean, variance and s.d. then be? (The conversion formula relating F and C, the corresponding temperatures on the F- and C- scales respectively, is $F = 1·8C + 32$.)

5. The following frequency table records the diameters of 200 grains of moulding sand in appropriate units.

Diameter d	8	10	12	14	16	18	20
Frequency	25	40	67	35	23	7	3

FRAME 75   (continued)

State the group in which the mode occurs, estimate the median and draw a histogram for the distribution.   Choose a suitable assumed mean and hence calculate the mean and standard deviation σ of the distribution.

The standard deviation calculated from the original measurements (before grouping) was 2·88.   Why is there a discrepancy between this and your value of σ?   (C.E.I.)

6.   The table shows a frequency distribution for spot speed of cars measured on a three-lane rural trunk road.

Class interval km/h	Frequency
30–39	3
40–49	6
50–59	24
60–69	64
70–79	50
80–89	29
90–99	14
100–109	6
110–119	3
120–129	1

(i)   A histogram can serve to show relative frequencies – in that case the area of each rectangle will represent the relative frequency in the group.   Draw the histogram representing the relative frequencies in this distribution of speeds.

(ii)   Draw the frequency polygon representing the frequency distribution. Traffic engineers use the term "pace" for the speed range of stated width (usually 20 km/h) which contains the most vehicles.   From the frequency polygon estimate the 20 km/h pace of the cars on this road.

(iii)   Form a table showing cumulative frequency and % cumulative frequency.

(iv)   Draw the ogive.

(v)   Estimate the median speed.

(vi)   Estimate the following percentile speeds:
(a)   the 15th, which shows the slower vehicles whose speed may be causing interference within the traffic stream,
(b)   the 85th, which can be used in the consideration of speed limit imposition or overtaking distances,
(c)   the 98th, which is often used as a design speed in geometric layout.

(vii)   Find the arithmetic mean, variance, standard deviation and coefficient of variation.

7.   Although it would be possible for the following frequency table to result from genuine observations, it would be very unlikely.   What special feature do you notice?

x	0·5–5·5	5·5–10·5	10·5–15·5	15·5–20·5	20·5–25·5	25·5–30·5	30·5–35·5
f	1	2	7	10	7	2	1

Find the arithmetic mean and the median.

8.   The frequency table on the next page shows the results obtained when the time between successive vehicles on a U.S. freeway were recorded.

Time gap (seconds)	Number of gaps observed
0-2	40
2-4	32
4-6	26
6-8	25
8-10	22
10-12	18
12-14	8
14-16	6
16-18	9
18-20	6
20-22	2
22-24	1
24-26	1
26-28	2
28-30	2

(i)   Draw the histogram representing this distribution.

(ii) In each of the three previous examples the arithmetic mean was in the modal group. Is that the case with this data?

(iii) Find the standard deviation.

9.   In order to make production in a factory more efficient, the manager called in consultants to do an investigation. An analysis, indicating the distribution of ages of the workers, was as follows:

Ages	16-19	20-29	30-39	40-49	50-59	60-64
Frequency	15	46	49	32	28	14

Calculate the mean and median. Draw a histogram of the data and indicate on it both the mean and median.

As a result of this study all those aged 60 and over, together with 6 others who are 59, were made redundant. Find the new mean and median.

(C.E.I.)

Answers to Miscellaneous Examples

1. $\dfrac{50 \times 26 + 25 \times 30 + 35 \times 20}{110} = 25$ mm

2.   Mean = 1·5,   Variance = 1·2,   Standard deviation = 1·095.

3. $u = (x - 129)/0\cdot1$ or $10(x - 129)$, $x = 129 + 0\cdot1u$, $\bar{u} = 1\cdot7$,
     $\bar{x} = 129\cdot17$, $\Sigma(u - \bar{u})^2 = 68\cdot1$, $\Sigma(x - \bar{x})^2 = 0\cdot681$.

4. $\bar{F} = 1\cdot8\bar{C} + 32 = 86$, $\text{var}(F) = 1\cdot8^2\text{var}(C) = 81$,   s.d.(F) = 9.

FRAME 76   (continued)

5.

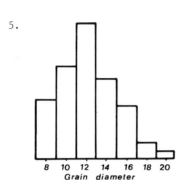

Grain diameter

The group whose central value is 12.

Median $= 11 + \dfrac{35}{67} \times 2 = 12 \cdot 0$

A suitable assumed mean (i.e. working origin) would be $d = 14$, but any of the other central values could be used.

Mean $= 12 \cdot 24$ $\sigma = 2 \cdot 74$

The difference between this value of σ and $2 \cdot 88$ is explained by taking all readings in a group as having its central value, whereas it is very unlikely that this was the case with the original data.

6.   (i)   Marking off bases of rectangles already discussed in quiz.   You probably realised that the shape of the histogram is the same whether it represents frequencies or relative frequencies.   For instance, the area of the rectangle corresponding to the group   50–59   must be   4   times the area of the rectangle corresponding to the group 40–49,   whether frequencies   24   and   6   are being represented or relative frequencies   24/200   and   6/200.

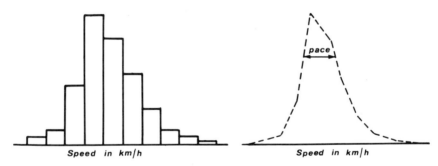

Speed in km/h   Speed in km/h

(ii)   59–79 km/h approx., i.e. where the width of the frequency polygon is 20.

(iii)

x	Cum. Freq. i.e. no. of speeds < x	% Cum. Freq.
29·5	0	0
39·5	3	1·5
49·5	9	4·5
59·5	33	16·5
69·5	97	48·5
79·5	147	73·5
89·5	176	88·0
99·5	190	95·0
109·5	196	98·0
119·5	199	99·5
129·5	200	100·0

(iv)

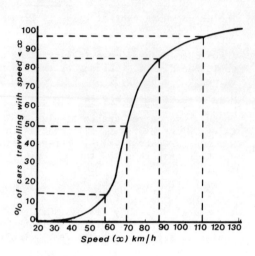

(v)   70 km/h

(vi)   (a) 58 km/h   (b) 87 km/h   (c) 109·5 km/h

(vii) 72·0,   230·75,   15·2,   21·1%

7. The distribution is symmetrical.   A.M. = 18   Median = 18

Note that the mean and median are equal, a property of symmetrical distributions.

8. (i)

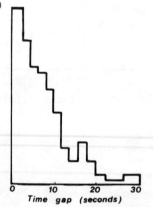

(ii)   No.   Mean = 7·5 s.   Notice the lack of symmetry of this distribution, which is termed skew.

(iii)   6·15 s.

9. Mean = 37·49, from 17·5, 24·5, 34·5, 44·5, 54·5, 62·0 for mid-points of groups.   The median is in the group 30–39,   its value can only be estimated.   Simple proportion gives $29 \cdot 5 + \frac{31}{49} \times 10 = 35 \cdot 8$.

FRAME 76   (continued)

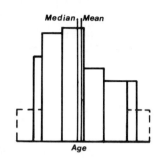

The bases of the rectangles have their boundaries at 15·5, 19·5, 29·5, 39·5, 49·5, 59·5, 64·5.

Did you remember that the frequencies are represented by the <u>areas</u> of the rectangles?   Hence, for instance, the heights of the rectangles for the two oldest age groups should be the same.

Alternatively you could make all groups the same width by taking the first and last to be 10-19 and 60-69 respectively.   The rectangles at each end would then be as shown by the dotted lines. However, you would then have ignored the fact that no workers are of age less than 16 or more than 64. 34·77,   33·8.

Probability

Introduction

The previous programme referred to the chance variation that affects the outcome
of, for example, titrating a certain volume of acid with an alkali or life-
testing a light bulb or counting disintegrations in a radioactive source or
throwing a die.   It is the uncertainty caused by this variation that gives rise
to the need for statistical methods.

Anyone who at any time has taken part in games of chance will know that although
the result (of throwing a die, tossing a coin etc.) is unpredictable, some
results are equally likely while others are not.   When the Oxford and Cambridge
boat race crews toss a coin to decide who will row on which side of the river,
they do so on the assumption that the two possible outcomes - heads and tails -
are equally likely.   But a player throwing a die, in a game in which success
depends on getting a six, is aware that "not a six" is a much more likely
outcome of a throw than "six".   Turning from games of chance to testing two
light bulbs, one Standard and one Longer-life, it is possible that the Standard
would last longer than the Longer-life but not very probable.

Whereas in conversation you might say that it was "very hot" yesterday, the
expert from the Meteorological Office would give the maximum temperature in ^{o}C
and though a person might describe himself as "tall and thin", when it comes to
buying clothes a more exact description in the form of measurements is needed.
In the same way, terms like "much more likely" and "not very probable" are too
vague for many purposes and so ways of measuring probability have been devised.

The aim of this programme is to give you a grounding in probability theory, on
which later to build and on which the understanding of statistical methods
depends.

The Classical (a priori) Approach

Any introduction to probability invariably uses, for illustration, examples
about coins being tossed or dice being thrown or cards being drawn from a pack.
This is not with the aim of encouraging a passion for gambling (a knowledge of
probability is, if anything, a deterrent in this respect) but because games of
chance provide as good a starting point for the student of to-day as they did
for the mathematicians of the past who developed the fundamental principles of
probability theory.

In the middle of the 17th century a French courtier, the Chevalier de Méré,
wanted to know how to adjust the stakes in gambling so that, in the long run,
the advantage would be his.   He took his problem to his fellow countryman,
Blaise Pascal, and it was in the correspondence between the latter and another
French mathematician, Pierre Fermat, that the theory of probability had its
beginnings.   Just as, in the course of time, further development of this theory
led to its application to problems in science and industry, so also by the end
of this programme you will have reached the point where you can see why this
topic is of interest to engineers and scientists.

Anyone who calls "Heads!" when a coin is tossed does so in the belief that this
prediction is as likely to be right as it is to be wrong.   The phrase
"fifty-fifty" is often used to describe the chances of winning or losing the

toss - this phrase is just a way of saying that the probability of the coin coming down with the head uppermost is 50%, and the probability of a tail resulting is 50%.   Putting it slightly differently, there are 2 possible outcomes, equally likely, and for each the chance of occurrence is $\frac{1}{2}$.   This may be so obvious that one is hardly aware of the reasoning behind it but we have to examine it more closely if we are to know how to deal with more complicated problems.

The tossing of the coin has 2 distinct, equally likely outcomes, of which 1 is "heads".

$\therefore$.   The probability of "heads" occurring = $\frac{1}{2}$

$\qquad\qquad$ i.e. $\dfrac{\text{Number of outcomes involving occurrence of a head}}{\text{Number of possible outcomes}}$

P( ) is a common notation to denote the probability of the event described in the brackets occurring.   Using H for the event "heads" we can write $P(H) = \frac{1}{2}$. Using T for the event "tails" similar reasoning to the above leads to $P(T) = \frac{1}{2}$.

Turning now to the throwing of a six-sided die, there are 6 distinct, equally likely, outcomes i.e. 1, 2, 3, 4, 5, 6.   Only 1 of these entails getting a 5, so

$\qquad P(5) = \dfrac{1}{6}$ i.e. $\dfrac{\text{Number of outcomes entailing occurrence of 5}}{\text{Number of possible outcomes}}$

Similar reasoning leads to $P(1) = \dfrac{1}{6}$, $P(2) = \dfrac{1}{6}$ and so on.

In many games, not getting a 6 is the player's misfortune.   Of the 6 possible outcomes, 5 entail the occurrence of this misfortune.

$\qquad \therefore$ $P(\text{not a } 6) = \dfrac{\text{Number of outcomes which entail not getting a } 6}{\text{Number of possible outcomes}} = \dfrac{5}{6}$

For each of the events listed below, write down how many of the 6 possible outcomes entail their occurrence.   Then deduce the probability of the event occurring.

(i)   An even number.   (ii)   A number greater than 2.   (iii)   7
(iv)   A number less than 7.

$\qquad\qquad$ ***

$\qquad\qquad\qquad\qquad\qquad\qquad\qquad\qquad\qquad\qquad\qquad\qquad\qquad\qquad$ 4A

(i)   3.   P(even number) = $\dfrac{3}{6}$ = $\dfrac{1}{2}$ $\qquad\qquad$ *(ii)   4.   P(number > 2) = $\dfrac{4}{6}$ = $\dfrac{2}{3}$*

(iii)   0.   P(7) = $\dfrac{0}{6}$ = 0 $\qquad\qquad\qquad$ *(iv)   6.   P(number < 7) = $\dfrac{6}{6}$ = 1*

In the last two frames probabilities have been assigned to particular events. The next step is to formulate in more general terms how a probability is calculated.   For lack of a better word, "experiment" is often used to cover what might be the tossing of a coin, the throwing of a die or the drawing of a card, i.e. whatever it is that has an unpredictable outcome and may, or may not, give rise to the event whose probability is being sought.   In every case, so far, we have expressed the probability of an experiment resulting in this event

FRAME 5   (continued)

as a fraction.   The denominator was always the total number of distinct, equally
likely outcomes of the experiment (2 in tossing the coin, 6 in throwing the
die) and the numerator was the number of these outcomes which entailed the
occurrence of the event.   Denoting the event by E we may write

$$P(E) = \frac{\text{Number of outcomes which entail the occurrence of the event } E}{\text{Number of equally likely outcomes of the experiment}} \qquad (5.1)$$

For the E's considered in the last two frames, P(E) has taken values
ranging from 0 to 1.   Are there E's for which P(E) has values outside this
range?   What kind of events give rise to the values 0 and 1?

****

5A

*No.   Number of outcomes can't be negative – it just wouldn't make sense – so
P(E) is never < 0.   Denominator of P(E)   embraces <u>all</u> possible outcomes so
number of outcomes involving E can't be greater and therefore P(E) can't be >1.
P(E) = 0   when numerator = 0   i.e. no outcomes entail occurrence of E, which
is another way of saying E never happens.   For example, you can't throw a 7
with the die.*

*P(E) = 1   when numerator = denominator   i.e. all outcomes entail E happening.
For example, when throwing the die you'll always get a number <7.*

FRAME 6

Probability, then, is measured on a scale from 0 to 1.   It can be given as a
decimal, a fraction or a percentage.   If a general value is to be indicated the
letter p is usually used.   We then have $0 \leqslant p \leqslant 1$.   As you have seen, for
events which are utterly impossible, p = 0, and for absolute certainties,
p = 1.

FRAME 7

It is very easy to be misled by fallacious arguments if one does not fully
understand the fundamental concepts on which probability, as defined in (5.1),
is based.   Before we enlarge further on this, examine each of the following
statements and say whether you think the argument is valid and if not, why not.

(i)   If two coins are tossed simultaneously, there are three possible outcomes,
      two heads, two tails or one of each.   Therefore for each of these events
      the probability of occurrence is $\frac{1}{3}$.

(ii) If a die is thrown there are two possible outcomes: an odd number or an
      even number.   Therefore the probability of getting an odd number is $\frac{1}{2}$
      and the probability of getting an even number is $\frac{1}{2}$.

****

7A

*(i) Not valid.   Although the outcomes can be classified like this, they are
     not then "equally likely", as the definition requires.   "One of each" can
     result from a head with coin No. 1 and a tail with coin No. 2 or from a
     tail with coin No. 1 and a head with coin No. 2.   This makes it twice as
     likely as two heads, for instance, which can only happen one way.*

7A   (continued)

*(ii)   Valid.   The two outcomes considered here are equally likely, so the
condition imposed by the definition is satisfied.   If you recalled how
P(even number) was found in FRAME 4, you may have said that the statement
is incorrect, as there are 6 outcomes, not 2.   Well, it all depends
what you mean by outcomes, doesn't it, so we'll have to look at this a bit
more closely in the next frame.*

FRAME 8

The time is now opportune for an explanation of the term ELEMENTARY OUTCOME,
often used in probability theory.   The outcomes "odd" and "even" in (ii) of the
preceding frame can each be broken down further, into the outcomes 1, 3 and 5
in the case of "odd" and 2, 4 and 6 in the case of "even", but with these
outcomes no further subdivision is possible – 1 is just 1, 2 is just 2, and
so on.   Thus throwing a die has 6 elementary outcomes: 1, 2, 3, 4, 5 and 6
on the uppermost face.

When P(even number) was found in FRAME 4 it was done working with elementary
outcomes, an approach to be recommended when the definition of probability as in
(5.1) is being applied.   The statement (i) of the preceding frame is, in fact,
similar to others wrongly propounded in the early stages of the development of
probability theory because of a lack of appreciation that elementary outcomes,
of equal likelihood, should be considered.   When two coins are tossed there are
4 elementary outcomes, which can be denoted by HH, HT, TH, TT.   Hence

$$P(2 \text{ heads}) = \frac{1}{4}, \quad P(2 \text{ tails}) = \frac{1}{4} \quad \text{and} \quad P(\text{one of each}) = \frac{2}{4} = \frac{1}{2}.$$

Now test your understanding of elementary outcomes by answering the following
questions.

A card is drawn from a pack of 52 playing cards (well shuffled, of course!).

(i)   What is the total number of elementary outcomes of this experiment?

(ii)   How many of these outcomes entail the occurrence of   (a) the ace of hearts,
(b) an ace,   (c) a heart,   (d) a card which is not a heart?   Deduce the
respective probabilities of each of these events.

   ****

8A

(i)   52
(ii)   (a) 1   (b) 4   (c) 13   (d) 39

$$\frac{1}{52}, \qquad \frac{4}{52} = \frac{1}{13}, \qquad \frac{13}{52} = \frac{1}{4}, \qquad \frac{39}{52} = \frac{3}{4}$$

FRAME 9

The Empirical Approach

In older textbooks, especially, you will often see the classical definition of
probability (5.1) given the Latin description 'a priori'.   What this is
stressing is that the definition can be applied prior to any experiment having
been carried out.   In the preceding frames we have calculated the probabilities
of events arising from coin tossing, die throwing and card drawing without
actually carrying out any experiment of this kind.   One might adapt a well-
known idiom and describe it as being "wise before the event".   Such an approach
is all very well when dealing with the games of chance type of problem, and it
solved the Chevalier de Méré's difficulties quite satisfactorily, but its field

of application is limited, as de Moivre found at the beginning of the 18th
century.   He was employed by an insurance firm in London and was engaged in the
calculation of annuities.   Briefly, in case you're not familiar with this type
of insurance, the client pays an annual sum (the premium) until the age of, say,
60 when the insurance company contracts to then pay him an agreed sum each year
until death.   Obviously both client and company take a chance - it's a good
bargain for the insurance company if the client dies aged 61 but a good bargain
for the client if he lives to be 100.   These chances must be carefully
balanced if the proposition is to be attractive to a potential client without,
at the same time, seriously risking the bankruptcy of the company.   Nowadays
this is the province of the actuary, whose professional training includes a
study of probability.

FRAME 10

If a person aged, say, 32, is a prospective customer for an annuity, payable
from the age of 60 onwards, probabilities such as P(person aged 32 will die
during next 28 years) and P(person aged 32 will live to age 100) are
relevant to the calculation of the premium.   Try to apply the classical
definition which we used with tossing coins and throwing dice, and you'll see
why de Moivre had to develop a new line of approach.   No longer can a list of
elementary outcomes, all equally likely, be enumerated just by considering the
problem.   However, even before we've discussed how to deal with this situation,
the following statements should provoke some comment from you:

(i)   P(person aged 32 will die during next 28 years) = 0·99
(ii)   P(person aged 32 will live to age 100) = 0

Well?

****

10A

(i) Don't believe it!
(ii) But some people <u>do</u> live to be 100, so it cannot be ruled out as impossible.

FRAME 11

No doubt your comments in the last answer frame were based on what you knew had
happened in the past.   You see so many people around you over 60 years of age
that it's just unbelievable that, for a person now aged 32, death before 60 is
almost certain (nearly said a dead cert!).   You've also heard of people
celebrating their 100th birthday and receiving a message of congratulations
from the Queen.   As it's unusual you would think that the probability of a
person aged 32 living to be 100 is very small, but not zero.   Looking back on
the past, then, would seem to offer an alternative way of assessing probabilities.
This led to the empirical definition (based on being wise <u>after</u> the event) which
may be summarised as

$$P(E) = \frac{\text{Number of times E occurred}}{\text{Number of times experiment was carried out}} \qquad (11.1)$$

As with all empirical formulae, it can only yield approximations and the larger
the number of experiments the better.

Here is an extract from a life table (or mortality table, depending on which
way you look at it!) for English males. ℓ_x is the number of men, out of a

million born, surviving to exact age x.

x	ℓ_x
90	16 090
91	11 490
92	8012
93	5448
94	3607
95	2320

Noticing that, of 16 090 men aged 90, 4600 (i.e. 16 090-11 490) died before reaching their 91st birthday, we estimate, using (11.1), that

P(man aged 90 will die within a year) $= \dfrac{4600}{16\ 090}$

Now obtain estimates of the following:

(i) P(man aged 90 will die before his 92nd birthday)
(ii) P(man aged 91 will live for at least 4 years)

****

11A

(i) $\dfrac{16\ 090 - 8012}{16\ 090} = \dfrac{8078}{16\ 090}$ (ii) $\dfrac{2320}{11\ 490}$

FRAME 12

In the first programme of this Unit, the lengths of life of 80 lamps were classified into a frequency table, repeated here for ease of reference. We shall now consider how this data might be used to estimate probabilities concerning the lives of lamps, of the same make, which had not been tested. The total number of lamps tested was 80, and of these 1 had a recorded life of from 201 to 400 hours i.e. an actual life between 200·5 and 400·5 hours as times were recorded to the nearest hour. The empirical definition (11.1) thus gives, for a lamp which has not been tested,

Interval mid-point (hours)	Frequency
300·5	1
500·5	2
700·5	5
900·5	12
1100·5	17
1300·5	20
1500·5	12
1700·5	7
1900·5	3
2100·5	1

P(life between 200·5 and 400·5 hours) $= \dfrac{1}{80}$

Similarly,

P(life between 400·5 and 600·5 hours) $= \dfrac{2}{80}$,

and so on.

Each of the values $\dfrac{1}{80}$, $\dfrac{2}{80}$, $\dfrac{5}{80}$ etc. is a relative frequency showing the proportion, rather than the actual number, of observations occurring in each group. The empirical approach uses this proportion as a probability estimate. From this table, estimate

(i) P(recorded life will exceed 2000 hours),
(ii) P(recorded life will not exceed 1000 hours).

****

12A

(i) $\dfrac{1}{80}$ (ii) $\dfrac{1}{4}$

Number of occupants x	Frequency f
1	15
2	12
3	8
4	4
5	1

Another frequency table in the first programme was formed from data on the occupants of 40 cars. It is shown again here, so that you can refer to it to obtain empirical values for:

P(only 1 occupant in car),

P(2 occupants in car),

P(more than 2 occupants in car).

****

13A

P(only 1 occupant in car)   i.e.   P(x = 1) = 15/40 = 3/8

P(x = 2) = 12/40 = 3/10

P(x > 2) = 13/40   Note: The event "more than 2 occupants" can be broken down into the elementary outcomes 3, 4 and 5 occupants.

It should be emphasised that probability values found empirically are only estimates. If another 80 lamps were tested or another 40 cars observed, different sets of data would almost certainly result, giving different probability estimates. For instance, in the second set of data, there might be no cars at all observed with 5 occupants, so that instead of estimating P(5 occupants in car) as 1/40 a value of zero would be obtained. This in itself would clearly not be exact, as it is not impossible for a car to have 5 occupants.

Large numbers of observations will, on the whole, give more reliable estimates and we can think of (11.1) as giving the true value of P(E) when the experiment is performed an infinitely large number of times, were that possible. Returning to the tossing of a coin, we can now reconcile the present approach to probability with the classical definition first given. To illustrate this a

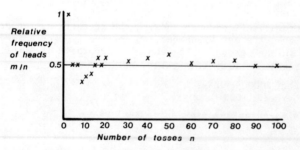

coin which, as far as could be seen, was a fair one, was tossed repeatedly. The number of heads, m, in n tosses was recorded as n increased up to 100. Successive estimates of P(H) given by m/n are plotted here against n.

You will notice that in this case the ratio m/n seems to be settling down around the value $\frac{1}{2}$ as n increases.

It will give you an insight into how chance effects operate if you now repeat this experiment yourself, and note the values of m/n when, say, n = 2, 4, 6, 8, 10, 20, 30, ... 100. Doubtless you will not have enough time on your hands

FRAME 14   (continued)

to emulate the feat of J.E. Kerrich who, while interned in Denmark as a British
subject during the Second World War, recorded 5067 heads in 10 000 tosses of
a coin!

FRAME 15

The Use of Sets

Most approaches to probability today make use of set theory, which is a feature
of modern mathematics syllabuses.   However, if you have followed a traditional
type of mathematics syllabus which did not include this topic, it is debatable
whether it would be worthwhile for you to embark on a study of it now, just in
order to help you think out probability problems.   In APPENDIX A on page 79
you will find a summary of those terms and symbols in set theory that are
referred to in this programme.   You may find that you can get the gist of it
from what is presented there but if you want more explanation you will find a
treatment of sets, adequate for present purposes, in Chapter 2 of Engineering
Mathematics by A.C. Bajpai, L.R. Mustoe and D. Walker (Wiley 1974).
Alternatively you may decide to gloss over this modern approach – the programme
does not commit you to using it.

FRAME 16

If you are familiar with set theory, you may have already spotted that the
possible outcomes of an experiment form a set.   This set, which we shall
denote by S, is called the SAMPLE SPACE or OUTCOME SPACE of the experiment and
its elements are called SAMPLE POINTS.   Thus, for the tossing of a coin
S = {H, T} and for the throwing of a die S = {1, 2, 3, 4, 5, 6}.   They
can be represented diagrammatically as:

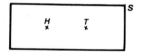

The number of sample points is finite in these two examples but it would be
infinite if, for instance, the outcomes are values of a continuous variate.   If
trains run at 10-minute intervals a traveller with no knowledge of the timetable
will, on arrival at the station, have a waiting time t minutes which can be
anything from 0 to 10 minutes.   In this case, S = {t : 0 < t < 10} which
is the set notation way of saying that S consists of all the elements t such
that 0 < t < 10.

FRAME 17

Continuing with the link-up with set theory, we now look at the event E whose
probability is being calculated. Clearly E is a subset of S.   In the
experiment of throwing a die we first considered, in FRAME 4, the event "getting
a 5".   For this E = {5}; it includes only one sample point and is therefore
sometimes described as a simple event.   On the other hand "not getting a 6",
which was considered next, is a compound event, with E = {1, 2, 3, 4, 5}.   A
simple diagrammatic representation of this is

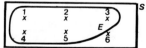

Now express as subsets the events listed
at the end of FRAME 4.

****

(i)   E = {2, 4, 6}   (ii)   E = {3, 4, 5, 6}
(iii) E = ∅ i.e. the null set.   This is the terminology for a set which has
*   no elements in it.*
(iv) E = {1, 2, 3, 4, 5, 6} i.e. S.

FRAME 18

You will now see that when the sample points represent equally likely outcomes
we have $P(E) = \dfrac{n(E)}{n(S)}$.

In the die-throwing experiment, $n(S) = 6$. For E as in (i) in the answers in
17A, $n(E) = 3$ and hence $P(E) = \dfrac{3}{6}$, as was obtained earlier in answering
FRAME 4.   Now write down $n(E)$, and hence $P(E)$, for E as in (ii), (iii) and
(iv).

****

18A

(ii) n(E) = 1   (iii) n(E) = 0   (iv) n(E) = 6
P(E) in each case as in 4A.

FRAME 19

Laws of Probability

When you started learning about the differential calculus you probably had the
concept of a differential coefficient explained to you and then differentiated,
from first principles, some simple functions.   However it would be tedious to
have to differentiate more complicated functions in this way so you found it
useful to have rules which could be applied to the various types of function.
To a lesser extent it is the same with probability.   There are some useful
rules which obviate the need to go back to first principles every time but,
owing to their wide diversity, probability problems cannot always be fitted into
standard categories as can functions for differentiation.

First, there is a simple relationship between the probability of an event
happening and the probability of it not happening, i.e. between $P(E)$ and
$P(\text{not } E)$.   In FRAME 4 it was noted that, in the throw of a die, $P(6) = 1/6$
and $P(\text{not } 6) = 5/6$.   In 8A, for a card drawn from a pack, you found that
$P(\text{heart}) = 1/4$ and $P(\text{not heart}) = 3/4$.   What do these results suggest to you
about $P(E)$ and $P(\text{not } E)$?

****

19A

$\dfrac{1}{6} + \dfrac{5}{6} = 1$ and $\dfrac{1}{4} + \dfrac{3}{4} = 1$, suggesting that P(E) + P(not E) = 1.

FRAME 20

From whichever viewpoint probability is defined, it can be shown that this
relationship will always hold.   For example, using the classical approach,
(5.1) gives

$P(E) = \dfrac{\text{Number of outcomes in E}}{\text{Number of possible outcomes}}$ and $P(\text{not } E) = \dfrac{\text{Number of outcomes not in E}}{\text{Number of possible outcomes}}$

∴   P(E) + P(not E) = $\dfrac{\text{Number of outcomes in E + Number of outcomes not in E}}{\text{Number of possible outcomes}}$

Clearly the numerator covers all possible outcomes and is therefore equal to the denominator.

Hence   P(E) + P(not E) = 1   (20.1)

In set notation, "not E" is the subset which is the complement of E and is denoted by E' or Ē.   The diagram showing this is on the left.

If you are familiar with set theory you will recognise this as a Venn diagram.   With this notation (20.1) may be restated as

P(E) + P(E') = 1

An alternative form of (20.1) is   P(E) = 1 - P(not E)   (21.1)

In some problems the calculation of P(E) from consideration of the event E may be complicated, whereas P(not E) is relatively simple to find and (21.1) then gives an easy way of arriving at P(E).   To illustrate this let us go back to the tossing of two coins simultaneously and try to find P(at least 1 head). First we'll solve the problem without the use of (21.1).   You have already seen that the elementary outcomes are HH, HT, TH, TT.   Write down the number of these outcomes in the event "at least 1 head" and deduce the required probability.

****

3 i.e. HH, HT, TH.   3/4

Listing the possible outcomes of this experiment was quite simple but it would be more complicated if a larger number of coins were being tossed.   Even with 4 coins it would be a bit lengthy - HHHH, HHHT, HHTT, etc., etc!   So we look for a different approach.   Firstly, it is not necessary to list all the possible outcomes in order to know how many there are.   When 2 coins are tossed, there are 2 possible outcomes for Coin No. 1 and for each of these there will be 2 possible outcomes for Coin No. 2.   Therefore the total number of possible outcomes is 2 × 2 i.e. 2^2.   Now use this line of argument to decide the total number of possible outcomes when the number of coins tossed is (i) 3,   (ii) 4.

****

(i)   2 × 2 × 2 = 2^3 (ii) 2^4

Next, instead of considering P(E), where E is the event "at least one head" we consider P(not E).   The event "not E" is very simple - what is it?   Give your answer in a form that applies however many coins are being tossed.

****

No heads.

If 2 coins are tossed, only 1 outcome (i.e. TT) is covered by "no heads".
It has been established that the total number of possible outcomes is 2^2 i.e. 4.

$$\therefore \quad P(\text{no heads}) = \frac{1}{4}$$

Then using (21.1), we get $P(\text{at least 1 head}) = 1 - \frac{1}{4} = \frac{3}{4}$.

Now find $P(\text{at least 1 head})$ in this way when the number of coins tossed is
(i) 3, (ii) 4, (iii) n.

****

(i) $\quad 1 - \frac{1}{8} = \frac{7}{8}$ *(ii)* $\quad 1 - \frac{1}{16} = \frac{15}{16}$ *(iii)* $\quad 1 - \frac{1}{2^n}$

The Addition of Probabilities

To illustrate the next property of probabilities we return to the experiment of
drawing a card from a pack. First write down $P(\text{drawing a diamond})$ and
$P(\text{drawing a red card})$.

****

$P(diamond) = \frac{13}{52} = \frac{1}{4}$, $P(red\ card) = \frac{26}{52} = \frac{1}{2}$

Now in 8A you found that $P(\text{heart}) = \frac{1}{4}$, so we notice that

$$P(\text{red card}) = P(\text{diamond}) + P(\text{heart})$$

i.e. $P(\text{diamond or heart}) = P(\text{diamond}) + P(\text{heart})$

This prompts the question: "Is $P(E_1 \text{ or } E_2) = P(E_1) + P(E_2)$ true for all
events E_1, E_2? Well, in 8A you also found that $P(\text{ace}) = \frac{1}{13}$

$$\therefore P(\text{ace}) + P(\text{heart}) = \frac{1}{13} + \frac{1}{4} = \frac{4}{52} + \frac{13}{52} = \frac{17}{52}$$

If this is $P(\text{ace or heart})$, then 17 of the outcomes of drawing a card from
the pack of 52 must be either an ace or a heart. Is this true?

****

*No.   There are 4 aces and 13 hearts, but the ace of hearts is common to both
and has been counted twice.*

In the first example, the events "drawing a heart" and "drawing a diamond" were
MUTUALLY EXCLUSIVE, that is, if the card you drew was a heart it could not
possibly be a diamond and vice versa.   The number of outcomes included in
"red card" was therefore the sum of the number of outcomes in "heart" and the
number of outcomes in "diamond".   In the second example, however, the events
"ace" and "heart" were not mutually exclusive, as there was one outcome (ace of
hearts) included in both events.   To sum up, if E_1 and E_2 are mutually
exclusive events (i.e. the occurrence of E_1 precludes the occurrence of E_2
and vice versa) then

$$P(E_1 \text{ or } E_2) = P(E_1) + P(E_2) \qquad (27.1)$$

This rule can be extended to any number of mutually exclusive events E_1, E_2,
E_3, ...

e.g. $P(E_1 \text{ or } E_2 \text{ or } E_3) = P(E_1) + P(E_2) + P(E_3) \qquad (27.2)$

In set theory notation (27.1) may be stated as

$$P(E_1 \cup E_2) = P(E_1) + P(E_2) \qquad (27.3)$$

when E_1 and E_2 are disjoint (i.e. having no elements in common).   The Venn
diagram is shown below.

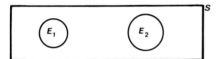

$E_1 \cup E_2$ is the notation for the union
of E_1 and E_2.   When they are disjoint
their union is the set of elements which
belong either to A or to B.

At the end of the last frame you decided that there were not 17 outcomes giving
either an ace or a heart, when a card is drawn from a pack.   What is the correct
number?

****

$17 - 1 = 16$

The correct value of P(ace or heart) is therefore $\frac{16}{52}$ and this can be written:

$$P(\text{ace or heart}) = \frac{4}{52} + \frac{13}{52} - \frac{1}{52}$$

$$= P(\text{ace}) + P(\text{heart}) - P(\text{ace of hearts})$$

The corresponding, more general, result for two events E_1 and E_2 is

$$P(E_1 \text{ or } E_2) = P(E_1) + P(E_2) - P(E_1 \text{ and } E_2) \qquad (28.1)$$

where the event "E_1 or E_2" may include both E_1 and E_2 happening.   You will
see that (27.1) is a special case of this, as when E_1 and E_2 are mutually
exclusive the event "E_1 and E_2" is impossible and hence $P(E_1 \text{ and } E_2) = 0$.
To avoid misunderstanding, you may prefer to think of the "or" in (28.1) as
"and/or", with the "and" option removed when E_1 and E_2 are mutually exclusive
as in (27.1).

In set theory notation (28.1) may be stated as

$$P(E_1 \cup E_2) = P(E_1) + P(E_2) - P(E_1 \cap E_2) \qquad (28.2)$$

where $E_1 \cap E_2$ is the intersection of E_1 and E_2 i.e. the set of elements belonging to both E_1 and E_2.

(27.3) was the special case of this when $E_1 \cap E_2 = \emptyset$. The Venn diagram for the present situation is shown alongside. The two circles represent E_1 and E_2 and the shaded area represents $E_1 \cap E_2$. The area bounded by the thick outline represents $E_1 \cup E_2$.

Here are two problems to test your understanding of this and previous frames.

(i)   Of the students attending a lecture, 50% could not see what was being written on the board and 40% could not hear what the lecturer was saying; a particularly unfortunate 30% fell into both of these categories.   What is the probability that a student picked at random was able to see and hear satisfactorily?   It is suggested that you first find the probability of this <u>not</u> happening, by applying (28.1) or its equivalent (28.2) with E_1 as the event "could not see" and E_2 as "could not hear".   Then deduce the required probability.

(ii) A card is drawn from a pack.   If E_1 = drawing a heart, E_2 = drawing a diamond and E_3 = drawing a black card, write down $P(E_1)$, $P(E_2)$ and $P(E_3)$.   Then find what (27.2) gives for $P(E_1$ or E_2 or $E_3)$ and comment on the result.

****

28A

(i) *P(could not see and/or could not hear) = 0·5 + 0·4 − 0·3 = 0·6*
     P(could see and hear) = 1 − 0·6 = 0·4

This Venn diagram shows the proportion of students in the various categories.   You can also see at a glance that, for instance,

P(could not see but could hear) = 0·2 and

P(could not hear but could see) = 0·1

(ii) $P(E_1) = \dfrac{1}{4}$, $P(E_2) = \dfrac{1}{4}$, $P(E_3) = \dfrac{1}{2}$. $P(E_1$ *or* E_2 *or* $E_3) = \dfrac{1}{4} + \dfrac{1}{4} + \dfrac{1}{2} = 1$,
as it should be, because between them, E_1, E_2 *and* E_3 *cover all the possible outcomes so it is certain that* E_1 *or* E_2 *or* E_3 *will happen. In terms of set theory, the event* "E_1 *or* E_2 *or* E_3" *would be described by* $E_1 \cup E_2 \cup E_3$ *which is, of course, the outcome space* S *and*
$P(S) = \dfrac{n(S)}{n(S)} = 1.$

Note: From this you will see that whenever mutually exclusive events $E_1, E_2, E_3, \ldots\ldots$ *between them cover all possible outcomes, the sum of their probabilities is 1.*

Multiplication of Probabilities - Independent Events

The tossing of two coins simultaneously is an experiment that has been referred
to on previous occasions in this programme.   The probabilities of various
events arising from it were calculated by considering the total number of
outcomes of the experiment and how many of these were covered by the event.
One event that was treated in this way was   "2 heads"   and it was found that

$P(HH) = \dfrac{1}{4}$.   You will now see that this answer could have been arrived at by an

alternative route.

First of all, it must be pointed out that the event   "2 heads" is in itself a
combination of two events, H from Coin No. 1 and H from Coin No. 2.   These
are INDEPENDENT EVENTS, that is, when the two coins are tossed, what happens to
one has no effect on what happens to the other.   Thus, for Coin No. 1,
$P(H) = \frac{1}{2}$ and for Coin No. 2, $P(H) = \frac{1}{2}$.

Now in FRAME 22 you saw that the total number of outcomes, i.e. 4 , comes from
(number of outcomes for Coin No. 1) × (number of outcomes for Coin No. 2),   i.e.
from 2 × 2 and this suggests breaking down P(HH) as follows:

$$P(HH) = \frac{1}{2 \times 2} = \frac{1}{2} \times \frac{1}{2} = P(H \text{ from Coin No. 1}) \times P(H \text{ from Coin No. 2})$$

It seems as though we're on to something here, so let us look at another
experiment, throwing a die and tossing a coin, and consider the probability of
getting 5 with the die and H with the coin.   Again, these events are
independent as the outcome of throwing the die does not affect the outcome of
tossing the coin.

Write down the total number of elementary outcomes of the combined experiment,
the number of these that constitute the event   "5 and H"   and deduce the
probability of it happening.

****

Total number of outcomes = 6 × 2 = 12.   Only 1 of these gives 5 and H.

∴   P(5 and H) = 1/12

Notice that $P(5 \text{ and } H) = \dfrac{1}{6 \times 2} = \dfrac{1}{6} \times \dfrac{1}{2} = P(5) \times P(H)$

Thus in both the examples of independent events examined, you have seen that the
probability of the two independent events occurring can be expressed as the
product of their probabilities.   This can be put into a general statement as
follows:

If E_1 and E_2 are independent events, then the probability of both happening

is given by $P(E_1 \text{ and } E_2) = P(E_1)P(E_2)$ (30.1)

or, using set theory notation, $P(E_1 \cap E_2) = P(E_1)P(E_2)$

Use this rule to find the probability of getting two spades when you draw a
card from a pack, replace it, reshuffle the cards and then draw a card again.

****

$$P(spade\ and\ spade) = \frac{1}{4} \times \frac{1}{4} = \frac{1}{16}$$

Conditional Probability

In the question which you have just answered the first card drawn was put back in the pack before the second card was drawn - a procedure known as "sampling with replacement". By so doing (and, of course, reshuffling the cards) P(spade) at the second draw was exactly the same as P(spade) at the first draw, i.e. we were dealing with independent events. But this would not have been so if the first card had not been put back i.e. if there had been "sampling without replacement".

By going back to first principles, write down, where possible, what P(spade) at the second draw would be if the first card is not replaced and if

  (i)   it is known that the first card drawn was a spade,
 (ii)   it is known that the first card drawn was a heart,
(iii)   it is known that the first card drawn was not a spade,
 (iv)   it is not known what the first card was.

****

(i) At the second draw, there are 51 possible outcomes of which 12 are spades

so $P(spade) = \frac{12}{51} = \frac{4}{17}$.

(ii) and (iii) $\frac{13}{51}$ (iv) Impossible to say.

Here, then, is an example where the probability of an event occurring (in this case, the second card being a spade) depends on the outcome of a previous experiment. For such conditional probabilities there is a convenient notation. $P(E_2/E_1)$ denotes the probability of the event E_2 happening, the event E_1 having occurred. Thus, in the last frame, you found that

$$P(spade\ second/spade\ first) = \frac{4}{17} \quad and \quad P(spade\ second/not\ spade\ first) = \frac{13}{51}$$

It will now be shown that the probability of getting two spades when drawing without replacement can be related to the conditional probability P(spade second/spade first). To do this we consider the outcome space S arising from the experiment of drawing two cards without replacement. There are 52 possible outcomes when the first card is drawn and for each of these there are 51 possible outcomes when the second card is drawn, so the total number of outcomes for the whole experiment is 52×51. How many of these are included in (i) "spade first", (ii) "spade first and spade second"?

****

(i) 13×51 (ii) 13×12

33A   (continued)

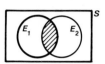

If you are using set theory, here is the Venn diagram.
E_1, *represented by the circle with the bold outline,*
consists of all outcomes with a spade first. E_2,
represented by the other circle, consists of all outcomes
with a spade second.

Then your answer to (i) *is* $n(E_1)$ *and your answer to*
(ii) *is* $n(E_1 \cap E_2)$. *The shaded area represents* $E_1 \cap E_2$.

___

FRAME 34

Now, as the probability of an event can be regarded as the proportion of
outcomes which entail its occurrence

P(spade second/spade first) = $\dfrac{\text{Number of outcomes in "spade first and spade second"}}{\text{Number of outcomes in "spade first"}}$

(34.1)

Check that this gives the same value for P(spade second/spade first) as you
obtained in 31A.

****

34A

$\dfrac{13 \times 12}{13 \times 51} = \dfrac{12}{51} = \dfrac{4}{17}$

In set theory terms this is $\dfrac{n(E_1 \cap E_2)}{n(E_1)}$ *i.e. the number of sample points in the*
shaded area in 33A as a proportion of the sample points in the circle outlined
boldly.

___

FRAME 35

Dividing both numerator and denominator of the R.H.S. of (34.1) by the total
number of outcomes in S leads to

P(spade second/spade first) = $\dfrac{\text{P(spade first and spade second)}}{\text{P(spade first)}}$ (35.1)

which may also be expressed as

P(spade first and spade second) = P(spade first)P(spade second/spade first)

(35.2)

Thus while the probability of getting two spades can be found from first

principles as the ratio of numbers of outcomes i.e. as $\dfrac{13 \times 12}{52 \times 51}$, it can also

be found by multiplying two probabilities, viz. $\dfrac{13}{52} \times \dfrac{12}{51}$.

___

FRAME 36

A general multiplication rule for any events E_1 and E_2 which are not
independent can be obtained by reasoning similar to that used in the preceding
frames to obtain (35.2). It is just a matter of substituting E_1 for "spade
first" and E_2 for "spade second".

(35.1) then becomes $P(E_2/E_1) = \dfrac{P(E_1 \text{ and } E_2)}{P(E_1)}$ (36.1) and (35.2) becomes $P(E_1$ and $E_2) = P(E_1)P(E_2/E_1)$ (36.2)

or, using set theory notation, $P(E_1 \cap E_2) = P(E_1)P(E_2/E_1)$ (36.3)

Note that (30.1), the multiplication rule for independent events, can be considered as a special case of (36.2).   For independent events E_1 and E_2, the probability of E_2 happening is the same whether E_1 has happened or not, so $P(E_2/E_1) = P(E_2)$.   Now test your understanding of the multiplication rule (36.2), or its equivalent (36.3), by applying it to this problem.

Four of the light bulbs in a box of ten have broken filaments.   If two bulbs are selected at random (i.e. all bulbs have an equal chance of being selected) what is the probability that neither has a broken filament?

****

36A

P(1st has unbroken filament) $= \dfrac{6}{10}$

P(2nd has unbroken filament/1st had unbroken filament) $= \dfrac{5}{9}$

$\therefore$ *P(2 bulbs have unbroken filaments)* $= \dfrac{6}{10} \times \dfrac{5}{9} = \dfrac{1}{3}$

FRAME 37

Now look back to question (i) at the end of FRAME 28.   If E_1 and E_2 were independent, i.e. the proportion of students unable to see properly was the same amongst those who could hear as amongst those who could not, what would be the probability that a student picked at random experienced both kinds of difficulty?   Deduce whether E_1 and E_2 were, in fact, independent.

****

37A

P(could not see and could not hear), i.e. $P(E_1$ *and* $E_2)$, *would be* $0 \cdot 5 \times 0 \cdot 4 = 0 \cdot 2$.

In fact, this probability was $0 \cdot 3$ *so* E_1 *and* E_2 *were not independent.*

FRAME 38

Answering the following questions will help you to ensure that you have understood the previous frames.

  (i) Refer again to question (i) at the end of FRAME 28.   If a student picked at random says he could not see satisfactorily, what is the probability that he could not hear either, i.e. what is $P(E_2/E_1)$?   If, on the other hand, the student says he could not hear satisfactorily, what is the probability that he could not see?

 (ii) Suppose that, of the people who contract an infectious disease, only one third have been recently treated with a trial vaccine.   The severity with which a victim is attacked by the disease is classified as "mild", "medium" or "severe".   If 50% of cases are "mild" and 30% are "medium", and if severity of attack is unaffected by the vaccine, find the probability that a victim selected at random

      (a) has a "medium" attack and has been vaccinated,

FRAME 38   (continued)

(b)   has a "mild" attack and has not been vaccinated,
(c)   has a "severe" attack and has been vaccinated.

****

38A

(*i*)   *From (36.1),* $P(E_2/E_1) = \dfrac{0 \cdot 3}{0 \cdot 5} = 0 \cdot 6$.

   Similarly P(could not see/could not hear), i.e. $P(E_1/E_2) = \dfrac{0 \cdot 3}{0 \cdot 4} = 0 \cdot 75$.

   You may find it helpful to refer to the Venn diagram in 28A.

(*ii*) *If severity of attack is unaffected by the vaccine, P("mild" attack) is
   the same whether the victim has been vaccinated or not.   Similar remarks
   apply to P("medium" attack) and P("severe" attack).   Thus we are
   dealing here with independent events and (30.1) gives*

   (*a*) $\dfrac{1}{3} \times \dfrac{3}{10} = \dfrac{1}{10}$ (*b*) $\dfrac{2}{3} \times \dfrac{1}{2} = \dfrac{1}{3}$ (*c*) $\dfrac{1}{3} \times \dfrac{1}{5} = \dfrac{1}{15}$

FRAME 39

Summary

This summary may help you to sort out in your own mind the various results
presented in FRAMES 25-36.

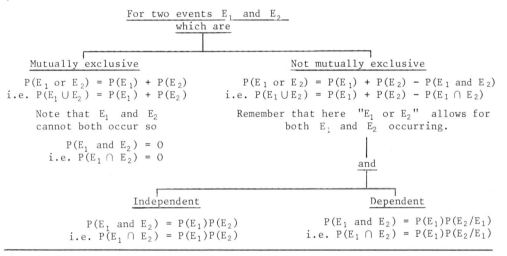

For two events E_1 and E_2
which are

Mutually exclusive	Not mutually exclusive
$P(E_1 \text{ or } E_2) = P(E_1) + P(E_2)$	$P(E_1 \text{ or } E_2) = P(E_1) + P(E_2) - P(E_1 \text{ and } E_2)$
i.e. $P(E_1 \cup E_2) = P(E_1) + P(E_2)$	i.e. $P(E_1 \cup E_2) = P(E_1) + P(E_2) - P(E_1 \cap E_2)$

Note that E_1 and E_2
cannot both occur so

$P(E_1 \text{ and } E_2) = 0$
i.e. $P(E_1 \cap E_2) = 0$

Remember that here "E_1 or E_2" allows for
both E_1 and E_2 occurring.

and

Independent	Dependent
$P(E_1 \text{ and } E_2) = P(E_1)P(E_2)$	$P(E_1 \text{ and } E_2) = P(E_1)P(E_2/E_1)$
i.e. $P(E_1 \cap E_2) = P(E_1)P(E_2)$	i.e. $P(E_1 \cap E_2) = P(E_1)P(E_2/E_1)$

FRAME 40

Use of ^nC_r

You solved the problem at the end of FRAME 36 by using the multiplication rule
(36.2), because that's the method you were asked to use.   It is worth looking
at the alternative method which goes back to first principles.   If that is done,
we have

$$P(2 \text{ bulbs have unbroken filaments}) = \frac{\text{Number of ways of selecting 2 bulbs with unbroken filaments}}{\text{Number of ways of selecting 2 bulbs from 10}}$$

(40.1)

The key to the evaluation of the numerator and denominator is the formula for ^nC_r, or $_nC_r$ or $\begin{pmatrix} n \\ r \end{pmatrix}$, as you may have seen it written. If this is not familiar to you, you can find a brief explanation in APPENDIX B at the end of this programme.

The denominator of (40.1) is easily seen to be $^{10}C_2$, the number of all possible pairs of bulbs that could be selected from the 10. Turning to the numerator, pairs of bulbs with unbroken filaments will have to come from the 6 in the box so there are $^6C_2$ possibilities.

Hence P(2 bulbs have unbroken filaments) $= \dfrac{^6C_2}{^{10}C_2} = \dfrac{6!}{4!2!} \times \dfrac{8!2!}{10!}$

$$= \frac{6 \times 5}{10 \times 9} \text{ as in 36A}$$

Going back to basic concepts makes the solution slightly more lengthy but it has been included here as a further illustration of those concepts and also to familiarise you with the use of ^nC_r in probability problems.

Continuing with the same box of light bulbs, consider them being checked by drawing a bulb at random, testing it and repeating the process (not replacing the bulb tested) until all the bulbs with broken filaments have been located. What is the probability that the number of tests required is 5?

One outcome covered by this event is the sequence of results UBBBB, where U signifies "unbroken filament" and B "broken filament". Begin the analysis of this problem by writing down, in similar fashion, all the other outcomes when 5 (and only 5) tests are necessary.

****

BUBBB, BBUBB, BBBUB. The last letter must always be B, because for 5 tests to be necessary the 4th broken bulb must be discovered at the 5th test.

Taking first the sequence UBBBB, the probability of this occurring can be found by repeated application of the general multiplication rule (36.2).

P(1st bulb is U) $= \dfrac{6}{10}$ and   P(2nd bulb is B/1st bulb is U) $= \dfrac{4}{9}$

∴ P(1st bulb is U and 2nd bulb is B) $= \dfrac{6}{10} \times \dfrac{4}{9}$

When this has happened, the probability of finding a broken filament at the 3rd test is $\dfrac{3}{8}$. Hence the probability of getting the sequence UBB is $\left(\dfrac{6}{10} \times \dfrac{4}{9} \right) \times \dfrac{3}{8}$. Continuing in this way, with repeated applications of (36.2), gives the probability of getting the sequence UBBB as $\left(\dfrac{6}{10} \times \dfrac{4}{9} \times \dfrac{3}{8} \right) \times \dfrac{2}{7}$ and finally P(UBBBB) $= \left(\dfrac{6}{10} \times \dfrac{4}{9} \times \dfrac{3}{8} \times \dfrac{2}{7} \right) \times \dfrac{1}{6} = \dfrac{1}{210}$.

FRAME 42   (continued)

Now use similar reasoning to obtain the probabilities corresponding to the outcomes listed in 41A, leaving the answers in factor form.

****

42A

$$P(BUBBB) = \frac{4}{10} \times \frac{6}{9} \times \frac{3}{8} \times \frac{2}{7} \times \frac{1}{6} \qquad\qquad P(BBUBB) = \frac{4}{10} \times \frac{3}{9} \times \frac{6}{8} \times \frac{2}{7} \times \frac{1}{6}$$

$$P(BBBUB) = \frac{4}{10} \times \frac{3}{9} \times \frac{2}{8} \times \frac{6}{7} \times \frac{1}{6}$$

FRAME 43

You may have noticed that all four probabilities have the same value, the factors in the numerators occurring in different orders.   As the four sequences of results are mutually exclusive events, the addition rule of FRAME 27 can be applied.

Thus P(5 tests required) = P(UBBBB or BUBBB or BBUBB or BBBUB)
$$= P(UBBBB) + P(BUBBB) + P(BBUBB) + P(BBBUB)$$
$$= 4 \times \frac{1}{210} = \frac{2}{105}$$

Now suppose we want to know the probability that the 4th broken filament is revealed at the 6th test.   For this event, one possible sequence of results is UUBBBB.   What is P(UUBBBB)?

****

43A

$$\frac{6}{10} \times \frac{5}{9} \times \frac{4}{8} \times \frac{3}{7} \times \frac{2}{6} \times \frac{1}{5} = \frac{1}{210}$$

FRAME 44

This time it is not suggested that you write down all the other possible sequences.   Just think what would be involved in this task and you will realise that the list of possibilities will be much longer than that in 41A.   We'll now see if we can calculate how many there are without actually writing them all down.   To do this let us look back at the treatment of the previous problem. For 5 tests to be necessary, the sequence of results had to be of the form * * * * B, with the four vacant places occupied by 3 B's and 1 U.   So when writing down the possible sequences, it was a matter of placing the U in a different place each time, and selecting one position out of 4 can be done in $^4C_1$ different ways.   Alternatively you can think of selecting 3 positions out of 4 for placing the B's, and the number of ways is then expressed as $^4C_3$. The answer is the same because $^4C_1 = {}^4C_3 = 4$.   Remember that $^nC_r = {}^nC_{n-r}$ as when you take a group of r things out of n, you leave a group of (n - r) things (see FRAMES B8 and B9, page 83, if you are not convinced).

For the present question, the sequence of results has to be of the form * * * * * B, with the 5 vacant places occupied by 3 B's and 2 U's.   In how many ways can this be done?   Deduce P(6 tests required).

****

44A

$^5C_2$ or $^5C_3$ = 10 $P(6 \ tests \ required) = 10 \times \dfrac{1}{210} = \dfrac{1}{21}$

FRAME 45

Probability Tree Diagrams

Tree diagrams are a form of graphical display with a variety of uses – in the analysis of network problems, in the formulation of problems in decision making and for generating the elements of Cartesian products of finite sets, to name just three.   Corresponding to this relevance to set theory is their use in probability problems which involve finding the outcome space of a composite experiment.   By a composite experiment is meant one which is a compounding of lesser experiments – the repeated tossing of a coin, for instance.

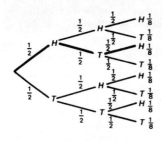

This is a probability tree for the tossing of a coin 3 times.   It shows that there are 8 elementary outcomes.   To obtain the probability of any one of them you start at the base at the L.H.S. and then follow the appropriate branches, multiplying the probabilities encountered along the way.   The path for the sequence HTH is shown by heavy lines in this diagram.

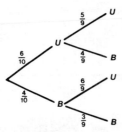

This is a probability tree for the testing of 2 light bulbs taken from the box of 10 that has been described previously, i.e. containing 4 with broken filaments.

Find the probabilities of each of the 4 elementary outcomes, check that they add up to 1 and deduce the probability that the 2 tests reveal one, and only one, broken filament.

****

45A

$P(UU) = \dfrac{6}{10} \times \dfrac{5}{9} = \dfrac{1}{3},$ $P(UB) = \dfrac{4}{15},$ $P(BU) = \dfrac{4}{15},$ $P(BB) = \dfrac{2}{15}.$

$P(1 \ broken \ filament \ found) = P(UB) + P(BU) = \dfrac{8}{15}$

FRAME 46

Problem Solving

Although, in justifying the rules for dealing with probabilities, the theoretical "equally likely outcomes" approach has mainly been employed in this programme, those rules are just as applicable when probabilities are estimated on an empirical, relative frequency basis or even when a subjective approach is used. The latter would be the case, for instance, if a manager wanted to assess the chance of a completely new product selling at a given level of profitability – the theoretical approach doesn't have any meaning, there is no past data

FRAME 46   (continued)
available and so the manager has to rely on his own experience and skill in putting a value on this probability.

We have obtained probability rules which apply to various categories of situation, but probability problems are very varied and don't always fall neatly into one of these categories.   You have really got to think each problem out for yourself, and you'll find this becomes easier as you gain experience.   Before being left on your own to work through the Miscellaneous Examples at the end of the programme, you will be guided through a succession of problems in the frames which now follow and, at the same time, you will also get a glimpse of some of the practical applications.

FRAME 47

A lot consists of 16 articles of which 10 are good, 4 have only minor defects and 2 have major defects.   Tiptop Traders will only accept articles which are good, but the Kwiksell Company will only reject articles which have major defects.

One article is drawn at random.   What is the probability that

(i)   it is acceptable to Tiptop Traders,
(ii) it is acceptable to the Kwiksell Company?

****

47A

(i) $\frac{10}{16} = \frac{5}{8}$

(ii) $\frac{7}{8}$,   *either from* $\frac{14}{16}$,   *there being 14 outcomes acceptable to the Kwiksell Company* ,

or from $\frac{10}{16} + \frac{4}{16}$,   *adding probabilities of "good" and "minor defects" which are mutually exclusive events,*

or from $1 - \frac{2}{16}$,   *i.e.   1 − P(not acceptable).*

FRAME 48

Now suppose that, starting with the same original lot, two articles are drawn at random.   What then would be the probability that

(i)   both are acceptable to Tiptop Traders,
(ii)   both are rejected by the Kwiksell Company,
(iii)   exactly one is acceptable to Tiptop Traders,
(iv)   neither is acceptable to Tiptop Traders,
(v)   both are acceptable to the Kwiksell Company,
(vi)   at least one is acceptable to Tiptop Traders,
(vii)   not more than one is acceptable to Tiptop Traders?

****

48A

(i)   P(1st acceptable) × P(2nd acceptable/1st acceptable) = $\frac{10}{16} \times \frac{9}{15} = \frac{3}{8}$
(ii) $\frac{2}{16} \times \frac{1}{15} = \frac{1}{120}$
(iii) P(1st acceptable and 2nd unacceptable)

    + P(1st unacceptable and 2nd acceptable) = $\frac{10}{16} \times \frac{6}{15} + \frac{6}{16} \times \frac{10}{15} = \frac{1}{2}$

(iv) $\frac{6}{16} \times \frac{5}{15} = \frac{1}{8}$

   (v) $\frac{14}{16} \times \frac{13}{15} = \frac{91}{120}$

(vi) *Either* $P(1\ acceptable) + P(2\ acceptable) = \frac{1}{2} + \frac{3}{8} = \frac{7}{8}$ *or*

   $1 - P(none\ acceptable) = 1 - \frac{1}{8} = \frac{7}{8}$

(vii) *Either* $P(none\ acceptable) + P(1\ acceptable) = \frac{1}{8} + \frac{1}{2} = \frac{5}{8}$ *or*

   $1 - P(both\ acceptable) = 1 - \frac{3}{8} = \frac{5}{8}$

FRAME 49

The Kwiksell company agrees to accept a lot of 16 articles if 3 articles taken from it at random have no major defects.   What is the probability that the lot described in FRAME 47 is   (i) accepted, (ii) rejected?

****

49A

(i) $\frac{14}{16} \times \frac{13}{15} \times \frac{12}{14} = \frac{13}{20}$ *(ii)* $1 - \frac{13}{20} = \frac{7}{20}$

FRAME 50

The blood groups of hospital patients in a particular region are distributed as follows: 44% have group O, 40% A, 10% B and 6% AB.   If half the patients are men and half are women, and there is no relation between a person's sex and their blood group, estimate the probability that a patient, chosen at random, will be (i) a man with blood group O,   (ii) a woman with blood group AB, (iii) a woman whose blood group is not AB.

****

50A

(i) $0 \cdot 5 \times 0 \cdot 44 = 0 \cdot 22$ *(ii)* $0 \cdot 5 \times 0 \cdot 06 = 0 \cdot 03$ *(iii)* $0 \cdot 5 \times 0 \cdot 94 = 0 \cdot 47$

Probabilities worked out on this basis will be required in Unit 2 when a statistical test will be carried out to see whether a set of data supports the hypothesis that sex and blood groups are independent.

FRAME 51

Four objects are distributed at random among six containers.   What is the probability that (i) all objects go into the same container, (ii) no two objects go into the same container?

****

51A

(i) *You can go back to first principles and say:*
   Total number of ways of distributing 4 objects $= 6 \times 6 \times 6 \times 6 = 6^4$
   Number of these where objects are in same container $= 6$

   $\therefore$ $P(all\ in\ same\ container) = \frac{6}{6^4} = \frac{1}{216}$

Alternatively you can use multiplication of probabilities.

P(2nd object in same container as 1st) = 1/6
i.e. P(First 2 objects in same container) = 1/6
P(3rd object in same container as 1st and 2nd) = 1/6
∴ P(First 3 objects in same container) = 1/6 × 1/6

and similarly P(4 objects in same container) = 1/6 × 1/6 × 1/6 = $\frac{1}{216}$

(ii)   First approach used in (i) gives:
Number of ways of distributing objects if no two are to be in same
container = 6 × 5 × 4 × 3
∴ P(no two objects in same container) = $\frac{6 \times 5 \times 4 \times 3}{6^4}$ = $\frac{5}{18}$

Second method outlined in (i) gives: $\frac{5}{6} \times \frac{4}{6} \times \frac{3}{6}$ = $\frac{5}{18}$

FRAME 52

An engineering company produces components which go through a high precision
superfinishing operation.   Experience has shown that 6% of the output from
this operation is substandard so the company has installed a pneumatic gauging
system to automatically eject substandard components.   However, the gauging
system is itself not totally reliable;   there is a 5% probability that it will
fail to eject a substandard component and a 10% probability that it will eject
a satisfactory one.   What is the probability that a component from the output
of the operation will be   (i) passed by the gauging system,   (ii) passed by the
gauging system and yet be substandard?   See if you can deduce what proportion
of components passed by the gauging system are substandard.

****

52A

Maybe you used a tree diagram.

(i)   0·003 + 0·846 = 0·849

(ii)   0·003

$\frac{0 \cdot 003}{0 \cdot 849}$ = $\frac{1}{283}$

FRAME 53

Climatic conditions are unpredictable, so when a civil engineer is designing a
system which has to withstand such conditions he must consider the risk of a
particular choice of design capacity proving inadequate during the lifetime of
the structure.   Given the design, he can usually estimate, for example, the
maximum flow possible through a spillway or the maximum wind velocity which a
structure can resist, and then he can use past data to estimate the probability
of the critical magnitude being exceeded in a given period of time.

Suppose that, for a proposed flood-control system, the probability of flood
level being reached or exceeded in any one year is 0·1.   This is what the
hydrology expert calls a 10-year flood because of the implication that, in the
long run, the flood would happen on the average once in 10 years.
Alternatively, he would say that 10 years is the average return period, often
abbreviated to "the return period".   The latter term is unfortunate.   It gives

people the impression that the flood occurs every 10 years which, of course,
it doesn't, just as saying that a 1 in 2 chance of getting a head when a coin
is tossed does not mean that there will be 1 head in every 2 tosses.

Now find the probability that

   (i)   flood level will not be reached or exceeded during (a) any one year,
         (b) 5 successive years,
   (ii) flood level will be reached or exceeded at least once in 5 successive
         years.

You will need to make the assumption, commonly made, that the probability of
flooding remains the same from year to year.

                 ****

53A

(i)   (a) 0·9   (b) 0·9^5 = 0·59
(ii) 1 - 0·59 = 0·41

───

Now find the probability that, for a flood-control system with an average
return period of T years, flood level will be reached or exceeded at least once
in n successive years.   Then use this formula to find the return period that
a highway engineer should use in his design of an underpass drain if he is
willing to accept only a 10% risk that flooding will occur in the next 4 years.

                 ****

54A

$1 - (1 - 1/T)^n$
Putting this equal to 0·10 with n = 4, and solving, gives T = 38·5.

───

Finally, you will now be shown how what you have learned about probability can
be used in measuring the likelihood of failure of a technical appliance, i.e.
in assessing the reliability of a system.

Let us first consider a very simple appliance made up of two components C_1
and C_2 which must both function for the appliance to do so.   Anyone who has
a gas-fired central heating system with small bore piping will understand this
all too well.   If the gas supply fails, the water in the boiler cannot be
heated and the system fails.   If the electricity supply fails, the electric
pump does not operate and the system fails.

You could also think of an electric current
passing from A to B, with components C_1 and C_2
(e.g. transistors, resistors etc.) in series in
the circuit and the failure of either C_1 or C_2 sufficient to interrupt the flow
of current.   Such a representation of logical conditions for the functioning or
non-functioning of a system is called a reliability network.   In all examples
in this programme it will be assumed that the probabilities of the components
functioning are independent of one another.   This being so, if p_1, p_2 are the
probabilities of the functioning of C_1, C_2 respectively, what is the
probability of this system (i) functioning, (ii) failing to function?

                 ****

55A

(i) $p_1 p_2$ *(ii)* $1 - p_1 p_2$

If $E_1 \equiv$ "C_1 functions" and $E_2 \equiv$ "C_2 functions",   then, in set theory terms,
(i) is $P(E_1 \cap E_2)$ and (ii) is $P\left[(E_1 \cap E_2)'\right]$.

FRAME 56

We now consider a system with the components in parallel, instead of in series.

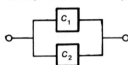

In terms of the electric circuit, the flow of current would only be stopped if both C_1 and C_2 fail.   In terms of a domestic hot water system, C_1 could represent a gas-fired boiler and C_2 an electric immersion heater, so that the water can be heated by either gas or electricity and there is only a breakdown if both supplies fail.

Again denoting the probabilities of C_1, C_2 functioning by p_1, p_2 respectively, what is the probability of this system functioning?

****

56A

$p_1 + p_2 - p_1 p_2$

There are various ways in which you might have obtained this:

(i)   You might have found P(system doesn't function), which is
(1 - p_1)(1 - p_2), and subtracted it from 1.

OR (ii) There are 3 outcomes in the event "system functions": C_1 functions
but not C_2, C_2 functions but not C_1, and C_1, C_2 both function, with
probabilities respectively $p_1(1 - p_2)$, $p_2(1 - p_1)$ and $p_1 p_2$.   The
addition rule of FRAME 27 for mutually exclusive events can then be
applied.

OR (iii) You could have considered the event as consisting of only two
outcomes: C_1 functions (and doesn't matter about C_2), C_1 doesn't
function but C_2 does, with respective probabilities p_1 and
(1 - p_1)p_2.   Addition rule for mutually exclusive events then applies.

OR (iv) As (iii) but with C_1, C_2 interchanged, and hence p_1, p_2 interchanged.

OR   (v) You may have noticed that p_1, p_2 are the probabilities of events
which are not mutually exclusive (C_1 and C_2 can both function) and
(28.1) can be applied.   If you prefer to think in terms of set
theory, then (28.2) is applicable.

FRAME 57

Having now seen two simple systems, one with the components in series and one with the components in parallel, try to decide, in each case, whether the reliability of the system is greater than or less than the reliability of either component.

****

57A

Series: Less than, as $p_1 p_2 < p_1$ and $p_1 p_2 < p_2$
Parallel: Greater than, as $p_1 + (1 - p_1)p_2 > p_1$ and $p_2 + (1 - p_2)p_1 > p_2$

*This means that if a component has a duplicate placed in <u>parallel</u> with it, the
reliability of the system is increased, as might be expected.*

FRAME 58

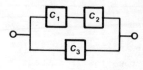

The failure of (i) both C_1 and C_3 or (ii) both C_2
and C_3 would be sufficient to stop the functioning of
the system whose reliability network is shown here.
Think of C_3 as the main petrol tank in a car which has a
reserve tank C_2 to which the driver can switch by using
C_1.   The car will stop if the petrol in the main tank
runs out and the driver does not switch over to reserve,
or if he does switch to reserve but the reserve tank is empty.

What is the probability of the system functioning when the components C_1, C_2, C_3
function with probability p_1, p_2, p_3 respectively?

****

58A

$$p_1 p_2 + (1 - p_1 p_2)p_3 = p_1 p_2 + p_3 - p_1 p_2 p_3$$

In set theory terms this comes from $P\left[(E_1 \cap E_2) \cup E_3\right].$

*You may have noticed that the results for the two previous systems can be
combined here, in that there are now effectively two components in parallel
whose probabilities of functioning are $p_1 p_2$ and p_3.*

FRAME 59

As was pointed out earlier, one way in which the reliability of a system can be
increased is by duplicates placed in parallel, and an interesting question that
arises here is whether it is more effective (i) to duplicate the whole
appliance or (ii) to duplicate the individual components.   In the case of the
simple system introduced in FRAME 55 the reliability networks for these two
alternatives would be as shown below.

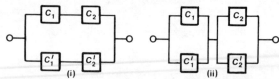

The duplicates C_1' and C_2' will,
of course, have the same
probability of functioning as
C_1, C_2 respectively.

Perhaps you have a hunch about the answer.   See whether it is confirmed by
calculating the probability of functioning for each of the two alternatives when
$p_1 = 0.9$ and $p_2 = 0.8$.

****

59A

*(i) 0.9216   (ii) 0.9504   Duplicating the components is more effective
than duplicating the appliance.   This is true for all values of p_1 and p_2,
also for other systems.*

Miscellaneous Examples

In this frame a collection of miscellaneous examples is given for you to try.
Answers are supplied in FRAME 61, together with a suggested method of approach
when a need for it is anticipated.   However it should be borne in mind that
there may be other methods which are equally good.

1. Suppose that 5 faulty electron tubes get mixed up with 8 good ones.

    (i)   What is the probability that if one is selected at random, it is
          good?

    (ii) If two tubes are drawn from the thirteen, what is the probability
          that
          (a) both are good,   (b) one is good and one faulty,
          (c) at least one is good?

    (iii) If eight tubes are selected from the thirteen, what is the
          probability that six are faulty?

2. The binary number system plays an important part in the operation of
    electronic computers.   The system involves the use of only the two digits
    0 and 1.   If the probability of an incorrect digit appearing is p, and
    errors in digits occur independently of one another, what is the
    probability of an n-digit number being incorrect?

3. In 1974 reports reached the press of experiments conducted by two
    scientists with Uri Geller, a young Israeli, who claimed to possess
    paranormal powers.   Two of the experiments will now be described.   They
    are both of the "double-blind" type, in which the experimenter himself does
    not know the answer the subject is trying to give, so there is no chance
    of clues being given unwittingly.

    (i)   A person who was otherwise not associated with the experiments went
          alone into a room and put an object into a can which he chose at
          random from 10 identical aluminium cans placed on a table.   The
          experimenter and Geller then entered the room and Geller was asked
          to identify the can containing the object, without touching either
          the cans or the table.   In 14 such trials, Geller twice refused to
          give an answer, but identified the can correctly on each of the
          other 12 occasions.   Thus he was right 12 times out of 12 when
          he claimed to be able to make the identification.   A newspaper
          commented: 'The odds against achieving this level of success by
          guesswork are one in a million million (1 in 10^{12})'.   Do you agree?

          Note: The term "odds", used more in common parlance than in
          probability theory, may need some clarification.   If, say, the
          probability of an event occurring is 3/4, the odds in favour of it
          happening are 3 to 1.   Giving odds of 3 to 1 against an event
          happening would mean that the probability of its occurrence is 1/4.

    (ii) A die was placed in a closed steel box, vigorously shaken and then
          placed on a table.   (This technique had been found in control runs
          to produce a distribution of uppermost die faces not differing
          significantly from what one would expect to happen by chance.)
          Geller was then asked to write down which die face was uppermost,
          something which at that stage was not known to the experimenters.
          In 10 trials, Geller twice refused to give an answer, but gave the
          correct response on each of the other 8 occasions.   He was
          therefore right 8 times out of 8 when he claimed to be able to
          state the result.   Do you agree with the comment: 'The probability

of this occurring by chance is approximately 1 in 10^6'?

4. A packed bed may be considered as an interconnected network of holes, each
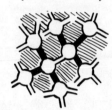
hole being linked to 4 other holes.   Under some
conditions a proportion p of all these links becomes
blocked.   Assuming that the blockages occur entirely
at random (and therefore independently of one another)
find an expression for the probability that two
particular holes are blocked off from the rest of the
network but not from each other.   You may find the
accompanying diagrammatic representation of the problem
helpful.   (Explanatory note for readers who are not
chemical engineers: Packed beds are used in processes such as the
filtration of dirty water through a bed of sand.)

5. For a certain river the probability that during any one year the discharge
will be greater that $1400 \, \text{m}^3\text{s}^{-1}$ is $0 \cdot 6$.   What is the probability that
this discharge will not be exceeded during a period of   (i) 1 year,
(ii) 4 years,   (iii) n years?   What is the probability that this discharge
will be exceeded during a 4-year period?

6. In its manufacture a product has to be processed first by a machine of
type 1, then by a machine of type 2 and lastly by a machine of type 3.
The probabilities of breakdown of the three types of machine   are p_1, p_2
and p_3 respectively.   What is the probability that machine breakdown will
occur and halt the flow of finished products

   (i)   if the factory has only one machine of each type,
   (ii)   if the factory has 1 machine of type 1, 2 of type 2 and 3 of
           type 3?

7. A person is given three cups of coffee to taste and told that in one case
ground coffee was used, in another instant coffee granules and in the
remaining one instant coffee powder.   The taster is asked to assign each
description to what he thinks is the corresponding cup of coffee.   If he
were unable to discriminate between the different kinds of coffee (i.e. if
the descriptions were assigned at random) what would be the probability of
just one kind being correctly identified?

8. A successful attack by an interceptor requires

       (a)   the reliable operation of a computing system,
       (b)   the transmission of correct directions
and (c)   the proper functioning of the striking mechanism.

When the probability of (a) is $0 \cdot 8$ and (b) is assured, the overall
probability of success is $0 \cdot 6$.   If the computing system is improved to
90% reliability, while the probability of (b) is reduced to $0 \cdot 8$ and that
of (c) remains unchanged, what is the new overall probability of success?

9. It is found that in manufacturing a certain article defects of one type
occur with probability $0 \cdot 1$ and of another type with probability $0 \cdot 05$,
also that the two types of defect occur independently of one another.
Calculate the probability that

   (i)   an article does not have both kinds of defect,
   (ii)   an article is defective,
   (iii)   a defective article has only one type of defect.

10. At each of a series of trials the probability of occurrence of a certain
event is $\frac{1}{2}$, except that it cannot result from consecutive trials.   Show

that the probability of it occurring just twice in (i) 3 trials is $\frac{1}{4}$,
(ii) in 4 trials is $\frac{1}{2}$.   What is the probability of it occurring just
twice in 5 trials?

11. A communications channel has two possible inputs X_1 and X_2 and two
     possible outputs Y_1 and Y_2.   For 60% of the time the input received by
     the channel is X_1 and for 40% of the time it is X_2.   The probability
     that X_1 will be correctly transmitted as Y_1 is 0·9 and that X_2 will be
     correctly transmitted as Y_2 is 0·8.   If an input X_1 is not transmitted
     correctly it yields Y_2 as output and similarly, if X_2 is not transmitted
     correctly the output is Y_1.

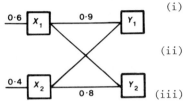

     (i)   State the probability that
           (a) an input X_1 is transmitted as Y_2,
           (b) an input X_2 is transmitted as Y_1.

     (ii) For what proportion of the time is
           (a) the input transmitted correctly,
           (b) the output Y_1 obtained?

     (iii) If the output is Y_1, what is the
           probability that the input was X_1?

12. Suppose that the probability of failure of an aircraft engine in flight
     is q and that an aircraft is considered to make a successful flight if at
     least half of its engines do not fail.   For what values of q is a
     two-engined aircraft to be preferred to a four-engined one?   (C.E.I.)

13. When a relay in an electric circuit is open a current is prevented from
     flowing.   Closing the relay allows the current to pass through.   Relays
     are subject to two kinds of failure: failure to open when they should and
     failure to close when they should.   For each of the relays in the circuit
     shown below, the probability of the first kind of failure is p and the
     probability of the second kind of failure is q.   Any failure in a relay
     occurs independently of failures in the other relays.   Find the
     probability of a current flowing between the terminals A and B

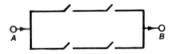

     (i)   if all the relays are closed and
           receive a command to open,

     (ii) if all the relays are open and receive
           a command to close.

14. In modern rocketry design an abort sensing system consists of a circuit of
     pressure switches which collectively can abort (terminate) a mission when
     the pressure drops significantly in the fuel manifold of the engine.
     Individual switches operate independently and fail to operate properly in
     two ways:
     (a) by not opening the circuit when the abort condition exists, this
          occurring with probability q_1,
     (b) by opening, i.e. breaking, the circuit when the abort condition does
          not exist, this occurring with probability q_2.
     The whole system fails if it does not sense an abort condition when it
     exists or when it erroneously senses an abort condition which does not in
     fact exist.
     If the probability of an abort condition is α, show that the probability
     of failure of a system of two switches in series (Diagram 1 overleaf) is

$$\alpha q_1{}^2 + (1 - \alpha)q_2(2 - q_2)$$

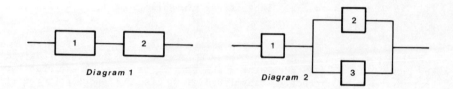

Diagram 1   Diagram 2

Find the probability of failure of the mixed parallel-serial system of Diagram 2, involving three switches.

State clearly in your analysis the manner in which you are applying the laws of probability.   (L.U.)

15. A person's blood is either Rhesus-positive or Rhesus-negative. It is an inherited characteristic determined by genes of two types, R and r. Each person has two genes, one inherited from each parent; only people with two r genes are Rhesus-negative.   Special medical treatment may be required when a Rhesus-negative mother gives birth to a Rhesus-positive child.   Suppose that the chances of a person (whether male or female) having one of the three possible gene combinations are: two R genes, 36%; two r genes, 16%; one R and one r, 48%. Assuming that each of the two genes of a parent have an equal chance of being transmitted to the offspring, what would you give as the chance of the mother-baby Rhesus combination mentioned above occurring if

   (i)   you knew the mother to be Rhesus-negative and the father to be
        Rhesus-positive,
  (ii)   you knew the mother to be Rhesus-negative,
 (iii)   you knew nothing about the Rhesus factor of either parent?

16.

     START

     TEST   F   TEST   F
      1   2

    S   S

   ACCEPT   S   TEST
              3

             F

       REJECT

    STOP

The diagram sets out an acceptance procedure laid down by a particular specification for concrete to be used in highway structures.

If the concrete passes (S) the first test, it is accepted outright. If it fails (F) it is subjected to a second test and failure at this stage means outright rejection.

Success at the second test, on the other hand, gives the concrete a chance of still being accepted by going on to a third test. Concrete which passes the third test is accepted, but failure means rejection.

Concrete of a certain quality has probabilities P_1, P_2, P_3 of passing tests 1, 2, 3 respectively. By following the appropriate paths in the diagram, find the probability of (i) acceptance, (ii) rejection, and check that your two answers add up to 1.

17. A micro-organism reproduces by dividing into two at intervals. After one division, it waits in 80% of cases 1 hour before dividing again, independently of its previous history, and in the remaining 20% it waits 2 hours.   If a biologist isolates one organism immediately after a division,

FRAME 60   (continued)

what are the possible numbers of organisms that could be present just
before the end of an interval of (i) 2 hours, (ii) 3 hours, and what
are the respective chances of these numbers occurring? If the organism
is introduced into an environment in which it has a 10% chance of being
eaten during any one hour, what do the answers to (i) become?

FRAME 61

Answers to Miscellaneous Examples

1. (i) 8/13   (ii) (a) 14/39 (b) 20/39 (c) 34/39   (iii) 0

2. $1 - P(\text{all } n \text{ digits are correct}) = 1 - (1 - p)^n$

3. (i) If answers are just guesses, the probability of 12 out of 12 being
         correct is 1 in 10^{12} and the odds against this result are $10^{12} - 1$
         to 1.   The journalist's statement is rather confused.

    (ii) Yes, if the approximation is only intended to indicate the order of
          magnitude.   The exact probability is 1 in 6^8 i.e. 1 in 1679 616,
          to which 1 in 10^6 is nearer than either 1 in 10^5 or 1 in 10^7.

4. $(1 - p)p^6$

5. (i) 0·4   (ii) 0·0256   (iii) $(0·4)^n$
         0·9744

6. (i) $1 - P(\text{each machine functions}) = 1 - (1 - p_1)(1 - p_2)(1 - p_3)$
    (ii) $1 - P(\text{at least one machine of each type functions})$
          $= 1 - (1 - p_1)(1 - p_2{}^2)(1 - p_3{}^3)$

7. Number of ways of assigning descriptions = $3 \times 2 \times 1 = 6$
    Number of ways of naming only one cup correctly = 3
    $\therefore$ $P(\text{just one kind correctly identified}) = \dfrac{3}{6} = \dfrac{1}{2}$

8. 0·54

9. (i) 0·995   (ii) 0·145   (iii) 28/29

10. 9/16

11. (i) (a) 0·1 (b) 0·2
     (ii) (a) 0·54 + 0·32 = 0·86   (b) 0·54 + 0·08 = 0·62   (iii)   27/31

12. For 2 engines, $P(\text{successful flight}) = 1 - q^2$
     For 4 engines, $P(\text{successful flight}) = 1 - 4q^3 + 3q^4$
     $1 - q^2 > 1 - 4q^3 + 3q^4$ if $q > 1/3$

13. (i) For each relay, $P(\text{closure}) = p$ $\therefore$ $P(\text{current flows}) = 2p^2 - p^4$
     (ii) For each relay, $P(\text{closure}) = 1 - q$
           $\therefore$ $P(\text{current flows}) = 2(1 - q)^2 - (1 - q)^4$

14. Let $E_1 \equiv$ abort condition exists but is not sensed
     and $E_2 \equiv$ abort condition does not exist but is sensed.
     For 1st system: $P(E_1) = \alpha q_1{}^2$, $P(E_2) = (1 - \alpha)\{1 - (1 - q_2)^2\}$
     $= (1 - \alpha)q_2(2 - q_2)$
     For 2nd system: $P(E_1) = \alpha q_1\{1 - (1 - q_1)^2\} = \alpha q_1{}^2(2 - q_1)$
     $P(E_2) = (1 - \alpha)\{q_2 + (1 - q_2)q_2{}^2\} = (1 - \alpha)q_2(1 + q_2 - q_2{}^2)$
     For each system, $P(\text{failure}) = P(E_1 \text{ or } E_2) = P(E_1) + P(E_2)$

FRAME 61   (continued)

15.   (i) Father could be RR or Rr, with respective probabilities 3/7 and
            4/7.
            If father is RR, baby is certain to be Rh-positive
            If father is Rr, baby has 50% chance of being Rh-positive.

            $\therefore$ P(baby is Rh-positive) $= \frac{3}{7} \times 1 + \frac{4}{7} \times \frac{1}{2} = \frac{5}{7}$

       (ii) $0 \cdot 36 \times 1 + 0 \cdot 48 \times 0 \cdot 5 = 0 \cdot 6$ (iii) $0 \cdot 16 \times 0 \cdot 6 = 0 \cdot 096$

16.   (i) $p_1 + (1 - p_1)p_2p_3$ (ii) $(1 - p_1)\{(1 - p_2) + p_2(1 - p_3)\}$
                                                    $= (1 - p_1)(1 - p_2p_3)$

17.   (i) 1, 2; P(1) = $0 \cdot 2$, P(2) = $0 \cdot 8$
       (ii) 2, 3, 4; P(2) = $0 \cdot 232$, P(3) = $0 \cdot 256$, P(4) = $0 \cdot 512$
             0, 1, 2; P(0) = $0 \cdot 1252$, P(1) = $0 \cdot 2916$, P(2) = $0 \cdot 5832$

APPENDIX A

Summary of terms and symbols in Set Theory

A collection of items can be represented by a SET, usually indicated by { }. For instance,

$$A = \{2, 4, 6, 8, 10, 12\}$$

denotes the set A composed of the even numbers from 2 to 12 inclusive and

$$B = \{all \ times \ between \ 0 \ and \ 10 \ minutes\}$$

denotes the set B composed of all times within the stated interval. We can also write this as

$$B = \{t : 0 < t < 10\}$$

if t is used to denote time in minutes.

Each item in a set is called an ELEMENT of the set. Thus, for example, 4 and 12 are both elements of the set A. The number of elements in a set may be finite, as in A, or infinite, as in B. The notation $n(A)$ can be used to denote the number of elements in the set A, so here $n(A) = 6$.

Any set of elements chosen from a set is called a SUBSET. Thus $\{4, 8\}$ forms a subset of A and $\{t : 0 < t < 5\}$ forms a subset of B.

A UNIVERSAL SET or UNIVERSE consists of all items under consideration. Suppose this were all the days of 1976. Then the days of 1976 during which more than 1 mm of rain fell at Marble Arch in London and the days on which the wind speed exceeded 10 km/h there would both be subsets of that universe. In probability theory the universe is often denoted by S.

The NULL SET or EMPTY SET is one containing no element, e.g. the number of days during 1976 when the sun shone for more than 21 hours at Marble Arch. The null set is usually denoted by $\emptyset$.

Those elements of a universe which do not belong to a given subset C form the COMPLEMENT of C, often denoted by C' or $\overline{C}$. Thus if S = {days of 1976} and C = {days of 1976 with rainfall exceeding 1 mm} then

$$C' = \{days \ of \ 1976 \ having \ railfall \leqslant 1 \ mm\}.$$

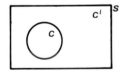

A VENN DIAGRAM is a pictorial representation of sets and subsets. For example, those in the previous paragraph can be represented by the diagram on the left.

If D denotes those days on which the wind speed exceeded 10 km/h, then two possibilities are as shown in diagrams (i) and (ii).

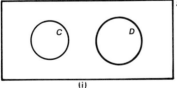

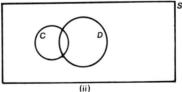

(i)   (ii)

In the situation represented by (i), the rainy and windy days did not coincide. The sets C and D are then said to be DISJOINT.

In the situation represented by (ii), some wet days were also windy. This is shown by the overlap of C and D. The days which were both wet and windy form the INTERSECTION of the sets C and D, denoted by C ∩ D. The days which were

wet and/or windy form the UNION of sets C and D, denoted by C ∪ D.   In the
Venn diagrams below, C ∩ D and C ∪ D are represented by the areas shaded
in (iii) and (iv) respectively.

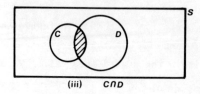
(iii)   C∩D

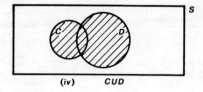
(iv)   C∪D

You will notice that, if the regions representing C and D overlap,
n(C) + n(D) will include n(C ∩ D) twice.   Hence to obtain n(C ∪ D),
n(C ∩ D) must be subtracted from the sum of n(C) and n(D), i.e.

$$n(C \cup D) = n(C) + n(D) - n(C \cap D)$$

In the situation represented by (i), where C and D are disjoint,

$$C \cap D = \emptyset \qquad \text{and} \qquad n(C \cup D) = n(C) + n(D)$$

APPENDIX B

Combinations and the notation ^nC_r

In FRAME 40 it is necessary to find the number of ways of selecting two electric light bulbs from a box of ten.   This number is denoted by one of three symbols:

$$^{10}C_2, \qquad _{10}C_2 \qquad \text{or} \qquad \binom{10}{2}$$

In the programme, $^{10}C_2$ is used.

More generally, ^nC_r represents the number of ways in which r objects can be selected out of n objects.   The letter C stands for COMBINATIONS.   When dealing with combinations, no regard is paid to the order of the objects.   Thus, if three letters are to be selected from the seven letters   a, b, c, d, e, f, g, the selection b e f is the same as e b f and this is the same as f b e, etc. When the order is important, then we are dealing with PERMUTATIONS instead of combinations.

First, let us find the number of arrangements (i.e. permutations) that can be formed when three letters are chosen from seven, each letter only being available for use once.

The letter for the first place can be chosen in any one of 7 different ways. Having chosen this letter, there are then only 6 left from which to fill the second place.   Now, any of these 6 letters in the second place can be used with any of the 7 in the first place and thus there are 7×6, i.e. 42, ways of filling the first two places.

In how many ways can the third place now be filled and in how many ways can all the three places be filled?

****

$5,$ $7 \times 6 \times 5 = 210$

This is now the number of permutations that can be formed from 7 letters, taken three at a time.   But this includes, for example,   b e f, e b f, f b e,   etc., i.e. different arrangements of the same three letters.   How many different arrangements of the three letters   b, e, f,   are there?

****

6

To arrive at this answer you may have written out all the six arrangements or you may have argued along lines similar to those just used, i.e. there are three letters available for the first place, two for the second (and hence 3×2 for the first two) and then just one left for the third, giving, all told, $3 \times 2 \times 1 = 6$ arrangements.

Now all these six arrangements have been included in the result 210 that you got in B2A. Similarly every other group of three letters, e.g. a b d or c e f, can be rearranged amongst themselves in 6 ways. But each of these six arrangements leads to only <u>one</u> combination. How many combinations are there, then, of the seven letters taken three at a time?

****

210/6 = 35

Now write down the number of combinations of

(i)   four objects chosen from six, i.e. $^6C_4$,

(ii) two objects chosen from ten, i.e. $^{10}C_2$.

****

(i) $\dfrac{6 \times 5 \times 4 \times 3}{4 \times 3 \times 2 \times 1} = 15$ *(ii)* $\dfrac{10 \times 9}{2 \times 1} = 45$

More generally, if we require the number of combinations or selections that can be formed when r objects are chosen out of n, i.e. ^nC_r, then we have

$$\frac{n(n - 1)(n - 2) \ldots\ldots (n - r + 1)}{r(r - 1)(r - 2) \ldots\ldots 1} \qquad (B6.1)$$

(Verify that when you put (i) n = 6, r = 4, (ii) n = 10, r = 2, in this formula, you get the same answers as you did in the preceding frame.)

Now, although at first it may seem to complicate matters, the result (i) in B5A can be written as

$$\frac{6 \times 5 \times 4 \times 3 \times 2 \times 1}{4 \times 3 \times 2 \times 1 \times 2 \times 1}$$

and (ii) in B5A as

$$\frac{10 \times 9 \times 8 \times 7 \times 6 \times 5 \times 4 \times 3 \times 2 \times 1}{2 \times 1 \times 8 \times 7 \times 6 \times 5 \times 4 \times 3 \times 2 \times 1}$$

However, these two results can be written more compactly by the use of factorials

Thus, the first fraction is $\dfrac{6!}{4!2!}$ and the second is $\dfrac{10!}{2!8!}$.

See if you can write (B6.1) in factorial form, by inserting the appropriate factors in its numerator and denominator.

****

$$\frac{n(n-1)(n-2)\ \dots\ (n-r+1)(n-r)(n-r-1)\ \dots\ 2\times1}{r(r-1)(r-2)\ \dots\ 1(n-r)(n-r-1)\ \dots\ 2\times1} = \frac{n!}{r!(n-r)!}$$

FRAME B8

We thus have

$$^nC_r = \frac{n!}{r!(n-r)!} \qquad (B8.1)$$

What does this formula become if you replace r by n − r?

****

B8A

$$\frac{n!}{(n-r)!(n-\overline{n-r})!} = \frac{n!}{(n-r)!\,r!}$$

FRAME B9

This therefore gives the result

$$^nC_{n-r} = {}^nC_r$$

Can you give a practical interpretation of this?

****

B9A

The number of ways in which we can choose r objects out of n is exactly the same as the number of ways in which we can choose to reject *the other n − r objects.*

FRAME B10

Now see if you can answer the following questions:

(1) Given that 0! is defined as having the value 1, what does (B8.1) give
     for ^nC_o ? Give an illustration to interpret the meaning of this result.

(2) Show that $r \times {}^nC_r = n \times {}^{n-1}C_{r-1}$

****

B10A

(1) 1.   There is just one way in which we can select none out of a group of n objects.   Selecting no object is, of course, equivalent to rejecting all of them.

(2) $r \times {}^nC_r = r \times \dfrac{n!}{r!(n-r)!} = \dfrac{n!}{(r-1)!(n-r)!} = n \times \dfrac{(n-1)!}{(r-1)!(n-r)!}$

$$= n \times {}^{n-1}C_{r-1}$$

Probability Distributions
for Discrete Variates (1)

Probability Distributions

In the first programme in this Unit you saw how the pattern of random variation
in a set of observations could be described by showing the frequencies with
which different values of the variate occurred.   The frequency distributions
which we looked at then were describing events which had actually taken place.
As has been pointed out before, if another 80 lamps had been tested or another
40 cars observed, different frequency distributions would almost certainly have
resulted.   Not startlingly different, admittedly, but different nevertheless.
A theoretical model, if one can be found, will give a more complete view of the
situation and from it further conclusions and predictions can be made.   The
model will be more widely applicable if it gives relative frequencies, rather
than frequencies (which are tied to a fixed total) and if it does that it is, in
effect, a PROBABILITY DISTRIBUTION.

We shall begin with models which apply to a particular kind of variate.
Included in this category of variate are: the number of dots on the face of a
die, the number of defective articles in a batch, the number of incoming calls
received by a telephone switchboard in a 5-minute period.   Do you remember the
name for this kind of variate?

****

Discrete

In the case of a discrete variate the probability distribution gives, for each
value that the variate can take, the probability of that value occurring.   We
shall use P(x) to denote the probability that the variate takes the value x.
The throw of a die affords a simple illustration.   The values of P(x) have
already been considered in the previous programme.   On the right you can see
a diagrammatic representation of the distribution.

x	P(x)
1	1/6
2	1/6
3	1/6
4	1/6
5	1/6
6	1/6

This is an example of a RECTANGULAR or UNIFORM distribution for a discrete
variate.   What do the values of P(x) add up to?

****

$\Sigma P(x) = 1$.   *This must, of course, always be the case for any probability
distribution for a discrete variate, when the summation is taken over all
possible values of the variate.*

From the probability distribution in the previous frame, we could calculate a theoretical frequency distribution for a total of, say, 600 throws.   These theoretical frequencies, called the EXPECTED FREQUENCIES, would be given by 600 P(x) i.e. 100 for each value of x.   Of course, this is not saying that it would be at all surprising if in 600 actual throws the frequencies were not all equal to 100.   You have already seen in the previous programme that where the empirical and theoretical approaches to probability are both possible there will not necessarily be complete agreement between the two and the same is therefore true of observed frequencies and expected frequencies.

For 600 throws, then, theory gives the frequency distribution shown below.

x	Expected frequency
1	100
2	100
3	100
4	100
5	100
6	100
	———
	600

The mean of this distribution is

$$\frac{100 \times 1 + 100 \times 2 + 100 \times 3 + 100 \times 4 + 100 \times 5 + 100 \times 6}{600}$$

$$= \frac{2100}{600} = 3 \cdot 5$$

This is the way that the calculation would usually be done, but the same result would be obtained from

$$\frac{100}{600} \times 1 + \frac{100}{600} \times 2 + \frac{100}{600} \times 3 + \frac{100}{600} \times 4 + \frac{100}{600} \times 5 + \frac{100}{600} \times 6$$

i.e. $\frac{1}{6} \times 1 + \frac{1}{6} \times 2 + \frac{1}{6} \times 3 + \frac{1}{6} \times 4 + \frac{1}{6} \times 5 + \frac{1}{6} \times 6$ (3.1)

If, instead, we considered the expected frequencies when the total number of throws is 1200, what would the mean of that distribution be?

****

3A

3·5.   (3.1) shows that the total frequency does not affect the value of the mean.

You will notice that (3.1) is obtained by multiplying each value of x by its probability and adding i.e. it is $\Sigma x P(x)$.   This is the formula for the mean of any probability distribution for a discrete variate.   You can see how it accords with the formula for the mean of a frequency distribution which you have already seen and used in the first programme of this Unit.   There we had

$$\overline{x} = \frac{\Sigma fx}{\Sigma f} = \frac{f_1 x_1 + f_2 x_2 + f_3 x_3 + \ldots}{N} \quad \text{where} \quad N = \Sigma f$$

$$= \frac{f_1}{N} x_1 + \frac{f_2}{N} x_2 + \frac{f_3}{N} x_3 + \ldots = \Sigma x \frac{f}{N}$$

The values of $\frac{f}{N}$ are the relative frequencies which, as you know, can be regarded as giving probabilities in the long run.

The term EXPECTED VALUE is used for the mean of a probability distribution. The notation for it is E(x), if the variate is x, and μ is the conventional symbol.   Note that the word "expected" is used here, as it also was with respect to frequencies in the previous frame, in a special, statistical sense

and not as you might understand it in its ordinary everyday sense.   Think of
an expected value, in statistical terminology, as representing 'the average
value in the long run'.

Returning to the frequency distribution given by theory for 600 throws of a
die, the calculation of the variance from its definition would be set out as
follows:

x	Expected frequency	$x - 3 \cdot 5$	$(x - 3 \cdot 5)^2$
1	100	$-2 \cdot 5$	$6 \cdot 25$
2	100	$-1 \cdot 5$	$2 \cdot 25$
3	100	$-0 \cdot 5$	$0 \cdot 25$
4	100	$0 \cdot 5$	$0 \cdot 25$
5	100	$1 \cdot 5$	$2 \cdot 25$
6	100	$2 \cdot 5$	$6 \cdot 25$

$$\text{Var}(x) = \frac{100 \times 6 \cdot 25 + 100 \times 2 \cdot 25 + 100 \times 0 \cdot 25 + 100 \times 0 \cdot 25 + 100 \times 2 \cdot 25 + 100 \times 6 \cdot 25}{600}$$

$$= \frac{1750}{600} \simeq 2 \cdot 92$$

The division by 600 could alternatively be done first, giving

$$\frac{1}{6} \times 6 \cdot 25 + \frac{1}{6} \times 2 \cdot 25 + \frac{1}{6} \times 0 \cdot 25 + \frac{1}{6} \times 0 \cdot 25 + \frac{1}{6} \times 2 \cdot 25 + \frac{1}{6} \times 6 \cdot 25 \qquad (5.1)$$

What would the variance be if, instead, we considered the distribution of
expected frequencies for 1200 throws?

****

5A

*It would still be the same, as (5.1) is independent of the total number of
throws.*

If you look at (5.1) you will see that it is $\Sigma(x - 3 \cdot 5)^2 P(x)$, the summation
being over all the values that x takes.   The general formula for the
variance, σ^2, of any probability distribution where the variate is discrete, is
$\sigma^2 = \Sigma(x - \mu)^2 P(x)$.   It is a simple matter to link this up with the general
formula for the variance of a frequency distribution.   If you wish to see this
for yourself, start with $\text{var}(x) = \frac{\Sigma f(x - \mu)^2}{\Sigma f}$ and then think along similar
lines to what was done in FRAME 4 for the mean.

****

6A

$$var(x) = \frac{\Sigma f(x - \mu)^2}{\Sigma f} = \frac{f_1(x_1 - \mu)^2 + f_2(x_2 - \mu)^2 + f_3(x_3 - \mu)^2 + \ldots}{N}$$

$$= \frac{f_1}{N}(x_1 - \mu)^2 + \frac{f_2}{N}(x_2 - \mu)^2 + \frac{f_3}{N}(x_3 - \mu)^2 + \ldots = \Sigma(x - \mu)^2 \frac{f}{N}$$

Three fundamental results have now been established concerning the probability distribution of a discrete variate x.   They are listed below with one side of each equation missing.   Fill in the gaps.

(i) $\Sigma P(x) =$ (ii) $= \mu$ (the mean)   (iii) $= \sigma^2$ (the variance)

****

7A

(i) $\Sigma P(x) = 1$ (7A.1)
(ii) $\Sigma x P(x) = \mu$ *(the mean)*   (7A.2)
(iii) $\Sigma (x - \mu)^2 P(x) = \sigma^2$ *(the variance)*   (7A.3)

FRAME 8

One further point about the variance.   You will remember that after this had been defined, in the first programme in this Unit, in terms of deviations from the mean, an alternative form was obtained which was often more convenient to work with.   The corresponding form of (7A.3) is

$$\sigma^2 = \Sigma x^2 P(x) - \mu^2 \qquad (8.1)$$

Try to derive it for yourself by expanding the terms in the summation on the L.H.S. of (7A.3) and using (7A.1) and (7A.2).

****

8A

$$\sigma^2 = \Sigma (x^2 - 2\mu x + \mu^2) P(x) = \Sigma x^2 P(x) - 2\mu \Sigma x P(x) + \mu^2 \Sigma P(x)$$
$$= \Sigma x^2 P(x) - 2\mu^2 + \mu^2$$
$$= \Sigma x^2 P(x) - \mu^2$$

FRAME 9

Bernoulli Trials and the Binomial Distribution

The uniform probability distribution has provided a simple illustration with which to start this programme, but it is not one which applies very widely. Of much greater practical importance is the model to which this programme is mainly devoted.   The introduction will, as before, be through tossing coins and throwing dice.

First let us look at some probability distributions where the variate x is the number of sixes when a die is thrown repeatedly.   Write down the values of $P(x)$ for x = 0 when the number of throws is   (i) 2,   (ii) 3,   (iii) 4. Leave your answers in factor form.

****

9A

(i) $\left(\dfrac{5}{6}\right)^2$ (ii) $\left(\dfrac{5}{6}\right)^3$ (iii) $\left(\dfrac{5}{6}\right)^4$

FRAME 10

Finding $P(x)$ when x = 1 is slightly more complex.   Take first the case when there are 2 throws.   Then the event "1 six" could happen in 2 ways, with the six occurring at either the first or second throw.

Thus $$P(1) = \frac{1}{6} \times \frac{5}{6} + \frac{5}{6} \times \frac{1}{6} = 2 \times \frac{5}{6} \times \frac{1}{6}$$

If there are 3 throws the event "1 six" could happen in 3 ways, with the six occurring at the 1st, 2nd or 3rd throw. You can think of it as being $^3C_1$ ways, as it is the number of ways of choosing 1 throw out of 3 for the occasion when the six is to occur. The respective probabilities of these three outcomes are $\frac{1}{6} \times \frac{5}{6} \times \frac{5}{6}$, $\frac{5}{6} \times \frac{1}{6} \times \frac{5}{6}$ and $\frac{5}{6} \times \frac{5}{6} \times \frac{1}{6}$. Notice that in each case there are 2 factors $\frac{5}{6}$ corresponding to the 2 throws yielding "not a six" and 1 factor $\frac{1}{6}$, corresponding to the throw yielding "six". Thus each has the value $\left(\frac{5}{6}\right)^2\left(\frac{1}{6}\right)$ and $P(1) = 3\left(\frac{5}{6}\right)^2\left(\frac{1}{6}\right)$.

Write down $P(1)$ when the die is thrown 4 times, leaving your answer in factor form.

****

10A

$4\left(\frac{5}{6}\right)^3\left(\frac{1}{6}\right)$.   *The 4 can be thought of as $^4C_1$ because it is the number of ways of choosing 1 throw out of 4 for the occurrence of the six.*

FRAME 11

Now find $P(2)$ when the number of throws is (i) 2, (ii) 3, (iii) 4, leaving each answer in factor form.

****

11A

(i) $\left(\frac{1}{6}\right)^2$ (ii) $3\left(\frac{5}{6}\right)\left(\frac{1}{6}\right)^2$ (iii) $6\left(\frac{5}{6}\right)^2\left(\frac{1}{6}\right)^2$ *The 6 comes from $^4C_2$ which is the number of ways of choosing from the 4 throws the 2 throws where sixes occur.*

FRAME 12

Here are the complete probability distributions for the number of sixes in 2, 3 and 4 throws of a die.

	2 throws		3 throws		4 throws
x	P(x)	x	P(x)	x	P(x)
0	$\left(\frac{5}{6}\right)^2$	0	$\left(\frac{5}{6}\right)^3$	0	$\left(\frac{5}{6}\right)^4$
1	$2\left(\frac{5}{6}\right)\left(\frac{1}{6}\right)$	1	$3\left(\frac{5}{6}\right)^2\left(\frac{1}{6}\right)$	1	$4\left(\frac{5}{6}\right)^3\left(\frac{1}{6}\right)$
2	$\left(\frac{1}{6}\right)^2$	2	$3\left(\frac{5}{6}\right)\left(\frac{1}{6}\right)^2$	2	$6\left(\frac{5}{6}\right)^2\left(\frac{1}{6}\right)^2$
		3	$\left(\frac{1}{6}\right)^3$	3	$4\left(\frac{5}{6}\right)\left(\frac{1}{6}\right)^3$
				4	$\left(\frac{1}{6}\right)^4$

FRAME 12   (continued)

Not all the values of P(x) have been calculated in the previous three frames.
You should check that you can see how the remaining ones have been found.
Then look closely at the distribution when there are 2 throws and notice that
the values of P(x) are the terms in the expansion of $\left(\frac{5}{6} + \frac{1}{6}\right)^2$.   Can you
arrive at a similar kind of result for each of the other two distributions?

****

12A

Values of P(x) are terms in the expansions, by the Binomial Theorem, of
$\left(\frac{5}{6} + \frac{1}{6}\right)^3$ *and* $\left(\frac{5}{6} + \frac{1}{6}\right)^4$ *respectively.*

FRAME 13

Let's see if we can find this kind of pattern in other probability distributions.
Take the variate x as the number of heads in repeated tosses of a coin and
obtain the distributions of P(x) for 2, 3 and 4 tosses.   You shouldn't find
this difficult as the reasoning is very similar to that used to obtain the
distributions in the previous frame.   Leave the values of P(x) in factor form
to make it easier for you to see whether you can identify them as terms in a
binomial expansion.

****

13A

2 tosses		*3 tosses*		*4 tosses*	
x	*P(x)*	*x*	*P(x)*	*x*	*P(x)*
0	$(\frac{1}{2})^2$	*0*	$(\frac{1}{2})^3$	*0*	$(\frac{1}{2})^4$
1	$2(\frac{1}{2})(\frac{1}{2})$	*1*	$3(\frac{1}{2})^2(\frac{1}{2})$	*1*	$4(\frac{1}{2})^3(\frac{1}{2})$
2	$(\frac{1}{2})^2$	*2*	$3(\frac{1}{2})(\frac{1}{2})^2$	*2*	$6(\frac{1}{2})^2(\frac{1}{2})^2$
		3	$(\frac{1}{2})^3$	*3*	$4(\frac{1}{2})(\frac{1}{2})^3$
				4	$(\frac{1}{2})^4$

Expansions of $(\frac{1}{2} + \frac{1}{2})^2$ *,* $(\frac{1}{2} + \frac{1}{2})^3$ *and* $(\frac{1}{2} + \frac{1}{2})^4$

FRAME 14

The probability distributions which we have obtained for die throwing and coin
tossing are examples of the BINOMIAL DISTRIBUTION, so named because of its
association with the terms of a binomial expansion.   Before trying to make
some general statement about this theoretical model, let us consider what the
die throwing and coin tossing experiments had in common that could have led to
the similarity of pattern in their probability distributions.   In both cases
the experiment consisted of repeated trials - the throwing of a die or the
tossing of a coin.   In both cases the outcome of each trial was looked at from
the viewpoint of whether a particular event happened or did not happen - whether
there was a six or not, whether there was a head or not.   In other words, the
outcome was regarded as a two-way affair and it was this that gave rise to the
binomial expressions $\frac{5}{6} + \frac{1}{6}$ and $\frac{1}{2} + \frac{1}{2}$ from which the various binomial
expansions originated.   One further point, those probabilities of $\frac{5}{6}$ and $\frac{1}{6}$,
and of $\frac{1}{2}$ and $\frac{1}{2}$ remained the same at each trial, the results of which were

independent of one another in that, for instance, whether a six occurred at the
first throw would not affect what happened at the second throw, and so on.

Now to describe in general terms the conditions under which the binomial model
operates.   Instead of thinking of "six" or "not a six", or "head" or "not a
head", we'll just think of "success" or "failure" at each trial, used in the
sense of "success" meaning that the event (getting a six or a head or whatever
it may be) happens and "failure" that it doesn't happen.

The series of trials (sometimes called BERNOULLI TRIALS after a member of the
famous Bernoulli family which produced eight mathematicians in three
generations), to which the binomial model applies, have the following
characteristics:

1. The number of trials is fixed.

2. The outcomes of each trial are divisible into two categories ("success" or
    "failure") which are mutually exclusive.

3. Whether a trial results in a "success" or not is unaffected by what
    happened at previous trials.

4. The probability of "success", usually denoted by p, is constant from trial
    to trial.

To which of the following would this description be applicable?

  (i)   x = number of hearts obtained when three cards are drawn from a pack
        (a) if each card is replaced in the pack before the next card is drawn,
        (b) if the cards are drawn without replacement.

 (ii)   x = number of times a tester is right when given 5 pieces of bread
        spread with either margarine or butter and asked to say which, in each
        case.   Assume that the tester is quite unable to distinguish between
        the two and gives answers which are pure guesses.

(iii)   x = number of engines which function throughout the flight of a
        4-engined aircraft, given that for each engine q is the probability of
        failing during the flight.

                ****

*(i) (a), (ii) and (iii) provided that the failure of one engine does not
affect the value of q for the other engines, an assumption which you had to
make when solving Misc. Ex. No. 12 of the previous programme.*

*In (i) (b) the probability of "success" i.e. getting a heart, would change at
each trial as the condition of independence is not met.*

If the conditions listed in the previous frame are satisfied, and
P("success") = p and P("failure") = q, obtain the probability distributions
for the variate x when x is the number of "successes" in 2, 3 and 4 trials
respectively, and show that $\Sigma P(x) = 1$ in each case.

                ****

16A

2 trials		3 trials		4 trials	
x	$P(x)$	x	$P(x)$	x	$P(x)$
0	q^2	0	q^3	0	q^4
1	$2qp$	1	$3q^2p$	1	$4q^3p$
2	p^2	2	$3qp^2$	2	$6q^2p^2$
		3	p^3	3	$4qp^3$
				4	p^4

$\Sigma P(x) = (q + p)^2$ $\Sigma P(x) = (q + p)^3$ $\Sigma P(x) = (q + p)^4$

As $q + p = 1$, $\Sigma P(x) = 1$ in each case.

FRAME 17

Once again you have seen that the values of $P(x)$ in the probability distribution are given by the terms in a binomial expansion. What power of $q + p$, when expanded, will give the values of $P(x)$ when the number of trials is n?

****

17A

The values of $P(x)$ will be given by the expansion of $(q + p)^n$.

FRAME 18

We can now make the general statement that if

   p is the probability of an event happening (i.e. a "success") at a single trial
                              and
   q is the probability of it not happening (i.e. a "failure")

then the terms of the binomial expansion

$$(q + p)^n = q^n + {}^nC_1 q^{n-1} p + {}^nC_2 q^{n-2} p^2 + \ldots\ldots + p^n$$

give the probabilities of the event happening 0, 1, 2, ... n times respectively in n independent trials.

Write down the probability of the event happening (i) 3 times, (ii) r times.

****

18A

(i) ${}^nC_3 q^{n-3} p^3$ (ii) ${}^nC_r q^{n-r} p^r$

FRAME 19

Here's a problem where these results can be applied:

It has been found that 2% of packages produced by an automatic packaging machine have defective seals. What is the probability that a case will contain more than 2 packages with defective seals if the packages are supplied in cases of (i) 20, (ii) 50?

Taking the event of a package having a defective seal as the so-called "success" we have $p = 0 \cdot 02$ and $q = 0 \cdot 98$. (Note that what is a "success" according to the meaning given to it by the binomial distribution is not necessarily a success from other points of view!)

For (i), n = 20, so terms in the expansion of $(0 \cdot 98 + 0 \cdot 02)^{20}$ are required.
The variate x being the number of packages with defective seals, we require
$P(x > 2)$. This could be expressed as $P(3) + P(4) + \ldots + P(20)$, but the
calculation of all those terms would be a very lengthy affair. Can you see
an easier way?

****

19A

*Find $P(x \not> 2)$, i.e. the probability that a case will <u>not</u> contain more than 2
packages with defective seals, and subtract from 1.*

Now $P(x \not> 2) = P(0) + P(1) + P(2)$

$$= (0 \cdot 98)^{20} + 20(0 \cdot 98)^{19}(0 \cdot 02) + \frac{20 \times 19}{2}(0 \cdot 98)^{18}(0 \cdot 02)^2 = 0 \cdot 9929$$

and hence $P(x > 2) = 1 - P(x \not> 2) = 0 \cdot 0071$, or about $0 \cdot 7\%$.

See if you can find the answer to (ii), i.e. for cases of 50, leaving the
answer in factor form if you have no calculating aid handy.

****

20A

n = 50.   Terms in the expansion of $(0 \cdot 98 + 0 \cdot 02)^{50}$ are required.

$$P(x \not> 2) = (0 \cdot 98)^{50} + 50(0 \cdot 98)^{49}(0 \cdot 02) + \frac{50 \times 49}{2}(0 \cdot 98)^{48}(0 \cdot 02)^2 \simeq 0 \cdot 922$$

$$P(x > 2) = 1 - P(x \not> 2) \simeq 0 \cdot 078, \text{ or about } 7 \cdot 8\%$$

Mean and Variance of the Binomial Distribution

It has already been established that the mean and variance of a discrete
probability distribution are given by $\Sigma x P(x)$ and $\Sigma (x - \mu)^2 P(x)$ respectively.
These formulae were previously listed as (7A.2) and (7A.3). Applying them to
the general binomial model described in FRAME 18 leads to

    Mean = np   Variance = npq   Standard deviation = $\sqrt{npq}$ (21.1)

Two distributions for which the values of $P(x)$ have already been worked out are
those for the number of heads in 4 tosses of a coin in answer frame 13A and the
number of sixes in 3 throws of a die in FRAME 12. Find the mean and variance
of these distributions

<u>either</u> by using (7A.2) and (7A.3), in which case you are advised to keep your
        working in fractions
    <u>or</u> by working with expected frequencies in, say, 16 coin tossing experiments
        or 216 die throwing experiments, and using the formulae for the mean and
        variance of a frequency distribution.

Check that your answers agree with the formulae that have been quoted above for
the binomial model.

****

4 tosses of a coin

x	Expected frequency $16P(x)$	$x \times 16P(x)$	$(x - 2)^2$	$(x - 2)^2 \times 16P(x)$	
0	1	0	4	4	
1	4	4	1	4	Mean $= \dfrac{32}{16} = 2$
2	6	12	0	0	
3	4	12	1	4	Var. $= \dfrac{16}{16} = 1$
4	$\dfrac{1}{16}$	$\dfrac{4}{32}$	4	$\dfrac{4}{16}$	

Check: $n = 4$, $p = \frac{1}{2}$, $q = \frac{1}{2}$, $np = 2$, $npq = 1$

3 throws of a die

x	Expected frequency $216P(x)$	$x \times 216P(x)$	$(x - \frac{1}{2})^2$	$(x - \frac{1}{2})^2 \times 216P(x)$	
0	125	0	1/4	125/4	Mean $= \dfrac{108}{216} = \dfrac{1}{2}$
1	75	75	1/4	75/4	
2	15	30	9/4	135/4	
3	$\dfrac{1}{216}$	$\dfrac{3}{108}$	25/4	$\dfrac{25/4}{90}$	Var. $= \dfrac{90}{216} = \dfrac{5}{12}$

Check: $n = 3$, $p = 1/6$, $q = 5/6$, $np = 1/2$, $npq = 5/12$

In these solutions expected frequencies have been used. If you chose the alternative method your 2nd, 3rd and 5th columns will not have been scaled up by factors of 16 and 216, but your values of mean and variance should, of course, be the same.

FRAME 22

Having verified for yourself the validity, in two particular cases, of the formulae np and npq for the mean and variance of a binomial distribution, you may be quite happy to accept them as being true in all cases. If, however, you want to see a proof for the general case you can find it in the APPENDIX at the end of this programme – it is not really difficult, just a bit tedious in places.

FRAME 23

Distribution of Proportion of Successes

Up to now the binomial model has been considered in relation to the variate x, where x is the <u>number</u> of successes in n trials. Sometimes it is considered in relation to the <u>proportion</u> of successes in n trials. This applies particularly to the situation where a "success" is "getting a defective item" and you may find "fraction defective" specified rather than "number of defectives". The difference is only one of scale. Whereas x, the number of successes, could take the values 0, 1, 2, ... n, obviously $\frac{x}{n}$, the proportion of successes, can take the values $0, \frac{1}{n}, \frac{2}{n}, \ldots . 1$. The respective probabilities are the same e.g. the probability of 2 successes in n trials is also the probability of the proportion of successes being 2/n.

Now look at the formulae given in FRAME 21 for the mean, variance and standard deviation of the number of successes x, and then write down the corresponding formulae when the variate is the proportion of successes.

****

23A

$$Mean = \frac{1}{n} \times np = p \qquad Variance = \frac{1}{n^2} \times npq = \frac{pq}{n}$$

$$Standard\ deviation = \frac{1}{n} \sqrt{npq} = \sqrt{\frac{pq}{n}}$$

If you had difficulty here, remember what you learned about coding in the first programme of this Unit.   That tells you that, if $x' = \frac{1}{n}\ x$, *then:*

$$mean(x') = \frac{1}{n}\ mean(x) \qquad var(x') = \frac{1}{n^2}\ var(x) \qquad s.d.(x') = \frac{1}{n}\ s.d.(x)$$

FRAME 24

Here is an example for you to try:

If, on average, 1 in 50 of the cans leaving a production line have their label insecurely attached and the cans are despatched to the retailer in boxes of 100, what are the mean and s.d. of

(i)   the number of cans in a box which are insecurely labelled,
(ii) the proportion of cans in a box which are insecurely labelled?

****

24A

(i) From (21.1): Mean = 100 × 0·02 = 2 $\qquad s.d. = \sqrt{100 \times 0·02 \times 0·98} = 1·4$

(ii) From the answers in 23A: Mean = 0·02 $\qquad s.d. = \sqrt{\frac{0·02 \times 0·98}{100}} = 0·014$

FRAME 25

Fitting a Binomial Model

An example will now be given to illustrate the fitting of a binomial model to a set of data.

The data in the following table was obtained from tests made on 250 nylon bars which had been moulded under similar conditions from the same batch of moulding powder.   Each bar was subjected to a test at 5 places along its length to see whether it would break under a particular applied force.   The number of breaks which occurred was recorded for each bar.

Number of breaks	0	1	2	3	4	5
Number of bars	141	62	31	14	1	1

The aim of the investigation was to discover whether brittleness was randomly distributed throughout the bars or whether it was concentrated in particular bars.   If the former were the case, the probability of a break occurring would be the same at every test.   Then, when a bar is tested at 5 points, at each point there is a two-way outcome - break or no break - and the probability p of a break is the same at each of the 5 points.   Under these circumstances what

FRAME 25   (continued)

deduction immediately follows about the distribution of x, the number of points
at which a bar breaks?

****

25A

*Binomial, with n = 5.   The terms in the expansion of $(q + p)^5$, where
$q = 1 - p$, will give the probabilities of 0, 1, 2, ... 5 breaks occurring.*

FRAME 26

To work out the theoretical frequencies that this model would give, it will be
necessary to have a value for p.   As a large number of trials were carried
out, a reasonable estimate of p can be obtained from the data.   Breaks
occurred at 175 of the 1250 test points, so p can be estimated as
$175/1250 = 0 \cdot 14$.   (If you need to see these calculations set out in detail,
refer back to FRAME 55 on page 31.)   Now write down the formula for P(x), the
probability of a bar breaking at x points.

****

26A

$$^5C_x \; 0 \cdot 86^{5-x} \; 0 \cdot 14^x$$

FRAME 27

The values of P(x) for x = 0, 1, 2, ... 5 are shown below, together with the
expected frequencies given by 250 P(x).

x	0	1	2	3	4	5
P(x)	$0 \cdot 4704$	$0 \cdot 3829$	$0 \cdot 1247$	$0 \cdot 0203$	$0 \cdot 0017$	$0 \cdot 0001$
Expected frequency	$117 \cdot 6$	$95 \cdot 7$	$31 \cdot 2$	$5 \cdot 1$	$0 \cdot 4$	$0 \cdot 0$

If you question the decimal values for the expected frequencies, remember that
an expected value is a mathematical concept and may be a value which could not
actually occur.   It's like getting $2 \cdot 1$ for the mean number of car occupants,
as happened in an earlier programme.

The frequencies calculated from the binomial model do not appear to show good
agreement with the actual results, suggesting that the premise on which the
binomial model was based may have been incorrect.   However it is unwise to
rely only on your own judgment when comparing the figures.   In Unit 2 you will
be told how to arrive at a decision objectively by the use of a statistical test.

FRAME 28

Miscellaneous Examples

In this frame a collection of miscellaneous examples is given for you to try.
Answers are supplied in FRAME 29, together with such working as is considered
helpful.

1. Given that the probability that any one of 4 telephone lines is engaged at an instant is 1/3, calculate the probability

   (i) that two of the four lines are engaged and the other two are free,
   (ii) that at least one of the four lines in engaged.   (L.U.)

2. In a chemical manufacturing plant, each batch of a product is purified by being passed over a series of 20 reacting grids which are renewed for each batch. The purity of the product is below standard if two or more grids in the sequence of 20 are inactive. The grids are supplied in bulk and contain 2% which are inactive. What percentage of batches will be below standard in purity after the purification process? Give an expression for the probability of x grids in a sequence of 20 being inactive.

3. There has been some criticism of the containers used for storing blood samples taken from motorists suspected of drunken driving. A doctor at a London medical college has suggested that 5% of these specimen containers are faulty because they leak alcohol and thus distort estimates of the blood alcohol level.

   The kit issued to police surgeons has four containers. If the doctor's allegation is correct, what percentage of kits will have (i) exactly 2 faulty containers, (ii) 2 or more faulty containers?

4. In the 1976 finals of BBC TV's "Young Scientists of the Year", the Oxford team's project concerned the behaviour of woodlice. The direction of movement was one aspect of their behaviour that was investigated. Some woodlice have an instinctive tendency to move towards the left – these the team termed "left-handed". In other woodlice there is either an instinctive tendency to move towards the right or else they are equally likely to move in either direction. These two categories were labelled by the team "right-handed" and "ambidextrous" respectively.

   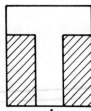 For some experiments "left-handed" woodlice were required. A woodlouse was placed at A in the T maze and the turn it made, either left or right, was recorded. This was done 10 times for each woodlouse, which was then classified as "left-handed" if it turned left at least 9 times.

   State the formula for the probability of an "ambidextrous" woodlouse making x left turns in the 10 trials. What was the probability of an "ambidextrous" woodlouse being classified by the team's procedure as "left-handed"?

5. The probability that parents with a trace of a certain blue pigment in otherwise brown eyes will have a child with blue eyes is 1 in 4. If there are six children in a family, what is the probability that at least half of them will have blue eyes?   (C.E.I.)

6. Observations have shown that 20% of all vehicles arriving at a particular traffic light in a town in the USA want to turn left. What is the probability that a left-turn lane with a capacity of three cars will not be adequate for accommodating all the drivers who want to turn left when the number of waiting vehicles is (i) 5, (ii) 6? Assume that the decision of a driver to turn left is not affected by the action of other drivers.

FRAME 28   (continued)

7. In a survey of a day's production from 400 machines making similar
    components, 4 items selected at random from the output of each machine
    were inspected in detail.   The number of machines m producing f faulty
    items was found to be

f	0	1	2	3	4
m	16	89	145	118	32

    Represent these data by a binomial distribution and calculate the
    theoretical distribution of faulty components.   (C.E.I.)

8. If x is the percentage of successes in N Bernoulli-type trials, the
    chance of a success at any individual trial being P%, state the mean and
    standard deviation of x.

    The Howard Mould Count is used by Port Health Authorities and by Food and
    Drugs Authorities to assess the degree of mould contamination of tomato
    products, especially tomato purée.   A specified volume of diluted purée
    is placed on a square area on a slide and examined under a microscope.
    The square area is marked off into 25 squares ("fields") of equal size.

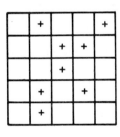

    A field where mould filaments of a specific length
    are observed is recorded as positive and the number
    of positive fields counted (the illustration shows
    a count of 8).   The percentage of fields which are
    positive is used to decide whether the purée should be
    accepted as wholesome.   Obviously this percentage is
    subject to chance variation.   What can be said of its
    distribution if the probability of a positive field
    occurring is constant and equal to 45%?   Under the
    same conditions what could be said about the
    distribution of the number of fields, out of 25,
    recorded as positive?

9. A machine is powered by three batteries, all of the same type, and will
    function provided that at least two of the batteries are in working order.
    The probability of a battery of this type failing during the first 8 hours
    of operation of the machine is 0·2;   if it survives the first 8 hours of
    operation the probability of failure during the next 8 hours of operation
    is 0·4.   Find the probability that the machine will function continuously
    for (i) 8 hours, (ii) 16 hours.

10. Three bolts are selected at random from a box of six bolts, and three nuts
    are selected at random from a box of six nuts.   If each box contains two
    faulty items, find (i) the probability that at least one of the six
    selected items is faulty, (ii) the mean number of satisfactory nut and
    bolt pairs that can be obtained from the six selected items.   (L.U.)

11. A mass-produced article is packed in cartons each containing 40 articles.
    Seven hundred cartons were examined for defectives with the results given
    in the table.

Defective articles per carton	0	1	2	3	4	5	6	More than 6
Frequency	390	179	59	41	18	10	3	0

    Obtain the proportion of defective articles p.

    Assuming that the total number of articles examined is so large that p can
    be taken to represent the proportion of defectives in the population, use

the Binomial distribution to calculate the probability that a random
sample of 5 of these articles will contain 2 defectives.   (L.U.)

(Note: The concepts of "population" and "sample" will be discussed in
Unit 2.   In this example all you need to know is that the population
consists of all the articles produced by the factory and that the random
sample consists of 5 of these articles chosen in such a way that every
article from the production line has the same chance of being chosen.)

12. In an experiment to investigate whether a species of fruit fly shows any
     response, either positive or negative, to light, each fly was forced to go
     through a maze in which at 5 successive points it had to choose between a
     light passage and a dark passage.   For each light passage chosen a fly
     scored 1, for each dark passage chosen the score was 0.   What values
     were possible for a fly's total score?   If this species is unresponsive
     to light what is the expected (i.e. mean) total score?   What is the least
     total score for which the probability of being equalled or exceeded is less
     than 20%?

13. In the inspection of components from a production line, an automatic device
     is used for detecting and rejecting substandard items, but it is found that
     there is a 10% chance of it making a wrong classification.   To reduce the
     number of misclassifications, the system is modified so that each component
     is tested by the device 5 times and only rejected as substandard if so
     classified by at least 3 of these tests.   What percentage of components
     will now be misclassified?

The next three questions are of a slightly more mathematical nature and some
readers may wish to omit them.

14. In the large-scale manufacture of a certain article the probability of a
     defective being produced remains constant and equal to p.   Periodically,
     items are taken from the production line and tested until a defective one
     is revealed.   Find the probability $P(x)$ that on such an occasion x items
     have to be taken and tested.   Verify that $\Sigma P(x) = 1$ and show that the
     mean value of x is $1/p$.   (This is another probability distribution for
     a discrete variate, called the geometric distribution.)

15. If the procedure outlined in the previous question for testing items from
     a production line were such that testing continued until r defective items
     had been found, what would be the probability $P(x)$ that x items have to
     be taken and tested?   State the possible values that x could take and
     show that, with the summation over that range, $\Sigma P(x) = 1$.   Also show

     that the mean value of x is r/p.   The expansion of $(1 - q)^{-r}$ and
     $(1 - q)^{-(r+1)}$ can be used in obtaining the last two answers, and that is
     why the distribution is often called the negative binomial distribution.
     It is also sometimes called the Pascal distribution or described as the
     binomial waiting-time distribution.   What distribution is obtained when
     $r = 1$?

16. In the previous two examples the trials were similar to those in the
     binomial distribution, in that the probability of a defective had the same
     value p at each trial.   This is not so in the example now described.

     From a consignment of N items, in which the proportion defective is p, n
     items are to be selected without replacement.   When the first is selected,
     all items in the consignment are to have an equal chance of being chosen
     and the probability of a defective one is thus p.   The second is then

selected in a similar manner from the remaining N - 1 items but the
probability of a defective will then be dependent on what has gone before
and will not remain constant.   The same will be true when the 3rd, 4th,
... nth items are selected, again without replacement.

Write down an expression for the number of possible selections of n items
from the consignment.   Also write down an expression for the number of
these outcomes that contain x defectives and deduce that

$$P(x) = \frac{{}^{k}C_{x} \cdot {}^{N-k}C_{n-x}}{{}^{N}C_{n}} \quad \text{where} \quad k = pN.$$

(This is the hypergeometric distribution.)

If N = 20, n = 5 and p = 0·1, what values are possible for x?   Using
the above formula, find P(x) for each of these values and check that
$\Sigma P(x) = 1$.   (The arithmetic is not too arduous if you cancel the factorials
and leave the answers as fractions.)

Answers to Miscellaneous Examples

1.   (i) $6(4/9)(1/9) = 8/27$ (ii) $1 - 16/81 = 65/81$

2. $1 - 0·98^{20} - 20 \times 0·98^{19} \times 0·02 \simeq 0·060$ i.e. about 6% below standard.

  $\frac{20!}{x!(20 - x)!} 0·98^{20-x} 0·02^{x}$

3.   (i) 1·35%   (ii)   1·40%

4. ${}^{10}C_{x} \, 0·5^{10-x} \, 0·5^{x} = \frac{10!}{1024(x!)(10 - x)!}$;   11/1024

5.   P(at least 3 have blue eyes) = 1 - P(less than 3 have blue eyes)
     $= 1 - \{P(0) + P(1) + P(2)\}$ where P(0), P(1), P(2) are the first three
                                terms in the expansion of $\left(\frac{3}{4} + \frac{1}{4}\right)^{6}$
     $= 347/2048 = 0·1694$

6.   (i) P(more than 3 want to turn) = P(4 want to turn) + P(5 want to turn)
          $= 5 \times 0·8 \times 0·2^{4} + 0·2^{5}$ i.e. sum of last two terms in expansion of
                                           $(0·8 + 0·2)^{5}$
        $= 0·006 72$

     (ii) Sum of last three terms in expansion of $(0·8 + 0·2)^{6} = 0·016 96$

7.   Mean = np = 2·1525   n = 4   ∴ p = 0·5381 and q = 0·4619
     Binomial distribution given by terms of $(q + p)^{4}$.   Multiplying
     probabilities by 400 gives theoretical values of m as   18·2, 84·8, 148·3,
     115·1, 33·5.

8.   P, $\sqrt{\frac{P(100 - P)}{N}}$
     Binomial, mean 45 and standard deviation $3\sqrt{11}$ or 9·95 to 2 d.p.
     Binomial, mean 11·25 and standard deviation $3\sqrt{11}/4$ or 2·49 to 2 d.p.

9.   (i) P(no batteries fail) + P(1 battery fails) = 0·896
     (ii) P(battery lasts for 16 hours) = $0·8 \times 0·6 = 0·48$
           P(3 batteries last for 16 hours) + P(2 batteries last for 16 hours)
                                                              $\simeq 0·47$

10.   (i) P(at least 1 faulty item) = 1 – P(no faulty items) = 24/25

       (ii) If x = number of satisfactory nut and bolt pairs, then x can take
             the values 1, 2, or 3.   (The distribution is not binomial.)
             Writing S for satisfactory, N for nut and B for bolt,
             P(1) = P(1 SN and at least 1 SB) + P(1 SB and at least 1 SN)
             – P(1 SN and 1 SB) = 9/25.   Similar reasoning leads to P(2) = 15/25.
             P(3) = P(3 SN and 3 SB) = 1/25.   Mean = $\Sigma x P(x)$ = 42/25 = 1·68.

11.   p = 0·02.   The use of the binomial distribution is based on the article
       being mass-produced, hence the articles for the sample are being selected
       from a very large number and the probability of getting a defective can be
       assumed to remain constant from the selection of one article to the next.

       P(2 defective) = $^5C_2$ $0·98^3 \times 0·02^2$ ≃ 0·003 76

12.   0, 1, 2, 3, 4, 5

       Score x = number of light choices.   Described by binomial model with
       n = 5, p = 0·5, if species not responsive to light.

       ∴ Mean value of x = np = 2·5
       P(5) = $0·5^5$ = 0·031 25,   P(4) = $5 \times 0·5^5$ = 0·156 25
       P(4 or 5) = 0·1875 which is < 20%,   P(3 or more) > 20% so required
                                                                      score is 4.

13.   If component O.K., P(device passes it) = 0·9, P(device rejects it) = 0·1.
       It will be classified substandard if at least 3 tests reject it.
       ∴ P(O.K. component misclassified) = Sum of last 3 terms in expansion of
                                                                    $(0·9 + 0·1)^5$
                                       = 0·008 56
       Similar reasoning leads to 0·008 56 for
       P(substandard component misclassified)
       ∴ 0·856% of components will be misclassified.

14. $P(x) = (1 - p)^{x-1} p$
       $\Sigma P(x) = p\{1 + (1 - p) + (1 - p)^2 + ...\} = p\{1 - (1 - p)\}^{-1} = 1$
       $\Sigma x P(x) = p\{1 + 2(1 - p) + 3(1 - p)^2 + ...\} = p\{1 - (1 - p)\}^{-2} = 1/p$

15.   The first x – 1 tests would have to reveal r – 1 defectives, and then
       the next item would have to be a defective.

       Thus, $P(x) = {}^{x-1}C_{r-1} \, p^{r-1} \, q^{x-r} \times p$ where   q = 1 – p

                  $= {}^{x-1}C_{r-1} \, p^r \, q^{x-r}$ x = r, r + 1, r + 2, ...

       $$\sum_{x=r}^{\infty} P(x) = p^r \left({}^{r-1}C_{r-1} + {}^rC_{r-1} \, q + {}^{r+1}C_{r-1} \, q^2 + ... \right)$$

       $$= p^r \left\{ 1 + rq + \frac{r(r + 1)}{2!} q^2 + \frac{r(r + 1)(r + 2)}{3!} q^3 + ... \right\}$$

       $$= p^r (1 - q)^{-r} = 1$$

       $$\sum_{x=r}^{\infty} x P(x) = p^r \left\{ r + r(r + 1)q + \frac{r(r + 1)(r + 2)}{2!} q^2 \right.$$

       $$\left. + \frac{r(r + 1)(r + 2)(r + 3)}{3!} q^3 + ... \right\}$$

$$= p^r \, r(1 - q)^{-(r+1)} = r/p$$

$r = 1$ gives the geometric distribution, described in the previous question.

16. Total number of possible outcomes $= {}^N C_n$

There are ${}^k C_x$ possible selections of x defectives and ${}^{N-k} C_{n-x}$ possible selections of $n - x$ items which are not defective.

$\therefore$ Number of possible selections of n items containing x defectives

$$= {}^k C_x \times {}^{N-k} C_{n-x}$$

Result for $P(x)$ follows.

$x = 0, 1, 2.$
$P(0) = 21/38$ $P(1) = 15/38$ $P(2) = 1/19$

APPENDIX

Mean and Variance of the Binomial Distribution

Mean $= \Sigma x P(x)$

$$= 0 \times q^n + 1 \times {}^nC_1 q^{n-1} p + 2 \times {}^nC_2 q^{n-2} p^2 + \ldots + r \times {}^nC_r q^{n-r} p^r + \ldots + n \times p^n$$

Now $r \times {}^nC_r = n \times {}^{n-1}C_{r-1}$ (set as an exercise in FRAME B10 on page 83)

$\therefore$ Mean $= np \left(q^{n-1} + {}^{n-1}C_1 q^{n-2} p + \ldots + {}^{n-1}C_{r-1} q^{n-r} p^{r-1} + \ldots + p^{n-1} \right)$

$$= np(q + p)^{n-1} = np$$

Variance $= \Sigma(x - np)^2 P(x)$ putting $\mu = np$ in (7A.3)
$\qquad\qquad = \Sigma x^2 P(x) - n^2 p^2$ from (8.1)

Now $\Sigma x^2 P(x) = 0^2 \times q^n + 1^2 \times {}^nC_1 q^{n-1} p + 2^2 \times {}^nC_2 q^{n-2} p^2 + \ldots .$

$$+ r^2 \times {}^nC_r q^{n-r} p^r + \ldots . + n^2 \times p^n$$

$= np \left(q^{n-1} + 2 \times {}^{n-1}C_1 q^{n-2} p + \ldots . + r \times {}^{n-1}C_{r-1} q^{n-r} p^{r-1} + \ldots . + np^{n-1} \right)$

$= np \left\{ \left(q^{n-1} + {}^{n-1}C_1 q^{n-2} p + \ldots . + {}^{n-1}C_{r-1} q^{n-r} p^{r-1} + \ldots . + p^{n-1} \right) \right.$

$\qquad \left. + {}^{n-1}C_1 q^{n-2} p + \ldots . + (r - 1) {}^{n-1}C_{r-1} q^{n-r} p^{r-1} + \ldots . + (n - 1) p^{n-1} \right\}$

$= np \left\{ (q + p)^{n-1} + (n - 1)p(q^{n-2} + \ldots . + {}^{n-2}C_{r-2} q^{n-r} p^{r-2} + \ldots . + p^{n-2}) \right\}$

$= np \left\{ 1 + (n - 1)p(q + p)^{n-2} \right\} = np\{1 + (n - 1)p\}$

$\therefore$ Variance $= np(1 + np - p) - n^2 p^2$
$\qquad\qquad\qquad = np(1 - p) = npq$

More concise proofs of these results exist but they use approaches for which
this text has not prepared you.

Probability Distributions
for Discrete Variates (2)

Introduction

In 1837 the French mathematician S.D. Poisson published the probability
distribution which bears his name. He had derived it from the binomial
distribution by considering the limiting case when $n \to \infty$ and $p \to 0$, with
the mean np remaining the same. This may sound rather formidable when
expressed mathematically but you will find the idea quite easy to understand
when it is illustrated by a practical example later in the programme. First
we will consider how "n infinitely large" and "p infinitely small" can be
interpreted in practical terms.

A much-quoted example of the fitting of a Poisson model to a set of data is that
which was originally published by L. von Bortkiewicz in Leipzig in 1898. He
had access to records of the deaths each year of cavalrymen who had died as a
result of being kicked by a horse. As these records were for each of 10
Prussian Army Corps and extended over a 20-year period (1875 - 1894) there
were 200 observations, enough to give a fairly clear indication of the model
that is appropriate. The variate x, of which there are 200 values, is the
number of occasions in a corps in a year when a cavalryman received a fatal
kick. Is it discrete or continuous?

            ****

2A

Discrete, as x can only take integer values.

Now you will recall that with the Bernoulli trials there were two possible
outcomes - "success" or "failure". If we designate the occurrence of a fatal
kick as the "success" (well, it was a success from the horse's point of view!)
then the non-occurrence of this unhappy event is the "failure". However,
whereas the number of "successes" in a year could be counted the number of
"failures" could not i.e. one cannot count the number of occasions on which a
cavalryman was not kicked to death by one of the horses. This is different
from the binomial distribution where an experiment consists of n trials, and
r "successes" entails n - r "failures". If a trial is taken as being the
opportunity for one of the horses to deliver a fatal kick, you will realise that
there are an infinite number of such trials. Fortunately for the cavalrymen
only a very small number of these opportunities were taken advantage of by a
vicious horse. Hopefully you are now beginning to relate with reality the
concept of "n infinitely large" and "p infinitely small".

The Poisson distribution can be said to describe the occurrence of isolated
events in a continuum. With the horse-kicks it was a continuum of time, as it
would also be for the modern counterpart - the number of accidents in a factory
in, say, a 6-month period. The continuum could alternatively be one of space,
either one-, two- or three-dimensional, in which case there are an infinite

number of points along a line, or in a given area or volume, where the "event"
can occur.   Examples are the number of faults in a length of cable or the
number of flaws in an area of paper or the number of suspended particles in a
volume of dusty gas.

Other applications of the Poisson distribution are widespread.   It has been
used as a model in:

  traffic flow theory, to describe, under certain conditions, the number of cars
  in a fixed length of roadway or the number of cars passing a point in a fixed
  time interval;

  telephony, to describe the number of calls made in a given time interval;

  microbiology, to describe bacteria counts and bloodcell counts;

  physics, to describe counts of α-particles in radioactive decay, of cosmic
  rays, of X-rays and of visible light photons;

  queueing theory, to describe the number of arrivals in an interval of time;

  the textile industry, to describe the number of warp breakages on a set of
  looms in a stated time interval.

A more comprehensive list of applications can be found in Handbook of the
Poisson Distribution by F.A. Haight (John Wiley & Sons, 1967).

FRAME 5

From Binomial to Poisson

The idea of considering the limiting case of the binomial distribution as $n \to \infty$
and $p \to 0$ will now be developed and the equation of the Poisson model obtained.
A better insight into what is happening can perhaps be obtained by reference to
a particular situation.   Suppose that a certain kind of electrical cable is
found to have on average 2 insulation faults per km length and the distribution
of the number of faults in 1-km lengths is required.

We could consider each 1-km length divided
into 10 sections of 100 m each.   To apply
the binomial model to this situation, two assumptions would then have to be made:
first, that no more than one fault can occur in each section, and second, that
the occurrence of a fault in a section is independent of the occurrence of a
fault in any other section.   For each section there are then two possible
outcomes – "fault" or "no fault" – and the probability p of a fault is the same
for every section.   The distribution of the number of faults in a 1-km length
would then be a binomial one.   State the mean of this distribution, the number
of trials n and deduce the value of p.   (Remember that the mean of a
binomial distribution is np.)

          ****

5A

$np = 2$ $n = 10$ $p = 2/10$

FRAME 6

One of the assumptions on which this model was based was that no more than one
fault could occur in each section.   You may have thought this was rather a
sweeping assumption but, even if you did, you will agree that it will be less

sweeping if the section length is smaller - say, 10 m instead of 100 m.   What
will the values of n and p then be for the appropriate binomial model?

****

6A

$n = 100$ $p = 2/100$

FRAME 7

Continuing in this way, decreasing the length of section by increasing n, the
assumption of no more than 1 fault in a section becomes more and more
reasonable.   Ultimately, the section will become a point and there can't be
more than 1 fault at a point, so the model and the physical reality will agree
on this.

You have seen that p is always 2/n and thus as n → ∞, p → 0.   To obtain the
distribution which occurs in this limit, we shall require the expression for the
probability of x faults in n sections of cable, as given by the binomial model.
Write this down, giving your answer in terms of x and n only.

****

7A

$$\frac{n!}{(n-x)!\,x!}\left(1-\frac{2}{n}\right)^{n-x}\left(\frac{2}{n}\right)^{x} \qquad (7A.1)$$

FRAME 8

The answer in 7A may be rewritten as

$$\frac{n(n-1)(n-2)\,\ldots\ldots\,(n-x+1)}{n^{x}}\;\frac{2^{x}}{x!}\;\frac{\left(1-\frac{2}{n}\right)^{n}}{\left(1-\frac{2}{n}\right)^{x}}$$

$$= \left(1-\frac{1}{n}\right)\left(1-\frac{2}{n}\right)\,\ldots\ldots\,\left(1-\frac{x-1}{n}\right)\frac{2^{x}}{x!}\;\frac{\left(1-\frac{2}{n}\right)^{n}}{\left(1-\frac{2}{n}\right)^{x}} \qquad (8.1)$$

For your own satisfaction you may care to check the above algebra.

(8.1) is now in a form such that the limit as n → ∞ can be seen, provided that

you know that $\lim\limits_{n\to\infty}\left(1+\frac{a}{n}\right)^{n} = e^{a}$.   You may have had the exponential function

introduced to you in this way.   If not, you can easily check that it is correct

by expanding $\left(1+\frac{a}{n}\right)^{n}$ by the binomial theorem and then taking the limit as

n → ∞, thus obtaining the exponential series.   Alternatively you can just take
our word for it!

Now write down the limit of (8.1) as n → ∞.

****

Putting $a = -2$ *gives* $\lim\limits_{n\to\infty}\left(1 - \dfrac{2}{n}\right)^n = e^{-2}$ *leading to* $\dfrac{2^x}{x!}\,e^{-2}$ *for the limit of the whole expression in (8.1).*

The formula arrived at gives the probability of x faults occurring in 1 km of cable, but it applies only to the case when the average number of faults in a 1-km length is 2.   To make it more general, let us call the average μ. Write down the corresponding formula, obtained by substituting μ for 2 in (7A.1) and then, where appropriate, in the subsequent working.

****

The probability of x faults occurring in 1 km of cable would then be

$\dfrac{\mu^x}{x!}\,e^{-\mu}$

The probability formula just obtained is that of a Poisson model.   In the illustration that has been used here the variate x represents the number of faults in 1 km of cable and μ its mean value.   Other situations in which similar assumptions can be made lead to the same formula giving, in general terms, the probability of x occurrences of an event in an interval (of time or length or area or volume, as appropriate).   Of course, the interval must be of a fixed size, as is the case, for example, in the number of vehicles arriving at a road junction in a 30-second interval or the number of particles contaminating 1 litre of sterile saline solution.

The Poisson Distribution

The probability function for the Poisson distribution

$$P(x) = \frac{\mu^x e^{-\mu}}{x!}$$ (11.1)

gives

$$P(0) = e^{-\mu} \qquad \text{(0! is defined as having the value 1.)}$$
$$P(1) = \mu e^{-\mu}$$
$$P(2) = \frac{\mu^2 e^{-\mu}}{2!}$$
$$P(3) = \frac{\mu^3 e^{-\mu}}{3!} \qquad \text{and so on.}$$

To make sure that you understand how to apply (11.1), return to the insulated electrical cable which had an average of 2 faults per km and write down the probability that in 1 km of cable

(i) there are no faults,   (ii) there is 1 fault exactly,
(iii) there is more than 1 fault.

****

11A

(i) $e^{-2} = 0 \cdot 135$ (ii) $2e^{-2} = 0 \cdot 271$ (iii) $1 - 3e^{-2} = 0 \cdot 594$

FRAME 12

Remembering that initially the assumption was made that faults occur independently of one another, deduce from the answers you have just written down the probability that in 2 successive 1-km lengths of cable

(i) there are no faults,
(ii) there is 1 fault exactly.   (Leave your answers as powers of e.)

****

12A

(i) $e^{-2} \times e^{-2} = e^{-4}$ (ii) $e^{-2} \times 2e^{-2} + 2e^{-2} \times e^{-2} = 4e^{-4}$

FRAME 13

Now $P(0) = e^{-4}$ and $P(1) = 4e^{-4}$ would be obtained from a Poisson distribution with $\mu = 4$.   Thus we could alternatively have arrived at the answers by saying that 2 successive 1-km lengths constitute a 2-km length, and the average number of faults per 2-km length is 4.   It is a feature of the situation to which the Poisson distribution applies that the average rate of occurrence of the events is constant overall, so that an average of 2 faults per km length can be translated into an average of 4 faults per 2-km length or 6 faults per 3-km length, and so on.

If vehicles pass a point on a road at an average rate of 300 per hour, what is the average number of vehicles passing in 1 minute and what is the probability of that actually being the number that pass during a particular period of 1 minute?

****

13A

$5, \quad 625e^{-5}/24$

FRAME 14

If you look at the formulae for $P(0)$, $P(1)$ etc. given in FRAME 11, you will see that each value of $P(x)$ can be obtained by multiplying the previous one by an appropriate factor.   Express each of $P(1)$, $P(2)$, $P(3)$ as a multiple of $P(0)$, $P(1)$, $P(2)$ respectively and state the relation between $P(r)$ and $P(r - 1)$.

****

14A

$P(1) = \dfrac{\mu}{1} P(0)$ $P(2) = \dfrac{\mu}{2} P(1)$ $P(3) = \dfrac{\mu}{3} P(2)$ $P(r) = \dfrac{\mu}{r} P(r - 1)$ (14A.1)

FRAME 15

This relation between successive Poisson probabilities can be used to advantage in their computation.   If you find flow diagrams helpful, a simple exercise would be for you to draw one for calculating $P(r)$ for $r = 0, 1, 2, \ldots n$, making use of (14A.1).   Read in the values of μ and n as data.

****

15A

One possible diagram is:

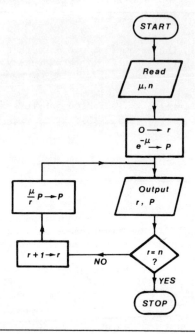

FRAME 16

In the previous programme it was established that, for all probability
distributions for a discrete variate, $\Sigma P(x) = 1$.   For the Poisson model the
variate always involves the number of occurrences of an event and is therefore
discrete.   Check that $\Sigma P(x) = 1$, for $P(x)$ as defined by (11.1).   (There
will be an infinite number of terms in this sum but that should not cause any
difficulty for you.)

****

16A

$$\Sigma P(x) = e^{-\mu} + \mu e^{-\mu} + \frac{\mu^2}{2!} e^{-\mu} + \frac{\mu^3}{3!} e^{-\mu} + \ldots$$

$$= e^{-\mu}(1 + \mu + \frac{\mu^2}{2!} + \frac{\mu^3}{3!} + \ldots) = e^{-\mu} e^{\mu} = 1$$

Did you recognise the exponential series in the brackets?

FRAME 17

Another formula that was established for discrete probability distributions was
that for the mean i.e. $\Sigma x P(x)$.   Check that this does give μ for the mean of
the Poisson distribution.

****

$$\Sigma x P(x) = 0 \times e^{-\mu} + 1 \times \mu e^{-\mu} + 2 \times \frac{\mu^2}{2!} e^{-\mu} + 3 \times \frac{\mu^3}{3!} e^{-\mu} + \ldots.$$

$$= \mu e^{-\mu}(1 + \mu + \frac{\mu^2}{2!} + \ldots.) = \mu e^{-\mu} e^{\mu} = \mu$$

FRAME 18

Now for the variance.   Bearing in mind the derivation of the Poisson
distribution from the binomial, what do you think its variance should be?

****

18A

Binomial: Variance $= npq = np(1 - p)$

Poisson: np $= \mu$, $p \to 0$ *so variance* $= \lim\limits_{p \to 0} np(1 - p) = \mu$

FRAME 19

Let's check this by finding the variance of the Poisson distribution itself.
The basic formula for the variance of a discrete probability distribution was
established in the previous programme as $\Sigma(x - \mu)^2 P(x)$.   It was shown that
this could be expressed in the alternative form $\Sigma x^2 P(x) - \mu^2$.   Using the
latter gives, for the Poisson model,

Variance $= 0^2 \times e^{-\mu} + 1^2 \times \mu e^{-\mu} + 2^2 \times \frac{\mu^2}{2!} e^{-\mu} + 3^2 \times \frac{\mu^3}{3!} e^{-\mu} + 4^2 \times \frac{\mu^4}{4!} e^{-\mu} \ldots. - \mu^2$

$$= \mu e^{-\mu}(1 + 2\mu + 3 \frac{\mu^2}{2!} + 4 \frac{\mu^3}{3!} + \ldots.) - \mu^2$$

$$= \mu e^{-\mu} \left\{ (1 + \mu + \frac{\mu^2}{2!} + \frac{\mu^3}{3!} + \ldots.) + (\mu + 2 \frac{\mu^2}{2!} + 3 \frac{\mu^3}{3!} + \ldots.) \right\} - \mu^2$$

Show that this simplifies to μ.

****

19A

$$\mu e^{-\mu}(e^{\mu} + \mu e^{\mu}) - \mu^2 = \mu + \mu^2 - \mu^2 = \mu$$

FRAME 20

Notice that the Poisson distribution has the special feature

Mean = Variance

This, of course, applies only to the theoretical model.   For an actual set of
data it is unlikely that the mean and variance will be exactly equal, because of
the random fluctuations from one set of data to another.   However their
approximate equality would be encouraging if the suitability of the Poisson
model is being considered.

FRAME 21

We now summarise the essential features of events to which the Poisson
probability model applies.

Such events occur singly at points in a continuum (of time, space etc.), e.g.
there are an infinite number of points in a length of cable where the insulation
can be faulty and there can be only one insulating fault at any one point.

They occur randomly, in that every point in the continuum has an equal chance
of being a point at which the event happens, with occurrences independent of
one another.   This is the case, for instance, if all points in a length of
cable have an equal chance of having faulty insulation and the occurrence of a
fault at any particular point does not affect the probability of faults
occurring at other points.

Thus the average rate at which they occur is uniform and the mean number of
occurrences is proportional to the size of the interval.   For example, if μ
is the mean number of faults in 2-km lengths of cable, then 2μ is the mean
number of faults in 4-km lengths, 3μ is the mean number in 6-km lengths, and
so on.

Fitting a Poisson model

A preliminary analysis of the circumstances out of which a set of data arises
will suggest whether or not the Poisson distribution might be a suitable
theoretical model.   Confirmation can then be obtained by calculating the
frequencies given by the model and comparing them with the observed ones.

The data that serves as an illustration here is quoted almost as often as that
on deaths from horse-kicks.   It dates from 1910 when Rutherford and Geiger
observed α-particles, emitted from a thin film of polonium in an exhausted
tube, making an electrical contact every time one caused a scintillation on
a zinc sulphide screen.   Each contact was recorded on a tape moving uniformly
and the observations were made during 2608 intervals, each of 7·5 seconds
duration.   The results are shown here in the form of a frequency table and give
a value of 3·8715 for the mean number of particles observed per interval.
Taking this as the value of μ in the Poisson model and multiplying each $P(x)$
by 2608 gives the theoretical frequencies which are shown alongside for
comparison.   Thus, for instance, the expected number of intervals with no
emissions is $2608 \times e^{-3 \cdot 8715} \simeq 54 \cdot 3$,   and so on.

Number of particles	Observed number of intervals (Rutherford–Geiger data)	Expected number of intervals (Poisson model)
0	57	54·3
1	203	210·3
2	383	407·1
3	525	525·4
4	532	508·6
5	408	393·8
6	273	254·1
7	139	140·6
8	45	68·0
9	27	29·3
10	10	11·3
11	4	4·0
12	0	1·3
13	1	0·4
14	1	0·1
	2608	2608·6

FRAME 22   (continued)

There appears to be good agreement between observation and theory, but
appearances can sometimes be deceptive and in Unit 2 you will learn how to carry
out a statistical test for "goodness of fit".

If you would like to try your hand at working out the theoretical frequencies
which a Poisson model gives, here is the famous data on which von Bortkiewicz
did the same exercise:

Number of deaths	0	1	2	3	4	5 and over
Number of years this number of deaths occurred in a corps	109	65	22	3	1	0

****

22A

Mean number of deaths per corps per year $= \dfrac{122}{200} = 0 \cdot 61$. *Taking this as the*
value of μ *gives theoretical frequencies of* $108 \cdot 7$, $66 \cdot 3$, $20 \cdot 2$, $4 \cdot 1$, $0 \cdot 6$ *and*
$0 \cdot 1$.

FRAME 23

Fitting a Poisson model to a set of observations can be used as a test of
randomness.   This is illustrated by an investigation that was carried out in
the Second World War with the object of finding out whether V2 rockets were
falling on London in an indiscriminate pattern or whether there was evidence
that they were being aimed at particular target areas.   On a map an area of
144 km^2 was divided into 576 squares of equal size and the number of rockets
which had fallen in each of these sub-areas was recorded.   From this a
frequency distribution was built up showing the number of sub-areas in which
0, 1, 2, ... rockets had fallen.   Randomness in this case would mean that
every point in the 144 km^2 had an equal chance of having a rocket land on it.
The theoretical frequency distribution would then be Poissonian, and it was, in
fact, shown that this model gave a very good fit.

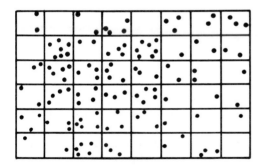

Investigations of this kind into the
way in which points are distributed
over an area can be of great interest
to geographers and geologists.   The
diagram represents an area on a map
which has been divided up into 48
equal sub-areas.   Each dot represents
the location of an oilwell.   Testing
for a pattern of randomness can be
done in a similar way to that used for
rockets falling on London.

FRAME 24

The Poisson distribution as an approximation to the Binomial

As the Poisson distribution can be derived as the limiting case of the binomial when $n \to \infty$ and $p \to 0$, it is evident that there should not be much difference between the two when n is large and p is small. The Poisson formula (which is the simpler) can then be used as an approximation, even though the binomial model is the true one, as is illustrated by the following example:

Electric light bulbs, of which 1% are defective on average, are packed in cartons of 100. It is required to calculate the percentage of cartons containing 0, 1, 2, ... defective bulbs.

Using the binomial model: $p = 0 \cdot 01$, $q = 0 \cdot 99$, $n = 100$:

Probability of x defectives in a carton $= \dfrac{100!}{(100 - x)! \ x!} (0 \cdot 01)^x (0 \cdot 99)^{100-x}$

Using the Poisson model with the same mean i.e. $\mu = np = 1$:
Probability of x defectives in a carton $= e^{-1}/x!$

Multiplying the probabilities by 100 to convert them to percentages the results below are obtained:

Number of defectives in a carton (x)		0	1	2	3	4	5	6
Percentage of cartons containing x defectives	Binomial	36·64	37·01	18·51	6·11	1·49	0·29	0·05
	Poisson	36·79	36·79	18·40	6·13	1·53	0·31	0·05

For larger values of p and smaller values of n, the approximation would not be as close as this. Ideas of what represents a satisfactory approximation will vary, but one can safely say that p needs to be less than 0·1.

Now try this example:

From extensive tests carried out in the past, it is known that 1·5% of filters of a certain type fail when tested against standard dust. State the exact formula (don't evaluate it) for the probability that out of 200 such filters just 4 will fail the test. Then give a suitable approximation.

****

24A

$\dfrac{200!}{196! \ 4!} (0 \cdot 015)^4 (0 \cdot 985)^{196}$ *Poisson approximation gives $27e^{-3}/8$*

FRAME 25

Miscellaneous Examples

In this frame a collection of miscellaneous examples is given for you to try. Answers are supplied in FRAME 26, together with such working as is considered helpful.

1. If 250 litres of water have been polluted with 10^6 bacteria, what is the probability that a sample of 1 ml of the water contains no bacteria?

2. Sheets of metal have plating faults which occur at random at an average rate of 1 per m^2. What is the probability that a sheet $1 \cdot 5 \, m \times 2 \, m$ will have at most one fault?

3. Values given by the Poisson distribution for the probability that an event will occur at least c times are required in some problems, the value of c

FRAME 25   (continued)

being determined by the particular situation in the problem.   For a
distribution with mean μ, obtain expressions for these probabilities when
$c = 0, 1, 2, 3$.   (Curves drawn on a special type of graph paper - Poisson
probability paper - are sometimes used for reading off such probabilities.
There is a curve for each value of c, μ is shown along one axis and the
probability on the other.)

4. Traffic engineers use the Poisson distribution as a model for the flow of
    vehicles past a point when the traffic is not dense and is flowing freely.
    For example, it can be used to describe the number of vehicles which arrive
    at an intersection during a certain time interval.   On this basis, if
    vehicles arrive at a signalised road intersection at an average rate of
    360 per hour and the cycle of the traffic light is set at 40 seconds, in
    what percentage of cycles will the number of vehicles arriving be
    (i) exactly 5, (ii) less than 5? If, after the lights change to green,
    there is time to clear only 5 vehicles before the signal changes to red
    again, what is the probability of waiting vehicles not being cleared in
    one cycle if (a) all vehicles were cleared in the previous cycle, (b) one
    vehicle was not cleared in the previous cycle?

5. Counting the oil wells in the 48 sub-areas of the map shown in FRAME 23
    gives the following frequency distribution:

Number of oil wells	0	1	2	3	4	5	6	7
Number of sub-areas	5	10	11	10	6	4	0	2

Calculate the mean number of oil wells per sub-area and find the
theoretical frequencies given by a Poisson distribution with the same mean.

6. If an average of 264 vehicles an hour enter a certain stretch of road,
    each taking 30 seconds to travel along it, find the probability that at a
    given instant there will be no vehicles on this stretch of road.

7. In a factory 2000 employees will be asked to use a barrier cream for which
    the probability of an initial reaction sufficient to cause absence from
    work is 0·001.   Determine the probability that more than two employees
    will be absent when the barrier cream is introduced.   (C.E.I.)

8. A scheme was prepared to improve a complicated road junction in a small
    town.   A full-sized roundabout had to be ruled out because it would involve
    very extensive, and expensive, demolition
    of buildings.   However, from a
    preliminary study, it seemed as if a small
    roundabout would be successful if entry
    from the side roads could be controlled by
    traffic lights.   There was just one snag -
    roads A and F converged very sharply, so
    if they both entered the roundabout
    frequent congestion might result.   To
    remove this potential source of trouble,
    it was suggested that road F be run into
    road A as shown in the figure and their
    junction X would then be controlled by
    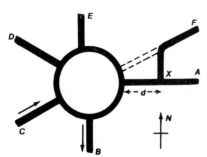
    traffic lights working in conjunction with those controlling other roads.
    But the distance d would then only have capacity for 5 east-bound
    vehicles to stand in it while the lights at X were against them.   If

there were more they would have to wait on the roundabout itself and so probably jam it.　Even 5 vehicles could cause this if not sufficiently close behind one another while waiting or if extra long.　To assess the probability of there being 5 or more vehicles in this queue, a count was taken of traffic entering roads A and F from roads C and E, which the scheme envisaged as being allowed to enter the roundabout together.　The table shows the result of recording the number of vehicles entering in successive 30-second intervals during the busiest hour of the day.

Number of vehicles (x)	0	1	2	3	4	5 or more
Number of intervals	47	44	21	4	4	0

Show that the mean number of vehicles entering in a 30-second interval is 0·95.　Taking this as the parameter μ, find the theoretical frequencies given by the Poisson model.　Notice that they show close agreement with the observations and that the assessment can therefore be made that, at that time of day, 5 or more vehicles may be expected in only 0·4 intervals out of 120.　This was a risk that could be taken but there was a possibility that traffic might increase in future years.　Assuming that the pattern of flow continues to be Poissonian, in how many intervals in the hour will 5 or more vehicles be expected if traffic increases by (i) 50%,　(ii) 100%?

(This problem is based on a similar project described by J.J. Leeming in Statistical Methods for Engineers.)

9.　Suppose that a biologist wishes to know the total number of cells present in an area of a glass slide which is being examined under the microscope and which is divided by a square grid into 20×20, i.e. 400, equal sub-areas.　If the cells are distributed at random throughout the grid, the number of cells in a sub-area may be assumed to follow a Poisson distribution.　On this assumption, state the formula for the probability of a sub-area containing no cells if the total number of cells in the whole area is N.　Deduce a formula for the number of sub-areas you would expect, on average, to contain no cells.　Equating this formula to the actual number of such sub-areas observed gives a "short-cut" method which has been used by some experimenters to estimate the value of N, it being much easier and quicker to count how many of the 400 sub-areas contain no cells than to count the number of cells present in the whole area.　Use this method to estimate the total number of cells present if 50 sub-areas were observed to have no cells.

10.　The "short-cut" method described in the previous question uses the observed frequency of one particular value, 0, of the variate to obtain an estimate of the parameter μ of the appropriate Poisson model.　What would this method have given for an estimate of μ for the distribution of oil wells as described in Qu. 5, if only the number of sub-areas with no oil wells had been counted?

When an oil well is on the boundary between two sub-areas the one to which it is allocated could depend on the particular map being used or on who was doing the counting.　For instance, instead of counting 5 sub-areas with no oil wells, other geologists might have recorded 4 or 6.　Find the estimates of μ given by each of these results, using the short-cut method, and compare them with the previous estimate and with the mean value obtained from the complete data in Qu. 5.

11. When wire is insulated by being enamelled, it is found that the occurrence
of weak spots in the insulation in a piece of wire ΔL units long is
proportional to ΔL, say $\lambda \Delta L$, and is independent of both the position on
the wire and the number of insulation weak spots that occur elsewhere in
the wire.   Hence the number of weak spots in the insulation in a length L
of wire will be described by a Poisson distribution with mean λL, where λ
is the mean number of insulation weak spots per unit length.   If a
particular enamelling process results in weak spots occurring at an average
rate of one per 2 m, find the probability that out of four 1-m lengths
less than two will have more than one weak spot.

12. An access road joins a motorway at A.   Vehicles arrive at A from the
access road at an average rate of α per minute and from the motorway
itself at an average rate of β per minute.   Assuming that in both cases
the Poisson model is appropriate, write down the probability that in a
1-minute interval the total number of vehicles passing the point A is
(i) 0,   (ii) 1,   (iii) 2.   If you look carefully at your answers you will
see that they are the values of   P(0), P(1), P(2)   given by a Poisson
distribution.   State the mean and variance of this distribution.

13. A manufacturer sells a certain article in batches of 5000.   By agreement
with a customer the following method of inspection is adopted:

A sample of 100 items is drawn at random from each batch and inspected.
If the sample contains 4 or fewer defective items, then the batch is
accepted by the customer.   If more than 4 defectives are found, every
item in the batch is inspected.

If inspection costs are 75p per hundred articles, and the manufacturer
normally produces 2% of defective articles, find the average inspection
cost per batch.   (C.E.I.)

Answers to Miscellaneous Examples

1. $e^{-4} = 0 \cdot 0183$,   assuming a random distribution of bacteria throughout the
250 litres.

2. $e^{-3} + 3e^{-3} = 4e^{-3} = 0 \cdot 199$.

3. 1, $1 - e^{-\mu}$, $1 - (1 + \mu)e^{-\mu}$, $1 - (1 + \mu + \mu^2/2)e^{-\mu}$

4. (i) $P(5) = 128e^{-4}/15$ i.e.   15·6%
   (ii) P(less than 5) = $103e^{-4}/3$ i.e.   62·9%
   (a) P(more than 5 arrive) = $0 \cdot 215$ (b) P(more than 4 arrive) = $0 \cdot 371$

5. 2·5;   3·9, 9·9, 12·3, 10·3, 6·4, 3·2, 1·3, 0·5, 0·2   are the theoretical
frequencies for   0, 1, ... 8   wells.

6. The stretch of road is empty if no vehicle has entered it during the
previous 30 s.   P(0) = $e^{-2 \cdot 2}$ = $0 \cdot 111$

7. The model which applies here is the binomial with   p = 0·001   and   n = 2000.
As p is small and n is large, the Poisson approximation can be used, with
$\mu = 2$.   P(more than 2 absent) = $1 - 5e^{-2} = 0 \cdot 323$

8. 0·95;   46·4, 44·1, 20·9, 6·6, 1·6, 0·4.
   (i) $\mu = 1 \cdot 425$ gives an estimate of 1·8 times in an hour.

(ii) $\mu = 1 \cdot 9$ gives $5 \cdot 3$.   It is therefore doubtful whether the scheme would offer a satisfactory long-term solution if it is envisaged that the traffic will increase to as much as double.

9. $\exp(-N/400)$, $400 \exp(-N/400)$, $N = 400 \ln 8 = 832$.

10. $\ln 9 \cdot 6 \simeq 2 \cdot 262$, $\ln 12 \simeq 2 \cdot 485$, $\ln 8 \simeq 2 \cdot 079$. Note that if these had been used to estimate N, as in the previous question, values of 109, 119 and 100 would have been obtained. The method may be a dubious proposition when the number of sub-areas is as small as 48, but for the biologist with 400 sub-areas, the estimate of N would be less susceptible to a slight change in the count.

11. For a 1-m length, $P(\text{more than 1 weak spot}) = 1 - 1 \cdot 5e^{-0 \cdot 5} = 0 \cdot 0902$
Then use binomial distribution with $p = 0 \cdot 0902$, $n = 4$.
$P(0) + P(1) = 0 \cdot 957$

12. (i) $P(0 \text{ vehicles arrive from access road}) = e^{-\alpha}$

$P(0 \text{ vehicles arrive from motorway}) = e^{-\beta}$

$P(0 \text{ vehicles arrive at A}) = e^{-\alpha} e^{-\beta} = e^{-(\alpha+\beta)}$

(ii) $e^{-\alpha}(\beta e^{-\beta}) + (\alpha e^{-\alpha})e^{-\beta} = (\alpha + \beta)e^{-(\alpha+\beta)}$ (iii) $\dfrac{(\alpha + \beta)^2 \, e^{-(\alpha+\beta)}}{2}$

Mean = variance = $\alpha + \beta$

13. The number of defective items in a sample of 100 is described by a binomial distribution with $p = 0 \cdot 02$, $n = 100$. Using Poisson approximation with $\mu = 2$, $P(4 \text{ or fewer defective}) = 7e^{-2} = 0 \cdot 9473$.

Probability that remaining 4900 items have to be inspected = $0 \cdot 0527$
Average number of items inspected per batch = $100 + 0 \cdot 0527 \times 4900 = 358 \cdot 2$
Average inspection cost per batch = $358 \cdot 2 \times 0 \cdot 75 \text{ p} = £2 \cdot 69$

Probability Distributions
for Continuous Variates

Introduction

The probability distributions so far considered have applied to discrete variates. When the variate is continuous, a different approach is needed. To illustrate this let us consider the time a passenger has to wait at a station if trains run every 10 minutes and if he has no knowledge of the timetable. The variate x is the waiting time in minutes and is obviously continuous. Is it restricted in its value in any way?

****

It can only have a value between 0 and 10.

As the passenger does not know the train departure times, it can be assumed that the length of time he has to wait is a matter of pure chance and that therefore all values of x between 0 and 10 are equally likely.

It is certain that the waiting time will lie between 0 and 10 and therefore the probability that x lies in this interval is 1. What would you say is the probability of a waiting time being between (i) 0 and 5 minutes, (ii) 5 and 10 minutes?

****

As (i) and (ii) are clearly equally likely, each has a probability of ½.

Similarly, if the interval is sub-divided into ten 1-minute intervals, it can be seen that the probabilities of a passenger having to wait between 0 and 1 minute, 1 and 2 minutes, etc. are each 1/10. Now, you have already used histograms to show the distribution of frequencies. They can just as well represent relative frequencies and, taking that view of the probabilities we have just found, the histograms shown here are obtained.

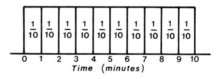

You will remember that, with frequency distributions, the area of each rectangle represents the frequency in that interval and the area of the whole histogram represents the total frequency. Here, the area of each rectangle represents the relative frequency, i.e. probability, and to emphasise this point the appropriate values are shown in the rectangles, although it would not normally be done in a histogram. The total area represents a probability of 1.

Now let us turn our attention to the <u>height</u> of the rectangles. When the base width represents 5 minutes and the area a probability of ½, the height must represent 1/10, the unit being probability per minute. Obviously the height

is the same in the histogram on the right, and will be 1/10 however the
10-minute interval is sub-divided.   It is, in fact, determined by the total
area having to represent 1 and the width of the base 10.

The vertical scale on these diagrams is said to represent PROBABILITY DENSITY.
In this example it is in units of "probability per minute".   In general, it
would be in units of "probability per unit of the variate x".

Write down the probability density corresponding to a waiting time (in minutes)
of (i) 4,   (ii) -4,   (iii) 14.

****

3A

(i) 1/10   (ii) 0   (iii) 0

FRAME 4

A probability distribution for a continuous variate can be described by the
function, denoted in this text by p(x), which defines the probability density
for every value of x.   It is called the PROBABILITY DENSITY FUNCTION, often
abbreviated to p.d.f.

The probability distribution for the waiting times is an example of a
RECTANGULAR or UNIFORM DISTRIBUTION for a continuous variate.   It is shown
here beside the similar type of distribution, for a discrete variate, that you
saw in a previous programme.

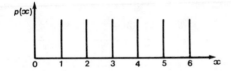
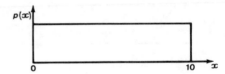

If the discrete distribution is analogous to a light rod bearing isolated point
loads, then the continuous distribution is analogous to a heavy rod where the
weight is distributed continuously (and, in this particular case, uniformly)
along its length.   This may help you to understand why the term probability
density is used.   For the waiting times, p(x) = 1/10 for values of x
between 0 and 10, and zero elsewhere.

Write down the probability of a passenger having to wait (i) more than 6
minutes, (ii) between x and x + h minutes, assuming that both x and x + h
are between 0 and 10.   In each case make a sketch to show the area which
represents the probability.

****

4A

(i) 4/10   *(ii) h/10*

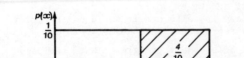
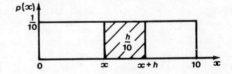

FRAME 5

Now, to test your understanding of the preceding frames, here is a simple
problem.   The breaking load (i.e. the load which is <u>just</u> sufficient to cause a
break) of a link in a chain is equally likely to have any value between 23 and
27 N.   Use a diagram to describe the probability distribution for the breaking
load of a link and write down the probability of a link breaking when subjected
to a load of 26 N.

****

5A

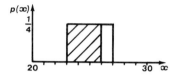

*The link will break when subjected to a load of
26 N if its breaking load does not exceed this
value.   The probability of this is given by the
shaded area and is 3/4.*

FRAME 6

Probability Curves

The rectangular probability distribution is very simple but, as has already been
noted of its discrete counterpart in an earlier programme, such a model is too
simple for most situations.

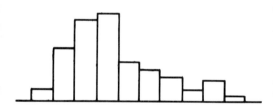

As relative frequencies give
estimates of probability, a table of
relative frequencies obtained from,
say, 100 observations of a
continuous variate would give an
approximation to its probability
distribution.   From the histogram
we would get some idea of what the
theoretical model should look like.

There are two reasons why the histogram shows only an approximation to the true
probability distribution.

(i)   Because of random fluctuations, different histograms will be obtained from
       different sets of observations.   With 100 observations we only see part
       of the picture.   An infinitely large number of observations would be
       required to reveal the whole of it.

(ii)   The probability density is treated as constant in each interval and
       changes suddenly at the interval boundaries.   If you think of a
       continuous variate such as the height of a man or the length of life of a
       lamp you will appreciate that this would be quite unrealistic.

As far as (i) is concerned, the histogram would give a better approximation if
based on a larger number of observations.   If this were done how would you also
attempt an improvement in relation to (ii)?

****

6A

*Decrease the interval width.   Then the way in which p(x) is changing will be
shown in more detail and the intervals over which it is assumed constant will be
smaller.*

Simultaneously increasing the number of observations and decreasing the interval width might result in a sequence of histograms as shown (the vertical lines have been omitted for simplicity).   As you will know from integral calculus, the area under a curve can be regarded as the limit of the sum of the areas of rectangles just such as there are in these histograms.   The logical outcome, therefore, is the PROBABILITY CURVE shown in the final diagram.

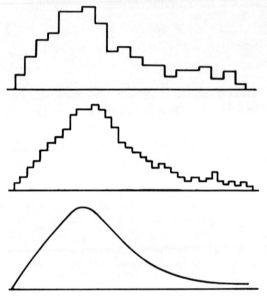

Just before the final stage is reached, the interval width is very small - let's call is δx - and the probability of getting an observation in the interval x to x + δx is given by $p(x)\delta x$. Summing over all the intervals and letting $\delta x \rightarrow 0$ leads to

$$\lim_{\delta x \rightarrow 0} \sum_{x=-\infty}^{\infty} p(x)\delta x, \quad \text{which is, of}$$

course, $\int_{-\infty}^{\infty} p(x)dx$.

If taking x from $-\infty$ to $+\infty$ does not seem to you to relate to what happens in practice, remember that $p(x)$ can be zero for part of the range (this happened with the waiting times).

For a discrete variate, you saw that $\Sigma P(x) = 1$, when summing over all the x's.   The corresponding result for a continuous variate is clearly

$$\int_{-\infty}^{\infty} p(x)dx = 1 \qquad (7.1)$$

This is saying that the total area under the probability curve must be 1, just as the total area of the histogram representing relative frequencies is always 1.   Verify, by integration, that (7.1) is true of the rectangular distribution for waiting times discussed in FRAMES 1-4.

****

$$\int_{-\infty}^{\infty} p(x)dx = \int_{-\infty}^{0} 0\ dx + \int_{0}^{10} \frac{1}{10}\ dx + \int_{10}^{\infty} 0\ dx = 0 + \left[\frac{x}{10}\right]_{0}^{10} + 0 = 1$$

Another obvious development of what has been said in the last frame is that the probability of getting an observation in the interval x = a to x = b is given by $\lim_{\delta x \rightarrow 0} \sum_{x=a}^{b} p(x)\delta x$ i.e. by $\int_{a}^{b} p(x)dx$, which is the area shown in the diagram on the next page.

FRAME 8   (continued)

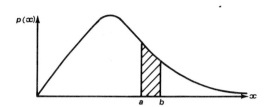

Verify, by integration, that the answer you obtained in 5A agrees with this.

****

8A

$$P(breaking\ load < 26\ N) = \int_{-\infty}^{26} p(x)dx = \int_{-\infty}^{23} 0\ dx + \int_{23}^{26} \frac{1}{4}\ dx = 0 + \left[\frac{x}{4}\right]_{23}^{26} = \frac{3}{4}$$

FRAME 9

Now look at the shaded area in the previous frame and say what will happen to it if b moves towards a and eventually coincides with it.

****

9A

The area will get smaller and eventually become zero.

FRAME 10

Thus if, instead of considering the probability of x occurring in the interval a to b, we were looking for the probability of x taking the value a, we would find that the area has vanished and so the probability has done likewise. Therefore, for a continuous variate, it is a probability density, instead of a probability, which is associated with a particular value of x.   Consequently we do not think of the probability of x taking a particular value but of the probability of x taking a value within a particular interval.

Returning to the case where the variate x is the waiting time for a train - if the time scale is measured in hours and the trains run every $\frac{1}{2}$ hour, what is the probability density for all values of x between 0 and $\frac{1}{2}$?

****

10A

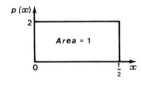

Probability density p(x) = 2 for $0 < x < \frac{1}{2}$.   Note that whilst a __probability__ can never have a value exceeding 1, a __probability density__ can have any positive value.

Cumulative Distribution Function

The breaking load problem is just one of many where the probability of the
variate being less than a stated value is what is required.   Denoting that
value by a, the general formula for this probability will be $\int_{-\infty}^{a} p(x)dx$.

This is a function of a, so we may write

$$F(a) = \int_{-\infty}^{a} p(x)dx$$

To every p(x) there will be a corresponding F(a), known as the CUMULATIVE
DISTRIBUTION FUNCTION (often abbreviated to c.d.f.).   If you recall the
cumulative frequencies found from frequency distributions in the first
programme in this Unit, you will recognise the same idea here applied to a
probability distribution.

For the train waiting times with a 10 minute service, p(x) = 1/10 for values
of x between 0 and 10 and zero elsewhere.   Thus the c.d.f. is given by

$$\begin{cases} F(a) = 0 & a < 0 \\ F(a) = a/10 & 0 < a < 10 \\ F(a) = 1 & a > 10 \end{cases}$$

A complete definition of F(a) is given, but as it represents the probability
of having to wait less than a minutes for a train, in practice negative values
of a would obviously not arise here.   However in other cases, a could be
negative as, for instance, if the variate were temperature in $^{\circ}$C.   Note that,
as F(a) is a probability, $0 \leqslant F(a) \leqslant 1$ for all a.

Now see if you can write down the equations giving the c.d.f. for the breaking
loads described in FRAME 5.   Also explain in words what F(a) actually
represents in this case.

****

11A

$$\begin{cases} F(a) = 0 & a < 23 \\ F(a) = (a - 23)/4 & 23 < a < 27 \\ F(a) = 1 & a > 27 \end{cases}$$

F(a) is the probability of a link having a breaking load less than a newtons.

FRAME 12

Mean and Variance

For a discrete variate you have seen that the mean, or expected value, of x is
given by ΣxP(x).   Adapting this to the case when the variate is continuous
leads to

$$\lim_{\delta x \to 0} \sum_{x=-\infty}^{\infty} xp(x)\delta x, \quad i.e. \quad \int_{-\infty}^{\infty} xp(x)dx \quad (12.1)$$

Use this formula to find the mean waiting time for a train.

****

$$\int_{-\infty}^{0} x \cdot 0 \, dx \; + \; \int_{0}^{10} x \cdot \frac{1}{10} \, dx \; + \; \int_{10}^{\infty} x \cdot 0 \, dx = 0 + \left[\frac{x^2}{20} \right]_{0}^{10} + 0 = 5 \; minutes$$

FRAME 13

From the third programme in this Unit you also know that the variance of a
discrete variate is given by $\Sigma(x - \mu)^2 P(x)$, which can be expressed in the
alternative form $\Sigma x^2 P(x) - \mu^2$. Maybe you can decide for yourself what the
corresponding formulae for the variance of a continuous variate are.

****

13A

$$\int_{-\infty}^{\infty} (x - \mu)^2 p(x) dx, \quad which \; in \; the \; alternative \; form \; becomes \quad \int_{-\infty}^{\infty} x^2 p(x) dx - \mu^2$$
$$(13A.1)$$

FRAME 14

Now find the variance of the distribution of train waiting times.

****

14A

$$Either \quad 0 \; + \; \int_{0}^{10} (x - 5)^2 \cdot \frac{1}{10} \, dx + 0 = \left[\frac{(x - 5)^3}{30} \right]_{0}^{10} = \frac{25}{3}$$

$$or \quad 0 \; + \; \int_{0}^{10} x^2 \cdot \frac{1}{10} \, dx + 0 - 25 = \left[\frac{x^3}{30} \right]_{0}^{10} - 25 = \frac{25}{3}$$

FRAME 15

The Exponential Distribution

(If you plan to miss out this topic, proceed straight to FRAME 22.)

In the previous programme we looked at events whose occurrence at points in an
interval of, say, length or time was a purely random (i.e. chance) affair and
whose average rate of occurrence remained constant. The variate which was
considered was the number of occurrences of such an event in an interval of
defined magnitude. For instance, in the case of faults in an insulated cable
the variate was the number of faults in a 1-km length, and in the emission
of α-particles it was the number of particles emitted in a 7·5-second interval.
Such variates, by their nature discrete, were seen to follow a Poisson
distribution.

If, instead, we consider as the variate the interval between two occurrences –
e.g. the distance between consecutive faults in the cable or the time between
consecutive emissions of α-particles – are we still dealing with a discrete
variate?

****

15A

No. Distance and time are continuous.

The model which describes the distance between faults or the time between emissions is the EXPONENTIAL DISTRIBUTION.   In the frames which follow you will discover that, in fact, it describes the intervals between the occurrences of other Poisson events.   It is also often adopted as an adequate model even when the occurrence of events does not comply with the conditions required by Poisson - for instance, it has been used for the time between vehicle arrivals even if the flow of traffic was not Poissonian.   The exponential distribution is made use of in queuing theory and in reliability engineering, where it applies to the time between chance failures of a component or system.

As has already been noted, the exponential distribution is a model for the continuous type of variate.   Its probability density function $p(x)$ can be shown to be

$$p(x) = \begin{cases} 0 & \text{for } x < 0 \\ \lambda e^{-\lambda x} & \text{for } x > 0 \end{cases} \qquad (16.1)$$

Probabilities, and hence probability densities, can't be negative, so $\lambda > 0$. With this in mind, sketch the graph of $p(x)$.

****

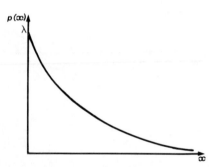

Note that this probability distribution rules out negative values for x, but theoretically permits values of x to extend to infinity in the positive direction.   From a practical point of view, however, there will be a point beyond which the probability of a value occurring may be considered negligible.

If you look back to the histogram representing time gaps between vehicles, shown in the answer to Misc. Ex. 8 on page 44, you will see that the exponential distribution might well be a suitable model for that data.

In FRAME 7 you saw that the area under a probability curve must always be 1. Verify that this is so for $p(x)$ as defined in (16.1), by evaluating

$$\int_{-\infty}^{\infty} p(x)dx.$$

Then, if you are familiar with integration by parts, use (12.1) and (13A.1) to obtain the mean and variance respectively of the exponential distribution and deduce the coefficient of variation.   (Refer back to FRAME 49 on page 28 if you have forgotten what this is.

****

$$\int_{-\infty}^{\infty} p(x)\,dx = 0 + \int_{0}^{\infty} \lambda e^{-\lambda x}\,dx = \left[-e^{-\lambda x}\right]_{0}^{\infty} = 1$$

$$Mean = \int_{0}^{\infty} x\,\lambda e^{-\lambda x}\,dx = \left[-xe^{-\lambda x}\right]_{0}^{\infty} - \int_{0}^{\infty} \left(-\,e^{-\lambda x}\right)dx$$

$$= 0 + \left[-e^{-\lambda x}/\lambda\right]_{0}^{\infty} = 1/\lambda$$

$$Variance = \int_{0}^{\infty} (x - 1/\lambda)^2\,\lambda e^{-\lambda x}\,dx \quad or \quad \int_{0}^{\infty} x^2\,\lambda e^{-\lambda x}\,dx - 1/\lambda^2$$

The second alternative is slightly easier, giving

$$\left[-x^2 e^{-\lambda x}\right]_{0}^{\infty} - \int_{0}^{\infty} -2xe^{-\lambda x}\,dx - 1/\lambda^2 = 0 + 2\int_{0}^{\infty} xe^{-\lambda x}\,dx - 1/\lambda^2$$

$$= 2/\lambda^2 - 1/\lambda^2 = 1/\lambda^2$$

Standard deviation = $1/\lambda$.   Coefficient of variation = 1,   i.e.   100%,   and is therefore the same for all λ.

Now obtain an expression for the probability, given by this distribution, of the variate having a value less than a, where $0 < a < \infty$, and deduce the probability of it exceeding a.   Also state the equations which define the c.d.f. F(a) for all a.

****

Area under curve between 0 and a = $\int_{0}^{a} \lambda e^{-\lambda x}\,dx = 1 - e^{-\lambda a}$
$e^{-\lambda a}$

$$\begin{cases} F(a) = 0 & a < 0 \\ F(a) = 1 - e^{-\lambda a} & 0 < a < \infty \end{cases}$$

Now to see how the exponential distribution can be linked up with the Poisson process.   If faults in a cable occur at a constant mean rate of λ per km, what is the mean number of faults occurring in lengths of ℓ km?   Use the Poisson model to deduce the probability that a length of ℓ km will have   (i) no faults, (ii) at least one fault.

****

$\lambda\ell$.   Taking $\mu = \lambda\ell$ in the Poisson model gives   (i) P(0) = $e^{-\lambda\ell}$, hence (ii) P(at least 1) = $1 - e^{-\lambda\ell}$.

Where there is a length of ℓ km of cable with no faults, the distance between faults in the cable is clearly greater than ℓ km. Thus, considering now the continuous variate x, the distance between faults in the cable, we see that your answer $e^{-\lambda\ell}$ gives $P(x > \ell)$. In the same way, if there is at least one fault in a length of ℓ km, the distance between faults must be less than ℓ km so your answer $1 - e^{-\lambda\ell}$ gives $P(x < \ell)$. It is impossible to have a negative distance between faults, so the c.d.f. which describes x is

$$\begin{cases} F(\ell) = 0 & \ell < 0 \\ F(\ell) = 1 - e^{-\lambda\ell} & 0 < \ell < \infty \end{cases}$$

If you compare this with your answer defining $F(a)$ in 18A, you will see that it is of the same form and is therefore the c.d.f. for an exponential distribution. In other words, if the number of faults per interval of length is Poisson distributed, then the length between faults is exponentially distributed. Note also that saying that the mean number of faults per km is λ is equivalent to saying that the mean number of km per fault is $1/\lambda$, which is just what, in 17A, you found the mean of the exponential distribution to be.

It has been suggested that the exponential distribution might be a suitable model for describing the time gaps between vehicles for which data was given in Misc. Ex. 8 on page 42. There were 200 observations of the variate t, the time between vehicles in seconds, and their mean was found to be 7·5. For an exponential distribution with the same mean:

(i)   State the p.d.f. $p(t)$.

(ii) State and evaluate the integral giving the probability of a time gap being less than t_1 seconds.

(iii) State and evaluate the integral giving the probability of a time gap being greater than t_1 but less than t_2.

(iv) For each of the first three groups in the frequency table, i.e. 0-2, 2-4, 4-6, find the probability of a value of t occurring in that group and deduce the theoretical frequency in a total of 200 observations.

****

(i) $p(t) = \lambda e^{-\lambda t}$

(ii) $\displaystyle\int_0^{t_1} \lambda e^{-\lambda t}\, dt = 1 - e^{-\lambda t_1}$ where $\lambda = 2/15$ as $1/\lambda = 7 \cdot 5$

(iii) $\displaystyle\int_{t_1}^{t_2} \lambda e^{-\lambda t}\, dt = e^{-\lambda t_1} - e^{-\lambda t_2}$

(iv) 0·2341, 46·8; 0·1793, 35·9; 0·1373, 27·5

At this stage, a comparison with the corresponding observed frequencies of 40, 32 and 26 would not unduly discourage the idea of an exponential model. A complete investigation of its suitability will be made later in the course.

The Normal (Gaussian) Distribution

The distribution to which the remainder of this programme will be devoted is by
far the most important of all the distributions described in this course on
statistical methods.   Its name – the Normal distribution – stems from an early
idea that it was the natural pattern which should be followed by distributions
and any divergence from it called for an explanation.   In fact, there is nothing
abnormal about observations which are not distributed Normally.   Among the
variates for which it does serve as a model are the dimensions of mass-produced
articles, experimental errors and measurable biological characteristics such as
a man's height, weight, chest girth or arm length.   Besides being put forward
by de Moivre in 1733, the Normal curve was also derived by Gauss in his study
of errors in observations in astronomy so you may see it referred to as the
Gaussian curve or Gaussian law of errors.

For this distribution, the probability density function is

$$p(x) = \frac{1}{\sigma\sqrt{2\pi}} \exp\left\{ - \frac{(x - \mu)^2}{2\sigma^2} \right\} \qquad (23.1)$$

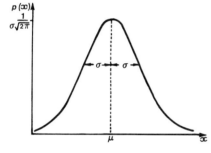

The curve has the following features:

    (i)   A maximum at $x = \mu$

    (ii) Points of inflexion at $x = \mu \pm \sigma$

    (iii) Symmetry about $x = \mu$

    (iv) The x-axis is an asymptote.

(For details of how these properties are
deduced from the equation of the curve, see
the answer to Misc. Ex. 9 in the programme
"Differentiation and its Applications" in Vol.
1 of Mathematics for Engineers and Scientists.)

After a moment's thought you should be able to state the mean and median of this
distribution.
              ****

*Mean = Median = μ because of the symmetry about x = μ.   (μ is also the mode
as it is where the peak probability density occurs.)*

With the Poisson model, you saw that a particular distribution was determined
by the value of one parameter, μ.   The Normal model has two parameters, μ and
σ.   You have already noted that μ is the mean.   The value of σ affects the
shape of the curve, with low values of σ corresponding to a high density of
observations around the mean.   The wider the spread of observations the bigger
is the value of σ.   You will find out more about σ later on.   Meanwhile look
at the two diagrams (i) and (ii) given on the next page, and also at the three
descriptions A, B and C, and choose an appropriate description for each diagram.

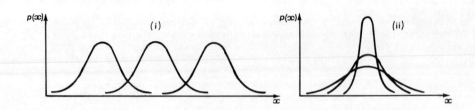

A.   Distributions with the same value of μ but different values of σ.
B.   Distributions with different values of μ and different values of σ.
C.   Distributions with the same value of σ but different values of μ.

        ****

24A

C describes (i).   A describes (ii).

FRAME 25

In FRAME 7 it was established that, for a continuous variate, $\displaystyle\int_{-\infty}^{\infty} p(x)\,dx = 1$.
When $p(x)$ is the function given in (23.1) this integral is

$\displaystyle\int_{-\infty}^{\infty} \frac{1}{\sigma\sqrt{2\pi}} \exp\left\{-\frac{(x-\mu)^2}{2\sigma^2}\right\}dx$,   which can be made to look less formidable by

the substitution $u = (x - \mu)/\sigma$.   If you are familiar with substitution methods
in integration, you should be able to find the corresponding integral in u (but
do not attempt to evaluate it).

        ****

25A

$du = \dfrac{dx}{\sigma}$ *Integral* $= \displaystyle\int_{-\infty}^{\infty} \frac{1}{\sqrt{2\pi}} e^{-u^2/2}\,du$

FRAME 26

This integral looks deceptively simple.   In fact, if you tried to find
$\int e^{-u^2/2}\,du$ you would not succeed (unless you avoided the difficulty by
expanding $e^{-u^2/2}$ as an infinite series).   However the integral can be
evaluated analytically when the integral has limits $-\infty$ and $+\infty$, by a special
technique involving double integration.   If you're not put off by that, you can
look it up in Mathematics for Engineers and Scientists Volume 2, where the
working is shown in full in the programme "Surface Integrals".   Otherwise, just

rest assured that it can be proved that $\displaystyle\int_{-\infty}^{\infty} e^{-u^2/2}\,du = \sqrt{2\pi}$, from which it

follows that $\displaystyle\int_{-\infty}^{\infty} p(x)\,dx = 1$, when $p(x)$ is as given in (23.1).

Deduce the value of $\displaystyle\int_{\mu}^{\infty} p(x)\,dx$.

        ****

0·5.   The total area under the curve from −∞ *to* +∞ *is 1 and the symmetry of the curve tells you that the line* x = μ *divides this area into two equal parts.*

The symmetry of the curve has told you that the mean is μ, but it should also be possible to obtain this result by using the general formula for the mean of

a continuous variate i.e. $\int_{-\infty}^{\infty} xp(x)dx$, as given in FRAME 12.   If you wish

to satisfy yourself on this point, make the substitution u = (x − μ)/σ and you should then find the integration quite simple.   Alternatively, you can proceed straight to the next frame without detriment to your understanding of the programme.

****

The substitution yields $\int_{-\infty}^{\infty} \frac{1}{\sqrt{2\pi}} (u\sigma + \mu)e^{-u^2/2} du$

$$= \int_{-\infty}^{\infty} \frac{\sigma}{\sqrt{2\pi}} ue^{-u^2/2} du + \mu \int_{-\infty}^{\infty} \frac{1}{\sqrt{2\pi}} e^{-u^2/2} du$$

$$= \frac{\sigma}{\sqrt{2\pi}} \left[-e^{-u^2/2} \right]_{-\infty}^{\infty} + \mu \times 1 = \mu$$

The variance of the Normal distribution can be found from the general formula

for the variance of a continuous variate, i.e. $\int_{-\infty}^{\infty} (x - \mu)^2 p(x)dx$, as given

in answer frame 13A.   With p(x) as in (23.1) this integral can be evaluated by making the same substitution as was used in the preceding frame, i.e. u = (x − μ)/σ, and then integrating by parts.   You may care to try this but if you find this prospect too daunting, just look at the end result in the answer frame.

****

The substitution leads to $\int_{-\infty}^{\infty} \frac{\sigma^2}{\sqrt{2\pi}} u^2 e^{-u^2/2} du.$

Treating $u^2 e^{-u^2/2}$ *as* $u.ue^{-u^2/2}$ *and integrating by parts,*

$$\int u^2 e^{-u^2/2} du = -ue^{-u^2/2} + \int 1.e^{-u^2/2} du$$

∴ *Variance* $= \frac{\sigma^2}{\sqrt{2\pi}} \left[-ue^{-u^2/2} \right]_{-\infty}^{\infty} + \sigma^2 \int_{-\infty}^{\infty} \frac{1}{\sqrt{2\pi}} e^{-u^2/2} du$

$$= 0 + \sigma^2 \times 1 = \sigma^2$$

<u>28A</u>   (continued)

Thus the parameter σ is the standard deviation of the distribution.

The Standard Normal Distribution

In problems where the Normal distribution serves as the model, it will be necessary to know what it gives for the probability of the variate having a value within a particular interval, i.e. of x having a value between x_1 and x_2, say.

This is represented by the shaded area.   We can write

$$P(x_1 < x < x_2) = \int_{x_1}^{x_2} \frac{1}{\sigma\sqrt{2\pi}} \exp\left\{-\frac{(x-\mu)^2}{2\sigma^2}\right\} dx \qquad (29.1)$$

It has already been explained that, even when simplified by a suitable substitution, the indefinite integral cannot be found as a function of x and therefore (29.1) cannot be evaluated in terms of x_1 and x_2.   However, in practical problems x_1 and x_2 will have numerical values and numerical methods of integration will thus be applicable. Such methods involve too many calculations for it to be practicable to evaluate an integral every time one is required – the Normal distribution would be much less popular if that had to be done.   Instead, tables are available.   Now, if you think of all the values that μ can take, and all the values that σ can take, and all the possible combinations of them, you will realise that a mammoth set of tables would be required if it were necessary to have separate tables for each Normal distribution.   Fortunately this is not so.   The secret lies in the change of variable $u = (x - \mu)/\sigma$.   This has been used in previous frames so it should be obvious to you that its substitution in (29.1) leads to

$$P(x_1 < x < x_2) = P(u_1 < u < u_2) = \int_{u_1}^{u_2} \frac{1}{\sqrt{2\pi}} e^{-u^2/2} du \qquad (29.2)$$

where $u_1 = (x_1 - \mu)/\sigma$ and $u_2 = (x_2 - \mu)/\sigma$

Notice that, although they will affect u_1 and u_2, μ and σ have disappeared from the integral itself.

Now look more closely at the formula $u = (x - \mu)/\sigma$ for the change of variable. It should remind you of what you learned about the coding of data in the first programme of this Unit.   Does it represent   (i) a change of origin,   (ii) a change of unit,   or   (iii) a change of origin combined with a change of unit?

****

<u>29A</u>

(iii).   The corresponding formula used in coding was $x' = (x - k)/h$.

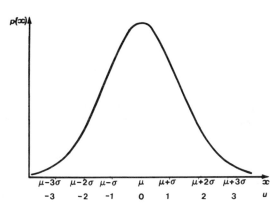

It is now apparent that all Normal distributions of x, whatever the values of μ and σ, will lead to the same distribution for u, with mean 0 and standard deviation 1. This distribution is called the STANDARD NORMAL DISTRIBUTION and u is called the STANDARDISED NORMAL DEVIATE. (In other books you may find it denoted by z instead of u.)

A convenient notation for saying that x is Normally distributed with mean μ and variance $σ^2$ is: x is $N(μ, σ^2)$. Thus u is $N(0, 1)$. Unfortunately the convenience of this notation has been somewhat diminished by the ambiguity caused by some authors using standard deviation instead of variance and writing $N(μ, σ)$. So, while in this text and some others $N(15, 9)$ stands for "Normally distributed with mean 15 and variance 9", you may possibly come across it used for "Normally distributed with mean 15 and standard deviation 9".

From (29.2) you can now see that for any Normal distribution the probability that is required can be expressed as a probability given by the Standard Normal Distribution. It is therefore only for the latter distribution that tables need be provided.

Use of tables

When using tables to evaluate probabilities for Normally distributed variates you are strongly advised to sketch the area which corresponds to the probability required. If you don't, it is all too easy to go astray. Not all tables give the same area. At the end of this volume, TABLE 1 gives values of the area shown in diagram (i) but in other books you might find the area in diagram (ii) tabulated or perhaps that in diagram (iii).

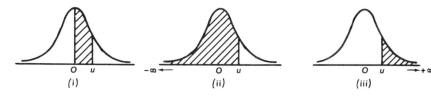

(i)   (ii)   (iii)

Obviously the area in (i) is zero when u = 0, and if you look in TABLE 1 you can check that that is what it gives. You will also see that the entry corresponding to u = 0·7 is 0·2580. What entries would you expect to find corresponding to u = 0 and u = 0·7 in a table giving areas as shown in (a) diagram (ii), (b) diagram (iii) ?

****

The total area under the curve is 1 and the area under each half is 0·5.
Hence:

(a) For u = 0, the entry would be 0·5 and for u = 0·7 it would be 0·7580.
(b) For u = 0, the entry would be 0·5 and for u = 0·7 it would be 0·2420.

When using tables of the Normal probability integral you should always check
what it is that is tabulated.   In this text we shall use TABLE 1, but if you
really understand what you are doing, you should not find any difficulty in
using other tables if the need arises.   One further, minor, point - until now,
in this text, Normal has been written with a capital letter to emphasise the
meaning.   Often this practice is not followed, the sense of the word being clear
from the context.   Its discontinuation in this programme should not now
mislead you.

A worked example will show you how to use TABLE 1.

In recent years the high incidence of heart attacks has promoted interest in the
cholesterol level in blood.   If, for the inhabitants of a certain country, the
values of this (in mg/100 ml) are normally distributed with a mean of 200 and
standard deviation of 20, find the probability that a person chosen at random
from this population will have a cholesterol level   (i) between 200 and 210,
(ii) between 190 and 200,   (iii) greater than 230,   (iv) less than 185,
(v) between 185 and 230.

(i)

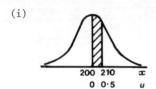

$x = 210$ $u = (210 - 200)/20 = 0·5$
$P(200 < x < 210) = P(0 < u < 0·5) = 0·1915$
from TABLE 1.

(ii)

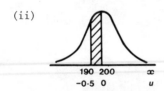

$x = 190$ $u = (190 - 200)/20 = -0·5$
The symmetry of the figure shows this answer to be
the same as for (i).   Because of this symmetry, the
table only needs to have entries for positive values
of u - another convenient feature of the normal
distribution.

(iii)

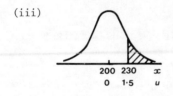

$x = 230$ $u = (230 - 200)/20 = 1·5$
Looking up u = 1·5 in TABLE 1 gives the area under
the curve from x = 200 to x = 230.   Subtracting
that from 0·5 gives the shaded area, which is what
is required.
$P(x > 230) = 0·5 - 0·4332 = 0·0668$

FRAME 32   (continued)

(iv)

185 200 x
-0·75 0 0·75 u

$x = 185$ $u = (185 - 200)/20 = -0·75$
The shaded area under the left tail is required.
By symmetry this equals the shaded area on the right.
$P(x < 185) = P(u < -0·75) = P(u > 0·75)$
$= 0·5 - 0·2734 = 0·2266$

(v)

185 200 230 x
-0·75 0   1·5 u

$P(185 < x < 230)$ = Sum of two shaded areas
Can you write down the answer?

****

32A

$0·2734 + 0·4332 = 0·7066$
(Symmetry gives the area between $u = -0·75$ and 0 as equal to that between
$u = 0$ and 0·75.)

FRAME 33

Now try the following problems on your own.   Don't forget to make a sketch each
time - it need only be rough.

1. When making up packets of sugar, and other commodities which are sold by
    weight, the producer has to control the process very carefully.   On the one
    hand, producing under-weight packets must be avoided or he will risk
    prosecution.   On the other hand he does not want to give too much away in
    over-weight packets.

    Suppose a machine, set for filling 1 kg packets of sugar, produces packets
    with contents whose weights are normally distributed with mean 1·02 kg and
    standard deviation 0·01 kg.   What proportion of packets will contain
    (i) less than 1 kg of sugar,   (ii) more than 1·03 kg of sugar ?

2. Resistors made by a certain manufacturer have a nominal rating of 100 Ω but
    their actual values are normally distributed with mean 100·6 Ω and standard
    deviation 3 Ω.   Find the percentage of resistors that will have values
    (i) higher than the nominal rating,   (ii) within 3 Ω of the nominal rating.

3. If, in repeated titrations of 5·00 ml of 0·1M HCL with 0·1M NaOH the
    results are normally distributed, the mean being 5·00 ml of alkali and the
    standard deviation 0·04 ml, in what proportion of titrations would the
    volume of alkali be expected to exceed 4·95 ml?

****

33A

1.   (i) $0·5 - 0·4772 = 0·0228$ or   2·28%
*   (ii) $0·5 - 0·3413 = 0·1587$ or   15·87%*

2.   *(i)* $0 \cdot 5 + 0 \cdot 0793 = 0 \cdot 5793$ *or*   *57·93%*
     (ii) $0 \cdot 3849 + 0 \cdot 2881 = 0 \cdot 6730$ *or*   *67·3%*

3. $0 \cdot 5 + 0 \cdot 3944 = 0 \cdot 8944$ *or*   *89·44%*

FRAME 34

By reference to TABLE 1 check the following statements about a normal
distribution:

>   The interval $\mu \pm \sigma$ contains approximately   68·3%   of the observations;
>   The interval $\mu \pm 2\sigma$ contains approximately   95·4%   of the observations;
>   The interval $\mu \pm 3\sigma$ contains approximately   99·7%   of the observations.

Notice that hardly any of the observations are more than 3 standard deviations
away from the mean.   In theory a normally distributed variate can take any
value between $-\infty$ and $+\infty$.   Perhaps this troubled you when considering the
examples in the preceding two frames, because theory did not accord with fact.
How could anyone's cholesterol level be infinitely high, or even just negative?
The same question can be asked of the weight of sugar, etc.   The difficulty is
not a practical one, however.   The normal curve gives only 0·3% of observations
outside the limits $\mu \pm 3\sigma$ and 0·006% outside the limits $\mu \pm 4\sigma$.   For most
practical purposes it is regarded as terminating at $\mu - 3\sigma$ and $\mu + 3\sigma$, giving
a range of 6σ.   The latter gives a very rough guide to the value of σ and can
help you to spot a really drastic error, such as the decimal point in the wrong
place, in a standard deviation calculated from a frequency distribution which
appears normal.

Take, for instance, one of the frequency tables in the first programme in this
Unit - that for the lives of 80 electric lamps.   The range was about 2000
hours and the distribution was roughly normal.   The calculation of the standard
deviation gave one of the following values: 346 hours,   35·7 hours,   1127 hours.
Without looking back, can you say which one it was?

>   **

34A

*346 hours.   It should be emphasised that only answers which are wildly wrong
are shown up by this check.*

FRAME 35

In using TABLE 1 you have looked up a probability corresponding to a stated
value of u but sometimes it is necessary to do things the opposite way i.e. to
find a value of u corresponding to a stated probability.   For instance, in the
last frame we started with the interval $\mu \pm 2\sigma$ for x, which converted to the
interval 0 ± 2 for u and we then found the probability of an observation
falling in that interval to be about 95·4%.   Suppose instead we had started
with a probability, 95%, say, and then tried to find the interval $\mu \pm k\sigma$ for
x, i.e. $0 \pm k$ for u, which contains this proportion of observations.   One
way of obtaining the answer would be to use Table 1 "backwards", finding the
required entry in the table and then seeing what value of u it is given by.

FRAME 35   (continued)

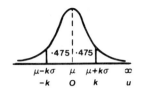

With the diagram as a guide, you should be able to do this.   Write down the value of k and hence the interval for x.

****

35A

$k = 1 \cdot 96$.   *Thus 95% of observations lie within the interval* $\mu \pm 1 \cdot 96\sigma$.

FRAME 36

Did you realise your luck when you found an entry of 0·4750 in TABLE 1? Another time things might not turn out so conveniently.   If, for example, you wanted limits containing 90% of the observations, you would be looking for an entry of 0·4500 and there isn't one.   You could get an answer by interpolation between the nearest entries, but it would be more convenient to use TABLE 2. It tabulates the value of u which has a P% chance of being exceeded.   To obtain the interval containing 95% of the observations you would look up P = 2·5, i.e. 2P = 5, as 5% of observations outside the interval means 2·5% under each tail.   Check that you find the value 1·96 and then, continuing to use TABLE 2, find the limits $\mu \pm k\sigma$ which contain (i) 90%, (ii) 99%, (iii) 50% of the observations.

****

36A

(i) $\mu \pm 1 \cdot 64\sigma$ *(ii)* $\mu \pm 2 \cdot 58\sigma$

(iii) $\mu \pm 0 \cdot 67\sigma$.   *If the deviations from* μ *are thought of as errors, this is saying that 50% of errors are less than* $0 \cdot 67\sigma$ *in magnitude and 50% are greater.   In the past some prominence was given to* $0 \cdot 67\sigma$ *(more exactly* $0 \cdot 6745\sigma$*), called the probable error, but it is not so much used nowadays.*

FRAME 37

A few examples illustrating some applications of the normal distribution will now be considered.

Tests for strength properties on clear specimens of timber have shown that, for a given species, the results can be assumed to follow the normal distribution pattern.   When calculating safe stresses, structural engineers apply a safety factor to the "statistical minimum failing stress", which is such that 99% of test results may be expected to exceed it.   Extensive tests have shown that specimens of Western Hemlock have maximum compression strengths (i.e. failing stresses) with mean $25 \cdot 44 \, \text{N mm}^{-2}$ and standard deviation $4 \cdot 65 \, \text{N mm}^{-2}$.   What value would you give for the statistical minimum failing stress for this species of timber?

****

37A

$25 \cdot 44 - 2 \cdot 33 \times 4 \cdot 65 = 25 \cdot 44 - 10 \cdot 83 \simeq 14 \cdot 6 \, N \, mm^{-2}$

FRAME 38

Reinforced and pre-stressed concrete structures are designed so that the compressive stresses are carried mostly by the concrete itself. For this and other reasons the main criterion by which the quality of concrete is assessed is its compressive strength. Specifications for concrete used in civil engineering jobs may require specimens to be made and tested on site. These specimens are of a stated size and shape (usually cubes) and the age at which they are to be tested is also specified. The normal model is judged suitable for the results of such cube strength tests. If the mean and standard deviation of this distribution are μ and σ respectively, use TABLE 2 to write down formulae for the "statistical minimum strength" when it is specified as the strength below which only (i) 1% of cubes may be expected to fail, (ii) 5% of cubes may be expected to fail.

****

38A

(i) $\mu - 2 \cdot 33\sigma$ (ii) $\mu - 1 \cdot 64\sigma$

FRAME 39

The uniformity of concrete quality depends on the works conditions. The coefficient of variation of cube strengths is sometimes used to describe the variability associated with a certain set of conditions. Using the definition of minimum strength as in (i) of the previous frame, a research laboratory report gave a figure of 75% for the ratio Minimum strength/Mean strength corresponding to conditions where the system of control was very good and there was constant supervision. What does this give for the coefficient of variation?

****

39A

$\mu - 2 \cdot 33\sigma = 0 \cdot 75\mu$
$\sigma/\mu = 0 \cdot 107$ i.e. Coefficient of variation = 10·7%

FRAME 40

A new code of practice redefined minimum strength as in (ii) of FRAME 38. Taking the coefficient of variation to be fixed for the conditions described, find the revised percentage for the ratio Minimum strength/Mean strength corresponding to these conditions.

****

40A

$(\mu - 1 \cdot 64\sigma)/\mu = 1 - 1 \cdot 64 \times 0 \cdot 107 \simeq 0 \cdot 82$ i.e. about 82%.

FRAME 41

Use of Normal Probability Paper

The use of a special type of graph paper can help in deciding whether the normal model is suitable for a set of data. Perhaps you are already familiar with the idea of graph paper with a logarithmic scale in one direction. If so, you may

FRAME 41   (continued)

have used it for deciding whether $y = ae^{kx}$ is a suitable law for your
experimental data, by taking the y-axis along the logarithmic scale and plotting
the points.   If they lie more or less on a straight line the law $y = ae^{kx}$,
which implies that the graph of log y against x is a straight line, is
confirmed.   You may also know that you could construct a logarithmic scale
yourself with the aid of a table of logarithms.   The same sort of idea is
embodied in normal probability paper which has a special scale in one direction.
You could construct such a scale for yourself with the help of tables of the
cumulative distribution integral such as were described in FRAME 31, diagram (ii).
For a normal variate, when percentage cumulative frequencies are plotted on
ordinary graph paper the curve (i.e. the ogive) is the shape of an elongated S.
When plotted on normal probability paper they give a straight line.

In the diagram the percentage cumulative frequencies for lives of electric
lamps are plotted on normal probability paper and show a marked pattern of
linearity, thus suggesting that the data is normally distributed.   Compare this
plot with that on ordinary graph paper shown in FRAME 20 on page 14.   If normal

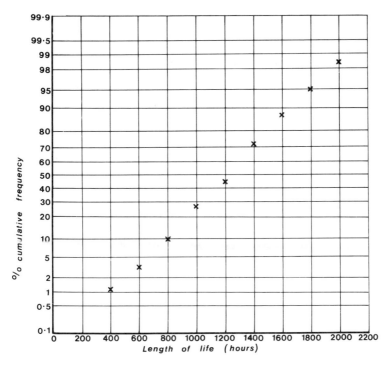

probability paper is available to you, use it to plot the % cumulative
frequencies which you obtained for car speeds in Misc. Ex. No. 6 on page 41.

Fitting a Normal Curve

Another way of deciding whether the normal model is a suitable one is to find
the frequencies which it would give and compare them with the actual frequencies
given by the data.   When fitting a Poisson model to a set of data we took the
mean of the data for the value of the one parameter μ.   Thus both the model
and the data had the same mean.   A normal distribution is determined by two
parameters - the mean μ and standard deviation σ.   When fitting a model, it
is chosen so that it has the same mean and standard deviation as the data.   For
example, if fitting a normal distribution to the data for 80 lamps, used for
illustration in the first programme of this Unit, we would take $\mu = 1225 \cdot 5$,
$\sigma = 346$,   as calculated in FRAME 71 on page 37.   The theoretical frequency for
each group would then be found by multiplying by 80 the proportion of
observations predicted as falling into that group.   For instance, consider the
group whose true end-points are $1400 \cdot 5$ and $1600 \cdot 5$.   The corresponding
standardised deviates are $175/346$ and $375/346$, i.e. $0 \cdot 506$ and $1 \cdot 084$.   Hence
the probability of an observation occurring between these limits
$= 0 \cdot 3608 - 0 \cdot 1936 = 0 \cdot 1672$,   and the frequency given by the normal model is
$80 \times 0 \cdot 1672 \simeq 13 \cdot 4$,   compared with the observed frequency of 12.

Moving on to the next group, the true end-points are $1600 \cdot 5$ and $1800 \cdot 5$ and
$x = 1800 \cdot 5$ gives $u = 1 \cdot 662$.   Calculate the theoretical frequency given by
the normal model for this group.

****

$7 \cdot 3$, compared with the observed frequency of 7.

*To complete the exercise theoretical frequencies would then be calculated for all
the remaining groups and an overall comparison made with the observed
frequencies.*

The Normal Approximation to the Binomial Distribution

When de Moivre obtained the normal distribution he did so by considering a
limiting case of the binomial distribution as $n \to \infty$.   This relation between the
two distributions explains why, for large n, binomial probabilities can be
approximated by those given by the normal model, whose convenience and ease of
use is now evident to you.   If you ask how large n should be, the answer is
"It depends".   It depends on how good an approximation is required and it
depends on the value of p.   The line diagrams on the next page represent three
different binomial distributions.   First look at diagrams (i) and (ii).   For
which of them do you think that the normal model will give a better approximation?
Then compare diagrams (ii) and (iii) and answer the same question for them.

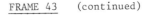

FRAME 43   (continued)

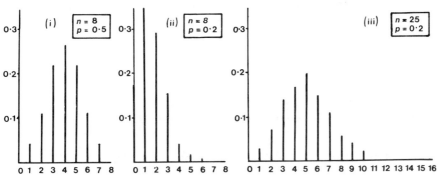

****

43A

The normal distribution is symmetrical and therefore looks more hopeful as an approximation for (i) than for (ii). Similarly it should be better for (iii) than for (ii).

FRAME 44

The comparisons just made illustrate how the values of n and p affect the suitability of the normal distribution as an approximation to the binomial. If p is near to 0·5 the approximation is quite close even for relatively small n, but the more p differs from 0·5 the larger n must be to achieve the same closeness.   A reasonable working rule is to use the normal approximation if $0·1 \leqslant p \leqslant 0·9$ and n is such that both $np > 5$ and $nq > 5$.

As a simple illustration, take the case of a coin being tossed 25 times.   The appropriate probability model for the number of heads occurring is the binomial, with $p = 0·5$ and $n = 25$.   Write down the mean and standard deviation of this distribution.

****

44A

Mean = np = 12·5   Standard deviation = $\sqrt{npq}$ = 2·5

FRAME 45

A normal distribution with the same mean and standard deviation can be expected to give a reasonable approximation here, as p has the optimum value for such an approximation.   The time is now opportune to remind you that the normal model is for a continuous variate whereas the binomial applies to a discrete variate.   If, therefore, the normal approximation is going to be used, we shall have to treat the variate as if it were continuous.

Suppose the probability of getting 13 heads is required.   For a continuous variate, a value recorded as 13, to the nearest integer, would represent a value in the interval 12·5 to 13·5.

    ∴ P(13 heads) ≃ P(12·5 < x < 13·5) where x is $N(12·5, 2·5^2)$.

Check that this is P(0 < u < 0·4) where u is N(0, 1).   The answer then obtained from TABLE 1 is 0·1555.   The binomial model itself gives 0·1550, to 4 d.p., so you can see that the normal approximation is close.

Now use the normal approximation to find the probability of getting
(i) 14 heads exactly,   (ii) 14 heads or more.

****

45A

(i)   P(13•5 < x < 14•5) = P(0•4 < u < 0•8) = 0•1326
(ii)   P(x > 13•5) = 0•3445

For comparison you may be interested to know that, to 4 d.p., the binomial model
gives 0•1328 and 0•3450 for (i) and (ii) respectively.

FRAME 46

The Normal Approximation to the Poisson Distribution

The normal distribution is also sometimes used as an approximation for a Poisson
model.   The circumstances under which this gives good results may be suggested
by the two diagrams shown here, one representing Poisson probabilities when
$\mu = 0•9$ and the other when $\mu = 5$.

For which of the two do you think that the normal model will give the better
approximation?   Can you suggest values of μ for which it would be even better?

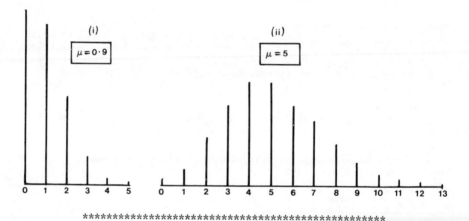

****

46A

The distribution in (ii) is the more symmetric and will therefore be better
fitted by the normal model.   Distributions with $\mu > 5$ will be even more
symmetric and so even better fitted.

FRAME 47

The larger the value of μ (which you will recall is both the mean and the
variance of the Poisson distribution) the closer will be the approximation given
by the normal model with the same mean and variance.   Remember that the Poisson
variate does not take negative values, so that symmetry is not possible if the
mean is near to zero.   A frequently adopted rule is that for Poisson
distributions with $\mu > 30$,   the normal distribution with mean μ and standard
deviation $\sqrt{\mu}$ gives an adequate approximation.

FRAME 47   (continued)

Suppose that counts during 2-minute intervals of the number of nuclear
disintegrations in an active source follow a Poisson distribution with mean 100.
Are the limits estimated from the normal distribution as those within which
there is a 90% chance of a count occurring   (i) 80·4 and 119·6 <u>or</u>
(ii) 83·6 and 116·4 ?

****

47A

(ii)   from $100 \pm 1·64 \times \sqrt{100}$

FRAME 48

The Lognormal Distribution

The normal distribution is symmetric and, in theory at any rate, describes a
variate which can take values from $-\infty$ to $+\infty$.   Where data reveals a distinctly
skew distribution and the normal model is inappropriate, it may be that the
logarithm of the variate is normally distributed.   If a variate x is such that
log x is normally distributed,
the distribution of x is said
to be LOGNORMAL.   As log x
ranging from $-\infty$ to $+\infty$ means x
ranging from 0 to $+\infty$, not
only does the lognormal model
accommodate the skewness but
also the essentially non-
negative nature of many variates
which occur in practice.
Special graph paper is available
for giving guidance as to its
suitability as a model for a

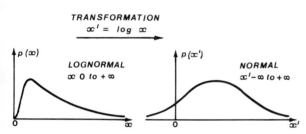

set of data - the vertical scale is as shown in FRAME 41 but the horizontal
scale for the variate is logarithmic.

The lognormal distribution has proved a useful model in civil engineering,
particularly in connection with hydrological data, as in flood frequency
analysis.   The distribution of small particle sizes and of the concentrations
of trace elements in rocks are among the examples of geological data with which
it has shown good agreement.   In medicine, experience has shown that the
threshold, or just-effective, dose of drugs and poisons is often distributed
lognormally.

FRAME 49

Distribution of Sums and Differences

Suppose that certain tablets produced by a pharmaceutical firm have a nominal
weight of 400 mg and are packed in bottles of 100.   Then the total weight X
of the contents of a bottle will be the sum of 100 variates each varying
independently of one another, i.e. $X = x_1 + x_2 + x_3 + \ldots + x_{100}$.

In this case x_1, x_2, x_3 etc. would all come from the same distribution but
this would not be so for R_1, R_2, R_3 in the next example.

Three resistances, rated at 2, 3 and 5 ohms respectively, are connected in
series.   The total resistance R is the sum of the three variates R_1, R_2, R_3

$$\text{i.e.   } R = R_1 + R_2 + R_3$$

and here the distributions of R_1, R_2, R_3 will be different from one another. Sometimes it may be a difference of variates which is of interest.   Thus if a cylindrical plug of diameter y is to be fitted into a socket of diameter x, the value of the difference z

$$\text{i.e.}   \quad z = x - y$$

determines whether there is a fit.

The questions which may need to be answered are:

If the distribution of tablet weights is known, what can be concluded about the distribution of the weights X contained in the bottles?

If the distributions of R_1, R_2, R_3 are known, what can be concluded about the distribution of the total resistance R?

If the plugs being manufactured for assembly have diameters with a known distribution and the distribution of socket diameters is known also, what can be concluded about the distribution of z?

There are two general results which apply to the distribution of sums and differences such as those described above.   These results can be derived mathematically, but the proofs rely on a fuller appreciation of the mathematics of statistics than is considered appropriate in a text of this kind.   In the remaining frames of this programme you will find out what these results are and see how they can be applied.

The examples described in the previous frame only involved simple sums and differences, but the results which you are now going to meet apply to the more general situation involving any <u>linear combination</u> of the variates and will therefore be given in this form.

If $X = a_1 x_1 + a_2 x_2 + a_3 x_3 + \ldots + a_n x_n$, where the a's are constants and x_1, x_2, x_3, $\ldots$ x_n are independent variates distributed with means μ_1, μ_2, μ_3, $\ldots$ μ_n respectively and variances σ_1^2, σ_2^2, σ_3^2, $\ldots$ σ_n^2 respectively then:

(1)   The distribution of X has mean $a_1\mu_1 + a_2\mu_2 + a_3\mu_3 + \ldots + a_n\mu_n$ and variance $a_1^2\sigma_1^2 + a_2^2\sigma_2^2 + a_3^2\sigma_3^2 + \ldots + a_n^2\sigma_n^2$.

Special cases of this result which will be of particular interest are:

(i)   If $X = x_1 + x_2 + x_3 + \ldots + x_n$ then $\mu = \mu_1 + \mu_2 + \mu_3 + \ldots + \mu$

i.e. $\text{mean}(X) = \text{mean}(x_1) + \text{mean}(x_2) + \text{mean}(x_3) + \ldots + \text{mean}(x_n)$

and $\sigma^2 = \sigma_1^2 + \sigma_2^2 + \sigma_3^2 + \ldots + \sigma_n^2$

i.e. $\text{var}(X) = \text{var}(x_1) + \text{var}(x_2) + \text{var}(x_3) + \ldots + \text{var}(x_n)$

(ii)   If $X = x_1 - x_2$

then $\mu = \mu_1 - \mu_2$ i.e. $\text{mean}(X) = \text{mean}(x_1) - \text{mean}(x_2)$
and $\sigma^2 = \sigma_1^2 + \sigma_2^2$ i.e. $\text{var}(X) = \text{var}(x_1) + \text{var}(x_2)$

(If the + sign in the variance surprised you, note that although $a_2 = -1$, $a_2^2 = +1$.)

(2) If the distributions of x_1, x_2, x_3, ... x_n are normal, then the
distribution of X is normal also.

It should be emphasised that result (1) is not restricted to normal variates
but applies generally.   You may remember Misc. Ex. 12 in the previous
programme where the sum of two Poisson variates, number of vehicles from access
road + number of vehicles from motorway, was involved.   You can now see that
the answers then obtained are in agreement with the present result.

FRAME 51

If the tablets described in FRAME 49 had weights which were distributed about a
mean of 400 mg with a standard deviation of 15 mg, then the distribution of the
weight X of 100 tablets would have

mean = 400 + 400 + 400 + ... + 400 = 100×400 = 40 000 mg or 40 g

variance = $15^2 + 15^2 + 15^2 + ... + 15^2 = 100 \times 15^2$

standard deviation = 150 mg

If tablet weights are normally distributed, what proportion of bottles will have
contents weighing less than 39·7 g?

****

51A

$u = \dfrac{39\cdot7 - 40}{0\cdot15} = -2$ $P(u < -2) = P(u > 2) = 0\cdot0228$

2·28% of bottles will have contents weighing less than 39·7 g.

FRAME 52

Furthermore, if the tablets were packed in bottles whose weights w were
distributed about a mean of 73 g with s.d. 1 g, then the total weight
W = X + w.   Find the mean, variance and s.d. of the distribution of W.

****

52A

Mean = 40 + 73 = 113 g   Variance = $0\cdot15^2 + 1^2 = 1\cdot0225 \, g^2$ s.d. = 1·011 g

---

FRAME 53

In answering the question in the last frame your line of reasoning was as
follows: W = X + w

$\therefore \mu_W = \mu_X + \mu_w$ and $\sigma_W{}^2 = \sigma_X{}^2 + \sigma_w{}^2$ (53.1)

i.e.   mean(W) = mean(X) + mean(w)   and   var(W) = var(X) + var(w)

But suppose you had been given the mean and standard deviation of w and W and
the problem had been to find the mean and s.d. of X.   You might have used the
above relationship and concluded from (53.1) that

$\mu_X = \mu_W - \mu_w$ and $\sigma_X{}^2 = \sigma_W{}^2 - \sigma_w{}^2$ (53.2)

i.e.   mean(X) = mean(W) − mean(w)   and   var(X) = var(W) − var(w)

FRAME 53   (continued)

On the other hand you might have first rewritten the relationship between the variables as $X = W - w$ and then treated this difference as in case (ii) of FRAME 50. What would that give for the mean and variance of X?

****

53A

$$\mu_X = \mu_W - \mu_w \qquad and \qquad \sigma_X^2 = \sigma_W^2 + \sigma_w^2 \qquad (53A.1)$$

i.e. $mean(X) = mean(W) - mean(w)$ *and* $var(X) = var(W) + var(w)$

FRAME 54

If you compare (53A.1) with (53.2) you will see that although the expressions for the mean of X agree, those for the variance do not. The explanation of this apparent contradiction is found by re-reading the statement in FRAME 50 and noting that the results apply to the case where x_1, x_2, x_3, ... x_n are

<u>independent</u> variates. This condition of independence is all-important because the mathematical proof of the result for the variance relies on it.

In the present example, where 100 tablets are counted out into a bottle, the weight of the tablets does not in any way affect the weight of the empty bottle in which they are placed, nor does the weight of the empty bottle affect the weight of the tablets placed in it. Thus, X and w are independent variates and conclusions (53.2) are correct. But W depends on both X and w, and so, if the relationship is reconsidered in the form $X = W - w$ it is not valid to conclude that

$$\sigma_X^2 = \sigma_W^2 + \sigma_w^2 \qquad \text{as in (53A.1)}$$

FRAME 55

The filling of containers, e.g. jars with coffee powder, cans with rice pudding, tins with paint, is a fairly widespread production operation. The ideal is for the quantity (e.g. weight) of the contents to be exactly the same for every container but this cannot be achieved in practice - there will inevitably be variation, however slight. The containers will also vary, even though nominally the same size. Thus, if

$$x = \text{weight of contents}$$
$$w = \text{weight of container}$$
$$\text{and} \quad W = \text{weight of container + contents}$$

x, w and W will all be variables. To say which two are independent it is necessary to know just how the filling process operates. Let us consider two possibilities:

1. When an empty container arrives at a certain point, the contents are released into it by a mechanism designed to let through a standard amount each time. The amount released is not influenced by the weight of the container being filled. Thus, x and w are independent and the total weight W will depend on the values taken by them.

2. The filling of a container proceeds until the total weight W reaches a specified level. Any variation in this total, from one filling operation to another, will be independent of how much the container actually weighs. Thus it is w and W that are independent. The weight of the contents will depend, for instance, on the weight of the container.

FRAME 55   (continued)

For each of these two possibilities, write down the equation connecting
(i) the means μ_x, μ_w, μ_W,   (ii) the variances σ_x^2, σ_w^2, σ_W^2.

****

55A

1. (i) $\mu_W = \mu_x + \mu_w$ (ii) $\sigma_W^2 = \sigma_x^2 + \sigma_w^2$

2. (i) $\mu_x = \mu_W - \mu_w$ (ii) $\sigma_x^2 = \sigma_W^2 + \sigma_w^2$

FRAME 56

You have been warned of one way in which the results of FRAME 50 can be
misapplied, if not properly understood.   The following example will illustrate
another:

   A resistance of 13 000 ohms is to be obtained by connecting up in series
   2 elements rated at 5000 ohms and 3 rated at 1000 ohms.   Elements of both
   types are supplied in bulk, those of the first type with resistances which are
   $N(5000, 100^2)$ and those of the second with resistances which are $N(1000, 50^2)$.
   From these supplies, elements are selected at random for the assembly.   What
   is the appropriate model to use to assess the likelihood of the constructed
   resistance being within 100 ohms of the requirement?

Two solutions are now proposed.   Consider each one carefully, then decide
which is correct and why the other is wrong.

Solution 1   Denoting resistances of elements of first and second types by R_1,
r_1 respectively, the overall resistance R is given by $R = 2R_1 + 3r_1$.   As R_1
is $N(5000, 100^2)$ and r_1 is $N(1000, 50^2)$,   R is distributed normally with

$\left.\begin{array}{l}\text{mean} = 2 \times 5000 + 3 \times 1000 = 13\,000 \\ \text{and variance} = 2^2 \times 100^2 + 3^2 \times 50^2 = 62\,500\end{array}\right\}$ putting $a_1 = 2$ and $a_2 = 3$ with
$n = 2$ in the results of FRAME 50

      i.e. R is $N(13\,000, 250^2)$

Solution 2   Using R_1, R_2 to denote the resistances of the two elements of the
first type and r_1, r_2, r_3 those of the other elements, the overall resistance
R is given by $R = R_1 + R_2 + r_1 + r_2 + r_3$.   As R_1 and R_2 are each
$N(5000, 100^2)$ and r_1, r_2, r_3 each $N(1000, 50^2)$,   R is distributed normally
with
      mean = 5000 + 5000 + 1000 + 1000 + 1000 = 13\,000
and   variance = $100^2 + 100^2 + 50^2 + 50^2 + 50^2 = 27\,500$

      i.e. R is $N(13\,000, 165 \cdot 8^2)$

****

56A

*Solution 2.   The overall resistance is the sum of 5 independent variates.
There is no reason, for instance, why the elements of the first type in the
assembly should both have the same resistance as is implied by Solution 1, which
assumes that this kind of thing must happen:*

Solution 2 allows for any combination of elements which could occur, such as:

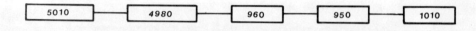

FRAME 57

Variance of a General Function

In FRAME 50 you were shown how a knowledge of the ways in which x_1, x_2, ... x_n vary tells you how X, a linear combination of them, will vary, but what of a combination which is not linear?   This question is particularly pertinent if the variation is caused by errors of measurement and we wish to assess the error in a result X calculated from measured values of x_1, x_2, ... x_n.

For instance, in a titration such as that described in the first frame of this Unit, the concentration of the solution in the burette is calculated from the ratio v_1/v_2, where v_1 is the volume of standard solution delivered by pipette into the flask at the outset and v_2 is the volume of standard solution delivered from the burette in the titration.   The question may arise of how errors in v_1 and v_2 affect the calculated value of R where

$$R = v_1/v_2 \qquad (57.1)$$

Another example is provided by the calculation of g, the gravitational acceleration, from the time T of one complete oscillation of a simple pendulum of length ℓ using the formula

$$g = 4\pi^2\ell/T^2 \qquad (57.2)$$

Obviously measurements of ℓ and T will be subject to error, and these errors will affect the calculated value of g.

As a third example, consider the determination of the density of a solid cylinder by weighing it to obtain its mass M and measuring its diameter D and height h with vernier calipers.   The density ρ can then be calculated from

$$\rho = M \div (\pi D^2 h/4) = 4M/\pi D^2 h \qquad (57.3)$$

It may be useful to know how errors in M, D and h contribute to the calculated value of ρ.

In (57.1), (57.2) and (57.3) the variates are combined in a non-linear fashion and we require a more general result than that given in FRAME 50.

FRAME 58

To begin with, we will consider a function z of two variates x and y, i.e. $z = f(x, y)$.   In the programme on partial differentiation in Mathematics for Engineers and Scientists Vol. 1, it is shown that the error δz in z, resulting from small errors δx and δy in x and y respectively, is given approximately by

$$\delta z \simeq \frac{\partial z}{\partial x}\,\delta x + \frac{\partial z}{\partial y}\,\delta y \qquad (58.1)$$

and this formula is then used to find the maximum possible error in z, when the maximum size of error is known for x and y.   However this is based on the extreme case when the worst possible combination of errors occurs, without regard to how seldom that would happen.   A more satisfactory approach would be to use the standard deviations σ_x and σ_y to describe the precision in measuring x and y respectively, and σ_z, the standard deviation of z, to describe the resulting variation in the calculated value of z.   To find how σ_x, σ_y and σ_z are related we first square both sides of (58.1), giving

$$(\delta z)^2 \simeq \left(\frac{\partial z}{\partial x}\right)^2 (\delta x)^2 + \left(\frac{\partial z}{\partial y}\right)^2 (\delta y)^2 + 2 \frac{\partial z}{\partial x} \frac{\partial z}{\partial y} (\delta x)(\delta y) \qquad (58.2)$$

Now δx, being the error, is the difference between the observed value of x and the true value.   If there is no systematic error, the true value will be μ_x, the mean of the distribution of x.   Thus δx may be expressed as $x - \mu_x$. If δy and δz are similarly expressed, (58.2) may be rewritten as

$$(z - \mu_z)^2 \simeq \left(\frac{\partial z}{\partial x}\right)^2 (x - \mu_x)^2 + \left(\frac{\partial z}{\partial y}\right)^2 (y - \mu_y)^2 + 2 \frac{\partial z}{\partial x} \frac{\partial z}{\partial y} (x - \mu_x)(y - \mu_y)$$

Now imagine this being repeated for a large number, N, of sets of observations and the sum being taken.   Dividing through by N will then give

$$\frac{\Sigma(z - \mu_z)^2}{N} \simeq \left(\frac{\partial z}{\partial x}\right)^2 \frac{\Sigma(x - \mu_x)^2}{N} + \left(\frac{\partial z}{\partial y}\right)^2 \frac{\Sigma(y - \mu_y)^2}{N} + 2 \frac{\partial z}{\partial x} \frac{\partial z}{\partial y} \frac{\Sigma(x - \mu_x)(y - \mu_y)}{N}$$

$$(58.3)$$

If x and y vary independently of one another, the values of $(x - \mu_x)(y - \mu_y)$ will tend to cancel each other out as the number of terms in the summation increases.   (You will understand this better when you have read the programme on correlation in Unit 3.)   Thus ultimately (58.3) becomes

$$\sigma_z{}^2 = \left(\frac{\partial z}{\partial x}\right)^2 \sigma_x{}^2 + \left(\frac{\partial z}{\partial y}\right)^2 \sigma_y{}^2$$

This is readily extended to functions of more than two variates.   If $X = f(x_1, x_2, x_3, \ldots, x_n)$ and $\sigma_1{}^2, \sigma_2{}^2 \ldots$ are the variances of $x_1, x_2, \ldots$ respectively, then the variance σ^2 of X is given by

$$\sigma^2 = \left(\frac{\partial X}{\partial x_1}\right)^2 \sigma_1{}^2 + \left(\frac{\partial X}{\partial x_2}\right)^2 \sigma_2{}^2 + \left(\frac{\partial X}{\partial x_3}\right)^2 \sigma_3{}^2 + \ldots + \left(\frac{\partial X}{\partial x_n}\right)^2 \sigma_n{}^2 \qquad (58.4)$$

Evaluate these partial derivatives when $X = a_1 x_1 + a_2 x_2 + a_3 x_3 + \ldots + a_n x_n$ and check that this leads to the same expression for the variance of X as was given in FRAME 50.

****

58A

$$\frac{\partial X}{\partial x_1} = a_1, \qquad \frac{\partial X}{\partial x_2} = a_2, \qquad \frac{\partial X}{\partial x_3} = a_3, \ldots\ldots\ldots \qquad \frac{\partial X}{\partial x_n} = a_n$$

leading to $a_1{}^2 \sigma_1{}^2 + a_2{}^2 \sigma_2{}^2 + a_3{}^2 \sigma_3{}^2 + \ldots + a_n{}^2 \sigma_n{}^2$ *for the variance of X.*

FRAME 59

Now let us return to the ratio of volumes v_1 and v_2 in (57.1).   Denoting the standard deviations of R, v_1 and v_2 by σ_R, σ_1 and σ_2 respectively,

$$\sigma_R^2 = \left(\frac{\partial R}{\partial v_1}\right)^2 \sigma_1^2 + \left(\frac{\partial R}{\partial v_2}\right)^2 \sigma_2^2 = \left(\frac{1}{v_2}\right)^2 \sigma_1^2 + \left(-\frac{v_1}{v_2^2}\right)^2 \sigma_2^2$$

$$= \frac{1}{v_2^2} \sigma_1^2 + \frac{v_1^2}{v_2^4} \sigma_2^2$$

This can also be expressed as $\left(\dfrac{\sigma_R}{R}\right)^2 = \left(\dfrac{\sigma_1}{v_1}\right)^2 + \left(\dfrac{\sigma_2}{v_2}\right)^2$, if it is preferable to think of the errors as proportions.

See if you can obtain the corresponding results when (58.4) is applied to (57.2) and (57.3) in turn.

****

59A

$$\sigma_g^2 = 16\pi^4 \left(\frac{1}{T^4} \sigma_\ell^2 + \frac{4\ell^2}{T^6} \sigma_T^2\right) \qquad or \qquad \left(\frac{\sigma_g}{g}\right)^2 = \left(\frac{\sigma_\ell}{\ell}\right)^2 + 4\left(\frac{\sigma_T}{T}\right)^2$$

$$\sigma_\rho^2 = \frac{16}{\pi^2} \left(\frac{1}{D^4 h^2} \sigma_M^2 + \frac{4M^2}{D^6} \sigma_D^2 + \frac{M^2}{D^4} \sigma_h^2\right) \qquad or \qquad \left(\frac{\sigma_\rho}{\rho}\right)^2 = \left(\frac{\sigma_M}{M}\right)^2 + 4\left(\frac{\sigma_D}{D}\right)^2 + \left(\frac{\sigma_h}{h}\right)^2$$

These examples serve to show you how the lack of precision in the various measurements affects the final result.   In practice, if you have some idea of the values of the variates involved and of their σ's, the relative contribution made by each of the terms on the R.H.S. of (58.4) can be assessed.   This can direct attention to where greater precision in measurement (i.e. reduction of the s.d.) would pay the highest dividend.   The error in the final result, as measured by the s.d. or coefficient of variation, is found by taking the square root of the R.H.S. of (58.4).   In this connection it is instructive to look at the calculations:

$$\sqrt{1 \cdot 0^2 + 0 \cdot 5^2} = 1 \cdot 12 \qquad\qquad \sqrt{2 \cdot 0^2 + 0 \cdot 5^2} = 2 \cdot 06$$

$$\sqrt{1 \cdot 0^2 + 0 \cdot 4^2} = 1 \cdot 08 \qquad\qquad \sqrt{2 \cdot 0^2 + 0 \cdot 4^2} = 2 \cdot 04$$

These show how dominant the larger component can be when the square root of a sum of squares is taken and how little improvement in the overall precision is achieved by reducing the error responsible for the smaller component.

Miscellaneous Examples

In this frame a collection of miscellaneous examples is given for you to try. (Do not attempt the first three if you skipped FRAMES 15-21.)   Answers are supplied in FRAME 62, together with such working as is considered helpful.

1.   The area over which the dispersal of seeds from a plant takes place is of relevance in ecology.   Suppose that in whichever direction seeds are dispersed the distance travelled from the plant has an exponential distribution with mean $0 \cdot 8$ m.   What proportion of seeds will be dispersed more than $1 \cdot 6$ m from the plant?

2. If the number of emissions per hour from a radioactive source has a Poisson
    distribution with mean 30, find the probability of the time between
    successive emissions being greater than 5 minutes, by considering

    (i)   a discrete variate and using the Poisson distribution,
    (ii) a continuous variate and using the exponential distribution.

3. (i)   The time to failure of a component is described by the exponential
          distribution if the mean failure rate is constant.   This is the case
          if there is no "wearing-out" effect, i.e. if, as long as it is
          functioning, the component is "as good as new".

          Suppose that an electronic device has a failure law given by an
          exponential distribution , the mean time to failure being 100 hours.
          Find the probability that it will still be functioning after
          (a) 100 hours,   (b) 200 hours,   (c) t_1 hours.

          From your answers to (a) and (b) deduce the probability that a device
          which has functioned for 100 hours will continue without failure for
          another 100 hours.

    (ii) The reliability function R(t) of a component or system is the
          probability that its time to failure exceeds t, i.e. that it will
          still be functioning after time t.   From your answer to (i) (c) you
          should be able to write down R(t), where t is in hours, for the
          device referred to there.   Deduce the reliability function of a
          system consisting of two such electronic devices in parallel.

4. Failures due to wearout, i.e. to a component having completed its
    anticipated useful life, follow the normal distribution pattern.   If
    components of a particular type have a mean wearout life of 1000 hours with
    standard deviation 25 hours, find the proportion of components that will
    have a wearout life, in hours,   (i) greater than 1040,   (ii) less than 955,
    (iii) between 1020 and 1040,   (iv) between 955 and 1020.

5. Analysis of past data has shown a manufacturer that the hub thickness of a
    particular type of gear is normally distributed about a mean of 50 mm with
    standard deviation 1 mm.

    Estimate how many such gears, in a production run of 5000, will have a hub
    thickness (i) greater than 51·5 mm,   (ii) between 49·2 and 50·8 mm,
    (iii) between 49·0 and 49·5 mm.

6. The weight of active ingredient in 60-mg phenobarbitone tablets produced
    by a pharmaceutical firm is normally distributed about mean 58·5 mg with
    standard deviation 1·2 mg.   If a regulation states that each tablet should
    contain at least 55·5 mg of active ingredient, what proportion of tablets
    fail to comply?

7. A certain dimension of a mass-produced mechanical part has a nominal value of
    100 mm with acceptable tolerances of ± 1 mm.   If the manufacturing process
    produces parts for which values of this dimension are normally distributed
    with mean 100·2 mm and standard deviation 0·5 mm, what percentage of parts
    will have to be rejected as outside the tolerance limits?

8. It has been found that, on weekdays, the speeds of free-moving vehicles on
    a certain section of roadway are normally distributed with mean 72 km/h and
    standard deviation 16 km/h.

    (i)   What is the median speed?
    (ii) Find the upper and lower quartiles of the distribution.

(iii) If there is a speed limit of 100 km/h, what percentage of vehicles are exceeding the speed limit?

9. Suppose that it has been established that boys in a certain age group have diastolic blood pressures (in mm Hg) which are normally distributed about a mean of 57 with standard deviation 8. Posing the question: "Would a blood pressure of 74 be unusually high for a boy of this age?" calls for 'unusually' to be exactly defined if the question is to be answered objectively. If 'unusual' is taken as meaning "having a probability of less than 1%" then the question can be more precisely phrased as: "Is the chance of a boy of this age having a blood pressure of 74 or more less than 1%?" Answer this question and also state what blood pressures would be considered 'unusually high' according to the criterion laid down here.

10. The lifetimes of a batch of radio components are known to be normally distributed with mean 500 hours and standard deviation 50 hours. A purchaser requires at least 95% of them to have a lifetime greater than 400 hours. Will the batch meet the purchaser's specification?

11. An automatic packing machine produces packets of caster sugar with contents normally distributed with standard deviation 2 g. What should the mean content weight be if 99% of packets are to contain at least 500 g of sugar

12. In the inspection of a mass-produced item, limit gauges are used to reject everything below a certain size. The dimension being controlled is normally distributed with coefficient of variation 20%, and 15% of items produced are rejected by the gauge. It is considered desirable to reduce this proportion to 5%. The coefficient of variation cannot be altered without installing new machinery but the mean value of the controlled dimension can be increased or decreased by a modification of the existing production process. What percentage change in this mean value will achieve the required reduction in rejects?

13. Rods are made to a nominal length of 100 mm but in fact their lengths form a normal distribution with mean 100·4 mm and standard deviation 0·8 mm. Each rod costs 12 p to make and is immediately usable if its length is between 99 mm and 101 mm. Rods shorter than 99 mm cannot be used but have a scrap value of 2 p. Rods longer than 101 mm can be shortened to an acceptable length at an extra cost of 4 p. Find the average cost of a usable rod.

14. The specification to which steel bolts of circular cross-section are being manufactured requires that their lengths be between 8·45 and 8·65 cm and their diameters between 1·55 and 1·60 cm. The steel bolts produced by a certain machine have lengths which are normally distributed about a mean of 8·56 cm with standard deviation 0·05 cm, and diameters which are independently normally distributed about a mean of 1·58 cm with s.d. 0·01 cm. For the bolts produced by this machine find:

   (i) the percentage that will not be within the specified limits for length,
   (ii) the percentage that will not be within the specified limits for diameter,
   (iii) the percentage that will not meet the specification.

15. A theory about the scattering of neutrons from a point source assumes that there is a constant probability α of any one neutron making a track between two fixed radial lines. If this assumption is correct and $\alpha = 0·4$, use the normal distribution to assess the likelihood that, out of 150 observed tracks, more than 70 will occur between the two fixed lines.

FRAME 61   (continued)

16. In your answer to Misc. Ex. 4 on page 96 you found 11/1024, i.e. 0·011
     approx., to be the probability of an "ambidextrous" woodlouse being
     classified by the Oxford team as "left-handed".   What estimate of this
     probability would be given by using the normal distribution as an
     approximation?   The value of n, in this case, does not quite meet the
     criterion np > 5 suggested in FRAME 44 and the approximation could be
     used with greater confidence if the woodlice were classified as a result
     of 20 trials.   In that case, what would it give as the rule for labelling
     a woodlouse "left-handed", if the risk of placing an "ambidextrous"
     woodlouse in this category is to be less than 5%?

17. Cylindrical metal pellets for use in a reactor are mass-produced and their
     lengths may be assumed to be normally distributed with mean 0·290 cm and
     s.d. 0·016 cm.   Nine pellets must fit end to end in a container,
     occupying a length not exceeding 2·670 cm.   If sets of nine are assembled
     at random what proportion of sets will not fit into the space allowed?

18. A manufactured product is regularly analysed for a particular chemical
     constituent, giving results which past records show to have a standard
     deviation of 7·8 units when the production process is under statistical
     control.   The variation in these results can be attributed to two sources:
     (i) the variation in the product itself and (ii) the error inherent in the
     method of analysis. The precision of the method has been assessed by using
     it on products of known chemical composition and the s.d. of the error of
     determination has in this way been found to be 3·0 units.   Find the s.d.
     of the actual amount of the chemical in the product.

19. At one stage of an assembly process a cylindrical plug has to be fitted
     into a circular socket, each being selected at random from a continuous
     supply.   Plug and socket diameters, in mm, are N(24·9, 0·03^2) and
     N(25, 0·04^2) respectively.   If a satisfactory fit requires a diametral
     clearance of at least 0·02 mm, on what proportion of occasions will there
     be an unsatisfactory fit?   (Diametral clearance = Socket diameter
     – Plug diameter.)

20. In weaving, the threads lengthwise in the fabric constitute the warp. They
     are positioned on the loom and the crosswise thread (the weft) is taken
     back and forth across the width to form the fabric.   The weft is supplied
     from a cop and when one weft-cop is used up
     another must be substituted.   In a fabric
     made from condenser weft, which tends to be
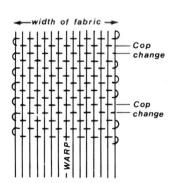
     rather variable in its fineness, a difference
     between the fineness of the weft in adjacent
     cops causes weft bars.   The bars can be seen
     when the fabric is held to the light.   The
     greater the difference in the weft at
     changeover, the greater the intensity of
     barring.   Experiments have shown that the bar
     is perceptible when the difference in fineness,
     as measured by linear density, is 8 tex
     (1 tex = 1 g/km) or more.   When the difference
     is as much as 16 tex the bar can be described
     as 'prominent'.

For a particular quality of condenser weft, linear density determinations
made on each of a large number of cops had a standard deviation of 7 tex.
Assuming linear density to be normally distributed, how many prominent bars

FRAME 61   (continued)
would occur on average in a length of fabric with 400 weft-cop changes? What would be the corresponding figure for bars which are perceptible but not prominent?

FRAME 62

Answers to Miscellaneous Examples

1. $e^{-2} = 0 \cdot 135$

2. (i) x = number of emissions in a 5-minute interval. Using Poisson distribution with $\mu = 2 \cdot 5$, $P(0) = e^{-2 \cdot 5} = 0 \cdot 082$.

   (ii) t = time in minutes between emissions. Using exponential distribution with $\lambda = 0 \cdot 5$, $P(t > 5) = e^{-2 \cdot 5} = 0 \cdot 082$.

3. (i) $\lambda = 0 \cdot 01$ (a) $e^{-1} = 0 \cdot 368$ (b) $e^{-2} = 0 \cdot 135$ (c) $\exp(-0 \cdot 01t_1)$
   A device which continues for a further 100 hours will have survived for 200 hours from the start.   Ratio of answer (b) to answer (a), i.e. $e^{-2}/e^{-1} = e^{-1}$, gives probability required.   Note that this is the same as the probability of functioning for 100 hours from the start, consistent with the concept of no "wearing-out" effect.

   (ii) $R(t) = \exp(-0 \cdot 01t)$
   $2 \exp(-0 \cdot 01t) - \exp(-0 \cdot 02t)$.   If in difficulties with the parallel system, refer back to FRAME 56 on page 71.

4. (i) $0 \cdot 0548$ (ii) $0 \cdot 0359$ (iii) $0 \cdot 1571$ (iv) $0 \cdot 7522$

5. (i) 334   (ii) 2881   (iii) 749

6. $0 \cdot 0062$

7. $6 \cdot 3\%$

8. (i) 72 km/h   (ii) Lower quartile = 61·21 km/h   (iii) 4·01%
                         Upper quartile = 82·79 km/h

9. No, the chance is about 1·7%.   Pressures greater than 75·6.

10. Yes, 97·72% have a lifetime exceeding 400 hours.

11. 504·65 g

12. At present, dimensions below $\mu - 1 \cdot 0364 \times 0 \cdot 2\mu$ are rejected, μ being the mean.   With new mean μ', dimensions below $\mu' - 1 \cdot 6449 \times 0 \cdot 2\mu'$ will be rejected.   Equating these two expressions for the critical dimension gives $\mu'/\mu = 1 \cdot 18$ i.e. an 18% increase in the mean value is required.

13. Average cost per rod made = $12 + 0 \cdot 2266 \times 4 - 0 \cdot 0401 \times 2 = 12 \cdot 8262$ p
    Proportion of rods which are finally usable = $0 \cdot 9599$
    Average cost per usable rod = $12 \cdot 8262/0 \cdot 9599 = 13 \cdot 36$ p.

14. (i) 5·0   (ii) 2·4
    (iii) 7·3   Most easily obtained by finding percentages which do meet
              specification and subtracting from 100.

15. True model binomial with p = 0·4, n = 150.   Use $N(60, 6^2)$ as approximation. $P(x > 70 \cdot 5) = 0 \cdot 0401$

16. P(9 or 10 left turns) $\simeq$ P(x > 8·5) where x is N(5, 2·5)
                          = P(u > 2·214) = 0·013
    If x is N(10, 5), there is a 5% chance that x > 13·7.   Hence a woodlouse would be labelled "left-handed" if it made 15 or more left turns.

Perhaps you think it should be 14 or more?   Remember that, as a
continuous variate, 14 represents a value between 13·5 and 14·5 and this
would not ensure x > 13·7, though only marginally.   (Tables of the
binomial distribution tell a similar story, giving P(14 or more) = 0·058
and P(15 or more) = 0·021.)

17. The total length of a set of 9 pellets is $N(2·61, 0·048^2)$ and hence
     P(total length > 2·670) = 0·1056, i.e. about 10·6% will not fit.

18. Result of analysis = Actual amount of chemical + Error of determination
     ∴   var(result) = var(amount) + var(error)
                 $7·8^2$ = var(amount) + $3·0^2$
          s.d.(amount) = 7·2

19. Difference between diameters is $N(0·1, 0·05^2)$.   Unsatisfactory fit on
     5·48% of occasions.

20. 42, 125, as difference between linear densities of weft on successive cops
     is $N(0, 2 \times 7^2)$

UNIT 1–Revision Examples

(Questions 22 and 27 are more mathematical, involving some integration, and may be regarded as an "optional extra" in this course.)

1. If X and Y are variates such that $Y = (1/c)(X + a)$, then

$$m(Y) = \frac{1}{c}\{m(X) + a\} \qquad \text{and} \qquad V(Y) = \frac{1}{c^2} V(X)$$

where $m(X)$ and $V(X)$ denote the mean and variance respectively of the variate X.

Tests on 80 specimens of a steel cable gave the following breaking loads (in appropriate units):

18·4	17·9	18·6	19·0	17·6	17·9	17·8	17·8	18·2	19·1
18·1	17·6	18·1	18·1	18·1	18·5	18·3	17·9	18·0	19·1
18·6	17·6	18·1	17·2	17·4	16·8	17·4	18·5	18·4	18·0
18·3	18·1	18·5	18·1	18·3	18·8	18·6	18·1	18·3	18·2
18·0	18·1	18·1	18·3	17·0	18·2	17·8	18·6	18·2	17·5
17·8	18·0	18·2	18·7	18·8	18·2	18·1	17·5	18·7	18·0
18·2	17·0	18·6	18·4	18·5	17·6	17·2	18·2	18·4	17·6
18·3	18·0	17·9	17·9	18·5	17·8	18·3	18·5	18·1	18·1

Classify this into a frequency table using twelve classes and from this determine the mean and variance of the distribution.   (C.E.I.)

2. A machine produces spindles of nominal length 5 cm. Each spindle produced is compared with a standard, deviations being recorded in thousandths of a centimetre. The results of 100 measurements are summarized as a grouped frequency table shown below.

range	frequency
−70 to −51	6
−50 to −31	10
−30 to −11	12
−10 to 9	14
10 to 29	19
30 to 49	27
50 to 69	12

Produce a histogram for this table. Find in terms of the original lengths the mean, median group and modal group of this distribution.

For purposes of producing control charts, it is necessary to compute $\bar{x} \pm 2\sigma$ and $\bar{x} \pm 3\sigma$, where $\bar{x}$ is the mean length and σ is the standard deviation. Determine these values.   (C.E.I.)

3. The breaking loads of 200 specimens of a certain material were measured and the results were arranged in the grouped frequency distribution on the next page:

Breaking load x_i (mid-interval values)	Number of specimens f_i
982·5	3
987·5	10
992·5	27
997·5	62
1002·5	56
1007·5	24
1012·5	12
1017·5	5
1022·5	1

Draw a histogram for these data.

State the modal group, the median group and the interquartile range.

Determine the mean and standard deviation of this distribution, using the change of variate

$$u_i = \frac{x_i - 1002 \cdot 5}{5}$$ (C.E.I.)

4. Given the quantities $x_1, x_2, \ldots x_n$, show that $S = \sum_{i=1}^{n} (x_i - a)^2$ is a minimum when $a = \bar{x} = \frac{1}{n} \sum_{i=1}^{n} x_i$.   (C.E.I.)

5. A temporary coffer dam is to be built to protect the construction activity for a major cross-valley dam. If the coffer-dam is designed to withstand a 20-year flood (i.e. a flood for which the chance of occurrence in any particular year is 1 in 20), what is the risk that the structure will be overtopped (i) in the first year, (ii) in the third year but not before, (iii) at no time during the 5-year construction period, (iv) at least once during this 5-year period?

6. A clause governing acceptance of 'designed' concrete on the results of works cube strengths requires that the mix proportions be modified to increase the strength if any of four named conditions are not satisfied. If p_1, p_2, p_3, p_4 are the respective probabilities of conditions 1, 2, 3 and 4 being satisfied, and the fulfilment of each condition is independent of the fulfilment of the others, what is the probability that (i) the mix proportions will have to be modified, (ii) only one of the four conditions is not met?

7. A component plays an essential part in the functioning of an appliance. If instead of installing just the one component, a system of identical ones in parallel is used, the reliability of the appliance is increased as it will then function provided at least one of the components does. If n components are used in this way, and for each the probability of functioning is p, what is the probability that the appliance will function? (The diagram shows the reliability network for $n = 3$.)

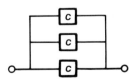

The smooth operation of a space craft depends upon a mechanism which has a 5% probability of failure. How many such mechanisms should be incorporated in the system to be

(i) 99% certain, (ii) 99·9% certain, (iii) 99·99% certain, that at least one mechanism will work satisfactorily?

8.   (i)   A single die is thrown six times. Write down expressions for the probability that (a) exactly one 'six' occurs, (b) at least two 'sixes' occur, (c) each face of the die occurs once.

         Find the probability that a die is thrown exactly r times before the first 'six' appears. Find the least value of r such that there is more than a 50% chance of obtaining a 'six' on the rth throw or earlier.

  (ii)   Three dice are thrown simultaneously. If S denotes the sum of the numbers on the uppermost faces of the three dice, calculate the following probabilities
       (a) $P(S = 5)$,   (b) $P(S = 11)$,   (c) $P(S \geqslant 16)$.   (L.U.)

9. A machine is powered by three similar storage batteries; it will function satisfactorily only if at least two of these batteries are serviceable. The probability of any one battery becoming unserviceable in less than 50 hours is 0·2, and of becoming unserviceable in less than 100 hours is 0·6. Find the probability that the machine will function satisfactorily for
(a)   at least 50 hours,   (b)   between 50 and 100 hours.   (L.U.)

10. Under the usual conditions of interference a certain type of communication channel transmits correctly with probability 0·9. That is, if the binary digit i ($i = 0$ or 1) is sent, the binary digit i is received with probability 0·9 and the digit $(1 - i)$ is received with probability 0·1.

If 0 is transmitted simultaneously over two such channels, the interference in one being independent of the interference in the other, what is the probability that the two receivers do not agree? If 0 is transmitted 5 times in succession over both channels, what is the probability that the two receivers agree at least four times?

If 0 is transmitted over a channel and the result received is transmitted over a second channel, the interference in the first being independent of the interference in the second, what is the probability that 0 is received in the second channel?   (L.U.)

11. A machine may be considered to operate under the following conditions. If it is in working order at the start of any day the probability is p that it will be in working order at the start of the next day. If it is broken down at the start of any day the probability is q that it will be repaired and in working order by the start of the next day.

If π_1 is the probability that the machine is working at the start of the first day find π_3, the probability that it is working at the start of the third day.

Express π_n, the probability that the machine is working at the beginning of the nth day, in terms of π_{n-1}, and hence show that as $n \to \infty$,
$$\pi_n \to \frac{q}{1 - p + q} .$$
      (L.U.)

12. Suppose that, in the previous question, $p = 0·8$, $q = 0·6$ and $\pi_1 = 0·75$. Show that, for all n, (i) $\pi_n = 0·75$, (ii) there is a probability of 0·072 that, in a period of 4 consecutive days beginning at the nth, the machine will be in working order at the start of only one day out of the four.

13. For a routine check of water supplies it is possible to use two methods. In the first method each source is tested independently and if the source is contaminated the test shows a positive reaction. In the second method the sources are combined into groups of three and for each group a composite sample prepared from water drawn from each of the three sources is tested. If any one of the three sources is contaminated the test shows a positive reaction and it is then necessary to test the three sources independently using the first method.

Show that, if the cost of testing a sample is c (whether it is drawn from three sources or one source) and the probability of a source being contaminated is p, the expected cost of testing 3n sources is 3nc by the first method and $nc\{4 - 3(1 - p)^3\}$ by the second method. Generalise this result by considering the testing of nr sources in groups of r sources. If $r = 3$, what is the range of p for which the first method is preferred?   (L.U.)

14. Jars of a food product pass through an automatic machine which labels them. The machine sometimes misses a jar, the misses occurring randomly and independently and the proportion of unlabelled jars leaving the machine being p. Show that the probability that the xth jar leaving the machine will also be the kth unlabelled jar is

$$\binom{x - 1}{k - 1} p^k (1 - p)^{x-k}, \qquad x = k, \quad k + 1, \quad k + 2, \quad \ldots\ldots$$

Also show that the probability that the second unlabelled jar will occur when the number having left the machine is N or more is given by

$$(1 - p)^{N-2}\{1 + (N - 2)p\}, \qquad N \geqslant 2 \qquad\qquad\qquad \text{(L.U.)}$$

NOTE: $\binom{x - 1}{k - 1}$ is here an alternative notation for $^{x-1}C_{k-1}$.

15. Of the electric lamps made by a factory, 80% give 1000 hours or more of service. What is the probability that of four lamps picked at random

   (i)   all will fail in less than 1000 hours,
   (ii) just two will so fail?

16. A production system is subject to a testing procedure which classifies every item as satisfactory or unsatisfactory. The testing procedure is itself subject to errors and has probability 0·95 of correctly identifying a satisfactory item and probability 0·98 of correctly identifying an unsatisfactory item. If it is known that 1% of the product is unsatisfactory find the proportion of items graded as satisfactory. Hence find the probability

   (i)   that an item graded as satisfactory is satisfactory,
   (ii) that an item graded as unsatisfactory is unsatisfactory.

The cost of producing each item is £1. Those graded as unsatisfactory, however, have to be reworked before being graded as satisfactory and cost a total of £1.50 each to produce. What is the expected cost of production of each item? The manufacturer may, at a cost of £2000, improve the testing procedure so that the probability of correctly identifying a satisfactory item would be 0·99. Can he expect to recoup this cost during the production of 100 000 items?   (L.U.)

17.   (i)   When a relay is tested, the probability that it fails to make
            satisfactory contact in a single trial is θ.   The outcomes of
            successive trials are independent and θ remains unchanged over a
            very large number of trials.   What is the probability that

            (a)   the first failure occurs at the sixth trial,
            (b)   the second failure occurs at the sixth trial,
            (c)   the kth failure occurs at the nth trial ($k \leqslant n$,   obviously)?

      (ii) The probability that a 20-watt bulb made by the Glowbrite Electric
            Company will fail in a 500-hour life test is 0·001.   Give,
            without evaluating, <u>exact</u> expressions for the probability that a sign
            constructed from 1000 such bulbs will remain lit up for 500 hours

            (a)   with no bulb failures,
            (b)   with just one bulb failure,
            (c)   with just k bulb failures.

            (Assume that the failure of one bulb is independent of the failure of
            any other in the sign.)

            State why the Poisson distribution could reasonably be used to give
            <u>approximate</u> answers to (a), (b) and (c), and what these answers
            would be.

18.   The frequency of accidents per day on a stretch of road is shown in the
      following table.

Accidents per day	0	1	2	3	4	5	
Frequency	667	266	56	10	1	0	Total = 1000

      Use the Poisson distribution to estimate the probability of there being

      (a) no accidents in a week,
      (b) more than 3 accidents in a week.   (C.E.I.)

19.   The number of days in a 100-day period during which x accidents occurred
      in a factory is tabulated below:

No. of accidents (x)	0	1	2	3	4	5
No. of days (n)	42	35	14	6	2	1

      (a)   Fit a Poisson distribution to this data to predict the probability of
            x accidents occurring.
      (b)   Compare the variance of the given and calculated distributions.(C.E.I.)

20.   Describe the binomial and Poisson distributions stating the circumstances
      in which each might be used.

      Random samples of fifty are examined from each batch of a large consignment
      of manufactured articles and in such samples the average number of defective
      articles was found to be 3·1.   A batch is rejected if the sample taken
      from it contains three or more defective articles.   Assuming a Poisson
      distribution, show that the probability of a batch being rejected is
      approximately 0·6.

      Calculate the probability that of six batches sampled three or more will
      be rejected.   Find also the probability that of 100 batches at least half
      will be accepted.   (L.U.)

21. The probability that any one machine will become defective in the small interval between time t and t + δt after maintenance is $\alpha e^{-\alpha t}\delta t$, where α is a constant.

A firm possessing 10 similar machines institutes a weekly maintenance of the machines, each of which operates for 44 hours per week, and $\alpha = 1/400$ when the unit of time is one hour.   Find

   (i)   the probability that all ten machines will continue to function throughout the week,

   (ii) the probability that more than two machines will become defective before the weekly maintenance is due.   (L.U.)

22. The time to failure, t, of a component is described by the exponential distribution if the mean failure rate λ is constant.   Write down the integral which represents the proportion of components that will not have survived after time τ.   Evaluate this integral and deduce that the median survival time is $(1/\lambda)\ln 2$.   (If you are familiar with the process of radioactive disintegration, you will recognise this as the half-life of a source where λ is the mean number of disintegrations per unit time.)

23. A scutcher is a machine used in the textile industry to open and clean new cotton and form it into a continuous fibrous layer called a lap.   From a large number of weighings made in the past it is known that the weights of 20-kg finisher laps produced on a particular type of scutcher can be assumed to be normally distributed with s.d. 75 g.   The mean μ of the distribution depends on the adjustment of the scutcher.   All laps differing from 20 kg by more than 200 g have to be reprocessed.   For what value of μ will the percentage of laps requiring reprocessing be a minimum?   Find this minimum percentage.

Narrowing the tolerance limits for lap weight would, of course, result in more reprocessing.   Where could the limits be set if the reprocessing of up to 2% of laps is acceptable?

24. In a study of the variation of a critical dimension of electric contacts, measurements of this dimension were made on a sample of 1000 such contacts. The results are shown here in the form of a frequency table.

Interval mid-point (mm)	10·3	10·4	10·5	10·6	10·7	10·8	10·9	11·0	11·1	11·2
Frequency	5	30	120	180	227	185	150	70	30	3

   (i) Describe exactly how this distribution would be represented by a histogram, making it clear where the bases of the rectangles would have their end points.

   (ii) Using coding, calculate the mean, variance and standard deviation of this distribution.

   (iii) What theoretical frequency for the interval whose mid-point is 10·7 would be given by a fitted Normal model (i.e. one with the same mean, standard deviation and total frequency as the data)?

25. Tests on 1000 single threads of sized yarn (i.e. yarn which has been treated so that it can be woven easily) showed that only 985 of them could be extended by 2% of their length without breaking. Of these, only 209 remained unbroken when the extension was increased to 5%. Assuming the % extensibility of single threads to be normally distributed, what mean and s.d. would be in accordance with the observations?

26. Suppose that 4 minutes is the median time taken by a factory's machine operators to complete a task which they perform many times a day. Then if any one of these performances is timed there is a 50% chance of a time greater than 4 minutes being recorded. If any 7 performances are timed, what is the probability of a time greater than 4 minutes being recorded (i) exactly once, (ii) not more than once?

    If 36 times, instead of 7, are recorded, use the normal distribution to estimate the probability that 25 or more will exceed 4 minutes.

27. If x is a random variable which is $N(\mu, \sigma^2)$, write down the integral that will give the arithmetic mean of those values of x which are greater than μ.

    Given that I.Q. is $N(100, 15^2)$ what is the mean I.Q. of people, who are of "above average" intelligence?

28. The required dosage of a particular drug is 200 mg. This can be supplied by a single tablet, such tablets having a mean drug content of 200 mg, with s.d. 10 mg. Alternatively, smaller tablets are available, whose mean drug content is 50 mg, with s.d. 3 mg. From the point of view of meeting the dosage requirement, would 4 of these tablets be preferable to the single tablet?

29. In a manufacturing process a piston of circular cross-section has to fit into a similarly shaped cylinder. The distributions of diameters of pistons and cylinders are known to be normal with parameters:

    Pistons: mean diameter 10·42 cm, standard deviation 0·03 cm.
    Cylinders: mean diameter 10·52 cm, standard deviation 0·04 cm.

    If the pistons and cylinders are selected at random for assembly

    (a) what proportion of pistons will not fit into cylinders?
    (b) what is the chance that, in 100 pairs selected at random, all the pistons will fit?
                                                                        (C.E.I.)

30. A type of sensor has a mean life of 15 000 hours with a standard deviation of 1000 hours. Three of these sensors are connected in a firewarning device so that when one fails another takes over. Assuming that the lifetimes are normally distributed, what is the probability that the device:

    (a) will function for 40 000 hours,
    (b) will fail before 39 000 hours?   (C.E.I.)

31. If the weights of passengers travelling by air on scheduled flights from a large metropolitan airport are normally distributed with mean 78 kg and standard deviation 10 kg, find limits (symmetrical about the mean) such that 95% of passengers will have a weight within these limits. What is the probability of the total weight of a random sample of 100 passengers exceeding 8000 kg?

32. Tests have shown that the highest temperature ($^{\circ}C$) which capacitors of a
particular type can withstand is $N(125, 9)$.   In the systems in which
they are used, the maximum temperature ($^{\circ}C$) to which an individual capacitor
is subjected is $N(116, 16)$.   What proportion of capacitors will fail
because of overheating?

ANSWERS

1. Using classes whose mid-points are $16 \cdot 85$, $17 \cdot 05$, ..., $19 \cdot 05$, frequencies
   are 1, 2, 2, 4, 5, 10, 19, 15, 10, 7, ?, 3.   Mean = $18 \cdot 1075$.
   Variance = $0 \cdot 2012$.

2. Histogram has rectangles with bases extending from $-70 \cdot 5$ to $-50 \cdot 5$,
   $-50 \cdot 5$ to $-30 \cdot 5$, ..., $49 \cdot 5$ to $69 \cdot 5$.   Mean = $5 \cdot 0113$.   Median group
   $5 \cdot 0095$ to $5 \cdot 0295$.   Modal group $5 \cdot 0295$ to $5 \cdot 0495$. $5 \cdot 0113 \pm 0 \cdot 0700$ i.e.
   $4 \cdot 9413$ and $5 \cdot 0813$. $5 \cdot 0113 \pm 0 \cdot 1050$ i.e. $4 \cdot 9063$ and $5 \cdot 1163$.

3. Histogram has rectangles with bases extending from 980 to 985, 985 to 990,
   ....., 1020 to 1025.   Modal group has mid-interval value $997 \cdot 5$, also the
   median group.   Interquartile range = $8 \cdot 48$.   Mean = $1000 \cdot 225$, s.d. = $7 \cdot 067$.

4. See FRAMES 26-27 on page 16.

5. (i) $0 \cdot 05$ (ii) $0 \cdot 045$ (iii) $0 \cdot 774$ (iv) $0 \cdot 226$

6. (i) $1 - p_1 p_2 p_3 p_4$

   (ii) $(1 - p_1)p_2 p_3 p_4 + (1 - p_2)p_1 p_3 p_4 + (1 - p_3)p_1 p_2 p_4 + (1 - p_4)p_1 p_2 p_3$

7. $1 - (1 - p)^n$ (i) 2   (ii) 3   (iii) 4

8. (i) (a) $\left(\dfrac{5}{6}\right)^5$ (b) $1 - \dfrac{11}{6}\left(\dfrac{5}{6}\right)^5$ (c) $\dfrac{5!}{6^5}$

   $\left(\dfrac{5}{6}\right)^{r-1}\left(\dfrac{1}{6}\right)$.   Least value of r is 4.

   (ii) (a) 1/36   (b) 1/8   (c) 5/108

9. (a) $0 \cdot 896$ (b) $0 \cdot 544$

10. $0 \cdot 18$, $0 \cdot 778$, $0 \cdot 82$

11. $\pi_1(p - q)^2 + q(1 + p - q)$, $\pi_n = \pi_{n-1}(p - q) + q$

13. $nc\{r + 1 - r(1 - p)^r\}$, $p > 1 - 1/\sqrt[3]{3}$

15. (i) 1/625   (ii) 96/625

16. $94 \cdot 07\%$ (i) $0 \cdot 999\,79$ (ii) $0 \cdot 165\,26$
    £$1 \cdot 029\,65$ No, as only £1980 would be saved in the production of
    100 000 items.

17. (i) (a) $(1 - \theta)^5 \theta$ (b) $5(1 - \theta)^4 \theta^2$ (c) $^{n-1}C_{k-1}(1 - \theta)^{n-k}\theta^k$

    (ii) (a) $(0 \cdot 999)^{1000}$ (b) $1000 \times (0 \cdot 999)^{999} \times 0 \cdot 001$

(c) $^{1000}C_k (0 \cdot 999)^{1000-k}(0 \cdot 001)^k$

The distribution of bulb failures is binomial, with $n = 1000$ and $p = 0 \cdot 001$. The Poisson distribution will give a good approximation because n is large and p is small. Answers: (a) e^{-1}, (b) e^{-1}, (c) $\dfrac{e^{-1}}{k!}$

18. (a) $0 \cdot 0559$ (b) $0 \cdot 327$

19. (a) $P(x) = (0 \cdot 94)^x e^{-0 \cdot 94}/x!$
    (b) Variance of observed distribution = $1 \cdot 14$
         Variance of Poisson model = $0 \cdot 94$

20. $0 \cdot 8208$, $0 \cdot 026$

21. (i) $e^{-1 \cdot 1} = 0 \cdot 3329$ (ii) $0 \cdot 0775$

22. $\displaystyle\int_0^\tau \lambda e^{-\lambda t}\, dt = 1 - e^{-\lambda \tau}$

23. $\mu = 20$ kg, i.e, when the limits of what is acceptable are symmetrically placed with respect to μ. $0 \cdot 8\%$.   Laps differing from 20 kg by more than 175 g would be reprocessed.

24. (i) The areas of the rectangles should be proportional to the frequencies and the bases should have their end points at $10 \cdot 25$, $10 \cdot 35$, ... $11 \cdot 25$.

     (ii) Mean = $10 \cdot 73$, Variance = $0 \cdot 0289$, s.d. = $0 \cdot 17$.
           Note: Mean and s.d. are in cm, but variance is in cm^2.

     (iii) $227 \cdot 7$

25. Mean = $4 \cdot 18\%$, s.d. = $1 \cdot 01\%$.

26. (i) $7/128$ (ii) $1/16$ $0 \cdot 015$

27. $\displaystyle\int_\mu^\infty xp(x)\,dx$ where $p(x) = (2/\sigma\sqrt{2\pi})\exp\{-(x - \mu)^2/2\sigma^2\}$
     $100 + 30/\sqrt{2\pi} = 111 \cdot 97$

28. Yes, as the s.d. of the dosage supplied by 4 of the 50-mg tablets is only 6 mg.

29. (a) $0 \cdot 0228$ (b) $0 \cdot 1$

30. (a) $0 \cdot 9981$ (b) $0 \cdot 0003$

31. $58 \cdot 4$ and $97 \cdot 6$ kg $0 \cdot 0228$

32. $0 \cdot 0359$

UNIT 2
THE DEDUCTION OF INFORMATION FROM SAMPLES

This Unit comprises five programmes:

(a) Confidence Limits for the Mean

(b) Tests of Significance (1)

(c) Tests of Significance (2)

(d) Nonparametric (Distribution-free) Tests

(e) Quality Control and Acceptance Sampling

Before reading these programmes, it is necessary that you are familiar with the following

Prerequisites

For (a): Probability (independent and dependent events).
          The normal distribution.   The distribution of sums and differences.
          For FRAMES 43-48, the Poisson distribution, but these frames may be
          omitted if desired.

For (b): Probabilities given by the binomial model.
          The contents of (a).
          For FRAMES 44-58, the use of the normal approximation to the binomial,
          but these frames may be omitted if desired.

For (c): The contents of the previous programmes in this Unit.

          Note: Some of the χ^2 goodness-of-fit test examples refer to standard
              distributions described in Unit 1 but those with which the reader is
              not familiar may be omitted.

For (d): The procedure of hypothesis testing.
          Calculation of probabilities (including those given by the binomial
          model).
          The normal distribution.

For (e): The distribution of sample means.
          The binomial distribution.
          For FRAMES 52 and 53, the ideas involved in hypothesis testing,
          but these frames may be omitted if desired.
          For Misc. Ex. 3, 8(iii) and 9(iii), the Poisson distribution,
          but these could be omitted if desired.

Confidence Limits for the Mean

Sample and Population

If a manufacturer of electric light bulbs wants to know about the length of life of all the bulbs produced in the factory, the only way of finding out with absolute certainty is to test all of them.   However, as the test is a destructive one, there would not then be any products left to sell!

If an analytical chemist wishes to establish, without a shadow of doubt, which of two methods is the more precise, then an infinitely large number of analyses by each method would have to be carried out.   Clearly this would be impossible and, in fact, practical restrictions usually allow only a small number of replicate analyses.

In the first example, the values of the length of life of all the bulbs in the factory's output constitute what statisticians call the POPULATION.   In the second example, the chemist is interested in two populations - the results of an infinite number of analyses using Method 1 and the results of an infinite number of analyses using Method 2.

In the case of the light bulbs, every one of them will have a length of life, although not known at the time of manufacture.   The population therefore consists of actual values of the variate, finite in number, though with mass production it would be so large as to almost be regarded as infinite.   The chemist's populations exist only in the imagination - all the analyses that might have been carried out - and would be thought of as being infinite.

If a few light bulbs from the factory's production are life-tested, the values thus obtained of their lengths of life will form a SAMPLE drawn from the population described in the previous frame.   Likewise, for Method 1, say, the results of analyses actually performed by the chemist represent a sample from the infinite population of all the Method 1 analyses that might have been.   The number of observations in the sample is known as the SAMPLE SIZE.

In testing the light bulbs, or any other mass-produced articles, a decision will have to be made on how to select those which are to be tested.   If every item has an equal chance of being selected, a RANDOM SAMPLE is obtained.   The question arises of how this is to be achieved.   Anyone who has witnessed the draw for raffle prizes has seen an attempt at random selection.   Pieces of paper, folded so that the numbers on them can't be seen, are placed in a container and well mixed.   The idea is that when someone is asked to draw out the ticket with the winning number on it, every ticket has an equal chance of being chosen.

A more sophisticated method is to use a table of RANDOM NUMBERS, such as can be found in any set of statistical tables.   A variety of ways of generating a set of random numbers have been devised, the principle always being that, for each digit, the chances of 0, 1, ... 9 occurring are all equal.   To choose a random sample of, say, articles for testing or persons for answering a questionnaire, every article or person in the population is allocated a number. Reference to the table of random numbers then determines which articles or persons should be selected.

Random sampling is not the only form of sampling. Stratified sampling aims at obtaining a representative sample, so that, for instance, a sample of students drawn from those attending a certain university would have roughly the same proportion studying engineering, science, arts etc. as the population of all students at the university. Similarly, in a British Standard specification for electric lamps, the selection procedure laid down guards against the sample being chosen from just a few containers in the batch and requires that the test lamps be taken from a prescribed minimum number of containers. Within that restriction, though, the selection is specified as random.

In this course, only random samples will be considered. When the text mentions samples you can take it that they are random, even if it is not specifically stated.

The broad outline of the problem facing the light bulb manufacturer and the chemical analyst is this:

    Information about the population is required.
    Only information about a sample is available.
    How can the information given by the sample best be used to make
    conclusions about the population?

That, in a nutshell, is what this and subsequent programmes in this Unit are all about.

You have seen in Unit 1 how some aspects of a distribution can be summarised by measures such as the arithmetic mean and standard deviation. Their values in the population are the POPULATION PARAMETERS. The lamp manufacturer would like to know the mean length of life of all the bulbs in the factory's output, i.e. the population mean. If, say, 5 bulbs chosen from the output are life-tested, their mean length of life is an example of a SAMPLE STATISTIC.

If a sample statistic is to be used to tell us something about a population parameter, we must investigate the relation between them. This will first be done for the mean.

Distribution of Sample Means

Referring to the example of the light bulbs, which of (a), (b) and (c) would you insert in each gap in the following statement to correctly complete it?

    The sample mean .... be equal to the population mean. If another 5
    bulbs are chosen at random and life-tested, their mean length of life ....
    be equal to the first sample mean.

(a) will definitely not   (b) will certainly   (c) might

                ****
7A

(c) in each case. Admittedly, one would expect it to be unlikely that the sample and population means will be equal, or that the two sample means will be equal, but neither is impossible.

Similar remarks could apply to the results of chemical analyses.   If, for
instance, some slag is sent to a laboratory and a chemist makes 4 determinations
of the percentage of silicon dioxide in it, there is no guarantee that the mean
of these 4 determinations will be the true percentage.   Furthermore, if
another 4 determinations were made, their mean might well be different from that
of the first 4.

Having realised that it is unlikely that a sample mean will be equal to the
population mean, we now ask "How large is the difference between them likely to
be?"   This question must be answered if a sample mean is to be used to make
conclusions about the population mean.   As sample means differ among themselves,
some will be nearer to the population mean than others.   What we now have to
consider is the concept of all the samples of the given size (5 in the case of
the light bulbs, 4 in that of the analyses) that could possibly arise from the
population concerned.   The pattern of variation of their means, i.e. the
DISTRIBUTION OF SAMPLE MEANS, is the key to the answer being sought.

Ordinarily the idea of taking all these samples is not put into practice and so
the distribution of sample means exists only in theory.   The following
experiment has been found helpful, not only in that an actual distribution of
sample means is generated in the classroom but also in that the properties of
this distribution are seen to support those derived theoretically.

On each of 20 small pieces of card is written the digit 0, on another 20 the
digit 1 is written, and so on for the digits 2, 3, 4, 5, 6.   These 140
numbered cards are then placed in a large envelope in which the numbers cannot
be seen from the outside.

The numbers in the envelope represent the population from which samples are to be
drawn.   As all the values 0, 1, ... 6 occur with equal frequency, the
distribution is rectangular.   It would be a useful revision exercise for you to
find the mean μ, variance σ^2 and s.d. σ of this distribution.

****

9A

$\mu = \Sigma x P(x) = 3 \qquad \sigma^2 = \Sigma x^2 P(x) - \mu^2 = 4 \qquad \sigma = 2$

Each student in the class takes 4 cards out of the envelope, notes the numbers
on them and returns the cards to the envelope.   He shakes up the contents
before passing it on to his neighbour and then calculates the mean of the
numbers which were drawn.   This is repeated as often as time allows.

Each set of 4 numbers recorded at a drawing may be regarded as a random sample
from the population in the envelope.   Some possible samples are shown below,
with their means boxed.

1st SAMPLE	2nd SAMPLE	3rd SAMPLE	4th SAMPLE	5th SAMPLE	
2 0	5 1	1 5	3 6	2 1	
1 4	5 5	6 2	1 0	0 6	and so on.
1·75	4·00	3·50	2·50	2·25	

FRAME 10   (continued)

The sample means can then be grouped into a frequency distribution and the mean and s.d. of this distribution found.   The results should show quite good agreement with those which will shortly be derived theoretically, especially if there has been time to draw a large number of samples.

FRAME 11

Before trying to develop a theory about the distribution of sample means in general, a little thought will be given to the sample selection procedure.

When the 4 cards are drawn from the envelope, one of the following two procedures could be adopted.   The cards may be drawn one at a time, each being replaced in the envelope before the next is drawn.   This is SAMPLING WITH REPLACEMENT.   The other way is to draw all four cards before returning them to the envelope.   This is SAMPLING WITHOUT REPLACEMENT and is the procedure suggested for the classroom experiment, not only because it would be less time-consuming but also because it appears to be more akin to what happens when, say, 5 light bulbs are selected for testing.   The question now is what effect, if any, the choice between the two procedures has on the samples that turn up.

Look, for instance, at the 2nd sample in the previous frame, consisting of three 5's and a 1, regardless of the order in which they were drawn.   Without actually working out the probabilities, would you say that the chance of getting the combination is the same whether the sampling is with or without replacement?

****

11A

Not the same.   Having drawn a 5 and not replaced it, the chance of getting another 5 is reduced.   When the number is replaced each time, getting a 5 and then subsequently getting another 5 are independent events, but when there is no replacement, the likelihood of drawing a 5 depends on what has happened before.

FRAME 12

Bearing in mind the remarks just made, write down expressions (don't evaluate them) for the respective probabilities of getting the 2nd sample with and without replacement in the selection procedure.

****

12A

With replacement: $4 \times \dfrac{20}{140} \times \dfrac{20}{140} \times \dfrac{20}{140} \times \dfrac{20}{140} = 4\left(\dfrac{1}{7}\right)^{4}$

Without replacement: $4 \times \dfrac{20}{140} \times \dfrac{20}{139} \times \dfrac{19}{138} \times \dfrac{18}{137}$ *(You may have combined the*

numerators and denominators in a different way - obviously it doesn't matter.)

FRAME 13

Notice, however, that although not replacing the card affects what happens after the first number has been drawn, the subsequent probabilities are not so very different from 1/7.   They would have been more different if the size of the population had been less than 140, but less different if the population had been larger.   Write down, again without evaluating them, expressions for the

probabilities of getting this sample with and without replacement in the
selection procedure when N, the number of cards in the envelope, is

(i) 21 (3 of each digit),   (ii) 700 (100 of each digit).

****

13A

$$(i)\quad N = 21 \qquad\qquad (ii)\quad N = 700$$

With replacement: $4\left(\dfrac{1}{7}\right)^{4}$ $4\left(\dfrac{1}{7}\right)^{4}$

Without replacement: $4 \times \dfrac{3}{21} \times \dfrac{3}{20} \times \dfrac{2}{19} \times \dfrac{1}{18}$ $4 \times \dfrac{100}{700} \times \dfrac{100}{699} \times \dfrac{99}{698} \times \dfrac{98}{697}$

*The value of N does not, of course, affect what happens in the "with
replacement" situation.*

FRAME 14

Evaluating the probabilities (to 5 d.p.) so that they can be compared:

	Without replacement		With replacement
N = 21	N = 140	N = 700	All N
0·000 50	0·001 49	0·001 63	0·001 67

As you see, not replacing the cards at each draw matters less and less as N
increases. Now imagine N to be infinite, still with equal proportions of the
cards carrying the digits 0, 1, ... 6.   What do you think will be the
probability then of getting this sample of three 5's and a 1, if the cards are
not replaced each time?

****

14A

$4\left(\dfrac{1}{7}\right)^{4}$.   *When there is an endless supply of digits, drawing a 5 the first time
and not returning it will not affect the probability of getting a 5 at the
second draw.*

FRAME 15

Many practical situations involve sampling from an infinite population (as with
the chemist's analyses) or from a population so large that it can be regarded
as infinite (as with the life-testing of lamps).   We shall therefore concentrate
on the imaginary concept of an envelope with an infinite supply of numbers in it,
which, as you have seen, is equivalent in terms of probabilities to using the set
of numbers in the experiment and replacing the card each time.   Each observation
in the sample is then a random variable which is independent of the others, i.e.
what number is drawn the first time does not affect what is drawn the second
time, etc.

$x_1 \qquad x_2$ If the 4 observations are denoted by x_1, x_2, x_3, x_4 then
$x_3 \qquad x_4$ their mean $\bar{x}$ is given by

$\boxed{\bar{x}}$

$$\bar{x} = \frac{1}{4}(x_1 + x_2 + x_3 + x_4)$$

FRAME 15   (continued)

Now x_1, x_2, x_3, x_4 all come from a population whose mean is 3 and whose s.d. is 2.   If you have not forgotten what you learned about the distribution of linear combinations of independent variates in the last programme of Unit 1, you should now be able to write down the mean and s.d. of $\bar{x}$.

****

15A

$$\bar{x} = \frac{1}{4} x_1 + \frac{1}{4} x_2 + \frac{1}{4} x_3 + \frac{1}{4} x_4$$

$$\therefore \quad Mean(\bar{x}) = \frac{1}{4} \times 3 + \frac{1}{4} \times 3 + \frac{1}{4} \times 3 + \frac{1}{4} \times 3 = 3$$

$$Var(\bar{x}) = \left(\frac{1}{4}\right)^2 \times 2^2 + \left(\frac{1}{4}\right)^2 \times 2^2 + \left(\frac{1}{4}\right)^2 \times 2^2 + \left(\frac{1}{4}\right)^2 \times 2^2 = 1$$

$$s.d.(\bar{x}) = 1$$

FRAME 16

Now find the mean and s.d. of $\bar{x}$ if the samples are drawn from a population with mean μ and s.d. σ and the sample size is (i) 4, (ii) n.

****

16A

(i)   Mean = μ Variance = $\sigma^2/4$ s.d. = $\sigma/2$

(ii) $\bar{x} = \frac{1}{n} x_1 + \frac{1}{n} x_2 + \ldots + \frac{1}{n} x_n$,   Mean = μ,   Variance = σ^2/n,   s.d. = $\sigma/\sqrt{n}$

It may be of interest to note that when the sample is taken, without replacement, from a population of size N, the mean of the $\bar{x}$'s is also μ, but the variance is $\frac{N-n}{N} \frac{\sigma^2}{n}$.   Obviously the multiplying factor $\frac{N-n}{N}$ will not differ greatly from 1 if N is large compared with n.   For 4 cards taken from 140, it would be 136/140 so even without replacement the classroom experiment should yield results agreeing quite well with those which you arrived at theoretically in the previous answer frame.

FRAME 17

With a reminder that in the last programme of Unit 1 it was stated that a linear combination of independent normal variates is itself normally distributed, what can you say about the distribution of $\bar{x}$ when the samples, of size n, are taken from a population which is $N(\mu, \sigma^2)$?

****

17A

$N(\mu, \sigma^2/n)$

FRAME 18

Two facts have now emerged about the distribution of sample means.   First, its mean is the same as that of the population but there is less spread, its standard deviation (called the STANDARD ERROR OF THE MEAN) being $\sigma/\sqrt{n}$ where σ is the s.d. of the population and n is the sample size.

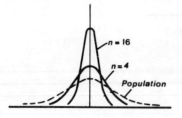

Secondly, if the population is normal so also is
the distribution of sample means.   This is
illustrated by the diagram on the left.

Not all populations, however, are normal, so this
result is of limited application.   A third
property, which will now be stated, is more
far-reaching.

The CENTRAL LIMIT THEOREM plays an important part in statistical theory.   It
tells us that, the larger the value of n, the nearer is the distribution of
sample means to the normal distribution with mean μ and s.d. $\sigma/\sqrt{n}$.   The
normal model therefore often gives a satisfactory approximation and this is one
of the main reasons for its importance.

The usual rules of guidance say that the distribution of sample means can be
assumed to be normal if the sample size is "not too small" and the population
from which the samples are drawn is "not too skew".   However an experiment
conducted by A.F. Ham with the aid of a computer, using some non-normal
populations, clearly illustrates the marked tendency of the distribution of
sample means to become symmetrical and bell-shaped even for samples as small as
4.   The experiment is really a computerised version of the classroom one
described earlier, the program using a method of selection equivalent to sampling
with replacement and repeating the procedure for three distributions besides

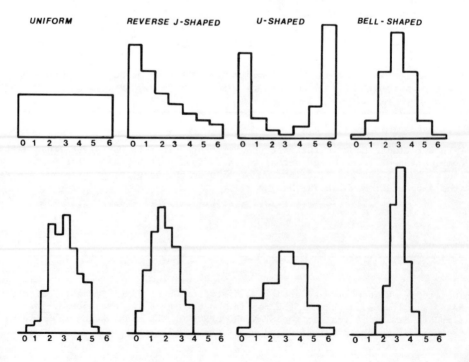

the uniform one.   For each population, 200 samples of size 4 were randomly selected and their means calculated and grouped into a frequency distribution.

The diagram on page 170 shows, on the top row, the histograms representing the populations from which samples were taken and below each the histogram representing the distribution of sample means obtained.   Notice that although the parent populations differ markedly one from another, all the sampling distributions show a tendency towards the symmetry of the normal distribution.

FRAME 20

Some questions about sample means will now test your understanding of what you have just read about their distribution.

The lives of Glowbrite light bulbs have a mean of 1000 hours and s.d. 160 hours. Consider the distribution of the mean lives of samples of 25 randomly selected bulbs.   State (i) its mean, (ii) its s.d., (iii) under what conditions it would be normal.

****

20A

(i)   1000 h   (ii)   32 h (this is the standard error of the mean)

(iii)   It would be normal if the lives of the light bulbs were themselves normally distributed.   If they were not, however, one would think the sample size of 25 large enough for the normal model to qualify as a reasonable approximation.

FRAME 21

Assuming a normal distribution for the sample means, find the chance of 25 randomly selected bulbs having a mean life   (i) less than 1000 h, (ii) less than 920 h.

****

21A

(i)   0·5   (ii)   0·0062

FRAME 22

In an example in Unit 1 you were asked the question "Would a diastolic blood pressure of 74 mm Hg be unusually high for a boy of a given age?   Your answer was to be based on the assumption that boys in that age group had blood pressures which were $N(57, 8^2)$ and "unusual" was to be interpreted as "having a probability of less than 1%".   You found that the chance of a boy of that age having a blood pressure as high as 74 (i.e. 74 or higher) was about 1·7% so it was not high enough to be considered "unusual".

Suppose that, instead, the question had been: "Would it be unusual for a group of 4 boys of that age to have a mean blood pressure as high as 74?"   Then we would need to know about the distribution of means of samples of 4 taken from a population which is $N(57, 8^2)$.   First, answer the following questions about this distribution of sample means:

(i) Is it normal?   (ii) What is its mean?   (iii) What is its s.d.?

****

(i) Yes.   No approximation here, as the population is known to be normal.
(ii) 57   (iii) 4

Interpreting "unusual" in the same way as before, we now have to find out whether the probability of a sample mean exceeding 74 is less than 1%.

Now as $\bar{x}$ is $N(57, 4^2)$, $P(\bar{x} > 74) = P(u > 4\cdot25)$ where $u = (\bar{x} - 57)/4$.

Is this less than 1%?   From your knowledge of the standard normal distribution you should be able to give the answer without needing to look at tables.

****

Values greater than 4·25 are very, very unusual for the standard normal deviate, the probability of them occurring being far less than 1%.   Thus, although 74 might not be considered high for an individual boy's blood pressure, it would be extraordinarily high for the mean of 4 boys' blood pressures.

Now look at the following problem and decide which of the five alternatives offered is correct.

A solution has a concentration of about $0\cdot2\ \mathrm{mol\ dm^{-3}}$.   It is known that, for solutions of this kind, repeated determinations have a standard deviation of $0\cdot0012\ \mathrm{mol\ dm^{-3}}$.   The minimum number of determinations which would be needed for their mean to have a standard error not greater than $0\cdot0005$ is:

(a) 3   (b) 4   (c) 5   (d) 6   (e) 7

Is your answer dependent on the determinations being normally distributed?

****

(d)   The sample size n must be such that $\dfrac{0\cdot0012}{\sqrt{n}} \leqslant 0\cdot0005$

i.e. $\dfrac{12}{\sqrt{n}} \leqslant 5$ *or* $\dfrac{144}{n} \leqslant 25$

This is not satisfied by n = 3, 4 or 5 but it is by n = 6.   Or, if you rewrite it as   25n ≥ 144   you get   n ≥ 5·76   and the smallest integer value of n for which this holds is n = 6.

No, the standard error of the mean is   σ/√n   whatever the pattern of distribution in the population.

Summary

The properties of the sampling distribution of the mean are very important, so they are summarised here for your convenience.

If x is distributed with mean μ and standard deviation σ, and if all possible samples of size n are drawn from this population, then the distribution of the sample mean $\bar{x}$ will

(i)   have mean μ and s.d. $\sigma/\sqrt{n}$,
(ii) approach the normal distribution with mean μ and s.d. $\sigma/\sqrt{n}$ as n
      increases,
(iii) itself be normal if the distribution of x is normal.

FRAME 26

Confidence Limits for Population Mean − σ known

You can now appreciate why it is that, when making measurements which are
subject to error, it is better to repeat the observations and take the mean
rather than to rely just on a single measurement.   Many people who do this
realise intuitively that the mean of, say, 4 measurements is likely to be
nearer the true value than one measurement is, without fully understanding why.
Moreover, they are also aware that the mean of, say, 10 measurements would be
likely to be even nearer.

Clearly the degree of confidence that can be placed in estimates of population
parameters, such as means and standard deviations, is closely related to the
size of the sample on which the estimate is based and to how much this estimate
then varies from sample to sample.   With a knowledge of the theoretical
background it is possible when saying, for instance, that a sample mean is
likely to be near the population mean, to specify how likely and how near.
Thus you will see that when using a sample mean as an estimate of the true value,
i.e. the population mean, this estimate should properly be quoted, not as a
single figure, but rather as an interval within which we are confident that the
true value lies.   "How confident?" you may ask.   As the answer to this must be
in terms of probability, the interval, when stated, will have to be accompanied
by an associated probability which is a measure of how confident we are that the
true value lies within this interval.

FRAME 27

To arrive at an interval such as that just proposed, let us consider random
samples of size n being taken from a population with mean μ and s.d. σ, in a
situation in which the sample means can be assumed to be normally distributed.
There is then a 95% probability of a sample mean $\bar{x}$ lying within the interval
$\mu \pm$ ....   Complete this statement.

            ****

27A

$\mu \pm 1 \cdot 96 \sigma/\sqrt{n}$

If you did not get this right, remember that $\bar{x}$ is $N(\mu, \sigma^2/n)$.

FRAME 28

Putting this another way, there is a 95% chance that the difference between $\bar{x}$
and μ does not exceed $1 \cdot 96\sigma/\sqrt{n}$ and therefore that the interval $\bar{x} - 1 \cdot 96\sigma/\sqrt{n}$
to $\bar{x} + 1 \cdot 96\sigma/\sqrt{n}$ contains μ.   This interval is called the 95% CONFIDENCE
INTERVAL, and its boundaries the 95% CONFIDENCE LIMITS, for the mean μ of the
population.

Returning to determinations of the concentration of a solution, which are known
to have a s.d. of $0 \cdot 0012 \, mol \, dm^{-3}$, suppose that 4 determinations of the
concentration of a particular solution have a mean value of $0 \cdot 205 \, mol \, dm^{-3}$.

The 95% confidence limits for the concentration of the solution are

$$0 \cdot 205 \pm 1 \cdot 96 \times 0 \cdot 0012 / \sqrt{4} \qquad i.e. \qquad 0 \cdot 2038 \text{ and } 0 \cdot 2062 \, \text{mol dm}^{-3}$$

Now try this problem:

A structural engineer concerned with the strength of reinforced concrete structures needs information about the force at which the tensile reinforcement will yield.   Tests on 25 specimens of mild steel reinforcing bars, all of the same nominal diameter, gave a mean yield force of 37·76 kN.   If past experience with tests on similar material has shown measurements of yield force to have a s.d. of 0·45 kN and to be approximately normally distributed, what are the 95% confidence limits for the yield force of this particular type of reinforcing bar?

****

28A

37·76 ± 1·96 × 0·45/5   i.e.   37·58 and 37·94 kN

(Based on the sampling distribution of the mean being normal, a reasonable assumption in this case.)

FRAME 29

Confidence limits can be associated with any probability.   While 95% is quite a common choice, you may also come across 90% and 99%.   Write down in terms of $\bar{x}$, σ and n, the respective formulae for 90% and 99% confidence limits for μ.

****

29A

$$\bar{x} \pm 1 \cdot 64 \sigma / \sqrt{n} \qquad and \qquad \bar{x} \pm 2 \cdot 58 \sigma / \sqrt{n}$$

FRAME 30

Sample Estimate of Population Variance

In both the determination of the concentration of a solution and the measuring of the yield force of reinforcing bars, a history of such tests existed and the standard deviation σ of their results was known.   This happens comparatively rarely.   The more usual situation is that the observations which form the sample are, in fact, the only data available and an estimate of σ has to be found from them.   That will entail first getting an estimate of σ^2.

Once again we are faced with the problem of obtaining from the sample an estimate of a population parameter; this time it is the population variance.   When estimating the population mean μ, the statistic that we used was the sample mean $\bar{x}$.   When the sampling distribution of $\bar{x}$ was investigated, its mean was seen to be μ.   Thus, when you use $\bar{x}$ as an estimate of μ, sometimes you will underestimate and sometimes you will overestimate, but on average you will be neither too high nor too low.   The sample mean $\bar{x}$ is therefore said to be an UNBIASED ESTIMATE of the population mean.

To obtain an estimate of σ^2, the idea that would naturally spring to mind would be to calculate $\frac{1}{n} \Sigma (x - \bar{x})^2$ from the sample.   However, investigation of the sampling distribution of this statistic shows that its mean is $\frac{n-1}{n} \sigma^2$,

FRAME 30   (continued)

not σ^2.   Thus the estimate would be biased, tending to underestimate σ^2.
This bias can be corrected by multiplying $\frac{1}{n} \Sigma(x - \overline{x})^2$ by a factor to produce
a statistic whose sampling distribution does have σ^2 for its mean.   What should
this multiplying factor be?

****

30A

$\frac{n}{n - 1}$ *(sometimes called Bessel's correction factor)*

FRAME 31

Multiplying $\frac{1}{n} \Sigma(x - \overline{x})^2$ by $\frac{n}{n - 1}$ gives $\frac{1}{n - 1} \Sigma(x - \overline{x})^2$ and this is
therefore used to obtain, from a sample, an unbiased estimate of the population
variance.   Mostly it is denoted by s^2, a practice which will be followed in
this text, but in some books s^2 is the notation for $\frac{1}{n} \Sigma(x - \overline{x})^2$, so beware!
The alternative symbol $\hat{\sigma}^2$ stresses the idea of its being an estimate of σ^2, the
"hat" being a conventional notation in statistics for "estimate of".   We have,
therefore,

$$\hat{\sigma}^2 = s^2 = \frac{1}{n - 1} \Sigma(x - \overline{x})^2$$

Now choose one of the five alternatives offered to complete correctly the
statement below.

The percentage yields of a chemical process in 6 successive runs under
apparently identical conditions were: 38, 45, 40, 39, 42, 42.   Regarding these
values as a random sample from the population of all such yields, the unbiased
estimate of the variance of this population is

(i) $\dfrac{(-3 + 4 - 1 - 2 + 1 + 1)^2}{5}$ (ii) $\dfrac{9 + 16 + 1 + 4 + 1 + 1}{6}$

(iii) $\dfrac{(-3)^2 + 4^2 + (-1)^2 + (-2)^2 + 1^2 + 1^2}{5}$ (iv) $\sqrt{\dfrac{32}{5}}$ (v) 41

****

31A

(iii)

FRAME 32

Only with small samples does it matter in practice whether $\Sigma(x - \overline{x})^2$ is
divided by n or n − 1 to obtain the variance estimate.   When n is large,
$\frac{n}{n - 1}$ is so near to 1 that it has little effect when applied as the correction
factor.

For instance, if n = 6, n/(n − 1) is 1·2 and as a multiplying factor it
causes a 20% increase.   For the percentage yields which you have just been
looking at, $\Sigma(x - \overline{x})^2 = 32$, giving 5·3 when divided by 6 but 6·4 when
divided by 5.   On the other hand, if the 250 nylon test bars mentioned in the
first programme of Unit 1 are regarded as a random sample from the population of

all such bars, then strictly speaking the population variance should be
estimated using 249 for denominator. $\Sigma(x - \overline{x})^2$ was found to be 230·5, which
gives 0·922 when divided by 250 and 0·926 when divided by 249.   When the
standard deviation (often the ultimate objective) is calculated, the values
are 0·960 and 0·962 respectively, so the difference is even less.

Degrees of Freedom

Obviously different samples from the same population will give different
estimates of its variance.   The variance estimate s^2 obtained from a sample
of n items is calculated from the sum of the squares of the n deviations
$(x - \overline{x})$.   Different values of s^2 arise from different sets of values of
$(x - \overline{x})$.   In using our imagination to write down a set which might occur when
n = 6, say, we might begin with

$$0·6 \qquad 1·2 \qquad -1·4 \qquad 1·3 \qquad -0·5$$

Only the 6th value remains to be written down.   Are we free to continue to
exercise our imagination or is there a restriction in choice?

****

*There is no freedom of choice in writing down the 6th value.   It must be −1·2
because $\Sigma(x - \overline{x}) = 0$.*

---

	x	x − $\overline{x}$	$(x - \overline{x})^2$
1		FREE	
2		FREE	
3		FREE	
.		.	
.		.	
.		.	
n − 1		FREE	
n		FIXED	
		0	

Thus, when the sample size is n,
although there are n terms (numbered 1
to n in the table on the left) in
$\Sigma(x - \overline{x})^2$ only (n − 1) are independent
and free from restraint.   The remaining
one is always fixed by the constraint
$\Sigma(x - \overline{x}) = 0$.   Hence it is said that there
are (n − 1) DEGREES OF FREEDOM in
$\Sigma(x - \overline{x})^2$ and consequently in the variance
estimate s^2.   The symbol conventionally
used for the number of degrees of freedom
(often abbreviated to d.f.) is the Greek
letter ν.   You will come across the concept again in subsequent programmes,
when it will be further developed.

Confidence Limits for Population Mean − σ estimated

Having discussed how to estimate σ from a sample, we can now go ahead with
showing how this estimate can be used in finding confidence limits for μ.

Previously, when σ was known, what distribution for $\dfrac{\overline{x} - \mu}{\sigma/\sqrt{n}}$ formed the basis
for the confidence limits obtained?

****

The standard normal distribution i.e. N(0, 1).

___

FRAME 36

Writing $u = \dfrac{\overline{x} - \mu}{\sigma/\sqrt{n}}$, and knowing from tables that there is a 95% chance that
$|u| < 1 \cdot 96$, led to the 95% confidence limits for μ. In the present
situation, with σ having to be estimated from the sample, we shall have, not
$\dfrac{\overline{x} - \mu}{\sigma/\sqrt{n}}$ but $\dfrac{\overline{x} - \mu}{s/\sqrt{n}}$. In the latter, not only does $\overline{x}$ vary from sample to sample,
but so also does s and this affects the pattern of the distribution, which is
no longer normal. The distribution of the new ratio is that of t, often
referred to as Student's t as it originated in 1908 in a paper "The Probable
Error of the Mean" written by someone calling himself "Student". It is now
known that the author was W.S. Gosset, employed in the brewing industry, but
because the firm (Guinness) did not allow their employees to publish the results
of their research, he wrote under a pen name.

___

FRAME 37

A STUDENT'S t-DISTRIBUTION is similar to the standard normal distribution in
that it is symmetrical about a zero mean, but it is more spread out because of
the variation in s. Variance estimates based on small samples will fluctuate
more wildly than those from larger ones, so how much s varies from sample to
sample depends on the sample size n, or more appropriately on the number of
d.f. ν, where $\nu = n - 1$. There are thus different t-distributions for
different values of ν. The equation of their curves is complicated, the
probability density function being of the form

$$k(\nu)(1 + t^2/\nu)^{-\frac{1}{2}(\nu+1)}$$

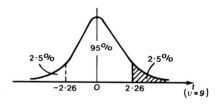

where $k(\nu)$ is a function of ν such as to make
the total area under the curve equal to 1. The
diagram shows the distribution curves for two
different values of ν and also the standard
normal curve, for comparison.

___

FRAME 38

In TABLE 3 at the end of the book you will find, for the distribution
corresponding to each given value of ν, the value of t for which the area
under <u>one</u> tail of the curve represents a probability of P%. If you look
along the row corresponding to $\nu = 9$ you will find, in the column headed $2 \cdot 5$,
the entry $2 \cdot 26$. Thus, for a t-distribution based on 9 d.f.:

There is a $2 \cdot 5$% chance of t being
greater than $2 \cdot 26$.
By symmetry, there is a $2 \cdot 5$% chance of t
being less than $-2 \cdot 26$.
Thus there is a 5% chance that $|t| > 2 \cdot 26$
and a 95% chance that $|t| < 2 \cdot 26$
i.e. a 95% chance that $-2 \cdot 26 < t < 2 \cdot 26$.

(For your convenience TABLE 3 shows values of

2P, below those of P, for use when the area under both tails is stipulated.)
Now complete the following:

For a t-distribution based on 5 d.f. there is

  (i)   a 2·5% chance that $t > \ldots$
  (ii) a 95% chance that $|t| < \ldots$ i.e. that $\ldots < t < \ldots$
  (iii) a 0·5% chance that $t > \ldots$
  (iv) a 99% chance that $|t| < \ldots$ i.e. that $\ldots < t < \ldots$

                    ****

38A

(i) 2·57   (ii) $|t| < 2·57$, $-2·57 < t < 2·57$ (iii) 4·03
(iv) $|t| < 4·03$, $-4·03 < t < 4·03$

FRAME 39

In the situation where σ was known and $\dfrac{\overline{x} - \mu}{\sigma/\sqrt{n}}$ was N(0, 1), the confidence

limits for μ were deduced to be $\overline{x} \pm u_c \sigma/\sqrt{n}$, where u_c was the value of u

appropriate to the stated % (1·96 for 95%, and so on). Now, with σ being

estimated from a sample and $\dfrac{\overline{x} - \mu}{s/\sqrt{n}}$ following a t-distribution with

(n − 1) d.f., the confidence limits for μ will be $\overline{x} \pm t_c s/\sqrt{n}$, where t_c is
the value of t appropriate to both the stated % and the number of d.f.   This
is best illustrated by an example.

Take the yields of successive runs of a chemical process, mentioned in FRAME 31,
for which n = 6, $\overline{x}$ = 41, s^2 = 6·4.   As ν = 5, the value of t_c for 95%
confidence limits is 2·57.

          $\therefore$ 95% confidence limits for population mean are $41 \pm 2·57 \times \dfrac{\sqrt{6·4}}{\sqrt{6}}$

                    i.e. 38·3 and 43·7

What would you substitute for 2·57 if (i) 99%, (ii) 90%, confidence limits
were required?

                    ****

39A

(i) 4·03   (ii) 2·02

FRAME 40

If 25 measurements (x) of the coefficient of thermal expansion of nickel give
$\Sigma x = 320·25 \times 10^{-6}$ and $\Sigma(x - \overline{x})^2 = 0·0384 \times 10^{-12}$, what is the 95%
confidence interval for the true coefficient of expansion?

                    ****

40A

$12·81 \times 10^{-6} \pm 2·06 \times 0·04 \times 10^{-6}/5$ i.e. $12·79 \times 10^{-6}$ to $12·83 \times 10^{-6}$

Relationship between t- and Normal Distributions

The use of t, when σ is estimated, is based on the underlying assumption of a normally distributed variate when σ is known. If a variate x is $N(\mu, \sigma^2)$ we know that $(x - \mu)/\sigma$ is $N(0, 1)$. It follows that, if s^2 is an unbiased estimate of σ^2, then $(x - \mu)/s$ is described by the t-distribution appropriate to ν, the number of degrees of freedom in s^2. Remembering that $\nu = n - 1$, what can you say about s as ν increases? Perhaps, from that, you can make a guess at what the distribution of $(x - \mu)/s$ becomes for ν infinite.

****

41A

As ν increases, s becomes a better estimate of σ. In the limit, for ν infinite, $(x - \mu)/s$ becomes $(x - \mu)/\sigma$, which is $N(0, 1)$.

The standard normal distribution is thus seen to be the limiting case of the t-distribution as $\nu \to \infty$. If you look at the values of t given at the end of TABLE 3 for ν infinite you will find that they are the values given for u in TABLE 2.

Note also that, just as the use of a t-distribution for $(x - \mu)/s$ is based on the assumption that $(x - \mu)/\sigma$ is $N(0, 1)$, so also does the use of a

t-distribution for $\dfrac{\overline{x} - \mu}{s/\sqrt{n}}$ depend on $\dfrac{\overline{x} - \mu}{\sigma/\sqrt{n}}$ being $N(0, 1)$. The confidence

limits obtained for the mean yield, as well as for the coefficient of expansion, therefore depend on $\overline{x}$ being normally distributed. You have seen that, as a consequence of the Central Limit Theorem, this is often a reasonable assumption.

Confidence Limits for a Count

When a count is made of radioactive disintegrations, or of red blood cells under a microscope, with the aim of estimating the population mean count μ, it will obviously be more informative to give confidence limits for μ rather than just the count obtained. You already know from Unit 1 that such counts are described by the Poisson distribution. You now need to recall two properties of this distribution. First see if you can do so for yourself.

For a Poisson distribution with mean μ, is the s.d. μ or $\sqrt{\mu}$? What distribution can be used as an approximation if μ is large enough?

****

43A

s.d. = $\sqrt{\mu}$ The normal distribution with the same mean and s.d.

If the count is not large enough for the normal distribution to be used, confidence limits must be based on the Poisson distribution itself and are available from special tables which can be found in Biometrika Tables for Statisticians Vol. 1 (Cambridge University Press). Here we shall deal only with the case where the count is large enough for the normal approximation to apply.

If x is a single observation from a population with known s.d. σ, what would
be the 95% confidence interval for the population mean μ?

****

44A

$x \pm 1 \cdot 96\sigma$

FRAME 45

In the present problem, $\sigma = \sqrt{\mu}$ but μ is the very thing that we don't know
and are trying to estimate.   The usual practice is to use $\sqrt{x}$ as an estimate of
$\sqrt{\mu}$, and hence of σ.   (The error in this estimate will be small compared with
the error in x as an estimate of μ.   Suppose, for instance, that μ = 100
and x = 110,   then   σ = 10   and $\sqrt{x}$ = 10·49,   showing a difference between $\sqrt{x}$
and σ which is small compared with the difference between x and μ.)   The 95%
confidence limits thus obtained from a single count x will be $x \pm 1 \cdot 96\sqrt{x}$.
What will the 90% confidence limits be?

****

45A

$x \pm 1 \cdot 64\sqrt{x}$

FRAME 46

A volume of $10^{-4} \, mm^3$ of blood taken from a hospital patient was placed in a
counting chamber and 484 red blood cells were counted under the microscope.
The doctor wants to know about the patient's blood as a whole, not just about
the minute amount examined under the microscope.   One way of expressing this
information would be to give 95% confidence limits for the patient's true mean
red blood cell count per mm^3.

Putting x = 484,   the 95% confidence limits for the mean number of red blood
cells in $10^{-4} \, mm^3$ of blood are $484 \pm 1 \cdot 96\sqrt{484}$ i.e. 441 and 527.   These
correspond to limits of 4·41 and 5·27 million cells per mm^3.

Now try to solve the following problem:

A single count of a radioactive source made during an interval of 5 minutes
gave the result 400.   Find 95% confidence limits for the population mean
count in a 5-minute interval and hence for the count rate per minute.

****

46A

$400 \pm 1 \cdot 96\sqrt{400}$ i.e.   361 and 439
72·2 and 87·8

FRAME 47

Suppose the problem you have just solved had been approached in a different way.
Converting the observed count of 400 in 5 minutes to a count rate of 80 per
minute, the 95% confidence limits for the count rate are then
$80 \pm 1 \cdot 96\sqrt{80} = 80 \pm 17 \cdot 5$ i.e. 62·5 and 97·5.   Or are they?   This is not the
same answer as that in 46A.   What is wrong in the argument leading up to it?

****

The confidence limits would have been correct if a count of 80 had been obtained in an interval of 1 minute. You will notice that they are further apart than the correct limits – this is because counting for only 1 minute produces less information, and hence greater uncertainty in conclusions, than counting for 5 minutes. The count rate of 80 should have been treated as a mean of 5 values.

FRAME 48

Treating 80 as a sample mean $\bar{x}$, with sample size 5, the estimate of the standard error should have been $\sqrt{80}/\sqrt{5}$ i.e. 4. The 95% confidence limits for the count rate are then $80 \pm 1\cdot96 \times 4$ and there is now agreement with the answer in 46A.

FRAME 49

Quiz

To prepare you for the Miscellaneous Examples which follow it, here is a quick quiz on what has been presented in this programme.

1. Complete the statements below by choosing which of the two alternatives offered in each pair of brackets is correct.

    Consider the distribution of the means of all possible samples of size n which can be selected from a population with mean μ and variance σ^2.

    The mean of this distribution (depends, does not depend) on the value of n. The standard error of the mean is the (mean, standard deviation) of this distribution. The larger the value of n, the (larger, smaller) the standard error of the mean.
    The distribution has mean (μ, zero) and variance (σ^2, σ^2/n) and is (normal, uniform) if the population from which the samples are taken is normal. If the population is not normal, the (larger, smaller) the value of n, the nearer is the distribution of sample means to being normal.

In Questions 2-4, only one of the alternatives offered correctly completes the statement. Which is it?

2. The weights in milligrammes of the precipitate in each of 5 analyses were: 20, 19, 25, 23, 18. Regarding these values as a random sample, the unbiased estimate of the variance of the population of all such precipitate weights is

    (i) $\dfrac{(-1 - 2 + 4 + 2 - 3)^2}{4}$ (ii) 21   (iii) $\sqrt{34/5}$

    (iv) $\dfrac{1 + 4 + 16 + 4 + 9}{5}$ (v) $\dfrac{(-1)^2 + (-2)^2 + 4^2 + 2^2 + (-3)^2}{4}$

3. Nine determinations of the specific gravity of a coal tar are made, using a method which is known from past experience to give values which are normally distributed, about the true specific gravity, with s.d. $0\cdot012$. The 9 values so obtained have a mean value of $1\cdot185$, so the 95% confidence limits for the specific gravity of this coal tar are:

    (i) $1\cdot185 \pm 1\cdot96 \times 0\cdot012$ (ii) $1\cdot185 \pm 1\cdot64 \times 0\cdot012$

    (iii) $1\cdot185 \pm 1\cdot96 \times 0\cdot012/3$ (iv) $1\cdot185 \pm 1\cdot64 \times 0\cdot012/9$

    (v) $1\cdot185 \pm 1\cdot28 \times 0\cdot012/3$

4. Sixteen determinations of the nicotine content (in milligrammes) in a certain quantity of a processed tobacco were made. The method used is known from past experience to give values which are normally distributed about the true content with s.d. 2·7.   The 16 values so obtained had a mean of 24·8 so the 99% confidence limits for the nicotine content are:

    (i)   24·8 ± 2·58 × 2·7   (ii)   24·8 ± 2·95 × 2·7

    (iii) 24·8 ± 2·33 × 2·7/4   (iv)   24·8 ± 2·58 × 2·7/4

    (v)   24·8 ± 2·95 × 2·7/4

5. If a variate x is $N(\mu, \sigma^2)$, which of (i), (ii) and (iii) apply to the distribution of $\frac{x - \mu}{\sigma}$?

    (i) zero mean   (ii) N(0, 1)   (iii) Student's t-distribution with
                                                    (n − 1) d.f.
            Note: More than one may apply.

    If s^2 is an unbiased estimate of σ^2, obtained from a random sample of size n using the formula $\frac{1}{n-1} \Sigma(x - \bar{x})^2$, which of (i), (ii) and (iii) apply to the distribution of $\frac{x - \mu}{s}$?

    Turning now to $\bar{x}$, the mean of a random sample of n values of x, we know that, if all possible samples are considered, the distribution of $\bar{x}$ is $N(\mu, \sigma^2/n)$.   Which of (i), (ii) and (iii) apply to the distribution of $\frac{\bar{x} - \mu}{\sigma/\sqrt{n}}$?   Each of these samples will give a value of s and therefore of $\frac{\bar{x} - \mu}{s/\sqrt{n}}$.   When all possible samples are considered, which of (i), (ii) and

    (iii) apply to the distribution of $\frac{\bar{x} - \mu}{s/\sqrt{n}}$?

    In Questions 6 and 7, only one of the alternatives offered correctly completes the statement.   Which is it?

6. An estimate of the mean μ of a population is to be made from a random sample of 16 observations.   If the mean of this sample is $\bar{x}$ and if $s^2 = \frac{1}{15} \Sigma(x - \bar{x})^2$, the 99% confidence limits for μ are

    (i) $\bar{x}$ ± 2·95s/4   (ii) $\bar{x}$ ± 2·92s/4
    (iii) $\bar{x}$ ± 2·95s   (iv) $\bar{x}$ ± 2·58s/4

7. The 95% confidence interval for the mean of the population of precipitate weights described in Qu. 2 is given by
    (i)   21 ± 1·96 × $\sqrt{1·7}$ (ii)   21 ± 2·78 × $\sqrt{1·7}$
    (iii) 21 ± 2·13 × $\sqrt{1·7}$ (iv)   21 ± 2·78 × $\sqrt{34}/2$

    ****

1. does not depend, standard deviation, smaller, μ, σ²/n, normal, larger.

2. (v)   3. (iii)   4. (iv)

5. (i) and (ii),   (i) and (iii),   (i) and (ii),   (i) and (iii).

6. (i)   7. (ii)

FRAME 50

Miscellaneous Examples

In this frame a collection of miscellaneous examples is given for you to try. Answers are supplied in FRAME 51, together with such working as is considered helpful.

1. A metallurgist carried out 4 determinations of the melting point of manganese obtaining, in $^{\circ}$C: 1261, 1268, 1264, 1267. Calculate an unbiased estimate of the variance of this metallurgist's determinations of the melting point of manganese.

2. A chemical is regularly tested for sulphur content by its manufacturer and over a period it has been found that the mean sulphur content is 0·35% with s.d. 0·05%. Batches of the chemical are delivered to a customer for whom the sulphur content is important and who therefore makes a check on the quality by carrying out determinations on 4 spot samples from each batch. If the mean sulphur content of the four exceeds 0·5% the manufacturer is under a heavy penalty clause. Can he be reasonably confident that this will not happen, if the manufacturing procedure remains under control?

3. If measurements of the specific gravity of a metal can be looked upon as a sample from a normal population having s.d. 0·05, what is the probability that the mean of a random sample of size 16 will be in error by at most 0·02?

4. A chart for use in controlling the quality of concrete is to be based on strength results of test cubes (of specified size and age) being normally distributed with mean 28 N mm^{-2} and s.d. 6 N mm^{-2}. (i) On this basis, what would be the probability of the mean strength of 4 test cubes being less than 25 N mm^{-2}? (ii) Limits, symmetrical about the design mean strength of 28 N mm^{-2}, are to be set such that the chance of the mean strength of 4 test cubes lying outside them is only 1 in 5, if the concrete meets the design requirement. Calculate these limits, and also what they would be if the chance were reduced to 1 in 20.

5. A British Standard specification for 240 V tungsten filament general service electric lamps aims at ensuring that they should have a minimum average life of 1000 hours. The procedure laid down involves a sample of lamps (the life test quantity or LTQ) being selected from the batch seeking approval. The number of lamps in this sample depends on the size of the batch, with an upper limit of 25, and their selection must take place in the way that is specified. The life of each lamp of the LTQ is determined by operating it on a 240 V electricity supply until failure occurs. During every 24 hours of operation the lamp must be switched off twice, each time for a period of at least 15 minutes; these periods are excluded from the life of the lamp.

The batch is approved if (a) no lamp in the LTQ has a life less than 700 hours and (b) the mean life of the LTQ is not below a specified minimum, which is 920 hours for an LTQ of 25 lamps.

Suppose that a manufacturer wants the quality of lamps coming off the production line to be such that the chance of an LTQ of 25 meeting requirement (b) is at least 99·9%.

  (i)   If the lives of lamps being manufactured have a mean of 1000 hours, what is their maximum permissible s.d.?

 (ii)   If the s.d. of lives of lamps being manufactured is 100 h, what is the minimum permissible value for their mean? If their mean has this value, give an expression for the probability of requirement (a) being met.

6. Find the chance of an LTQ of 25 lamps meeting requirement (b) of the specification described in the previous question, when the mean and s.d. of the population from which it is taken are respectively

    (i)   1400 h and 300 h,   (ii)   900 h and 100 h.

    As was stated in the previous question, the size of LTQ required is related to the size of batch seeking approval, the larger batches calling, on the whole, for larger samples to be tested. For LTQ's of 13 through 19, the minimum mean life specified in (b) is 890 h. If the lamps described in (i) and (ii) are submitted in smaller batches, for which the LTQ is 16, what are the respective probabilities of requirement (b) being met?

7. For a type of varnish the drying time (in hours) was recorded when it was tried out on 9 test specimens.   The results were:

    6·0   5·7   5·8   6·5   7·0   6·3   5·6   6·1   5·0

    (i)   Calculate the mean drying time for the 9 specimens.

   (ii)   Obtain an unbiased estimate of the variance of the population of all drying times when this type of varnish is used.

  (iii)   Find the 95% confidence limits for the mean of this population
          (a) if it is known from past experience that drying times of any type of varnish have a s.d. of 0·6 hour,
          (b) if no previous information about drying times is available.

    State whether any of your answers are dependent on drying times being normally distributed.

8. The mean weight of suitcase carried by passengers on non-stop jets between Phoenix and Chicago is to be estimated from the weights of 25 such suitcases selected at random.   What will be the 95% confidence limits for this mean weight if the 25 values of suitcase weight x (in kg) give $\Sigma x = 335$ and $\Sigma x^2 = 4705$?

9. When a radioactive source was observed for 25 minutes, a total count of 1225 was recorded.   Using a suitable approximation, obtain 90% confidence limits for the population mean count rate per minute.

10. Two grades of light bulbs - "standard" and "longer-life" - made in a factory have lives (in hours) which are $N(1400, 200^2)$ and $N(2000, 250^2)$ respectively.   If 1 bulb of each grade is life-tested, what is the probability of the "standard" one being the longer lasting?

If 4 bulbs of each grade are life-tested, what is the probability of the mean life of the "standard" ones being greater than the mean life of the "longer-life" ones?

11. Suppose that a method of measuring the hardness of metals is known to give results which are normally distributed about the true value (i.e. there is no systematic error) with s.d. σ.   The method is to be used in estimating the difference in hardness between two alloys A and B, i.e. in estimating $\mu_A - \mu_B$, where μ_A, μ_B are the hardness values (unknown) of the two alloys.   Thus tests on alloys A and B will give results which are $N(\mu_A, \sigma^2)$ and $N(\mu_B, \sigma^2)$ respectively.   Write down what the distributions of each of the following would be:

   (i)   mean $\bar{x}_A$ of n_A tests made on alloy A,

   (ii) mean $\bar{x}_B$ of n_B tests made on alloy B,

   (iii) $\bar{x}_A - \bar{x}_B$.

   Having satisfied yourself, from your answer to (iii), that $\bar{x}_A - \bar{x}_B$ will give an unbiased estimate of $\mu_A - \mu_B$, complete the following statements:

   There is a 95% chance that $\bar{x}_A - \bar{x}_B$ will not differ from $\mu_A - \mu_B$ by more than ....

   The 95% confidence limits for $\mu_A - \mu_B$ are therefore ....

12. To estimate the percentage chlorine content in each of two batches of polymer, 9 determinations were made on the first batch and 16 on the second, giving mean values of 58·18 and 56·97 respectively.   The analytical method used is known from past experience with similar batches using the same sampling procedure to give results which have a s.d. of 0·80.   Find the 99% confidence interval for the amount by which the true percentage of chlorine in the first batch exceeds that in the second.

13. A problem sometimes met by the analytical chemist is that of determining the average amount of a particular ingredient in supposedly uniform "units" of material.   One example of this would be the determination of the amount of active ingredient in a type of medicinal tablet, another would be the analysis of bottles of hydrogen peroxide solution for the quantity of hydrogen peroxide present in the solution.   Two sources of variation in the results must be taken into consideration - the variation of the actual amount of ingredient from one unit to another and the error due to the analytical method employed (we shall assume that there is no systematic error).   Two possible procedures for obtaining an estimate from n units are:

   (i)   Analyse each unit separately and average the results.   Each observation (x') would be related to the actual amount (x) of the ingredient and the error (e) in the analysis by $x' = x + e$. Thus the n determinations could be represented by: $x_1' = x_1 + e_1$, $x_2' = x_2 + e_2$, ... $x_n' = x_n + e_n$ and $\bar{x}'$ would give the required estimate.

(ii)   Thoroughly mix the units together, carry out one determination on the
       pooled mixture and divide the result by n.   Here the
       observation (X') could be represented by $X' = X + E$, where
       $X = x_1 + x_2 + \ldots + x_n$ and E is the error in the analysis, and
       X'/n would be used as the estimate.

       If the s.d. of the amount of ingredient present in a unit is denoted
       by σ_1 and the error in determining this amount has a s.d. of σ_2,
       find the variance of the final estimate obtained by each of the above
       procedures
       (a)   when, as might occur, for example, in a trace analysis, the error
             of determination is the same whatever amount of ingredient is
             being determined, and thus   s.d.(E) = s.d.(e) = σ_2
       (b)   when, as frequently happens in chemical analysis, the s.d. of the
             error of determination is proportional to the magnitude of the
             amount being determined.   This corresponds to a constant
             relative precision and   s.d.(E) = n × s.d.(e) = $n\sigma_2$.

Answers to Miscellaneous Examples

1.   10.   Perhaps you made use of what you learned about coding in Unit 1, and
     first subtracted 1260 from the data.   This leaves 1, 8, 4, 7, which
     give the same variance estimate as the original data because, if
     $x' = x - 1260$, $\text{var}(x') = \text{var}(x)$.

2.   Yes.   When $\bar{x} = 0 \cdot 5$, $u = 6$ and the chance of this being exceeded is so
     small as to be negligible by any standards.   Had the result not been so
     decisive, it would have been necessary to ask for 'reasonably confident' to
     be defined more exactly.

3. $0 \cdot 8904$

4.   (i) $P(\bar{x} < 25) = P(u < -1) = 0 \cdot 1587$
     (ii) $28 \pm 1 \cdot 28 \times 3$ i.e. $24 \cdot 2$ and $31 \cdot 8 \, \text{N mm}^{-2}$
           $28 \pm 1 \cdot 96 \times 3$ i.e. $22 \cdot 1$ and $33 \cdot 9 \, \text{N mm}^{-2}$

5.   (i)   129 h   (ii)   982 h $(0 \cdot 9976)^{25}$

6.   (i) $P(u > -8)$, which can be regarded as certainty.
     (ii) $P(u > 1) = 0 \cdot 1587$

     For an LTQ of 16:   (i) $P(u > -6 \cdot 8)$, which would also be regarded as
                                certainty.
                          (ii) $P(u > -0 \cdot 4) = 0 \cdot 6555$

7.   (i) $6 \cdot 0$ hours   (ii) $0 \cdot 33 \, \text{h}^2$
     (iii) (a) σ is known to be $0 \cdot 6$.   .˙.   95% confidence limits are
                $\bar{x} \pm 1 \cdot 96\sigma/\sqrt{n}$, with $\bar{x} = 6 \cdot 0$, $n = 9$, giving $5 \cdot 61$ and $6 \cdot 39$ h.
           (b) σ must be estimated from the sample.   For $\nu = 8$,
                $P\{|t| < 2 \cdot 31\} = 0 \cdot 95$.   .˙.   95% confidence limits are
                $\bar{x} \pm 2 \cdot 31s/\sqrt{n}$, where $s = \sqrt{0 \cdot 33}$, giving $5 \cdot 56$ and $6 \cdot 44$ h.

     In (iii) (a) and (b) the answers are based on the assumption that sample
     means are normally distributed.   This would be exact if the distribution
     of individual drying times is normal, but an approximation (usually quite
     satisfactory) otherwise.

FRAME 51   (continued)

8. Obtain variance estimate by using the formula $\Sigma(x - \bar{x})^2 = \Sigma x^2 - \bar{x}\Sigma x$
    95% confidence limits are $13 \cdot 4 \pm 2 \cdot 06 \times 3/5$ i.e. $12 \cdot 2$ and $14 \cdot 6$ kg.

9. $46 \cdot 7$ and $51 \cdot 3$

10. Denoting lives of "standard" and "longer-life" bulbs by x_S, x_L respectively
    $x_L - x_S$ is $N(600, 250^2 + 200^2)$

    $P(x_S > x_L) = P\{(x_L - x_S) < 0\} = P(u < -1 \cdot 874) = 0 \cdot 030$

    $\bar{x}_L$ is $N(2000, 125^2)$ and $\bar{x}_S$ is $N(1400, 100^2)$

    $\therefore \ \bar{x}_L - \bar{x}_S$ is $N(600, 125^2 + 100^2)$

    $P\{(\bar{x}_L - \bar{x}_S) < 0\} = P(u < -3 \cdot 748) = 0 \cdot 0001$

11.   (i) $N(\mu_A, \sigma^2/n_A)$ (ii) $N(\mu_B, \sigma^2/n_B)$

    (iii) $N\left(\mu_A - \mu_B, \ \dfrac{\sigma^2}{n_A} + \dfrac{\sigma^2}{n_B}\right)$ As the mean of this distribution is $\mu_A - \mu_B$,

        $\bar{x}_A - \bar{x}_B$ will give an unbiased estimate of $\mu_A - \mu_B$.

        There is a 95% chance that $\bar{x}_A - \bar{x}_B$ will not differ from $\mu_A - \mu_B$

        by more than $1 \cdot 96\sigma\sqrt{\dfrac{1}{n_A} + \dfrac{1}{n_B}}$.

        The 95% confidence limits for $\mu_A - \mu_B$ are therefore

        $$\bar{x}_A - \bar{x}_B \pm 1 \cdot 96\sigma\sqrt{\dfrac{1}{n_A} + \dfrac{1}{n_B}}$$

12. $1 \cdot 21 \pm 0 \cdot 86$ i.e. $0 \cdot 35$ and $2 \cdot 07$

13. For both (a) and (b),   (i) gives $\text{var}(\bar{x}') = (\sigma_1^2 + \sigma_2^2)/n$

    For (a),   (ii) gives $\text{var}(X') = n\sigma_1^2 + \sigma_2^2$,   whence
                   $\text{var}(X'/n) = \sigma_1^2/n + \sigma_2^2/n^2$

    For (b),   (ii) gives $\text{var}(X') = n\sigma_1^2 + n^2\sigma_2^2$,   whence
                   $\text{var}(X'/n) = \sigma_1^2/n + \sigma_2^2$

    Note: This shows that (ii) gives better precision for (a), and (i) for (b).
    You may say that this is obvious anyway.   However, with the statistical
    analysis before you, and estimates of σ_1 and σ_2, you could see how just
    much better one procedure would be overall than the other.   You could also
    go further and compare the precision of these procedures with that of
    other possible ones such as, for instance, making more than one
    determination on the pooled mixture.

Tests of Significance (1)

Introduction

There are many situations where a statistical test is called for, although this
may not be appreciated by someone unfamiliar with the basis of statistical
methods.   Typical of such situations are the two examples which will now be
described.

(1)   Daily determinations of the octane number of a petroleum product from a
pilot-plant, during the first 11 days of its operation, gave the following
results:

88·2,   86·7,   87·2,   88·4,   87·2,   86·8,   86·1,   87·3,   86·5,   86·6,   87·1

How should one view the designers' claim that the product would have an
octane number of 87·5, now that these results have been obtained?

Of course, if octane number determinations were not affected by random
variation a decision would be clear-cut.   Only one analysis would be
necessary in the first place: if it gave 87·5 the claim would be accepted,
if it did not the claim would be rejected.   As it is, there clearly is
variation and while some values are greater than 87·5, others are less.
To attempt to resolve the problem, one might calculate the mean of the 11
values, which is 87·1.   However, even the fact that this is not 87·5 is
not in itself grounds for rejecting the claim, because, as you know, if
there is variation in individual observations there is also variation in
sample means.   The question is: "Does the difference between 87·1 and
87·5 really suggest that the product is not what it is claimed to be, or
can it be satisfactorily explained by the random variation of the results?"

(2)   In an experiment seeking to discover whether a particular drug affects the
blood glucose of diabetic rats, 6 such rats were treated with the drug
and their blood glucose levels (in mg/ml) were then found to be:

2·01   1·73   2·05   1·49   1·84   1·68

In 6 control rats, which had not been treated with the drug, the levels
were

2·23   2·04   1·77   1·91   2·15   1·78

The means of the two samples are 1·80 and 1·98 respectively, but is this
difference large enough to be treated as evidence that the drug affects the
blood glucose, considering the variation that exists from one rat to
another?

In both these cases the problem is to decide whether an observed difference
is "significant".   In (1) the difference is between the sample mean 87·1
and the quoted value of 87·5, and the question is whether this difference
signifies a difference between the actual octane number of the product and
that claimed for it.   In (2) the difference is between the mean blood
glucose levels of the two groups of rats and the question is whether this
signifies a difference between the levels of glucose in the blood of
treated and untreated rats in general.

To point the way to a general procedure for answering such questions, let us look at a similar situation that might arise from tossing a coin.   When you agree to settle an issue by the toss of a coin, you do so in the belief that heads and tails are equally likely outcomes.   Would your belief be shaken by any of the following results happening when a coin was repeatedly tossed?   Just give your immediate reaction without recourse to exact calculations and then compare with the remarks in the answer frame.

(i)	no heads in	2	tosses	(ii)	no heads in 10	tosses
(iii)	no heads in	20	tosses	(iv)	20 heads in 20	tosses
(v)	12 heads in	20	tosses	(vi)	15 heads in 20	tosses

****

2A

We think that your belief would have been affected thus:

(i) and (v) unshaken,   (ii) shaken,   (iii) and (iv) shattered.

Your reaction to (vi) is less predictable.

FRAME 3

Starting off with the assumption that the coin is an honest one, you would become suspicious if repeated tossing gave results which would be very unusual for an honest coin.   The more unusual the results, the greater your suspicions would be.   Even without having studied probability theory, an intelligent person would sense that no heads in 10 tosses would be an extraordinary result if heads and tails were equally likely and that the coin's fairness is therefore in doubt.   But what about no heads in 6 tosses or 2 heads in 10 tosses or 15 heads in 20 tosses?   Using your "judgment" or "common sense" now begins to fail you and a statistical approach is called for.

Suppose, for the sake of argument, that a coin is to be tested for being fair by tossing it 8 times.   What number of heads should lead to its rejection? Starting from the hypothesis that the coin is fair, we can deduce the probability distribution of the number of heads occurring in 8 tosses.   Describe this distribution.

****

3A

Binomial, with $p = 0 \cdot 5$, $q = 0 \cdot 5$, $n = 8$.

FRAME 4

The terms in the expansion of $(0 \cdot 5 + 0 \cdot 5)^8$ give the respective probabilities of 0, 1, 2, ... 8 heads occurring.   They are shown to 3 d.p. in the table below.

x	0	1	2	3	4	5	6	7	8
P(x)	0·004	0·031	0·109	0·219	0·273	0·219	0·109	0·031	0·004

We might decide to reject the coin if either 0 or 8 heads occur, as each would be so unlikely in the event of the coin being a fair one.   This decision rule can be portrayed thus:

Number of heads	0	1	2	3	4	5	6	7	8
Decision	REJECT	←			ACCEPT			→	REJECT

This would mean taking a small chance of rejecting a fair coin.   What would
that chance be?

                 ****

                                                                              4A

0·008

                                                                        FRAME 5

If, on the other hand, the number of heads is within the acceptance region, can
you be sure that the coin is a fair one?

                 ****

                                                                              5A

*No.   Just as it is possible to get, say, 0 heads with a fair coin so it would
also be possible to get, say, 1 head with a biased coin.*

                                                                        FRAME 6

The probability of accepting a coin which is biased could be reduced by
narrowing the acceptance region thus:

    Number
    of heads   0   1 | 2   3   4   5   6 | 7   8
    Decision   ←REJECT →| ←——————   ACCEPT   ——————→ |← REJECT→

But what is now the chance of rejecting a fair coin?

                 ****

                                                                              6A

0·070

                                                                        FRAME 7

Notice that wherever the line is drawn between acceptance and rejection, there
is always the risk of

 (i)   rejecting a coin that is fair,
(ii)   accepting a coin that is biased.

Moreover, if one risk is decreased the other is automatically increased.   Only
by increasing the number of tosses could you be more certain about the nature of
the coin, and reduce both risks.   Outside the realms of coin tossing, however,
the number of repeated trials would usually be restricted by time and resources.

                                                                        FRAME 8

A parallel can now be drawn between testing the hypothesis of the fairness of
a coin and the problem about the octane number described in the first frame.
In the case of a coin, the usual belief is that p, the probability of a head,
is $0·5$.   That belief is adhered to unless experimental results are obtained
which would be unlikely if, indeed, $p = 0·5$.   The appropriate probability model,
the binomial, can be used to find just how unlikely particular results are.

In the case of the petroleum product, design calculations have credited it with
an octane number of $87·5$ and it is now a matter of deciding whether to accept
that value in view of the values which have been obtained.   With the coin we

FRAME 8   (continued)

were looking at an observed proportion of heads (e.g. 0/8 or 1/8) in relation
to a theoretical proportion 1/2, and the binomial distribution was appropriate.
With the octane number determinations we shall have to look at an observed
mean $\bar{x}$ (= 87·1) in relation to a theoretical mean μ (= 87·5) and the first
task will be to decide on an appropriate probability model.

FRAME 9

Test of a stated value for a population mean - σ known

Testing the claim about the octane number of the petroleum product could be
interpreted as asking the question "If the octane number were 87·5, is it
likely that the mean of 11 determinations would be as far away from 87·5 as
87·1?" To answer this, it is necessary to consider the distribution of means
of samples of size 11 taken from a population with mean 87·5.   This
distribution of sample means will be assumed to be normal, but to be able to
describe it completely we require to know something further about the population
from which the samples are taken.   What is it?

         ****

9A

Its standard deviation.

FRAME 10

The solution is simplest when past history tells us what the s.d. σ of the
population is.   Suppose that many determinations of the octane number of
similar petroleum products have been made before and a value of 0·6 has been
established for σ.

Now, what were found in the previous programme to be the mean and s.d. of the
distribution of means of samples of size n taken from a population with mean μ
and s.d. σ?
         ****

10A

Mean = μ s.d. = $\sigma/\sqrt{n}$

FRAME 11

If the sample means are normally distributed, as is being assumed here, then $\bar{x}$
is $N(\mu, \sigma^2/n)$.   What, therefore, can you say about the distribution of
$\dfrac{\bar{x} - \mu}{\sigma/\sqrt{n}}$?

         ****

11A

It is $N(0, 1)$

FRAME 12

Deciding whether a value of $\bar{x}$ is unusually far away from μ is thus a matter of
deciding whether the corresponding value of u, where $u = \dfrac{\bar{x} - \mu}{\sigma/\sqrt{n}}$, is unusually
far away from zero.   That raises the question of what is "unusual".   If it

were defined as "occurring on less than 5% of occasions", what range of values of u (in either the positive or negative direction) would be regarded as unusually far away from 0?   What would this range of values become if 1% were substituted for 5%?

****

12A

$u < -1.96$ and > 1.96,   i.e. $|u| > 1.96$
$|u| > 2.58$

FRAME 13

In the present example, $\bar{x} = 87.1$, $\mu = 87.5$, $\sigma = 0.6$, $n = 11$,   giving

$u = \dfrac{87.1 - 87.5}{0.6/\sqrt{11}} = -2.21$.   Being less than -1.96 this comes within the range of

values of u which would occur on less than 5% of occasions if the hypothesis that $\mu = 87.5$ is correct.   It might be concluded, therefore, that it is not the unusual event that has occurred but that the original hypothesis was wrong. If we decide to do that, in a test of this kind, whenever $|u| > 1.96$ we have to face a 5% risk of rejecting a correct hypothesis.   If this risk is acceptable, the claim that the octane number is 87.5 would be rejected.   If, however, such a risk is too high, it might be reduced to, say, 1% and then the original hypothesis would only be rejected if $|u| > 2.58$.   That is not the case with the octane number data, so at this level of risk the figure of 87.5 would not be disputed.

FRAME 14

You have just been introduced to a TEST OF SIGNIFICANCE.   In this particular example the test was being applied to the difference between a sample mean and a value claimed to be the mean of the population from which it was taken.   The starting point was to put forward a hypothesis (called the NULL HYPOTHESIS) which was that the claim about the octane number was valid i.e. $\mu = 87.5$.

The value of $\dfrac{\bar{x} - \mu}{\sigma/\sqrt{n}}$ was then calculated.   If this showed a difference between

$\bar{x}$ and μ which would, on the basis of the hypothesis, be unusually large, then the null hypothesis was rejected in favour of the ALTERNATIVE HYPOTHESIS (in this case $\mu \neq 87.5$).   A probability, the LEVEL OF SIGNIFICANCE, was needed to define what was to be regarded as unusual.   In practice, a choice of either 5% or 1% has been found to meet most requirements.

In the octane number example, the difference between $\bar{x}$ and 87.5 was shown to be unusually large if "unusual" was defined as "having a probability of 5% or less of occurring by chance".   The difference is therefore said to be SIGNIFICANT AT THE 5% LEVEL.   Note that this is saying that the difference is statistically significant.   Whether there is a difference of practical importance is another matter.

The difference between $\bar{x}$ and 87.5 was, however, shown to be not significant at the 1% level.   Would it be possible for a difference to be significant at the 1% level but not at the 5% level?

****

No.   The diagram explains why.

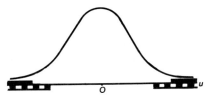

━ ▪▪▪ ━   *Range of values of u for significance*
          at the 5% level

━━━━━   *Range of values of u for significance*
          at the 1% level

<u>FRAME 15</u>

For your convenience, here is a summary, in general terms, of the test
procedure which was adopted in the octane number problem.

PROBLEM: A random sample of n items, taken from a population whose s.d. is
           known to be σ, has mean $\bar{x}$.   Test the claim that the population mean
           is some specified value μ_0.

PROCEDURE:

1.   Formulate null hypothesis and alternative hypothesis.
     NULL HYPOTHESIS: The population mean is μ_0 i.e. $\mu = \mu_0$.
     ALTERNATIVE HYPOTHESIS: The population mean is not μ_0 i.e. $\mu \neq \mu_0$.

2.   Decide on the LEVEL OF SIGNIFICANCE α.
     α (usually either 0·05 or 0·01) is the risk of rejecting the N.H. when in
     fact it is true, i.e., in this case, concluding that $\mu \neq \mu_0$ when, in fact,
     $\mu = \mu_0$.

3.   Calculate $u = \dfrac{\bar{x} - \mu_0}{\sigma/\sqrt{n}}$ (assuming sample means to be normally distributed).

4.   If you chose α = 0·05   and if $|u| > 1·96$ ⎫   reject the N.H. and adopt
                                                            ⎬   the A.H., i.e. decide $\mu \neq \mu_0$.
     If you chose α = 0·01   and if $|u| > 2·58$ ⎭   Otherwise accept the N.H.

Note: Some texts use the notation H_0 for the null hypothesis and H_1 for the
alternative hypothesis.   In this text the abbreviations N.H. and A.H. will be
used.

<u>FRAME 16</u>

Now a question for you to answer.

The purity of a product was regularly checked by the chemical analysis of a
sample from each batch.   Analyses for nitrogen content, averaged over a long
period, had given a figure of 4·02% with a s.d. of 0·06%.   Then samples taken
from 4 successive batches were found to have a mean nitrogen content of 4·14%.
Does this indicate a significant change in the composition of the product
(i) at the 5% level, (ii) at the 1% level?   In your answer state both the
hypothesis that you are testing and the one that you will substitute for it if
you reject it.   Is choosing a level of significance (e.g. 5% or 1%) at the
outset a matter of deciding the risk one is prepared to take of concluding that
the composition of the product has changed when in reality it hasn't?

****

N.H.:   *The composition of the product is unchanged, i.e. the nitrogen content is 4·02%.*

A.H.:   *The composition of the product has changed, i.e. the nitrogen content is no longer 4·02%.*

$$u = \frac{4 \cdot 14 - 4 \cdot 02}{0 \cdot 06/\sqrt{4}} = 4$$

(i) $|u| > 1 \cdot 96$ *so the change is significant at the 5% level.*
(ii) $|u| > 2 \cdot 58$ *so the change is significant at the 1% level.*
Yes.

To be even surer about a decision that a change in the nitrogen content had taken place, a 0·1% level of significance could have been used.   Find from TABLE 2 the appropriate critical value of $|u|$ and decide whether the difference is significant at this level.

****

3·29

As the data gives a value of $|u|$ which exceeds this, the difference is significant at the 0·1% level.

Clearly the risk of being wrong in concluding that the nitrogen content has changed is so small as to be almost negligible and the result would be described as being very highly significant.   When a difference is as marked as this, the conclusion may seem obvious to the observer who may therefore question whether the procedure of the significance test achieves anything.   Well, just as there are optical illusions which deceive the eye, so also can data be deceptive and it is therefore better not to rely on a subjective judgment.   Moreover, it is not usual for such a marked difference to be revealed and in less well defined situations it is even more advisable to reach a conclusion by the reasoning of the significance test, with its controlled risk of deciding that a real difference exists when in fact it doesn't.

Suppose that instead of the sample mean being 4·14% it had been 4·09%.   Would you then have said that the nitrogen content had changed, if in so doing you were prepared to take a 5% risk of being wrong?   Would your answer be the same if this risk had not to be more than 1%?   What would your answer to both these questions be if the sample mean were 4·06%?

****

$\bar{x} = 4 \cdot 09$, $u = 2 \cdot \dot{3}$.   *With the 5% level of risk, this indicates a change of nitrogen content, but not for the 1% level.*

$\bar{x} = 4 \cdot 06$, $u = 1 \cdot \dot{3}$.   *This is not significant at either the 5% or 1% levels and the null hypothesis of no change would be retained.*

Test of a stated value for a population mean - σ estimated

So far, in this programme, the hypothesis tested has been concerned with the
mean of a population with known s.d.   We shall now turn to the case where a
value for σ is not available.   As you know from the previous programme, an
unbiased estimate of the population variance can be obtained from the sample,
using the formula $s^2 = \dfrac{1}{n-1} \Sigma(x - \overline{x})^2$.   Now, if $\dfrac{\overline{x} - \mu}{\sigma/\sqrt{n}}$ is $N(0, 1)$,   as was
assumed in the preceding tests, what can you say about the probability
distribution of $\dfrac{\overline{x} - \mu}{s/\sqrt{n}}$?

****

It is a t-distribution, with $(n - 1)$ d.f.

The question about the octane number of the petroleum product, in a situation
where previous data had not established a value for σ, will now be used as an
illustration.   From the 11 readings, $\Sigma(x - \overline{x})^2 = 4 \cdot 82$ and hence $s^2 = 0 \cdot 482$.
As before,

$$\text{N.H.:} \quad \mu = 87 \cdot 5, \qquad \text{A.H.:} \quad \mu \neq 87 \cdot 5$$

This time the statistic that is calculated is

$$t = \frac{87 \cdot 1 - 87 \cdot 5}{\sqrt{0 \cdot 482}/\sqrt{11}} \approx -1 \cdot 91$$

Reference to TABLE 3 shows that, for $\nu = 10$, the critical value of $|t|$ at the
5% level is $2 \cdot 23$.   As the value of $|t|$ obtained from the octane number data
is less than this, it would not be significant at the 5% level and at this
level the statement that the octane number of the product is $87 \cdot 5$ would be
accepted.   Would this statement have been accepted if a 10% level of
significance had been chosen?

****

*No.   The critical value of $|t|$ at the 10% level is $1 \cdot 81$ so $-1 \cdot 91$ is outside
the acceptance region.*

The same type of test is required by the next problem.

A measuring technique is biased if the population mean of replicate measurements
made by it differs from the true value of what is being measured.   In "Selected
Values of the Thermodynamic Properties of the Elements" (American Society for
Metals, 1973) a value of $1246^{\circ}C$ is given for the melting point of manganese.
Suppose that 4 determinations carried out by a metallurgist gave, in $^{\circ}C$:
1247, 1254, 1250, 1253.   Taking the published value to be the true value, would
you judge the metallurgist's results to be biased if you were prepared to take
a 5% risk of making a false accusation of bias?   Would your answer be the same
if this chance had to be only 1%?   What judgment would you make in this
respect about the data given in Misc. Ex. 1 on page 183?

****

N.H.: That the population mean μ of the metallurgist's measurements is 1246, i.e. there is no bias.

A.H.: $\mu \neq 1246$

Sample mean = 1251   Unbiased estimate of population variance = 10

$$t = \frac{1251 - 1246}{\sqrt{10}/\sqrt{4}} \simeq 3 \cdot 16$$

For $\nu = 3$, the 5% critical value of $|t|$ is $3 \cdot 18$. Strictly speaking, the value of $|t|$ obtained from the data is not quite large enough to indicate significant bias in the metallurgist's results, though only marginally. At the 1% level the decision is no longer a borderline one, the critical value being $5 \cdot 84$, and you would confidently retain the hypothesis of "no bias". Perhaps the test has revealed fainter evidence of bias than you would have expected from the original data, in which all 4 values were higher than 1246.

For the previous data, the variance estimate was the same as for the present data, i.e. 10, but the sample mean was 1265, giving: $t = \dfrac{1265 - 1246}{\sqrt{10}/\sqrt{4}} \simeq 12 \cdot 0$

The discrepancy between those observations and the published figure is therefore significant at the 1% level (and almost, but not quite, at the $0 \cdot 1\%$ level).

---

t-Test applied to Paired Observations

FRAME 1 showed you some data on the blood glucose levels of 6 diabetic rats which had been treated with a drug and 6 diabetic rats which had been not so treated.   In both groups of rats there was variation in the blood glucose levels found.   This could be explained partly by the error of the laboratory method for determining the amount of blood glucose present but mainly, one would think, by the variation from one rat to another.   The presence of these sources of variation makes it more difficult to detect any effect the drug may have had. The remedy lies in conducting the experiment differently, and this illustrates the importance of careful advance planning in experimental investigations.   By recording the blood glucose levels of the same 6 rats, before and after treatment with the drug, our attention would be focussed on the difference in level observed for each rat.   This would lead to a more sensitive statistical test than is possible for the data given in FRAME 1.

There are other situations where planning the experiment on a "paired comparison" basis is desirable.   If two chemical processes are to be compared for yield it is desirable to remove from consideration, as far as possible, variation in yield caused by factors other than the nature of the process itself.   One such contributory factor might be the composition of the raw material used in the process, this composition being subject to variation from one batch to another. If circumstances permit, the best plan then would be to carry out paired trials of the two processes, each pair of trials using raw material from the same batch.   The percentage yields (x_A and x_B) of a medicinal product in such a set of trials are shown below.

Batch number	1	2	3	4	5	6
x_A	$60 \cdot 1$	$57 \cdot 0$	$58 \cdot 6$	$58 \cdot 8$	$60 \cdot 2$	$58 \cdot 0$
x_B	$63 \cdot 9$	$60 \cdot 3$	$58 \cdot 5$	$61 \cdot 3$	$59 \cdot 7$	$61 \cdot 0$

FRAME 22   (continued)
It is important to appreciate the way in which the data are paired.   What
links (i) 60·1 and 63·9,   (ii) 57·0 and 60·3?

****

22A

(i) They are both yields obtained using raw material from Batch No. 1.
(ii) They are both yields obtained using raw material from Batch No. 2.

FRAME 23

The difference to be looked at here is the difference between the % yields
obtained by the two processes at each pair of trials.   The values of this
difference $d (= x_B - x_A)$ are:

$$3·8 \qquad 3·3 \qquad -0·1 \qquad 2·5 \qquad -0·5 \qquad 3·0$$

Now, if there were no difference between the true mean % yields of the two
processes, i.e. $\mu_A = \mu_B$, these values of d would constitute a random sample

from a population whose mean μ_d is .... Can you fill in the value of μ_d?

****

23A

$\mu_d = \mu_B - \mu_A = 0$

FRAME 24

The problem therefore reduces to that of testing a hypothetical population mean
and in this programme you have already learned how to deal with that.   We
begin by stating:

N.H.:   That there is no difference between the true mean % yield of the two
        processes i.e. $\mu_d = 0$.

A.H.: $\mu_d \neq 0$

The variance of d is not known and will have to be estimated from the sample.

$\bar{d} = 2·0 \qquad \Sigma (d - \bar{d})^2 = 16·84 \qquad$ Estimate of $\mathrm{var}(d) = s_d^2 = 3·368$

The value of the test statistic then required is $\dfrac{2·0 - 0}{\sqrt{3·368/\sqrt{6}}}$ i.e. 2·67.

To decide whether the result is significant at, say, the 5% level, it will be

necessary to refer to the distribution of $\dfrac{\bar{d} - 0}{s_d/\sqrt{6}}$.   What is this distribution,

if that of $\bar{d}$ is assumed to be normal?

****

24A

t-distribution with 5 d.f.   It would have been N(0, 1) if we had known the
population variance instead of having to use a sample estimate.

FRAME 25

Reference to TABLE 3 shows the 5% critical value of $|t|$ for 5 d.f. to be 2·57 and so the value of 2·67 obtained here is just significant. Thus, at this level of significance, the N.H. would be rejected in favour of the A.H. that the processes differ in their overall mean yields. What would your decision be if the acceptable level of risk of wrongly concluding that a difference exists were only 1%?

****

25A

The 1% critical value of $|t|$ for 5 d.f. is 4·03, so the N.H. would be retained i.e. you would decide that there is not sufficiently strong evidence to say that there is a difference between the two processes.

FRAME 26

If two analysts or two analytical methods are to be compared, an experimental design based on matched pairs is especially advantageous if the variation in the composition of the substance being analysed is large compared with the analytical errors. The following is an illustration of such a design.

Nine specimens of unalloyed steel were taken and each was halved, one half being sent for analysis to a laboratory at the University of Loughingham and the other half to a laboratory at the University of Derborough. The determinations of % carbon content were as follows:

Specimen No.	1	2	3	4	5	6	7	8	9
University of Loughingham	0·22	0·11	0·46	0·32	0·27	0·19	0·08	0·12	0·18
University of Derborough	0·20	0·10	0·39	0·34	0·23	0·14	0·13	0·08	0·16

By following a similar procedure to that adopted for the process yields, test the hypothesis that there is no real difference between the two laboratories in their determinations of % carbon. Allow for a 5% risk of concluding that such a difference exists when in fact it doesn't.

****

26A

$$\bar{d} = 0 \cdot 02 \qquad s_d^2 = 0 \cdot 0108/8 = 0 \cdot 001\ 35 \qquad t = \frac{0 \cdot 02 - 0}{\sqrt{0 \cdot 001\ 35/9}} \simeq 1 \cdot 63$$

For 8 d.f., 5% critical value of $|t| = 2 \cdot 31$. Thus the value obtained here is not large enough to be significant and the hypothesis of no difference between the laboratories would be retained.

Note: To avoid decimals in the working, the data could be coded. Making a change of unit by multiplying all observations by 100 gives

$$\bar{d} = 2 \qquad s_d^2 = 108/8 = 13 \cdot 5 \qquad t = \frac{2 - 0}{\sqrt{13 \cdot 5/9}} \simeq 1 \cdot 63$$

As t is a ratio in which numerator and denominator are both multiplied by the same factor when the unit is changed, there is no need to convert back to the original units.

Comparison of two Sample Means – σ known

Not all comparisons of two sets of observations can be made on a paired basis.
For instance, if the effect of an additive to the diet on the growth rate of
pigs were being investigated, this would need to be observed over a period of
time and each animal can only go through its growing stage once.   It would not
be possible to "set the clock back" and see how the same pigs would have grown
with a different diet.   Instead, one group of pigs could receive the diet with
the additive, and a control group could be given a diet without the additive.

In many situations it is not a matter of whether pairing is feasible or not –
it may simply not be relevant, as in the following example.   The pH value of
a solution is a measure of its alkalinity (or acidity, depending on which way
you look at it) not just of interest to chemists but also to keen gardeners who
want to know whether the soil is right for the plants they want to grow.
Suppose that 9 determinations of the pH of a solution are made, giving a mean
value of 8·31, and that 9 determinations made by the same method of the pH of
another solution give a mean of 8·28.   To decide whether the alkalinity of the
two solutions is the same, or not, it would be necessary to apply a statistical
test to the difference between the two sample means to see if it can reasonably
be explained by the fluctuations in the pH determinations.

The experiment with the pigs' diet would require a similar type of test, applied
in that case to the difference between the mean growth rate of the group
receiving the additive and the mean growth rate of the control group.

Suppose that, in the case of the pH determinations, it is known that the method
used gives, for solutions of that type, measurements which are approximately
normally distributed about the actual pH with s.d. 0·02.   It is then known
that the two samples are from populations with the same s.d. and the question is:
"Do these populations have the same mean?"

To answer this question you will need to apply what you have learned about the
distribution of sample means.   If the actual pH of the first solution is μ_1,
what are the mean and variance of the distribution of the mean $\bar{x}_1$ of 9
determinations of its pH?   Similarly, if the pH of the second solution is μ_2,
what are the mean and variance of the distribution of the mean $\bar{x}_2$ of 9
determinations of its pH?

****

28A

$\bar{x}_1$: Mean = μ_1 Variance = $0 \cdot 02^2/9$

$\bar{x}_2$: Mean = μ_2 Variance = $0 \cdot 02^2/9$

The normal model should be satisfactory for these distributions, so we can say
$\bar{x}_1$ is $N(\mu_1, 0 \cdot 02^2/9)$ and $\bar{x}_2$ is $N(\mu_2, 0 \cdot 02^2/9)$.   Taking any value of $\bar{x}_1$
at random and any value of $\bar{x}_2$ at random, we now consider the difference
$\bar{x}_1 - \bar{x}_2$.   What can you say about the distribution of all such differences?

****

$$N\left(\mu_1 - \mu_2, \quad \frac{0 \cdot 02^2}{9} + \frac{0 \cdot 02^2}{9}\right)$$

The hypothesis to be tested is that the two solutions have the same pH i.e.
$\mu_1 = \mu_2$. If this hypothesis is correct, then $\bar{x}_1 - \bar{x}_2$ is $N(...?..., ...?...)$
and $\frac{\bar{x}_1 - \bar{x}_2}{..?..}$ is $N(0, 1)$. Fill in the gaps in this statement.

****

$$\bar{x}_1 - \bar{x}_2 \quad is \quad N\left(0, \quad \frac{0 \cdot 02^2}{9} + \frac{0 \cdot 02^2}{9}\right) \quad and \quad \frac{\bar{x}_1 - \bar{x}_2}{\sqrt{\frac{0 \cdot 02^2}{9} + \frac{0 \cdot 02^2}{9}}} \quad is \quad N(0, 1)$$

The test takes the following form:

N.H.: That the two solutions have the same pH i.e. $\mu_1 = \mu_2$
A.H.: $\mu_1 \neq \mu_2$

The appropriate test statistic is u, where $u = \dfrac{\bar{x}_1 - \bar{x}_2}{\sqrt{\frac{0 \cdot 02^2}{9} + \frac{0 \cdot 02^2}{9}}}$.

If a 5% significance level is chosen, and we get a value of $|u| > 1 \cdot 96$, we
would decide that the difference between $\bar{x}_1$ and $\bar{x}_2$ is large enough to indicate
a difference in the pH of the two solutions.

For the data here, $\bar{x}_1 = 8 \cdot 31$, $\bar{x}_2 = 8 \cdot 28$, $u = \dfrac{0 \cdot 03}{0 \cdot 02\sqrt{2}/3} \simeq 3 \cdot 18$.

Therefore at the 5% level the difference is large enough to be considered
significant and the N.H. would be rejected in favour of the A.H. that the two
solutions do not have the same pH.

Would the same decision be reached if there were a maximum permitted risk of
only 1% of wrongly concluding that the solutions have different pH values?

****

Yes, as $|u| > 2 \cdot 58$

The data which has just been tested was rather special, in that the number of
observations in each sample was the same. However, by adopting the same
approach, you should be able to see how to deal with unequal sample sizes. To
make the problem more general, suppose that n_1 determinations are made with the
first solution and n_2 with the second, and that the s.d. of determinations is
σ. Write down $\text{var}(\bar{x}_1)$, $\text{var}(\bar{x}_2)$ and $\text{var}(\bar{x}_1 - \bar{x}_2)$. If the two solutions have
the same pH, i.e. $\mu_1 = \mu_2$, what will be the distribution of $\bar{x}_1 - \bar{x}_2$?

****

$$var(\overline{x}_1) = \sigma^2/n_1 \qquad var(\overline{x}_2) = \sigma^2/n_2 \qquad var(\overline{x}_1 - \overline{x}_2) = \sigma^2/n_1 + \sigma^2/n_2$$

$\overline{x}_1 - \overline{x}_2$ is $N(0, \ \sigma^2/n_1 + \sigma^2/n_2)$

It follows that $\dfrac{\overline{x}_1 - \overline{x}_2}{\sigma \cdot \sqrt{\dfrac{1}{n_1} + \dfrac{1}{n_2}}}$ is $N(0, 1)$ and that the appropriate test

statistic to calculate is u, where $u = \dfrac{\overline{x}_1 - \overline{x}_2}{\sigma \sqrt{\dfrac{1}{n_1} + \dfrac{1}{n_2}}}$

$$= \frac{\text{difference between sample means}}{\text{standard error of the difference}}$$

So far we have considered the same method of determination being used for the two solutions, past experience telling us that for both solutions it would give results with s.d. σ. Now, suppose, instead, that the method used for determining the pH of the first solution is known to give results with s.d. σ_1 and another method, which gives results with s.d. σ_2, is used for the second solution. What then will be the distribution of $\overline{x}_1 - \overline{x}_2$, if the two solutions have the same pH? What will be the appropriate test statistic to calculate?

****

$$\overline{x}_1 - \overline{x}_2 \ is \ N\left(0, \ \frac{\sigma_1^2}{n_1} + \frac{\sigma_2^2}{n_2}\right) \qquad u = \frac{\overline{x}_1 - \overline{x}_2}{\sqrt{\dfrac{\sigma_1^2}{n_1} + \dfrac{\sigma_2^2}{n_2}}}$$

The following problem will give you the opportunity to see whether you have understood what has been said about testing the difference between two sample means.

Machines of two different types are being used to package tins of talcum powder with the same nominal content. From past experience with the machines it is known that the weights of fillings produced by type A have a s.d. of $1 \cdot 1$ g and those produced by type B have a s.d. of $1 \cdot 4$ g. When 25 tins filled by machines of type A are emptied and the contents carefully weighed, the mean weight of filling is found to be $173 \cdot 2$ g. When the same is done for 20 tins filled by machines of type B, the mean weight is $174 \cdot 1$ g. Show that, at the 5% level of significance there is evidence that the two types of machine are producing different mean filling weights. Would the same conclusion be reached using a 1% level of significance? To make sure that you haven't forgotten what you learned in the previous programme, find the 95% confidence limits for the difference between the mean weights of filling produced by the two types of machine.

****

$$u = \frac{174 \cdot 1 - 173 \cdot 2}{\sqrt{\frac{1 \cdot 1^2}{25} + \frac{1 \cdot 4^2}{20}}} = 2 \cdot 35$$

As $|u| > 1 \cdot 96$, this would lead to the rejection, at the 5% level, of the N.H. that $\mu_A = \mu_B$.

However, as $|u| < 2 \cdot 58$, the N.H. would not be rejected if a 1% significance level were chosen. 95% confidence limits for

$\mu_B - \mu_A$ *are* $(174 \cdot 1 - 173 \cdot 2) \pm 1 \cdot 96 \sqrt{\frac{1 \cdot 1^2}{25} + \frac{1 \cdot 4^2}{20}} = 0 \cdot 15$ *and* $1 \cdot 65 \, g$.

Notice that this confidence interval does not include zero. This is linked with the fact that the N.H. $\mu_A - \mu_B = 0$ is rejected at the 5% level.

Similarly linked are the acceptance of the N.H. at the 1% level and the fact that the 99% confidence interval, which is $-0 \cdot 09$ to $1 \cdot 89 \, g$, does include zero. You may already have realised that hypothesis tests and confidence intervals are different ways of looking at the same data and applying the same basic theory. Which is used depends on the nature of the particular situation.

Comparison of two Sample Means – σ estimated

So far, in devising a test for comparing the means of two samples, each sample has been considered to be from a population with known variance. Suppose, for instance, that the method of obtaining the 9 determinations of pH for each of the two solutions in FRAME 27 had not been known to have a s.d. of 0·02, what then? When a similar lack of knowledge about the s.d. of octane number determinations was encountered in a previous example, the observations in the sample were used to supply an estimate. In the present problem there are two samples and by combining the information which they give, a variance estimate can be obtained. The appropriate way of doing this, in these circumstances, is to use the formula

$$s^2 = \frac{\Sigma(x_1 - \overline{x}_1)^2 + \Sigma(x_2 - \overline{x}_2)^2}{n_1 + n_2 - 2} \qquad (35.1)$$

where one sample consists of n_1 values of x_1 with mean $\overline{x}_1$ and the other of n_2 values of x_2 with mean $\overline{x}_2$.

The variance estimate $\frac{\Sigma(x - \overline{x})^2}{n - 1}$, given by a single sample, is based on $(n - 1)$ degrees of freedom. This was explained in the previous programme by showing that only $(n - 1)$ of the n components of $\Sigma(x - \overline{x})^2$ are independent, the remaining one then being fixed. Now look at the numerator in (35.1) and, for each sum, state how many of the terms in it are independent and free from restraint. Deduce the number of d.f. in the whole numerator.

****

$n_1 - 1, \quad n_2 - 1, \quad n_1 + n_2 - 2$

	$x_1 - \overline{x}_1$		$x_2 - \overline{x}_2$
1	*FREE*	*1*	*FREE*
2	*FREE*	*2*	*FREE*
3	*FREE*	*3*	*FREE*
⋮	⋮	⋮	⋮
$n_1 - 1$	*FREE*		
n_1	*FIXED*	$n_2 - 1$	*FREE*
		n_2	*FIXED*

The following may help you to understand this, if you had difficulty:

Notice that the denominator of (35.1) is the number of d.f. in the numerator,
showing a similarity with $\frac{\Sigma(x - \bar{x})^2}{n - 1}$.

FRAME 36

Obviously (35.1) only makes sense if there is a common variance to estimate,
i.e. if both samples are from populations with the same variance.   With the pH
values there are practical grounds for this being so.   For each solution the
variation among replicate determinations is caused by the method used, which is
the same for both solutions.   This suggests a common variance.   (As a check,
confirmation can be obtained by applying a suitable statistical test, as you
will discover in the next programme.)

For the pH data, $n_1 = n_2 = 9$, $\bar{x}_1 = 8 \cdot 31$, $\bar{x}_2 = 8 \cdot 28$.   Suppose that further
calculations give $\Sigma(x_1 - \bar{x}_1)^2 = 0 \cdot 0024$ and $\Sigma(x_2 - \bar{x}_2)^2 = 0 \cdot 0048$.

Then $s^2 = \dfrac{0 \cdot 0024 + 0 \cdot 0048}{16} = 0 \cdot 000\ 45$

What is the number of d.f. in this estimate?

****

36A

16

FRAME 37

The estimation of σ^2 has paved the way for testing the hypothesis that the
two samples are from the same population.   As before we have:

N.H. :   That the two solutions have the same pH i.e. $\mu_1 = \mu_2$.
A.H. : $\mu_1 \neq \mu_2$

In the previous test σ was known and it followed from the N.H. that, if

$$u = \frac{\bar{x}_1 - \bar{x}_2}{\sigma\sqrt{\dfrac{1}{n_1} + \dfrac{1}{n_2}}} \qquad (37.1)$$

then u is N(0, 1).   In the present test, estimated σ replaces known σ.
You have already had some experience of the effect of that when considering a
single sample from a population.   When s replaced σ in $u = \dfrac{\bar{x} - \mu}{\sigma/\sqrt{n}}$, u being
N(0, 1),   what replaced the standard normal distribution?

****

37A

The t-distribution corresponding to $\nu = n - 1$, this being the number of d.f.
in s^2.

In a similar way, the replacement for (37.1) will be

$$t = \frac{\overline{x}_1 - \overline{x}_2}{s\sqrt{\dfrac{1}{n_1} + \dfrac{1}{n_2}}}$$

and the appropriate t-distribution is that for $\nu = n_1 + n_2 - 2$, the number of d.f. in s^2.

For the pH data the value of this t-statistic is

$$\frac{8\cdot 31 - 8\cdot 28}{\sqrt{0\cdot 000\ 45}\ \sqrt{\dfrac{1}{9} + \dfrac{1}{9}}} = \frac{0\cdot 03}{0\cdot 01} = 3 \qquad \text{and} \qquad \nu = 16$$

Reference to TABLE 3 shows the 5% critical value of $|t|$ to be $2\cdot 12$. Thus the N.H. would be rejected if that significance level were chosen. What if the 1% level were chosen?

****

38A

The 1% critical value of $|t|$ is $2\cdot 92$ and the N.H. would still be rejected, though only very marginally.

In the test just carried out the values of n_1 and n_2 were equal but obviously this does not need to be so. You should have no difficulty in applying the same type of test in the following problem, in which the sample sizes are different. Try it and see.

In an experiment to compare two different diets on which to rear pigs, 13 young pigs of the same age and breed were randomly divided into two groups of 7 and 6 respectively. One group was fed on Diet A and the other on Diet B. The weight gains (in kg) after a 20-week period are shown below. Is there evidence that pigs on one diet gain more weight than pigs on the other? (You can assume that the variance of weight gains is the same for both diets.)

Diet A	68	73	63	65	75	74	72
Diet B	65	71	69	57	67	55	

****

39A

$$\overline{x}_A = 70 \qquad \overline{x}_B = 64 \qquad \Sigma(x_A - \overline{x}_A)^2 = 132 \qquad \Sigma(x_B - \overline{x}_B)^2 = 214 \qquad s^2 = 346/11$$

$$t = \frac{70 - 64}{\sqrt{\dfrac{346}{11}\left(\dfrac{1}{7} + \dfrac{1}{6}\right)}} = 1\cdot 92$$

For 11 d.f. the 5% critical value of $|t|$ is $2\cdot 20$, so the value obtained here is not large enough to cause the rejection of the hypothesis that there is no difference between the diets as far as weight gain is concerned.

Confidence Limits for Difference between Means

As has been pointed out before, finding confidence limits for a difference may be more useful than testing for its significance.   The data on the weight gains of pigs will serve as an illustration of how to find confidence limits for the difference between two population means when the common variance has to be estimated from the samples.   You have already found, in Misc. Ex. 11 of the previous programme, how to deal with the corresponding situation when σ^2 is known, and you have applied that knowledge in FRAME 34 of this programme.   Just to remind you of the background - as $\overline{x}_A - \overline{x}_B$ is $N\left(\mu_A - \mu_B, \dfrac{\sigma^2}{n_A} + \dfrac{\sigma^2}{n_B}\right)$, then

$$\frac{\overline{x}_A - \overline{x}_B - (\mu_A - \mu_B)}{\sigma\sqrt{\dfrac{1}{n_A} + \dfrac{1}{n_B}}} \qquad \text{is} \qquad N(0, 1) \qquad (40.1)$$

and the 95% confidence limits for $\mu_A - \mu_B$ are

$$\overline{x}_A - \overline{x}_B \pm 1 \cdot 96\ \sigma\sqrt{\frac{1}{n_A} + \frac{1}{n_B}} \qquad\qquad (40.2)$$

What must be substituted for the standard normal distribution in (40.1) if σ is unknown and is replaced by the estimate s, obtained in the way described in this programme?

****

t-distribution with $n_A + n_B - 2$ *d.f.*

Thus, if s replaces σ in (40.2),   1·96 must be replaced by the value pertaining to the appropriate t-distribution.   What would this value be in the case of the pig diet data?

****

$n_A = 7$ $n_B = 6$ $\nu = 11$ $\therefore$ *The value is* 2·20.

The 95% confidence limits for the difference $\mu_A - \mu_B$, i.e.
Mean weight gain with diet A - Mean weight gain with diet B,   are therefore

$$\overline{x}_A - \overline{x}_B \pm 2 \cdot 20\ s\sqrt{\frac{1}{n_A} + \frac{1}{n_B}}$$

$$\text{i.e.} \quad 70 - 64 \pm 2 \cdot 20 \times \sqrt{\frac{346}{11}} \times \sqrt{\frac{1}{7} + \frac{1}{6}}$$

$$\text{giving} \quad -0 \cdot 9 \qquad \text{and} \qquad 12 \cdot 9$$

Note that these limits include zero, which links up with the significance test
having found insufficient evidence of a difference at the 5% level.   If 99%
confidence limits for the difference in mean weight were required, what value
should be used instead of 2·20 in the preceding calculations?

****

42A

3·11

_____

FRAME 43

As another example, let us consider the pH readings which were used to
illustrate a significance test in FRAMES 36-38.   For Solution No. 1, 9
readings gave a mean pH of 8·31, for Solution No. 2 the mean of 9 readings
was 8·28 and s^2, the estimated variance of the method of measurement used, was
0·000 45.   Find 95% confidence limits for the difference in pH of the two
solutions.

****

43A

For (pH of Solution 1 - pH of Solution 2)   the 95% confidence limits are

$$0{\cdot}03 \pm 2{\cdot}12 \times \sqrt{0{\cdot}000\ 45}\ \sqrt{\frac{1}{9} + \frac{1}{9}}\qquad i.e.\qquad 0{\cdot}009\ and\ 0{\cdot}051$$

_____

FRAME 44

Test of difference between proportions

(i) Between an observed proportion and a hypothetical one

At the beginning of this programme some thought was given to deciding which
results of tossing a coin a number of times would provide grounds for declaring
it to be biased.   You saw that if the number of tosses was 8 and the coin was
to be rejected if either 0, 1, 7 or 8 heads occurred, the chance of rejecting
a fair coin was 0·070.

Number of heads (x)	0	1	2	3	4	5	6	7	8
Decision	← REJECT →		←		ACCEPT		→	← REJECT →	
P(x) for fair coin	0·004	0·031	0·109	0·219	0·273	0·219	0·109	0·031	0·004
	0·035							0·035	

In the language of significance testing, choosing these acceptance and rejection
regions is equivalent to choosing a 7·0% level of significance.   Suppose you
wanted to reduce the risk of rejecting a fair coin, and decided to reject the
coin only if the number of heads was either 0 or 8.   What significance level
would you, in effect, be choosing?

****

44A

0·8%

The normal and t-distribution models deal with a continuous variate, and therefore in the significance tests based on them it was possible to define acceptance and rejection regions corresponding <u>exactly</u> to a 5% or 1% level of significance.   With the binomial model you have seen that this is not possible, as it applies to a discrete variate.   Thus, in the example of 8 tosses of a coin, you have to settle for a $0 \cdot 8\%$ level or a $7 \cdot 0\%$ level, there is nothing in between.   In such a situation you can't define a rejection region so that the probability of rejecting a fair coin is <u>equal</u> to, say, 5%, but you can define the region so that this probability does not exceed 5%.   If the coin were tossed only 6 times, what rejection region would satisfy this criterion? After you have written down your answer, try to answer the same question for the coin being tossed 5 times, and see what difficulty you find yourself in. Would the same difficulty be encountered if the coin were tossed less than 5 times?

****

45A

For 6 tosses, reject the coin if either 0 or 6 heads occur.

x	0	1	2	3	4	5	6
Decision	*REJECT*	←		*ACCEPT*		→	*REJECT*
P(x) for fair coin	*0·0156*	*0·0937*				*0·0937*	*0·0156*

The probability of a fair coin being rejected would then be $3 \cdot 12\%$.

For 5 tosses, there is no rejection region which would meet the requirement.
Yes.

Note, therefore, that imposing a maximum on the risk of rejecting a fair coin results in the imposition of a minimum on the number of tosses on which a decision is to be based.

What is the minimum number of tosses required to decide whether or not a coin is biased, if the risk of rejecting an unbiased coin is not to exceed 1%?

****

46A

8.   You could have arrived at this by trial and error, starting at 7 as you know from 45A that the number has to be more than 6.

Alternatively, you may have solved $0 \cdot 5^n + 0 \cdot 5^n < 0 \cdot 01$ for the smallest integer value of n.

We have been looking at the proportion of heads observed in a given number of tosses in relation to the hypothesis that the proportion of heads in an infinitely large number of tosses was $\frac{1}{2}$.   This is just a particular example of the general problem of looking at an observed proportion of "successes" in n trials in the light of a hypothesis that the proportion overall is p.

    Let x = number of "successes" in n trials, the probability of success at each trial being equal to p.

Then x can take the values 0, 1, ..., n and its distribution will be binomial.   State the mean and s.d. of its distribution.

****

47A

Mean = np.   *s.d. = $\sqrt{npq}$ where q = 1 - p*

FRAME 48

In the coin tossing examples, the values of n were small and p was 0·5, thus making calculations quite easy, but the evaluation of binomial probabilities can involve a lot of tedious calculations when the values of n and p are less convenient.   Tables for use in significance tests based on a binomial model are available and can be found in books of statistical tables such as those mentioned in the Bibliography.   Here we shall concentrate on the case where there is a convenient approximation available.   If p is not too different from 0·5 and n is large enough, so that the binomial distribution is fairly symmetrical, what distribution can be used as an approximation?

****

48A

The normal distribution with the same mean and s.d., i.e. x is N(np, npq).

FRAME 49

Now, if x is N(np, npq), what can you say about the distribution of $\frac{x - np}{\sqrt{npq}}$?

****

49A

It is N(0, 1).

FRAME 50

When an observed value of x is to be used to test the hypothesis of a population proportion p, the test statistic to calculate is therefore

$$u = \frac{x - np}{\sqrt{npq}} \qquad\qquad (50.1)$$

where the critical values of |u| are given by the standard normal distribution.

(50.1) can also be written as $u = \dfrac{x/n - p}{\sqrt{pq/n}}$ (50.2)

which is convenient if you are thinking in terms of the observed <u>proportion</u> of successes, i.e. x/n, rather than the <u>number</u> of successes, x.

As an example of a test where either (50.1) or (50.2) could be used, suppose that a coin has been tossed 64 times and shown 41 heads, and the question is whether this casts doubt on the fairness of the coin.   Following the usual test procedure, we begin with:

N.H.:   The coin is fair, i.e. P(heads) = $\frac{1}{2}$

A.H.:   P(heads) $\neq$ $\frac{1}{2}$

As $p = \frac{1}{2}$ and $n = 64$, the normal approximation can be used.   The observed number of heads was 41, but remember that the normal distribution deals with a continuous variate.   The question of whether 41 or more is unusual for the discrete variate then becomes a question of whether 40·5 or more is unusual for the continuous variate.   Allowing for this correction for continuity gives

$$u = \frac{40 \cdot 5 - 32}{\sqrt{16}} = 2 \cdot 125$$

As $|u| > 1\cdot96$, this is significant at the 5% level.   Thus the N.H. would be rejected if a 5% risk of declaring a fair coin to be biased is acceptable.   If only a 1% risk were acceptable, would the fairness of the coin then be challenged?

****

50A

No, as $|u| < 2\cdot58.$

FRAME 51

If you have understood the reasoning behind this test, you should be able to work out what results from 64 tosses would lead to the rejection of the hypothesis of a fair coin.   See if you can do this, giving answers for 5% and 1% levels of significance.

****

51A

5% level: Rejection regions are $\qquad u < -1\cdot96 \qquad$ *and* $\qquad u > 1\cdot96$
$\qquad\qquad\qquad\qquad$ *i.e.* $\quad x - 32 < -1\cdot96 \times 4 \quad$ *and* $\quad x - 32 > 1\cdot96 \times 4$
$\qquad\qquad\qquad\qquad\qquad\qquad x < 24\cdot16 \qquad$ *and* $\qquad x > 39\cdot84$

Thus either less than 24 heads, or more than 40 heads, would lead to the rejection of the hypothesis of a fair coin.

1% level: Using 2·58 instead of 1·96 shows required range of results to be:
$\qquad\qquad$ *21 heads or less, or 43 heads or more.*

FRAME 52

If records show that the sex ratio at birth in domestic cattle is 51 males to 49 females, what normal distribution would approximately describe the number of bull calves in a sample of 100 births?

****

52A

N(51, 24·99), from p = *probability of a male* = 0·51, n = 100, *whence mean* = np = 51 *and variance* = $np(1 - p)$ = 51 × 0·49.

FRAME 53

Now suppose that observations on wild cattle show that in a sample of 100 births there were 64 males.   Does this provide evidence, at the 5% level of significance, that the sex ratio in wild cattle differs from that in domestic cattle?

****

$u = \dfrac{63 \cdot 5 - 51}{\sqrt{24 \cdot 99}} = 2 \cdot 5.$ *Thus, at the 5% level, the hypothesis of no difference in the sex ratio would be rejected in favour of the alternative hypothesis that there is a difference.   If you did not make the correction for continuity, and used 64 instead of 63·5, you will have got u = 2·6 and still have arrived at the same decision.*

(The 1% critical value of $|u|$ being 2·58, the difference does not reach this level of significance, when the correction for continuity is made, though only by a very narrow margin.)

The hypothesis of 51% male births having been rejected, the question may arise: In wild cattle, what is the proportion of births in which the calves are male? As we only have records of 100 births, this proportion can only be estimated. Now if, for wild cattle generally, p is the proportion of male births, what are the mean and s.d. of the proportion of males in a random sample of n births? (If in difficulty, refer back to FRAME 47 and take x as the number of males in n births.   You now have to consider the variate x/n.)

****

Mean = p   s.d. = $\sqrt{pq/n}$ where   q = 1 - p

As the sample proportion x/n is distributed with mean p, it provides an unbiased estimate of the population proportion and is therefore sometimes denoted by $\hat{p}$.   In the present problem, $\hat{p} = 0 \cdot 64$.   A more informative statement would say how near this sample estimate is likely to be to the population value and you already know that confidence limits do just that. Clearly the values of n and p allow for the normal approximation to be used again, but the standard error of the estimate is needed before the confidence limits can be written down.   You have already found the general formula for this standard error (i.e. the s.d. of x/n) to be $\sqrt{p(1 - p)/n}$.   Here n = 100 but p is unknown, so the only thing to do is to use its estimated value. Substituting 0·64 for p then gives $\sqrt{0 \cdot 64 \times 0 \cdot 36/100}$ i.e. 0·048 for the standard error and the 95% confidence limits are

$$0 \cdot 64 \pm 1 \cdot 96 \times 0 \cdot 048$$
i.e.   0·546 and 0·734   or   54·6% and 73·4%

Now write down the general formula for the 95% confidence limits for p based on an observed proportion $\hat{p}$ in a sample of size n.   (Assume n and p to have values for which a normal approximation is adequate.)

****

$\hat{p} \pm 1 \cdot 96 \sqrt{\hat{p}(1 - \hat{p})/n}$

(ii)   Between two observed proportions

So far, in testing differences between proportions, you have been comparing a sample with a population.   In other problems, it may be a comparison between two samples that is required.   For instance, in one area a geologist might find that, in a random sample of 80 pebbles, 30 are limestone, whereas when a random sample of 120 pebbles is collected in another area, 66 are limestone. The question may then be asked: Is the proportion of limestone pebbles really different in the two areas or can the difference in the observed proportions, 30/80 and 66/120, be attributed to sampling fluctuations?

Expressed in general terms, this problem is one of comparing a sample of n_1 observations of which x_1 are "successes" with a sample of n_2 observations of which x_2 are "successes".   The question is whether the difference between the observed proportions x_1/n_1 and x_2/n_2 is significant.   To answer this question, we test the hypothesis that both samples are from the same population. If that hypothesis is true, and the proportion of "successes" in the population is p, what will be the mean and variance of the distribution of

(i) $\dfrac{x_1}{n_1}$,   (ii) $\dfrac{x_2}{n_2}$,   (iii) $\dfrac{x_1}{n_1} - \dfrac{x_2}{n_2}$?

****

(i) p, pq/n₁;   (ii) p, pq/n₂;   (iii) 0, pq(1/n₁ + 1/n₂) where q = 1 − p.

Writing $p_1 = x_1/n_1$ and $p_2 = x_2/n_2$, then under the conditions for which the normal approximation applies, $p_1 - p_2$ is $N\left\{0,\ pq\left(\dfrac{1}{n_1} + \dfrac{1}{n_2}\right)\right\}$.   However, to use this to see whether we have an unusual value of $p_1 - p_2$, it would be necessary to have a value for p.   The actual value of p is unknown, so the next best thing is to use an estimate.   Both p_1 and p_2 are estimates, but a better estimate can be obtained by combining the two samples.   According to the hypothesis both samples are from the same population and hence $(x_1 + x_2)/(n_1 + n_2)$ will also be an estimate of p.

Writing $\hat{p} = (x_1 + x_2)/(n_1 + n_2)$,   it can now be stated that

$$p_1 - p_2 \text{ is } N\left\{0,\ \hat{p}(1 - \hat{p})\left(\frac{1}{n_1} + \frac{1}{n_2}\right)\right\}$$

and, therefore, $\dfrac{p_1 - p_2}{\sqrt{\hat{p}(1 - \hat{p})\left(\dfrac{1}{n_1} + \dfrac{1}{n_2}\right)}}$ is N(0, 1).

The background theory necessary for solving the geologist's problem has now been thought out.   What values will have to be substituted for p_1, p_2, n_1, n_2 and $\hat{p}$?

****

$p_1 = 0{\cdot}375$ $p_2 = 0{\cdot}55$ $n_1 = 80$ $n_2 = 120$ $\hat{p} = 0{\cdot}48$

It doesn't, of course, matter if you have labelled the samples the other way round, i.e. $p_1 = 0{\cdot}55$, $n_1 = 120$, etc.

The test statistic to calculate is then

$$u = \frac{0 \cdot 375 - 0 \cdot 55}{\sqrt{0 \cdot 48 \times 0 \cdot 52 \left(\frac{1}{80} + \frac{1}{120} \right)}} = -2 \cdot 43$$

Comment on the significance of the result.

****

58A

As $|u| > 1 \cdot 96$, the hypothesis that the proportion of limestone pebbles is the same in both areas would be rejected at the 5% level. However, as $|u| < 2 \cdot 58$, it would not be rejected at the 1% level.

FRAME 59

Type 1 and Type 2 Errors

The significance tests in this programme have all been carried out correctly, with the working free from mistakes, yet the conclusions reached could have been wrong. The two solutions could have had the same pH, yet the test led us to decide that this was not so, and the petroleum product might not have had the octane number claimed for it when we accepted that it had. The deficiency is not in the significance tests, but in the data to which they were applied. Suppose, for instance, that Glomor light bulbs are claimed by their manufacturer to have a mean life of 2000 hours, what would be the only way of establishing, with complete certainty, whether or not this claim is correct?

****

59A

The entire production of Glomor bulbs would have to be tested and their mean length of life found.

FRAME 60

You see, therefore, that if you want to make conclusions from a sample about the population from whence it came, you just don't have enough information to be 100% certain about your conclusions. It is inevitable that, whichever decision is made as the result of a significance test, there is always a risk of it being the wrong one. The most we can hope for is to be able to make an assessment of this risk.

There are two ways in which your decision can be wrong:
(1) You may decide that the observed difference is significant when, in fact, no real difference exists. In other words, you may reject the N.H. when, in fact, it is correct.

(2) You may decide that the observed difference is not significant when, in fact, there is a real difference. In other words, you may accept the N.H. when, in fact, it is wrong.

The significance level represents the maximum risk you are prepared to take of wrong decisions of type ..... being made. Fill in the gap with (1) or (2).

****

As you have realised, the chance of a Type 1 error occurring is the significance
level.   It is denoted in general by α, and the chance of a Type 2 error
occurring is correspondingly denoted by β.   The following table summarises
what can happen in hypothesis testing.

		Hypothesis is actually	
		TRUE	FALSE
Hypothesis is	ACCEPTED	✓	Type 2 error (Probability = β)
	REJECTED	Type 1 error (Probability = α)	✓

The values of α and β are related to one another.   To illustrate this, let
us look at the first type of test described in this programme where the
hypothesis of a population mean, $\mu = \mu_0$, was being tested in the light of an
observed sample mean $\bar{x}$.   The basis of the test was that, if $\mu = \mu_0$, such
sample means would be $N(\mu_0, \sigma^2/n)$.   This distribution is the lower one shown
in the diagram.

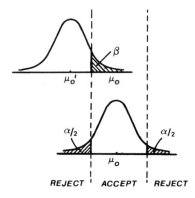

HYPOTHESIS FALSE $\mu \neq \mu_0$

HYPOTHESIS TRUE $\mu = \mu_0$

REJECT ' ACCEPT ' REJECT

On the other hand, if the N.H. is incorrect and the population mean is not μ_0,
but some other value μ_0' , say, then the sample means would be $N(\mu_0', \sigma^2/n)$
and this is the upper distribution in the diagram.

The vertical lines divide the range of values of $\bar{x}$ into those which would lead
to rejection of the hypothesis and those which would lead to acceptance.   The
shaded areas then represent α and β, as shown.

By reference to the diagram, answer these questions:

(i)   If the significance level α has been chosen, and the population mean is
      not μ_0 but some other value μ_0' , will the risk β depend on what that
      value μ_0' is?   (Imagine keeping the dotted lines fixed and displacing
      the upper distribution as μ_0' varies.)

(ii) For μ_0' as shown in the diagram, what will be the effect on β of
      reducing the value of α?   (Imagine keeping the upper distribution fixed
      and moving the dotted lines so that they are wider apart.)   What must be
      done to α to reduce β?

              ****

                                                                              62A

(i) Yes
(ii) β will be increased. α must be increased.

FRAME 63

The distributions in the diagram in the previous frame are for a sample size n.
What would be the effect on the distributions of quadrupling the sample size?

              ****

                                                                              63A

It would halve the s.d. and, therefore, the width of spread of each distribution.

FRAME 64

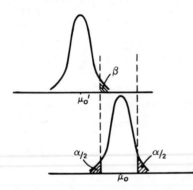

This diagram describes the situation in which
this has happened, with μ_0' and α remaining
as they were before.   Notice that as the
dotted lines have now moved closer to μ_0
and the tails of the upper distribution have
moved closer to μ_0' , the area β has been
diminished.

Increasing n by a factor of 4 was chosen
here for the sake of argument, but it should
now be obvious that the effect of any increase
in the sample size will, for a chosen
significance level α, decrease the risk β.

FRAME 65

Let us now consider the implications, in significance testing, of what has been
noticed about β in the previous three frames.   Having realised that test
conclusions are subject to two kinds of error, your natural reaction would be
to try to minimise the chances of their occurrence.   Perhaps, in the earlier
stages of this programme, you wondered why a 5% significance level should be
chosen in preference to a 1% level with its reduced risk of what has since been
identified as a Type 1 error.   Now you know why - decreasing α causes an
increase in β and vice versa.   The only way of decreasing one risk without

increasing the other is to simultaneously make the sample larger, but practical
difficulties will always place some restriction on the sample size.   It is
therefore a matter of achieving a suitable balance between the two kinds of
risk.   In trying to achieve that, it would be helpful to know what value of β
would correspond to a chosen α.   Taking the case of the octane number problem
at the beginning of this programme, the hypothesis being tested was $\mu = 87 \cdot 5$.
You knew the value of σ and the sample size was 11, but if, say, a 5%
significance had been chosen, i.e. $\alpha = 0 \cdot 05$,   would it have been possible to
calculate the corresponding risk β?   If not, why not?   (You may find it
helpful to refer back to the diagram in FRAME 62.)

****

65A

No, because it would be necessary to know the true value of μ, *if indeed it is
not* $87 \cdot 5$, *and if we knew that we wouldn't be making the test!   In the diagram
this unknown quantity is denoted by* μ_0'.

FRAME 66

It is a feature of all the significance tests in this programme that, whilst the
N.H. is quite specific, the A.H. covers a multitude of possibilities and
therefore you can't say what β is.   For instance, in testing the hypothesis
$\mu = \mu_0$,   the alternative was $\mu \neq \mu_0$ (thus covering a multitude of possible
values) and as that doesn't specify a particular value for μ it doesn't fix a
value for β, either.   Nevertheless, take any value of μ and you can find the
corresponding value of β.   This functional relationship is given by the
POWER FUNCTION of the test, a topic which will be enlarged on in a later
programme.

FRAME 67

Perhaps you have wondered how the standard values for α, mostly $0 \cdot 05$ and $0 \cdot 01$,
have been arrived at.   The answer is that picking them has been purely a matter
of convenience and they have not been obtained by any mathematical formula.
They apparently represent, in round terms, the levels of risk that most users
are prepared to take.   Which is chosen depends on what is at stake.

For instance, if it was of the utmost importance that the nitrogen content of a
product should not deviate from $4 \cdot 02\%$, then in a test such as that in FRAME 16
you might choose a 5% significance level, preferring to take the risk of being
needlessly alarmed rather than increase the risk of letting a difference slip
through undetected.

On the other hand, if a new process for producing nylon cord is being tested to
see whether it produces cord that is stronger than that made at present, you
may deem a 1%, or even $0 \cdot 1\%$, level of significance advisable, if changing
over to the new process requires a large capital outlay.   In this case, you will
want a low risk of installing a new process which doesn't, in fact, produce
stronger cord, even if that means a greater risk of missing an opportunity to
improve the process.

In a textbook example it is not possible to convey all the background information
needed for weighing up the choice of α.   In any case, as you have seen, the
choice of α is not decided statistically and is therefore not properly part of
this course.   In future examples, unless a particular significance level is

stated, you should indicate whether you find a result (i) not significant at
the 5% level, (ii) significant at the 5% level but not at the 1% level, or
(iii) significant at the 1% level.   Why is it unnecessary to include the
categories   (iv) significant at the 1% but not at the 5% level, and
(v) significant at both the 5% and 1% levels?

****

67A

(iv) is impossible.   (v) is implied by (iii).

FRAME 68

Traditional v. Bayesian approach

In this programme you have been introduced to the general procedure used in the
testing of hypotheses.   It may be summarised as follows:

Formulate a null hypothesis.

State the alternative hypothesis.

From the data calculate the value of the appropriate test statistic.

The N.H. predicts the distribution of this statistic and hence its range
of values can be divided into those which are "likely" and those which are
"unlikely", where "unlikely" is defined as having a probability less than
α.   The value of α is the significance level, usually chosen as 0·05 or
0·01.

If the value of the test statistic falls in the "unlikely" category the
N.H. is rejected in favour of the A.H.

Otherwise the N.H. is upheld.

This is the traditional method of testing, widely accepted and used in the past
and still continuing in favour with many of today's practitioners of statistical
techniques.   For instance, t-tests of the kind described in this programme
were used extensively in the analysis of biomedical data recorded during the
Apollo space flights.

Since the 1960's there has been growing support for an alternative approach,
based on a theorem in probability originally published by the Rev. Thomas Bayes
in 1763.   A dialogue (sometimes heated) continues between the two schools of
thought.   It is beyond the scope of this course to explain how the two
viewpoints differ and the traditional one will be adhered to throughout.   A
description of Bayesian ideas and methods, in reasonably simple language, can be
found in Bayesian Statistics for Social Scientists by L.D. Phillips (Nelson,
London 1973).

FRAME 69

Which test?

The greatest difficulty experienced by the beginner in applying tests of
significance is in identifying the appropriate one for the problem posed.   The
aim of this course is that you should understand <u>what</u> is being done and <u>why</u> it is
being done.   This understanding, combined with experience with a variety of
problems, should result in your being able to make a correct diagnosis of which
test to use.   To help you get off to a good start, the salient features of five

FRAME 69   (continued)

of the tests described in this programme are set out in the table below.   They
cover the types of test required in Misc. Ex. 1-5 of the next frame, there
being one example corresponding to each of the tests (i)-(v).   Can you match
them up?

Difference being tested for significance	Test statistic to calculate	Distribution of test statistic
(i) Between observed sample mean $\bar{x}$ and supposed population mean μ. σ known.	$\dfrac{\bar{x} - \mu}{\sigma/\sqrt{n}}$	Standard normal distribution
(ii) As for (i) but σ unknown, only sample estimate s available.	$\dfrac{\bar{x} - \mu}{s/\sqrt{n}}$	t-distribution based on $(n - 1)$ d.f.
(iii) Between two samples, observations recorded on a paired basis.	$\dfrac{\bar{d} - 0}{s_d/\sqrt{n}}$ where d = difference between pair of observations	t-distribution based on $(n - 1)$ d.f.
(iv) Between two sample means $\bar{x}_1$ and $\bar{x}_2$. Both samples from populations with same σ, unknown, estimated from $s^2 = \dfrac{\Sigma(x_1 - \bar{x}_1)^2 + \Sigma(x_2 - \bar{x}_2)^2}{n_1 + n_2 - 2}$	$\dfrac{(\bar{x}_2 - \bar{x}_1) - 0}{s\sqrt{\dfrac{1}{n_1} + \dfrac{1}{n_2}}}$	t-distribution based on $(n_1 + n_2 - 2)$ d.f.
(v) Between an observed proportion x/n and a supposed proportion p in the population.	$\dfrac{x - np}{\sqrt{np(1 - p)}}$ or $\dfrac{x/n - p}{\sqrt{p(1 - p)/n}}$	Approximated by standard normal distribution, if p not too different from 0·5 and n large enough.

****

69A

1, (ii)   2, (iv)   3, (i)   4, (v)   5, (iii)

FRAME 70

Miscellaneous Examples

In this frame a collection of miscellaneous examples is given for you to try.
Answers are provided in FRAME 71, together with such working as is considered
helpful.   Although this does not continue throughout to include a statement of
the null and alternative hypotheses, you should yourself always be quite clear
about what they are when embarking on a significance test, especially if you
intend to go on to the next programme.

1. Ten diesel engines selected at random from a production batch consumed fuel
    at the following rates (measured in litres per hour):

    15·2,   18·4,   12·8,   22·0,   17·6,   16·0,   20·0,   14·8,   18·0,   17·2

    when tested under identical conditions.

If the population from which the sample was taken follows a normal
distribution, justify the maker's claim that the fuel consumption of this
type of engine under the test conditions is 16·0 litres per hour.   (C.E.I.)

2.   Members of a consumer association investigated two brands of canned peas
selling at the same price for the same size of can.   A random selection
of 5 cans of each brand was made and the drained weights (in grams) were
as follows:

| Brand A | 297 | 292 | 312 | 307 | 317 |
| Brand B | 280 | 308 | 311 | 292 | 314 |

On the basis of this data, should the investigating team have recommended
one brand as being better value than the other?   (A statistical test shows
that neither brand is more variable in its drained weight than the other.)

3.   A test of significance can assist a geologist in deciding the name of a
particular fossil.   For instance, suppose that, on looking at a slab of
rock containing brachiopods, he thinks that the fossils look as if they
belong to the species Composita ambigua.   Suppose also that he finds the
mean length of 9 of the specimens before him to be 17·8 mm and that past
examination by fossil experts of a large number of specimens of the
brachiopod Composita ambigua has shown their lengths to be normally
distributed with mean 14·2 mm and s.d. 4·8 mm.   By applying a significance
test, decide what guidance you would give the geologist as to the correctness
of his preliminary identification of the brachiopods.

4.   Suppose that it is claimed that 40% of households in the U.K. own at least
one car.   Would doubt be cast on this claim if a survey of 120 randomly
selected households showed car ownership in 57 of them?

5.   It is thought that the yield of waxy substances from tobacco leaves may
depend upon the solvent used for extraction.   For each of 5 different
sources from which leaves were obtained, two extractions were carried out,
one using solvent A and the other using solvent B.   The yields were as
shown in the table:

Source	1	2	3	4	5
Solvent A	2·3	3·2	2·5	4·8	4·2
Solvent B	3·0	4·7	2·8	6·4	5·1

Use a suitable test to decide whether the two solvents produce significantly
different estimates of wax content, assuming you are prepared to accept
a 5% risk of concluding that a difference exists when in fact it does not.
Would your answer be the same if you were only prepared to take a 1% risk
of making such an error?

6.   Now ignore the headings showing source in the data in the previous question
and suppose that, for each solvent, the yields were obtained from tobacco
leaves selected at random without regard to source.   The problem of
deciding whether there is a difference between the two solvents is then one
of comparing the mean of 5 yields from extractions using solvent A with the
mean of 5 yields resulting from the use of solvent B, i.e. of testing the
significance of the difference between two sample means.   Find whether
such a test would lead to the same decisions as you arrived at in Qu. 5.

(An appropriate test shows no significant difference between the variance of yields obtained using solvent A and the variance of yields obtained using solvent B, so you can use the "pooled sum of squares" estimate of variance as given in (35.1).)

7. Rods are being cut to a nominal length of 96 cm.   The lengths of a random sample of 150 rods are given in the following grouped frequency table:

Length (cm)	92·5	93·5	94·5	95·5	96·5	97·5	98·5	99·5
Frequency	2	13	21	36	39	20	14	5

Find 95% confidence limits for the mean length of rod.

A second random sample of 120 rods has mean length 95·91 cm with s.d. 1·50 cm.   Is the difference in the mean values of the two samples significant?
                                                                (L.U.)

(HINT: The samples here are large enough for the variance estimates which they give to be treated as population values.   Your answer to FRAME 33 gives you the theory on which to base the significance test called for in this question.)

8. In finding out what the integral calculus is all about, a group of Loughborough University students in the first year of a degree course in Business Administration drew, on squared paper, the graph of $y = x(4 - x)$.   They then estimated the shaded area by counting squares and compared the answer with that obtained from $\int_0^4 x(4 - x)\,dx$.   The estimates obtained graphically by 15 students were:

10·76 10·10 10·74 10·10 10·45 10·55 10·46 10·58
10·80 10·77 10·51 10·55 10·44 10·58 10·41

The exact value obtained by evaluating the integral is $10\frac{2}{3}$.   On the basis of these results would you say that the square-counting method is biased?

9. The table gives the number of lost-time accidents which befell workers in a factory over a period of many years, classified according to the sex of the worker involved.

	Number of accidents	Number employed	Rate per 100 workers
Men	144	900	16·0
Women	45	360	12·5
Total	189	1260	15·0

To say whether one sex is more accident prone than the other, these figures must be viewed in relation to the number of each sex employed.   (It will be assumed that the men and women worked the same hours.)   It is then seen that the data shows a higher accident rate for men than for women.   Is this difference significant or can it reasonably be attributed to chance?
(HINT: If neither sex is more accident prone than the other the expected proportion of accidents which involve men will be 900/1260 and that involving women 360/1260.   Take either of these as the hypothetical value of p.   Supposing you take p = 360/1260, then you have to test whether the observed proportion of accidents involving women is significantly different.)

10. The results of an experiment with diabetic rats were given in FRAME 1.
     Test the hypothesis that the drug does not affect the blood glucose level
     of such rats.   (You may assume that the variation in blood glucose level
     from rat to rat is the same for treated and untreated rats.)

11. A manager is considering the purchase of several electronic calculators to
     be used for general computational purposes in the company offices.   The
     prices of two competitive models are comparable and the sales representative
     for each model claims that his model has features that will result in less
     time being spent doing the computational work required in the offices.   To
     compare the two calculators the manager obtains one of each on loan for a
     trial period and records the time taken by each of 5 operators to perform
     a sequence of computational routines that are typical of the work done in
     the office.   Each operator is timed with each calculator, and the times
     (in minutes) are as follows:

MACHINE \ OPERATOR	A	B	C	D	E
Wundaworka	13·5	13·1	12·4	12·6	13·9
Supaspeedi	12·5	12·7	12·0	13·7	12·6

     Should the manager conclude that there is a significant difference between
     the Wundaworka and the Supaspeedi, as far as speed of operation is
     concerned?   Assume that, in the event of there being no real difference in
     the long run, he is prepared to take a 5% risk of wrongly concluding that
     there is.

12. Of 100 new cars purchased at the same time by a car hire company, 50 are
     model A and 50 are model B.   After a period of time has elapsed, during
     which all cars have been in use, an inspection is carried out.   This
     reveals rusting of the bodywork in 15 of the cars of model A and 23 of
     those of model B.   Is this evidence of a real difference between the finish
     of these two models of car?

13. Two yarns A and B were tested for single-thread strength.   The results are
     given below, the breaking strengths (in newtons) having been recorded for 7
     test pieces of yarn A and 5 test pieces of yarn B.

     Yarn A   2·18   3·17   2·46   2·70   2·78   3·35   3·52
     Yarn B   3·13   3·07   3·92   3·51   2·92

          Calculations give $\Sigma x_A = 20·16$ $\Sigma x_A^2 = 59·4842$

                                $\Sigma x_B = 16·55$ $\Sigma x_B^2 = 55·4347$

     where x_A, x_B refer to the observations in the respective samples.

     Assuming the variation in the results of single-thread strength tests to be
     the same for both types of yarn, estimate the common variance.   Find 95%
     confidence limits for the difference $\mu_B - \mu_A$, where μ_A, μ_B are the
     population mean single-thread strengths for yarns A and B respectively.

14. Gregor Mendel, the abbot of a monastery, was a 19th century pioneer in the study of how characteristics are inherited. The theories which he put forward were suggested by plant-breeding experiments which he carried out. With regard to seed colour in garden peas one of his laws forecasts that if a pure yellow is crossed with a pure green, and the first generation hybrids are then crossed randomly with one another, the ratio of yellow to green in the second generation population is 3:1. If carrying out this procedure experimentally led to a count of 246 yellow peas out of a total of 300 in the second generation, would you consider the results to be inconsistent with Mendel's theory?

15. In an investigation into the effect of exercise on the heart rates of 18-year old male students, measurements were recorded for 25 such students randomly selected from freshmen at a university. Each student was subjected to a set programme of physical exertion lasting 5 minutes. His heart rate (in beats per minute) was recorded immediately before and immediately after this bout of exercise. Let this pair of observations be denoted by x_1 and x_2 respectively and their difference $x_2 - x_1$ by d. It is required to estimate μ_d, the mean increase in heart rate after the exercise programme, among all 18-year old male students. If $\bar{d}$ is the sample mean and $s_d^2 = \frac{1}{24}\Sigma(x - \bar{x})^2$, what can you say about the distribution of $\dfrac{\bar{d} - \mu_d}{s_d/5}$? Deduce 95% confidence limits for μ_d.

16. In the Apollo series of space flights, crew members underwent intensive medical examination before and after flight. As part of the examination of the cardiovascular system, the lower body was subjected to a pressure lower than that of the atmosphere by being placed in a chamber, with an airtight waist seal, connected to a regulated vacuum source. Heart rates, in beats per minute, were recorded when a pressure of $6700\ \mathrm{Nm}^{-2}$ below atmospheric had been reached. A simplified version of the results for 4 Apollo missions is shown here.

Apollo	Crew member	Pre-flight	Heart Rate 1st post-flight	3rd post-flight
	CDR	76	100	93
9	CMP	71	81	68
	LMP	70	87	65
	CDR	61	76	65
15	CMP	80	131	93
	LMP	59	–	78
	CDR	74	109	83
16	CMP	62	99	79
	LMP	79	112	98
	CDR	72	112	78
17	CMP	84	87	90
	LMP	63	82	60

CDR = Commander   CMP = Command Module Pilot   LMP = Lunar Module Pilot

The first post-flight evaluation took place on the recovery ship shortly after splashdown.   Second and third evaluations took place at intervals of approximately 24 hours thereafter – only the latter are included in this summary.   The test on the Apollo 15 LMP on recovery day was abandoned because of symptoms which he developed during the early stages of the reduction of pressure.

Comparing the first post-flight evaluation heart rates with the pre-flight ones, the increase is so marked that a significance test hardly seems necessary (if carried out it shows a difference which is significant at the 0·1% level).   Leaving aside the Apollo 15 LMP, so that the data can be treated as paired, calculate the immediate post-flight mean increase in heart rate found in the remaining 11 crew members and find the 95% confidence limits for its population value.

At the 3rd post-flight evaluation, heart rates appear to be returning to pre-flight levels.   Is the difference between them still significant? Having answered this question using a paired comparison test, see whether the same conclusion is reached if the pre- and post-flight values are treated as two independent samples, each of size 12, and the difference between their means is tested.   (It can be shown that the variation in heart rate from one crew member to another can be taken to be the same after flight as it was before.)   If you reach a different conclusion this time, suggest the reason for it.

17.   In the 1976 finals of BBC TV's "Young Scientists of the Year", the Oxford team's project involved studying the direction of movement of woodlice. The team applied the term "ambidextrous" to a woodlouse if it was equally likely to turn left or right in a T-maze.   The decision as to whether a woodlouse fell into this category was made by observing how many turns in each direction it made in repeated trials.   It was not considered to be "ambidextrous" if the number of left turns was outstandingly low or outstandingly high.   This procedure could be regarded as testing the N.H. $p = \frac{1}{2}$, against the A.H. $p \neq \frac{1}{2}$, where p is the probability of making a left turn.

Suppose the number of trials to be 6.

(i)   What is the probability of an "ambidextrous" woodlouse being wrongly classified, if the label "ambidextrous" is to be rejected when the number of left turns is   (a) either 0 or 6,   (b) either 0, 1, 5 or 6?

(ii)   For each of the criteria in (i), what is the probability of a woodlouse being wrongly classified as "ambidextrous" if it is really (a) a "left-handed" specimen, with $p = 0·9$, (b) a "right-handed" specimen, with $p = 0·4$?

18.   Suppose that a sample of 9 determinations is to be used to test the hypothesis that the octane number μ of a petroleum product is 87·5 and that the s.d. of such determinations is known to be 0·6.

(i)   What range of values of the sample mean will lead to the rejection of the N.H. $\mu = 87·5$, in favour of the A.H. $\mu \neq 87·5$, if a 5% significance level is chosen?   What is the chance of the N.H. not being rejected if μ is actually (a) 87·5, (b) 87·4, (c) 88·0?

(ii)   Answer the questions in (i) with the significance level changed to 1%.

Answers to Miscellaneous Examples

1. N.H.: That the maker's claim is correct, i.e. $\mu = 16 \cdot 0$ A.H.: $\mu \neq 16 \cdot 0$

$t = \dfrac{17 \cdot 2 - 16 \cdot 0}{\sqrt{6 \cdot 368/9}} \simeq 1 \cdot 43$ As $|t| < 2 \cdot 26$, the 5% critical value of $|t|$ for 9 d.f., the maker's claim would not be rejected at that level of significance (nor, of course, at the 1% level).

2. N.H.: $\mu_A = \mu_B$ A.H.: $\mu_A \neq \mu_B$

$t = \dfrac{305 - 301}{\sqrt{\dfrac{1270}{8}\left(\dfrac{1}{5} + \dfrac{1}{5}\right)}} \simeq 0 \cdot 50$ As $|t| < 2 \cdot 31$, the 5% critical value of $|t|$ for 8 d.f., there is insufficient reason for recommending either brand as better than the other.

3. $u = \dfrac{17 \cdot 8 - 14 \cdot 2}{4 \cdot 8/3} = 2 \cdot 25$ As $|u| > 1 \cdot 96$ but $< 2 \cdot 58$, the identification of the brachiopods as Composita ambigua should be rejected if a 5% significance level had been chosen, but not if the choice had been 1%.

4. Correcting for continuity, $u = \dfrac{56 \cdot 5 - 48}{\sqrt{120 \times 0 \cdot 4 \times 0 \cdot 6}} = 1 \cdot 58$ which is not large enough to cast doubt on the claim.

5. $\bar{d} = 1 \cdot 0$ where $d = x_B - x_A$, $s_d{}^2 = 0 \cdot 30$, $t = \dfrac{1 \cdot 0 - 0}{\sqrt{0 \cdot 30/5}} \simeq 4 \cdot 08$

For $\nu = 4$, the 5% critical value of $|t|$ is $2 \cdot 78$ so it would be decided, at that level of risk, that the two solvents produce significantly different estimates of wax content.   This decision would not be arrived at if the 1% risk level is chosen, as $|t| < 4 \cdot 60$.

6. $|t| = \dfrac{4 \cdot 4 - 3 \cdot 4}{\sqrt{1 \cdot 72\left(\dfrac{1}{5} + \dfrac{1}{5}\right)}} \simeq 1 \cdot 2$, based on 8 d.f.   The difference is not significant at the 5% level.

This test applies only to independent samples and it would be wrong to apply it if the data had been obtained on a matched basis, as in the previous question.   Using the same figures in the two examples serves to illustrate how, in this case, the variation in yield from source to source can mask a difference between the two solvents.   The value of s^2 is larger here because it includes a contribution due to source-to-source variation and so a larger value of $\bar{x}_1 - \bar{x}_2$ is required for significance than was the case with the paired comparison.

7. $95 \cdot 84$ and $96 \cdot 34$
$|u| \simeq 0 \cdot 95$ The difference is not significant at the 5% level.

8. $|t| \simeq 2 \cdot 67$ which, for 14 d.f., is significant (indicating bias) at the 5% level but not at the 1%.

9. Using test (v) in FRAME 69 with $p = 360/1260 = 2/7$, $x = 45$ (really $45 \cdot 5$ if you correct for continuity but the effect is negligible) and $n = 189$

gives $|u| \simeq 1 \cdot 4$, which does not reach the 5% significance level. Thus there is no convincing evidence of one sex being more accident prone than the other.

10. $s^2 = 0 \cdot 040\ 76$, $|t| \simeq 1 \cdot 54$, $\nu = 10$ The hypothesis would not be rejected at the 5% significance level.

11. Paired comparison test gives $|t| \simeq 0 \cdot 97$.   5% critical value of t for 4 d.f. $= 2 \cdot 78$.   No significant difference.

12. Using the test described in FRAMES 56-58 with $p_1 = 0 \cdot 3$, $p_2 = 0 \cdot 46$, $\hat{p} = 0 \cdot 38$, $n_1 = n_2 = 50$ gives $|u| = \dfrac{0 \cdot 46 - 0 \cdot 3}{\sqrt{0 \cdot 38 \times 0 \cdot 62 (0 \cdot 02 + 0 \cdot 02)}} = \dfrac{40}{\sqrt{19 \times 31}}$
$\simeq 1 \cdot 65$.   This does not reach the 5% significance level and there is insufficient justification for saying that there is a difference between the two models.

13. $\Sigma(x_A - \bar{x}_A)^2 = 1 \cdot 4234$ $\Sigma(x_B - \bar{x}_B)^2 = 0 \cdot 6542$ Estimate of common variance $= 0 \cdot 207\ 76$ 95% confidence limits for $\mu_B - \mu_A$ are $3 \cdot 31 - 2 \cdot 88 \pm 2 \cdot 23 \times 0 \cdot 2669$ i.e. $-0 \cdot 165$ and $1 \cdot 025$.

14. $|u| = 2 \cdot 8$ The difference is significant at the 1% level, indicating inconsistency with Mendel's theory.

15. t-distribution with 24 d.f. $\bar{d} \pm 2 \cdot 06\ s_d/5$ i.e. $\bar{d} \pm 0 \cdot 412\ s_d$

16. $25 \cdot 82$ beats per minute $16 \cdot 05$ and $35 \cdot 59$

Paired comparison test, with pre-flight and 3rd post-flight results for all 12 crew members, gives $\Sigma(d - \bar{d})^2 = 864 \cdot 25$, $|t| \simeq 3 \cdot 22$, which for 11 d.f. is significant at the 1% level.

$t \simeq 1 \cdot 89$ which, for 22 d.f., is not significant. This shows how, with this type of test, the variation in heart rate from one astronaut to another could obscure a real difference between pre- and post-flight heart rates.   The use of such a test would not, of course, be valid for data obtained as described in this question, as the heart rates in one sample are not independent of those in the other, both being recorded for the same crew members.

17. (i) Note that these answers represent the risk α of a type 1 error.
     (a) $0 \cdot 5^6 + 0 \cdot 5^6 = 0 \cdot 031\ 25$
     (b) $0 \cdot 5^6 + 6 \times 0 \cdot 5^6 + 6 \times 0 \cdot 5^6 + 0 \cdot 5^6 = 0 \cdot 218\ 75$

     (ii) Note that these answers represent, for each value of p, the risk β of a type 2 error.
     (a) For (i) (a), $0 \cdot 4686$; for (i) (b), $0 \cdot 1142$
     (b) For (i) (a), $0 \cdot 9492$; for (i) (b), $0 \cdot 7258$

Notice that the value of the risk β, corresponding to a stated α, depends on the actual value of p.   Also notice that when $p = 0 \cdot 9$, β decreases as α increases, and that the same thing happens when $p = 0 \cdot 4$.

18.   (i) $\bar{x} < 87 \cdot 11$ or $> 87 \cdot 89$ (a) $0 \cdot 95$ (b) $0 \cdot 9194$ (c) $0 \cdot 2912$

     (ii) $\bar{x} < 86 \cdot 98$ or $> 88 \cdot 02$ (a) $0 \cdot 99$ (b) $0 \cdot 9811$ (c) $0 \cdot 5398$

For each value of α, the answers to (a), (b) and (c) give the values of β for μ as given.   Notice that, for each α, the risk β depends on the actual value of μ.   Also notice that, for each μ, β increases as α decreases from $0 \cdot 05$ to $0 \cdot 01$.

Tests of Significance (2)

One-tailed and Two-tailed Tests

All the tests in the previous programme were concerned with deciding whether a
real difference existed, without regard to whether that difference represented
an increase or a decrease.   For instance, in looking at the fairness of a coin,
we would have rejected it as biased whether it was producing too few heads or
too many heads.   Denoting P(head) by p, the null hypothesis being tested was
$p = \frac{1}{2}$ and the alternative hypothesis was $p \neq \frac{1}{2}$, which covers both $p < \frac{1}{2}$ and
$p > \frac{1}{2}$.

Similarly, in deciding whether a population mean had a given value or not, the
N.H. was of the form $\mu = \mu_0$, with the A.H. $\mu \neq \mu_0$, which includes both
$\mu < \mu_0$ and $\mu > \mu_0$.   The N.H. was rejected if the sample mean $\bar{x}$ was either
unusually low or unusually high.   The rejection region thus covered the two
extremes of the range of values for $\bar{x}$.

Such tests are called TWO-TAILED or TWO-SIDED.   In some problems, however, it
is an increase, not simply a difference, that we are seeking to detect;   in
others, it is a decrease.   In either case, a ONE-TAILED (or ONE-SIDED) test is
appropriate and this programme begins with some illustrations that will show you
how to make such tests.

Suppose that, for a number of years, a standard method has been used for
manufacturing a particular chemical product.   It is thought that the addition
of a small quantity of a certain substance during the process will improve the
yield.   Five experimental runs with this additive present gave the following
yields (expressed as a percentage of the theoretical yield):

$$78 \qquad 85 \qquad 84 \qquad 81 \qquad 86$$

The question to be answered is whether there is a real improvement in yield,
compared with the standard method which gives a mean yield of 80 with s.d. 3·5.

Notice that the only change in mean yield which is of interest here is an
increase.   If there is no clear indication of an increased yield, the additive
will not be used and whether it would have caused a decrease, or left the yield
unchanged, is of no consequence.   The null hypothesis is taken as $\mu = 80$,
and the alternative as $\mu > 80$.   The one-sided nature of the test affects only
the boundary between acceptance and rejection regions.   The test statistic
and distribution table used will be the same as for a two-sided test.

Calculate the test statistic which you think is appropriate to this problem and
state which tables you would refer to for the critical value.   (There is no
reason to suppose that the presence of the additive will affect the variation
in yield and, as you will find later, this is confirmed when a statistical test
is applied to the data.)

****

2A

$$u = \frac{82 \cdot 8 - 80}{3 \cdot 5/\sqrt{5}} = 1 \cdot 789 \qquad \textit{Standard normal distribution}$$

Now comes the question of what range of values of u should lead to the
rejection of the N.H.   In the previous programme, where we were looking for
evidence of a <u>difference</u>, the rejection region covered values of u which, on
the basis of the N.H., would be either unusually low or unusually high.   This
is shown in diagram (i), where the area under the two tails is the significance
level α, i.e. the chance of rejecting the N.H. when it is correct.

Two-tailed test	One-tailed test	One-tailed test
N.H. $\mu = \mu_0$	N.H. $\mu = \mu_0$	N.H. $\mu = \mu_0$
A.H. $\mu \neq \mu_0$	A.H. $\mu > \mu_0$	A.H. $\mu < \mu_0$

$\alpha/2$ $\alpha/2$ α α

REJECT   ACCEPT   REJECT   ACCEPT   REJECT REJECT   ACCEPT

(i)   (ii)   (iii)

In the present problem we are looking for evidence of an <u>increase</u> in yield and
this can only be provided by a <u>high</u> value of the sample mean.   Thus the
rejection region covers values of u which, on the basis of the N.H., would be
unusually high and this is shown in diagram (ii), where α is the area under the
right-hand tail.

For $\alpha = 0 \cdot 05$, the rejection region in diagram (i) is given by $|u| > 1 \cdot 96$ and
this was used in two-tailed tests in the previous programme.   What range of
values of u will be considered significant at this level when a one-tailed test,
as in diagram (ii), is being used?

                         ****

3A

$u > 1 \cdot 64$ *(obtained from TABLE 2)*

As the yields of the trial runs gave a value of u in this range, the N.H. would
be rejected if a 5% significance level had been chosen, and it would be
concluded that the overall mean yield had increased.

However, because of the cost involved in changing over to the new process, the
manufacturer might only be willing to take a 1% risk of making a change which
does not really improve the yield.   If that were the case, would you still
conclude that the additive increases the yield?

                         ****

4A

No.   A 1% risk would require u > 2·33 for a significant increase to be shown.

Thus the mean yield of the trial runs was high enough to claim an improvement on
the standard method at the 5% level, but not high enough to signify an
improvement at the 1% level.   For 5 trial runs what is the minimum mean yield
that would be required to show a real increase (i) at the 5% level,

(ii) at the 1% level?   (If you don't have a calculator handy, just give
expressions without evaluating them.)

****

5A

(i) $80 + 1 \cdot 64 \times 3 \cdot 5/\sqrt{5} = 82 \cdot 6$ *(ii)* $80 + 2 \cdot 33 \times 3 \cdot 5/\sqrt{5} = 83 \cdot 6$

FRAME 6

Now let us consider a different problem relating to the same plant process as
before.   Suppose a modification to the process is proposed, which would have
some advantage (e.g. lower cost) over the standard method if it does not cause
a decrease in yield.   In this case the decision which has to be made is whether
or not there is a decrease.   If there is, the existing method will be retained,
but otherwise the modification will be introduced.   Thus, if μ is the overall
mean yield of the modified process, we must this time test the N.H. $\mu = 80$
against the A.H. $\mu < 80$.   The acceptance and rejection regions are as shown
in diagram (iii) in FRAME 3.

If, as before, it can be assumed that the modification does not affect the
variation in yield from batch to batch, i.e. σ is still $3 \cdot 5$, the normal
distribution will again be appropriate.   Suppose that, if it were the case that
the modification would not decrease the overall mean yield, you would be
prepared to take a risk of up to 5% of missing the benefits of the modified
process.   (i) What values of u would then lead to you deciding to retain the
existing method?   (ii) If, as before, the number of trial runs with the
modified process is 5, what is the minimum mean yield from this sample that
would lead to the modification being made?

****

6A

(i) $u < -1 \cdot 64$ *(ii)* $80 - 1 \cdot 64 \times 3 \cdot 5/\sqrt{5} = 77 \cdot 4$

FRAME 7

Both the examples just considered have been concerned with testing a value of μ
where σ was known, and hence the normal distribution was used.   Here are two
problems for you to try.   They require other types of test whose two-sided
versions you are already familiar with.   It is now just a matter of making
these tests on a one-sided basis and you should not find this too difficult.

1. An organisation concerned about the health hazards of smoking is making
    checks on the nicotine content of various brands of cigarettes and comparing
    the results obtained in its laboratory with the figures quoted by the
    manufacturers.

    According to its manufacturer, the mean nicotine content of a brand of
    cigarettes does not exceed 20 mg.   The organisation's laboratory found the
    nicotine content in 5 of these cigarettes selected at random to be:
    22, 21, 20, 23, 24 mg.   Should the manufacturer's claim be contested if it
    is acceptable to take a risk of up to 5% of making a false accusation?
    Would the answer to this question be the same if the greatest acceptable
    risk were 1%?

    (HINT: Take the N.H. as $\mu = 20$, this being the maximum mean allowed by the
    manufacturer's claim.   As the organisation is only looking for evidence of
    a value of μ <u>higher</u> than this, the A.H. is $\mu > 20$.)

FRAME 7   (continued)

2. It is required to determine whether a new kind of synthetic fibre is
    weakened by dyeing.   Ideally each strength test would be carried out first
    on an undyed thread and then on the same thread after dyeing, but this is
    impossible because the test is destructive.   The best that can be done is
    to use two pieces of thread which initially are as alike as possible.
    With this in view, 6 lengths (numbered 1 to 6) are halved and one half
    of each pair (chosen randomly) dyed.   The strength tests gave the following
    results (in coded form):

Length no.	1	2	3	4	5	6
x_U (undyed)	14·5	14·4	11·6	14·0	13·4	12·1
x_D (dyed)	13·7	13·6	10·9	12·0	11·6	12·5

Has dyeing produced a significant decrease in strength?

****

7A

1. *Sample mean = 22   Unbiased estimate of variance = 2·5*

$$t = \frac{22 - 20}{\sqrt{0·5}} \simeq 2·83$$

*For 4 d.f., there is a 5% chance of getting a value of t greater than
2·13 and hence the rejection region for the 5% significance level is
t > 2·13.   At this level of risk the manufacturer's claim would be
contested, but not at the 1% level as that requires t > 3·75.*

2. *Denoting the population means by μ_U and μ_D, the N.H. is $\mu_D = \mu_U$ and the
    A.H. is $\mu_D < \mu_U$.   As the data is paired, we must consider the difference,
    $x_D - x_U$ or $x_U - x_D$, it doesn't matter which.   Taking $d = x_U - x_D$, the
    N.H. is then $\mu_d = 0$ and the A.H. $\mu_d > 0$, where μ_d is the population
    mean for d.*

    $\bar{d} = 0·95$ Unbiased estimate of var(d) = 0·751

    $$t = \frac{0·95 - 0}{\sqrt{0·751/6}} \simeq 2·69$$ *This is significant at the 5% level, but not at the*

    *1% level, as for 5 d.f. the rejection regions are respectively t > 2·02
    and t > 3·36.*

    *(If you were bothered about the data being coded, think of the effect that
    a change of origin will have on the values of d.   None.   As the
    t-statistic is a ratio it is unaffected by any change of unit that is made.
    Thus coding makes no difference to the value of t obtained.)*

FRAME 8

The Variance Ratio F

You now know how to apply a significance test when comparing (i) an observed
sample mean with a supposed population mean, or (ii) two observed sample means.
You also know that these tests can be made on either a one-tailed or a
two-tailed basis, depending on the particular question that is being asked.

However, a mean describes only one aspect of a distribution.   Consider errors
of measurement, for instance.   The accuracy of a technique is a matter of how

near the mean of observations made by it is to the true value.   On the other
hand, the precision is concerned with the variation between observations and
that is not described by their mean but by their ....   Suggest how this
sentence could be completed.

****

8A

*By any of the following: Range, mean deviation, interquartile range,
variance,   standard deviation.*

FRAME 9

You are now going to learn about a test that can be used in comparing variability.
Of the measures of variability available, you have seen that the standard
deviation and its square, the variance, are the ones most commonly met with.
For reasons of mathematical convenience, this test uses the variance.

Such a test might be applied when the precision of a method of chemical analysis
or of a measuring instrument has been established from past experience.   The
test could then be used to decide, for instance, whether an analyst is competent
in using the method i.e. whether the variation in his results can reasonably be
attributed to that inherent in the method itself, or whether it is partly
caused by carelessness or inexperience.   In this type of situation, the
required comparison is between a sample of observations (made by the analyst)
and a population (based on past experience).

A more common need for the test occurs when two samples have to be compared.
This would happen if, from the results of a small number of analyses carried out
by each of two methods, you had to decide whether one method leads in general to
results of better reproducibility than the other.   It also happens, as you have
already seen, in the use of a t-test to compare two sample means, if you want
to check that it is valid to use (35.1) on page 202 to obtain a pooled estimate
of variance from the two samples.

FRAME 10

Once again it must be emphasised that the need for statistical methods in
general, and significance tests in particular, is caused by the necessity to
base conclusions on only a limited number of measurements.   If an infinitely
large number of analyses could be carried out by one method and an infinitely
large number by a second method, then it would be possible to find the actual
variances σ_1^2 and σ_2^2 for results obtained by the first and second methods
respectively, and it could be stated definitely that the method with the lower
variance gives results of better reproducibility.   But, of course, in practice
only a limited number (often small) of analyses can be made, so only sample
estimates of σ_1^2 and σ_2^2 can be found.   A difference between the values
s_1^2, s_2^2 of these estimates does not in itself mean that σ_1^2 and σ_2^2 must be
different.   Does $s_1^2 > s_2^2$ necessarily imply $\sigma_1^2 > \sigma_2^2$?

****

10A

*No.   Obviously, arguments apply here which are similar to those previously
applied to means, where you have seen that, because of chance fluctuations, it is
possible to have $\bar{x}_1 > \bar{x}_2$ without having $\mu_1 > \mu_2$.*

To decide whether s_1^2 and s_2^2 are different enough to show statistical
significance, it would be necessary to test the hypothesis $\sigma_1^2 = \sigma_2^2$.   To test
the hypothesis that two samples are from populations with the same variance, we
shall need to know how different the variance estimates obtained from two such
samples are likely to be.

When making a test to decide whether two samples were from populations with the
same <u>mean</u>, it was $\bar{x}_1 - \bar{x}_2$ that was considered, because the distribution could
be readily deduced from the N.H. $\mu_1 = \mu_2$.   When making a test to decide
whether two samples are from populations with the same <u>variance</u>, it is s_1^2/s_2^2
that is considered because it is the distribution of this ratio, rather than
that of the difference $s_1^2 - s_2^2$, that can be readily deduced from the N.H.
$\sigma_1^2 = \sigma_2^2$.   The distribution is that of the variance ratio F, so named by
G.W. Snedecor in honour of R.A. Fisher, a pioneer in the use of statistical
methods.

You will remember that, in the case of Student's t, there is not just one
t-distribution, but many.   In thinking about what would happen if, for instance,
we had s instead of σ in $\dfrac{\bar{x} - \mu}{\sigma/\sqrt{n}}$, we saw that the distribution would be
affected by the fact that s varies from sample to sample.   Moreover, it seemed
reasonable that how much $\dfrac{\bar{x} - \mu}{s/\sqrt{n}}$ varies is affected by how much s varies.
That in turn depends on the sample size, as the larger the sample the more
reliable is the estimate s and the less it varies from sample to sample.

With this in mind, it will probably come as no surprise to you to learn that
there is not just one F-distribution.   How much s_1^2 varies from sample to
sample will depend on the size of the sample and the same is true of s_2^2.
Consequently there is a different F-distribution for each possible combination
of sample sizes.

Each t-distribution, you will recall, is usually identified by the number of
degrees of freedom, ν, in the variance estimate, rather than with the size of
sample on which this estimate is based.   In a similar way, each F-distribution
is usually associated with the number of d.f. ν_1, ν_2 in the respective
estimates s_1^2, s_2^2.   How are ν_1, ν_2 related to the respective sample sizes
n_1, n_2?

        ****

$\nu_1 = n_1 - 1$ $\nu_2 = n_2 - 1$

Briefly, if s_1^2, s_2^2 are independent unbiased estimates, based on samples of
n_1, n_2 items respectively, of the same population variance, then s_1^2/s_2^2
satisfies an F-distribution.   (There is a requirement that populations be
normal.   In examples in this text this assumption will be made, though it may
only be approximate.)   Which F-distribution is needed depends on the number of
degrees of freedom ν_1, ν_2 in the estimates s_1^2, s_2^2 respectively.   To
specify the F-distribution being referred to, it is convenient to use the

notation $F_{\nu_2}^{\nu_1}$ for $\dfrac{s_1^2}{s_2^2}$.   This indicates that ν_1 is the number of d.f. in the numerator and ν_2 is the number of d.f. in the denominator.   You may find the notation F_{ν_1, ν_2} used elsewhere.

The probability density function for F is complicated and will not be given at this stage.   Obviously it must be a function of ν_1, ν_2.   What must it be for F < 0?

****

13A

$p(F) = 0$ for $F < 0$, as $s_1{}^2/s_2{}^2$ cannot be negative.

FRAME 14

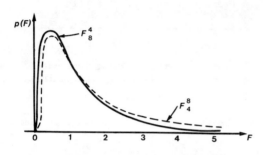

Whilst theoretically there is no upper limit to the value F can take, the larger the value the more unlikely it becomes.   The probability curves in the diagram, one shown by a continuous line and the other by a broken line, are those for F_8^4 and F_4^8 respectively.

As has already been noted, getting a value of $s_1{}^2/s_2{}^2$ which is not equal to 1 does not in itself give grounds for rejecting the hypothesis $\sigma_1{}^2 = \sigma_2{}^2$.   However, a value of $s_1{}^2/s_2{}^2$ which is unusually far away from 1, either below or above it, would throw suspicion on the hypothesis.   In TABLE 4 you will find values of the variance ratio which would have only a P% chance of being exceeded if the hypothesis were correct, for P = 5, 2·5 and 1.   Values of ν_1 are given along the top and values of ν_2 down the left-hand side.   Remember that ν_1 is the number of d.f. in the <u>numerator</u> and ν_2 the number of d.f. in the <u>denominator</u>.   Thus if, for example, $s_1{}^2$ is obtained from a sample of 5 observations and $s_2{}^2$ from a sample of 9 observations, the distribution of $s_1{}^2/s_2{}^2$ is that of F_8^4 as $\nu_1 = 5 - 1 = 4$ and $\nu_2 = 9 - 1 = 8$.

Turn to TABLE 4 and looking down the column for $\nu_1 = 4$ to the row for $\nu_2 = 8$, you will see that there is a 5% chance of getting a value of $s_1{}^2/s_2{}^2$ greater than 3·84, and that the corresponding values of this variance ratio for chances of 2·5% and 1% are 5·05 and 7·01 respectively.

If the sample sizes had been reversed, i.e. $s_1{}^2$ based on 9 observations and $s_2{}^2$ on 5, what value of $s_1{}^2/s_2{}^2$ would have a P% chance of being exceeded if

(i) P = 5,   (ii) P = 2·5,   (iii) P = 1 ?

****

14A

(i) 6·04   (ii) 8·98   (iii) 14·8

Note that these answers, which refer to the distribution of F_4^8, are not the same as those which were obtained for F_8^4.   That's why it is essential to take ν_1 as the number of d.f. in the numerator.

One-tailed F-test

As an example of a significance test based on an F-distribution, consider two
substances A and B which have to be mixed in a vat.   To examine the
effectiveness of the mixing process, 7 samples were taken from different places
in the vat after 10 minutes operation.   The percentage of substance A in each
sample was then obtained, giving the following results:

      35·4   36·4   35·2   34·8   33·3   34·6   35·3

Samples were again taken after a further 5 minutes mixing and the percentages
then obtained were:

      33·6   35·2   34·7   34·9   35·9   35·3   36·1

The decision that has to be made is whether the extra 5 minutes of mixing has
been effective, i.e. has it increased the uniformity of the mixture?

If the first 7 results are from a population with variance σ_1^2 and the
second 7 from a population with variance σ_2^2, the N.H. to be tested is
$\sigma_1^2 = \sigma_2^2$.   As the extra mixing time is only worth-while if the uniformity is
increased, i.e. the variance is decreased, a one-sided test is called for and
the A.H. is $\sigma_2^2 < \sigma_1^2$, i.e. $\sigma_1^2 > \sigma_2^2$.

For the 1st set of results: $\Sigma(x_1 - \bar{x}_1)^2 = 5 \cdot 34$

$$\text{Best estimate of population variance} = \frac{5 \cdot 34}{6} = 0 \cdot 89$$

For the 2nd set of results: $\Sigma(x_2 - \bar{x}_2)^2 = 4 \cdot 14$

$$\text{Best estimate of population variance} = \frac{4 \cdot 14}{6} = 0 \cdot 69$$

Taking $s_1^2 = 0 \cdot 89$ with $\nu_1 = 6$ and $s_2^2 = 0 \cdot 69$ with $\nu_2 = 6$, gives

$$F_6^6 = \frac{0 \cdot 89}{0 \cdot 69} \simeq 1 \cdot 3$$

We now have to decide whether this is significantly higher than 1.   Look up in
TABLE 4 the 5% critical value of F_6^6, i.e. the value which has only a 5% chance
of being exceeded if the N.H. is correct.   Deduce the range of values of F_6^6
for which the hypothesis of equal population variances would be (i) accepted,
(ii) rejected.

        ****

$4 \cdot 28$ *(i)* $< 4 \cdot 28$ *(ii)* $> 4 \cdot 28$

The value of F_6^6 which we have obtained is considerably less than $4 \cdot 28$.   Thus,
although they gave a lower variance estimate, the second set of results could
well have come from a population with the same variance as the first set.   At
the 5% level, the difference in variance estimates is not significant.   The
conclusion is that the further 5 minutes of mixing has not made the mixture
more homogeneous.

Now, the procedure of the mixing experiment involved first the mixing of the
ingredients and then the determination of the percentage of A present in each

of 7 samples taken from different parts of the vat.   There are thus two possible sources of variation in the results : (i) lack of homogeneity in the mixture, so that the actual percentage of A present differs from sample to sample, and (ii) error in determining this percentage for each sample.   We have found that the extra 5 minutes of mixing has produced no significant reduction in the variation of results, so it has evidently not reduced component (i), but is this component still present, i.e. is the mixture still not uniform?   If the mixture is uniform, the only remaining source of variation will be (ii), so the question can be rephrased as: Can the variation that still exists from one result to another be entirely accounted for by the method of determining the percentage of A present, or is it partly due to incomplete mixing?

Let us suppose that past analysis of mixtures of known composition has shown that the method of determination of the amount of substance A present gives results whose variance is 0·46.   The question is then answered by making the hypothesis that the mixture is uniform and the 7 determinations are therefore from a population whose variance is 0·46.   This will have to be tested against the alternative that the variance has another component, due to lack of uniformity in the mixture, and is therefore greater than 0·46.   The test thus takes the form:

$$\text{N.H.:} \quad \sigma^2 = 0\cdot46$$
$$\text{A.H.:} \quad \sigma^2 > 0\cdot46$$

To decide whether a variance estimate of 0·69, based on 6 d.f., is consistent with this N.H., the variance ratio 0·69/0·46 is considered.   The denominator is a population value, so the number of d.f. on which it is based is infinite, and we have $F_\infty^6 = \dfrac{0\cdot69}{0\cdot46} = 1\cdot5$.

By referring to TABLE 4, decide whether the N.H. should be rejected if a 5% significance level is chosen.

            ****

17A

You should have found that a value of at least 2·10 would be required to justify rejecting the N.H.   Hence the N.H. is retained and we would conclude that the variability of the percentages could well have been caused by the method of determination and is not evidence of lack of uniformity in the mixture.

FRAME 18

You have now participated in two F-tests.   In the second one, an estimate s^2 was being compared with a population value σ^2.   This is rather a special case in that one of the ν's is infinite, and there is an alternative approach using another distribution which you will meet later.   The more common use of F is illustrated by the first test, in which two estimates s_1^2 and s_2^2 were being compared.   That is how F-tests are used in analysis of variance, an important statistical technique which you will learn about in Unit 3.

Here are two problems, both requiring one-sided tests.   They will give you some practice in applying what you have learned about F up to this point, before you proceed to the extension to two-sided tests.

(1) With the aim of improving its precision, a modification to a standard method of analysis is proposed.   Five repeat tests using the standard method gave results from which the unbiased estimate of variance was calculated to be

FRAME 18   (continued)

2·025.   Six repeat tests using the modified method gave an unbiased
variance estimate of 0·450.   Would you conclude that the reproducibility
of results is improved by the modification?

(2)   In a factory where boxes of tablets are packed by hand, the distribution of
the weights of full boxes is normal, with variance 0·12.   It is essential
that this variance should not increase, if the contents of the boxes are
to be kept within permitted limits, and a check is made periodically by
weighing 10 full boxes taken at random.   From this sample an unbiased
estimate of the population variance is calculated.   If a value of 0·24
were obtained for this estimate would you regard the situation as
satisfactory?   Would your answer be the same whether you were using the 5%
significance level or the 1%?

****

18A

(1)   *Obviously the modification will only be adopted if it improves the precision
i.e. it decreases the variance.   Hence the test is one-tailed and if the
variances of the standard and modified methods are σ^2, σ_m^2 respectively,
then:*

N.H.: $\sigma^2 = \sigma_m^2$

A.H.: $\sigma_m^2 < \sigma^2$ *i.e.* $\sigma^2 > \sigma_m^2$

$F_5^4 = \dfrac{2 \cdot 025}{0 \cdot 450} = 4 \cdot 5$, *but a value of at least 5·19 would be required for
significance at the 5% level.   Thus you should have decided that the
lower variance estimate with the modified method could well have arisen by
chance and does not represent a real improvement in the method.*

*NOTE: Perhaps you weren't sure which variance ratio to consider –
2·025/0·450 or 0·450/2·025.   It is purely a matter of convenience.
Deciding whether 0·450/2·025 is significantly less than 1 is equivalent
to deciding whether 2·025/0·450 is significantly greater than 1.   The
latter viewpoint is chosen because the tables give critical values of F
at the upper end of the distribution.*

(2)   *N.H.: $\sigma^2 = 0 \cdot 12$*
      A.H.: $\sigma^2 > 0 \cdot 12$

$F_\infty^9 = \dfrac{0 \cdot 24}{0 \cdot 12} = 2$ *which is greater than the 5% critical value but not the 1%.*

*Thus, if a 5% significance level were chosen, the situation would not be
regarded as satisfactory, but the sample variance estimate is not high
enough to justify the same conclusion at the 1% level.*

FRAME 19

Two-tailed F-test

The greatest use of F occurs in analysis of variance, where the test is always
one-sided.   There are, nevertheless, situations where a two-sided F-test is
called for.   You have already met such a situation in the previous programme,
where there was a need to check the validity of using a pooled estimate of
variance in a t-test to compare two sample means.   For the time being, you were
just told that a statistical test showed no significant difference between the
sample estimates of variance.   That statistical test is an F-test and you are
now going to see how it is made.

In a two-tailed test, values of the test statistic at both extremities of its distribution lead to rejection of the N.H.   With the normal and t-distributions there was symmetry about zero, which made it a simple matter to deduce what was happening at the lower end from what was happening at the upper end.   For example, TABLE 2 gives $P(u > 1 \cdot 96) = 2 \cdot 5\%$, from which it can be deduced that $P(u < -1 \cdot 96) = 2 \cdot 5\%$ and $P(|u| > 1 \cdot 96) = 5\%$.

An F-distribution lacks such symmetry, but it is still possible to find out from TABLE 4 what is happening at the lower end of the distribution.   Let us denote by F_P the value of $F^{\nu_1}_{\nu_2}$ which has a P% chance of being exceeded.   Then, if $s_1{}^2$ and $s_2{}^2$ are estimates of σ^2 based on ν_1 and ν_2 d.f. respectively, the probability of $s_1{}^2/s_2{}^2$ being greater than F_p is P%.   Which of the following statements would it be correct to deduce from this?

   (i)   There is a P% probability of $s_1{}^2/s_2{}^2$ being less than $1/F_p$.

  (ii)   There is a P% probability of $s_2{}^2/s_1{}^2$ being greater than $1/F_p$.

(iii)   There is a P% probability of $s_2{}^2/s_1{}^2$ being less than $1/F_p$.

                    ****

(iii)

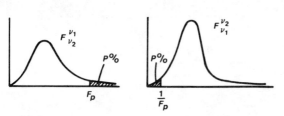

The distribution of $s_2{}^2/s_1{}^2$ being that of $F^{\nu_2}_{\nu_1}$, you will see that we have arrived at the result depicted in the diagram, in which the shaded areas are equal.

Now fill in the gaps in the following statement for

(i) $\nu_1 = 4$, $\nu_2 = 12$,   (ii) $\nu_1 = 12$, $\nu_2 = 4$.

In the distribution of $F^{\nu_1}_{\nu_2}$,   2·5% of values are greater than ....
and 2·5% are less than ....

                    ****

(i) *4·12,* *1/8·75*   *(ii)* *8·75,* *1/4·12*

FRAME 22

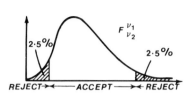

When the N.H. $\sigma_1^2 = \sigma_2^2$ is being tested on a two-tailed basis, the A.H. is $\sigma_1^2 \neq \sigma_2^2$. The diagram shows the range of values of s_1^2/s_2^2 for which the N.H. would be accepted and the range for which it would be rejected, if the 5% testing level had been chosen.

What would these ranges be for   (i) $\nu_1 = 4$, $\nu_2 = 12$,   (ii) $\nu_1 = 12$, $\nu_2 = 4$?

****

22A

(i) *Accept for* $\dfrac{1}{8\cdot75} < \dfrac{s_1^2}{s_2^2} < 4\cdot12$ *Reject for* $\dfrac{s_1^2}{s_2^2} < \dfrac{1}{8\cdot75}$ *or* $> 4\cdot12$.

(ii) *Accept for* $\dfrac{1}{4\cdot12} < \dfrac{s_1^2}{s_2^2} < 8\cdot75$ *Reject for* $\dfrac{s_1^2}{s_2^2} < \dfrac{1}{4\cdot12}$ *or* $> 8\cdot75$.

FRAME 23

You have found that with $\nu_1 = 4$, $\nu_2 = 12$, the N.H. is rejected if either $s_1^2/s_2^2 > 4\cdot12$ or $s_1^2/s_2^2 < 1/8\cdot75$, i.e. if either $s_1^2/s_2^2 > 4\cdot12$ or $s_2^2/s_1^2 > 8\cdot75$.   Now, you will recall that $4\cdot12$ and $8\cdot75$ are the upper $2\cdot5\%$ points obtained from the distributions F_{12}^4 and F_4^{12} respectively.

Generalising from this, it can be seen that the N.H. is rejected at the 5% level if either

$$s_1^2/s_2^2 > \text{the upper } 2\cdot5\% \text{ point on the } F_{\nu_2}^{\nu_1} \text{ distribution}$$

$$\text{or } s_2^2/s_1^2 > \text{the upper } 2\cdot5\% \text{ point on the } F_{\nu_1}^{\nu_2} \text{ distribution}$$

Hence, in practice, if s_1^2 is the larger estimate you compare the value of s_1^2/s_2^2 with the critical value given by $F_{\nu_2}^{\nu_1}$, but if s_2^2 is the larger you take the ratio s_2^2/s_1^2 and compare it with the critical value given by $F_{\nu_1}^{\nu_2}$.
Thus the F-tables are easily used for two-sided tests, though TABLE 4 would not be adequate for this purpose if a 1% level of significance were chosen. Why not?

****

23A

Upper $0\cdot5\%$ points are not included.   (They have been omitted in the interest of brevity and in this course you will not meet any problems which require them.)

FRAME 24

In the previous programme the gains in weight made by 7 pigs fed on diet A were compared with the gains made by 6 pigs fed on diet B.   The t-test made to compare the means $\overline{x}_A$ and $\overline{x}_B$ was based on the assumption of a common variance — in other words, it was assumed that the variation in weight gain from

one pig to another was the same whichever diet the pigs were receiving.   That
assumption will now be justified by the application of an F-test.

The weight gains x_A of the 7 pigs on diet A gave a mean $\bar{x}_A$ of 70 and
$\Sigma(x_A - \bar{x}_A)^2 = 132$.   For the 6 pigs on diet B, the mean $\bar{x}_B$ was 64, with
$\Sigma(x_B - \bar{x}_B)^2 = 214$.

We have to test the hypothesis that the x_A's and x_B's are from populations
with the same variance, against the alternative that the variances are different.
With the usual notation, this can be expressed as:

$$\text{N.H.:} \quad \sigma_A^2 = \sigma_B^2$$

$$\text{A.H.:} \quad \sigma_A^2 \neq \sigma_B^2$$

If s_A^2, s_B^2 are the unbiased variance estimates obtained from the 7 values
of x_A and the 6 values of x_B respectively, what are their values and on how
many degrees of freedom is each based?

****

24A

$s_A^2 = 132/6 = 22 \qquad 6 \; d.f.$

$s_B^2 = 214/5 = 42 \cdot 8 \qquad 5 \; d.f.$

FRAME 25

The N.H. will be rejected if s_A^2 is either significantly lower than s_B^2 or
significantly higher than s_B^2, i.e. the test is two-sided.   As the data has
given s_B^2 as the greater estimate of the two, we consider the ratio s_B^2/s_A^2.
This has 5 d.f. in the numerator and 6 d.f. in the denominator, so the
appropriate distribution is that of F_6^5.   If the 5% significance level is
chosen, the 2·5% upper critical value is required from TABLE 4.   Check that it
is 5·99.   As $s_B^2/s_A^2 = 42 \cdot 8/22 \simeq 1 \cdot 95$, which is considerably less than 5·99,
the N.H. would not be rejected and the assumption of a common variance is
justified.

The 10% significance level is not often used, but if it were chosen in this
case, would the N.H. still be retained?

****

25A

*Yes.   The 5% upper critical value of F_6^5 is 4·39, still well above the
observed ratio.*

FRAME 26

If s_A^2 had been the larger variance estimate, for what values of the ratio
s_A^2/s_B^2 would the N.H. have been rejected at (i) the 5% level, (ii) the 10%
level?

****

(i) $s_A^2/s_B^2 > 6 \cdot 98$ *(ii)* $s_A^2/s_B^2 > 4 \cdot 95$

FRAME 27

In Misc. Ex. 2 of the previous programme you used a t-test to compare the
drained weights of two brands, A and B, of canned peas.   A random selection
of 5 cans of each brand gave results from which it was calculated that
$\Sigma(x_A - \bar{x}_A)^2 = 430$ and $\Sigma(x_B - \bar{x}_B)^2 = 840$.   Verify the statement then made that
a statistical test shows that neither brand is more variable in its drained
weights than the other.

****

27A

$s_B^2/s_A^2 \simeq 1 \cdot 95.$ *A value of F_4^4 of at least $9 \cdot 6$ would be required to show a
difference between the two brands at the 5% level.*

FRAME 28

Confidence Limits for σ^2 using F

You have already learned that, when a sample mean is used to give an estimate
of the population mean μ, it is more informative to give a confidence interval
for μ instead of just stating the value of $\bar{x}$.   Something similar can be done
when a population variance σ^2 is being estimated.   If you fill in the gaps in
the statements below you will get the idea of how it is done.   Suppose that s^2
is the unbiased estimate, obtained from a sample of 25 observations, of a
population with variance σ^2.

   (i)   There is a 2·5% chance that $\sigma^2/s^2 >$ ....
   (ii) There is a 2·5% chance that $\sigma^2/s^2 <$ ....
   (iii) There is a 95% chance that σ^2/s^2 is between .... and ....
   (iv) There is a 95% chance that σ^2 is between .... and ....

****

28A

(i) $1 \cdot 94$ *(ii)* $1/1 \cdot 64 = 0 \cdot 61$ *(iii)* $0 \cdot 61, \ 1 \cdot 94$ *(iv)* $0 \cdot 61 s^2, \ 1 \cdot 94 s^2$

FRAME 29

The statements in the previous frame led up to a 95% confidence interval for
σ^2, given in (iv).   Now see if you can obtain 90% confidence limits by
similar reasoning.

****

29A

$0 \cdot 66 s^2$ *and* $1 \cdot 73 s^2$

FRAME 30

The Chi-squared Distribution

You have seen that the F-distribution can be used to compare s^2 and σ^2, either
when finding confidence limits, as in the previous two frames, or when testing a
hypothetical value for σ^2, as was done earlier.   This use of the variance

ratio F is rather special in that either ν_1 or ν_2 is infinite, because σ^2 is
the population variance, and it has already been mentioned that in such cases an
alternative approach is available.   The alternative arises from the fact that
while the distribution of s^2/σ^2 falls into the category of an F-distribution,
it is also described by a related type of distribution, which we are now going
to consider and which provides the basis of some useful significance tests
where F does not offer a possible alternative.

If x_1 is a variate which is $N(\mu_1, \sigma_1{}^2)$, x_2 is $N(\mu_2, \sigma_2{}^2)$, ... and x_n
is $N(\mu_n, \sigma_n{}^2)$, describe the distributions of the variates $u_1, u_2, ..., u_n$,
where $u_1 = \dfrac{x_1 - \mu_1}{\sigma_1}$, $u_2 = \dfrac{x_2 - \mu_2}{\sigma_2}$, ..., $u_n = \dfrac{x_n - \mu_n}{\sigma_n}$.

****

They are all N(0, 1), i.e. the standard normal distribution.

As you know, the range of possible values of each of $u_1, u_2, ... u_n$ extends
from $-\infty$ to $+\infty$.   Admittedly there will be values in this range which are
highly improbable, but the probability density is never actually zero.   What is
the range of possible values of (i) $u_1{}^2$, (ii) $u_1{}^2 + u_2{}^2$,
(iii) $u_1{}^2 + u_2{}^2 + ... + u_n{}^2$?

****

0 to ∞, in each case.

Variates such as those defined in (i), (ii) and (iii) of the previous frame are
conventionally denoted by χ^2, χ being the Greek letter chi.   (Pronounce the
ch as in Scottish words such as loch, if you want to be really expert about it.)
χ^2, rather than χ, is used because of its essentially non-negative nature.

Thus we may write $\chi_1{}^2 = u_1{}^2$

$\chi_2{}^2 = u_1{}^2 + u_2{}^2$

$\vdots$

$\chi_n{}^2 = u_1{}^2 + u_2{}^2 + ... + u_n{}^2$

As $x_1, x_2, ... x_n$ vary independently of one another, so also will
$u_1, u_2, ... u_n$, and $\chi_n{}^2$ is thus the sum of n components which are free to
vary independently of one another.   The term "degrees of freedom" is again
applicable and for $\chi_n{}^2$ the number of d.f., ν, is obviously n.

State the values of ν for $\chi_1{}^2$ and $\chi_2{}^2$ respectively.

****

For $\chi_1{}^2$, $\nu = 1$.   *For* $\chi_2{}^2$, $\nu = 2$.

It can be shown mathematically that the mean value of $u_1{}^2$ is 1, and clearly the same will be true of $u_2{}^2$, $u_3{}^2$, ... $u_n{}^2$. Remembering what you have learned about the distribution of sums, state the mean of the distribution of

(i) $\chi_1{}^2$,   (ii) $\chi_2{}^2$,   (iii) $\chi_n{}^2$ (iv) χ^2 with ν d.f.

****

(i) 1   (ii) 2   (iii) n   (iv) ν

If you also remember that the variance of a sum of independent variates is the sum of their variances, you will realise that the variance of a χ^2-distribution will be proportional to the number of terms which go to make up χ^2, i.e. the variance will be proportional to ν (it can be shown to be 2ν), and so the higher the value of ν the more spread out the distribution will be.

It will already be evident that, as in the case of t and F, there is not just one distribution.   There are different χ^2-distributions, one for each value of ν.   Recalling that the Central Limit Theorem tells us that the distribution of a sum of independent variates approaches the normal distribution as the number of terms in the sum increases, we see that the larger the value of ν the nearer will the χ^2-distribution be to a normal distribution.

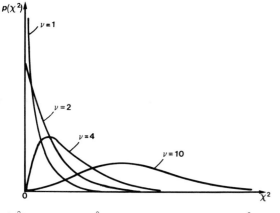

The properties of χ^2 which have now been deduced are illustrated in the diagram, which shows the probability curves for four values of ν.   The p.d.f. is $k(\nu)(\chi^2)^{\frac{1}{2}\nu-1} e^{-\frac{1}{2}\chi^2}$ where $k(\nu)$ is a function of ν that makes the total area under the curve equal to 1.   You might like to check that the curves for $\nu = 1$ and $\nu = 2$ differ from those for all other values of ν in the way they behave as $\chi^2 \rightarrow 0$.   If this interests you, show that for $\nu = 1$,

$p(\chi^2) \rightarrow \infty$ as $\chi^2 \rightarrow 0$; for $\nu = 2$, $p(\chi^2) = k(2)$ when $\chi^2 = 0$; and for $\nu > 2$, $p(\chi^2) = 0$ when $\chi^2 = 0$.   If you are not interested you can proceed directly to the next frame without impairing your understanding of subsequent frames.

Use of tables of χ^2

In TABLE 5 at the end of this volume you can find the value of χ^2, with
ν d.f., which has a P% probability of being exceeded.   Check that, for
$\nu = 24$,   there is a   2·5%   chance that $\chi^2 > 39·36$,
                      a   97·5%   chance that $\chi^2 > 12·40$,
     and hence a   2·5%   chance that $\chi^2 < 12·40$.

Then fill in the gaps in the following:

$$\text{For} \quad \nu = 6, \qquad P(\chi^2 > ....) = 0·05$$
$$P(\chi^2 > ....) = 0·95$$
$$P(\chi^2 < 1·64) = ...$$

****

36A

12·59,   1·64,   0·05

FRAME 37

χ^2 and the Sampling Distribution of s^2

If s^2 is the estimate of the population variance σ^2, obtained from a sample of
size n using the formula $\dfrac{1}{n-1} \Sigma(x - \bar{x})^2$,   then, as you are aware, s^2 will
vary from sample to sample.   It can be shown that the distribution of
$\dfrac{\Sigma(x - \bar{x})^2}{\sigma^2}$,   i.e. of $\dfrac{(n-1)s^2}{\sigma^2}$,   is a χ^2-distribution with   (n − 1)   d.f.
State the mean of this distribution and hence confirm that the statement in the
previous sentence is consistent with s^2 being an unbiased estimate of σ^2.

****

37A

n − 1.

As the mean value of $\dfrac{(n-1)s^2}{\sigma^2}$ *is* *n − 1,* *the mean value of* s^2 *is*

$\dfrac{\sigma^2}{n-1} \times (n-1),$ *i.e.* σ^2, *and thus* s^2 *is an unbiased estimate of* σ^2.

FRAME 38

Hitherto we have solved problems concerning the variance ratio s^2/σ^2 by
considering the F_∞^{n-1} distribution.   You will now see that an alternative is
to use the χ^2-distribution with   n − 1   d.f. for $(n-1)s^2/\sigma^2$.

Take first the problem of testing the hypothesis that σ^2 has a given value, in
the light of an observed value of s^2.   An example of this occurred in
FRAME 17 where the test was to decide whether the variance estimate of 0·69
given by a sample of 7 observations, was significantly higher than 0·46, the
known variance attributable to the method of determination.   As n = 7, the
χ^2-distribution for $\nu = 6$ applies.   Your first answer in 36A now tells us
that there is a 5% chance of getting a value of $6s^2/\sigma^2$ greater than 12·59,
i.e. of getting a value of s^2/σ^2 greater than 2·10.   (Note that this
critical value is the same as you obtained in 17A using F_∞^6.)   From this point
onwards the reasoning is the same as it was before − the observations give
$s^2/\sigma^2 = 0·69/0·46 = 1·5$, which is not high enough to be significant at the 5%

level and the N.H. that $\sigma^2 = 0 \cdot 46$ is retained.

In problem (2) in FRAME 18, the value of s^2 obtained from the weights of 10
full boxes was $0 \cdot 24$ and the test was to decide whether this was significantly
higher than the maximum permissible population variance of $0 \cdot 12$.   Repeat the
test now, using χ^2 instead of F.   The procedure is outlined below, all you
have to do is fill in the gaps.

For $\nu = \ldots\ldots$, $P(\chi^2 > \ldots\ldots) = 0 \cdot 05$ and $P(\chi^2 > \ldots\ldots) = 0 \cdot 01$

$\therefore$ There is only a 5% chance of getting a value of $9s^2/\sigma^2 > \ldots\ldots$
i.e. of getting a value of $s^2/\sigma^2 > \ldots\ldots$
and only a 1% chance of getting a value of $9s^2/\sigma^2 > \ldots\ldots$
i.e. of getting a value of $s^2/\sigma^2 > \ldots\ldots$

Observed value of $s^2/\sigma^2 = \ldots\ldots\ldots$
The result is significant at the $\ldots\ldots\ldots$ level.

****

38A

*9, 16·92, 21·67, 16·92, 1·88, 21·67, 2·41, 2, 5% (it does not reach the 1%
level of significance).*

FRAME 39

Confidence Limits for σ^2 using χ^2

χ^2 can also be used instead of F in finding confidence limits for σ^2 .
Consider, as in FRAME 28, the case where s^2 is obtained from a sample of 25
observations.   The distribution of $24s^2/\sigma^2$ is then that of χ^2 with $\nu = 24$
and the result given in FRAME 36 can be restated as:

There is a 2·5% chance that $24s^2/\sigma^2 > 39 \cdot 36$.
There is a 2·5% chance that $24s^2/\sigma^2 < 12 \cdot 40$.

By making use of these statements, complete (i) and (ii) below and then check
that your answers are the same as were obtained for (i) and (ii) in FRAME 28.

(i)   There is a 2·5% chance that $\sigma^2/s^2 > \ldots\ldots$
(ii) There is a 2·5% chance that $\sigma^2/s^2 < \ldots\ldots$

****

39A

(i) $\dfrac{24s^2}{\sigma^2} < 12 \cdot 40$ *gives* $\dfrac{\sigma^2}{s^2} > \dfrac{24}{12 \cdot 40}$ *which is 1·94 as in (i) in 28A.*

(ii) $\dfrac{24s^2}{\sigma^2} > 39 \cdot 36$ *gives* $\dfrac{\sigma^2}{s^2} < \dfrac{24}{39 \cdot 36}$ *which is 0·61 as in (ii) in 28A.*

95% confidence limits for σ^2 then follow as in (iii) and (iv) in FRAME 28.

FRAME 40

χ^2-tests for Goodness of Fit

Mention was made in Unit 1 of experiments conducted to investigate the
paranormal powers claimed by Uri Geller.   In one of these experiments a die was
placed in a closed steel box which was shaken and then placed on a table, and
Geller was asked to say which die face was uppermost.   It was stated that

control runs, in which the die had been shaken in this way, had been found 'to produce a distribution of uppermost die faces not differing significantly from what one would expect to happen by chance'.   You are now going to find out how a significance test can lead to such a conclusion.

Suppose that 60 control runs had been made, giving the following distribution of numbers on the uppermost die faces.

Number on face of die	1	2	3	4	5	6
Observed frequency	14	7	6	11	6	16

The problem is to determine whether these observed frequencies are compatible with the hypothesis that all faces of the die have an equal chance of landing uppermost.   What theoretical frequencies would be given by this hypothesis?

****

The theoretical distribution would be a uniform one, with $P(x) = 1/6$ for
$x = 1, 2, \ldots.6$,   and corresponding expected frequencies:

10, 10, 10, 10, 10, 10

This is just one instance - there are many more - of how we may need to compare observed frequencies with those given by a hypothesis being tested.   As the observed frequencies are subject to chance variation it is highly unlikely that they will coincide with the corresponding expected values, even if the theory is correct.   The question that has to be answered is - how great a difference between the two sets of frequencies can reasonably be attributed to chance variation?   Assessing the effect of chance variation calls for a probability model and in this type of problem it is a χ^2-distribution which meets the need.

Let us consider the general case where there are n intervals in the frequency table and the observed and expected frequencies in the ith interval are denoted by 0_i, E_i respectively.   Provided that no values of E_i are too small (the usual criterion is $\not< 5$) the distribution of

$$\sum_{i=1}^{n} \frac{(0_i - E_i)^2}{E_i}$$

will approximate to a χ^2-distribution with the appropriate number of d.f.   In the 60 control runs with the die, n = 6.   What are the values of 0_i and E_i for i = 1 to 6?

****

The values of 0_i are   14, 7, 6, 11, 6, 16.   The corresponding values of E_i
are all 10.

The calculation of the value of X^2 for the data is set out below:

O_i	E_i	$O_i - E_i$	$(O_i - E_i)^2$	$(O_i - E_i)^2/E_i$
14	10	4	16	1·6
7	10	-3	9	0·9
6	10	-4	16	1·6
11	10	1	1	0·1
6	10	-4	16	1·6
16	10	6	36	3·6

$$X^2 = 9·4$$

Add up the figures in the column $O_i - E_i$. Would the result be the same for any set of values of O_i and E_i?

****

42A

$\Sigma(O_i - E_i) = 0$. This would always happen because ΣO_i and ΣE_i must be the same. When doing the calculations yourself (as opposed to using a computer) check that this column adds to zero before proceeding.

The value of X^2 now has to be examined to see whether it gives any indication of bias in the die. What set of values of O_i would have given $X^2 = 0$? What would your reaction have been to such a set of observations?

****

43A

$O_i = E_i = 10$ for all i. Suspicion! Even without working out any probabilities it is obvious that such a set of results would be very unlikely to occur by chance and one would suspect that they had been manoeuvred.

You have noticed that complete agreement between the observed and theoretical frequencies would give zero for X^2. It will also be obvious to you that the poorer is the agreement between the two sets of frequencies, the larger will be the values of $(O_i - E_i)^2/E_i$ and hence the larger will be their sum. What you have to decide is whether this sum has a value too large to be reasonably attributed to chance variation in the observed frequencies. Use of the X^2-distribution will enable you to make this decision, with TABLE 5 telling you what would be an unusually large value for X^2, once you have defined what you consider to be "unusual".

By now you have no doubt guessed that this is leading up to a significance test. The N.H. to be tested is that the die is a fair one, against the A.H. that it is not. If you are prepared to take a 5% risk of rejecting a fair die, then the critical value of X^2 is that which would have only a 5% chance of being exceeded because of random fluctuations. If the value of 9·4, which we have obtained, is greater than this critical value, then the difference between the O_i's and the E_i's would be judged significant at the 5% level and we would

FRAME 44   (continued)

conclude that the die was not a fair one.

What information do you require before you can find the 5% critical value of χ^2 from TABLE 5?

****

44A

The value of ν, i.e. the number of degrees of freedom.

FRAME 45

You will perhaps recall that, in the introduction to χ^2 earlier on, the number of d.f. was explained as being the number of terms in its sum free to vary independently of one another.   Now, there were 6 terms in the sum that gave 9·4 in FRAME 42, but each of those terms was derived from a value of $O_i - E_i$ and not all 6 values of $O_i - E_i$ are free to vary independently.   How many are?

****

45A

Only 5, the sixth being then restricted by the fact that $\Sigma(O_i - E_i)$ must be zero.   Or, think of it this way, if you prefer.   The results of the 60 trial runs were, in fact, figments of the authors' imagination.   We wrote down 14, 7, 6, 11, 6 for the first 5 frequencies but then we no longer had any free choice – the last frequency had to be 16 to make the total 60.

FRAME 46

Thus in the sum that gave 9·4 there were only 5 terms free to vary independently, and so it is to the χ^2-distribution for $\nu = 5$ that we must refer.   Turning to TABLE 5 you will find the entry 11·07.   Hence a value of χ^2 as large as 9·4 would occur more than 5% of the time, it is not significant at the 5% level and on this basis you would go ahead with the experiments to test Geller, satisfied that the die and the process for shaking it are such that all 6 faces have an equal chance of landing uppermost.

The solution of this problem has illustrated the use of χ^2 in testing for GOODNESS OF FIT.   In this case we were testing the fit between the data and the uniform distribution defined by $P(x) = 1/6$ for $x = 1, 2, \ldots. 6$.   Here is a similar problem for you to try on your own:

When reading a scale where the last figure is estimated, some observers show a marked preference for particular digits.   The table below shows the distribution of the last figure in 200 randomly chosen routine readings made by one observer.

Last figure	0	1	2	3	4	5	6	7	8	9
Frequency	35	16	15	17	17	19	11	16	30	24

Test whether there is evidence of such a preference, if the chance you are prepared to take of wrongly accusing the observer of bias is (i) 5%, (ii) 1%.

****

46A

In randomly chosen readings all 10 digits should be equally likely to appear in the last place.

O_i	E_i	$O_i - E_i$	$(O_i - E_i)^2/E_i$
35	20	15	11·25
16	20	−4	0·80
15	20	−5	1·25
17	20	−3	0·45
17	20	−3	0·45
19	20	−1	0·05
11	20	−9	4·05
16	20	−4	0·80
30	20	10	5·00
24	20	4	0·80

$$\chi^2 = 24\cdot90$$

Here there are 10 values of $O_i - E_i$ but, as their sum must be zero, freedom to vary independently is available to only 9 of them, and consequently to only 9 of the terms contributing to χ^2. Or, to put it another way, if you try to imagine all the other sets of observations which might have occurred when the 200 readings were chosen, each set of O_i's would be such that their sum is 200. Thus your imagination would only have free rein for 9 out of 10 values of O_i, the last always being fixed by the

constraint $\Sigma O_i = 200$, and in consequence only 9 out of the 10 values of $(O_i - E_i)^2/E_i$ would be varying freely.

For $\nu = 9$, χ^2 must exceed 16·92 to be significant at the 5% level and 21·67 to be significant at the 1% level.

In either (i) or (ii) the data would be considered to show evidence of bias on the part of the observer. Note that amongst the contributions to the value of 24·90 for χ^2, 11·25 stands out. This suggests either a preference or a distaste for 0 as the last figure – in this case, a preference.

FRAME 47

In the fourth programme of Unit 1, the Rutherford–Geiger data on the emission of α-particles served to illustrate the fitting of a Poisson model. The expected frequencies were calculated from the formula $\dfrac{Ne^{-\mu}\mu^x}{x!}$, x being the number of α-particles emitted during a 7·5 s interval, N the total number of intervals and μ the mean value of x. The values of N and μ were the same as for the data, i.e. 2608 and 3·8715 respectively. Calculations then gave:

Number of particles	Observed number of intervals (Rutherford–Geiger data)	Expected number of intervals (Poisson model)
0	57	54·3
1	203	210·3
2	383	407·1
3	525	525·4
4	532	508·6
5	408	393·8
6	273	254·1
7	139	140·6
8	45	68·0
9	27	29·3
10	10	11·3
11	4	4·0
12	0	1·3
13	1	0·4
14	1	0·1
	2608	2608·6

At that stage it was commented that 'there appears to be good agreement between observation and theory', but you were promised a test for assessing the goodness of fit statistically.   Now you will realise that this is the kind of test being dealt with at the moment.   Before proceeding to the routine calculation of χ^2, re-read the second paragraph of FRAME 41 and then look at the column of E_i values as given on the previous page.   What requirement for the use of χ^2 is not met by these E_i?

****

47A

The requirement $E_i \not< 5$ is not met at the bottom end of the table.

FRAME 48

To get round this difficulty, adjacent groups are combined until an expected frequency of at least 5 is obtained.   In this example, the last 4 groups need to be amalgamated.   The calculations then proceed in the usual way.

O_i	E_i	$O_i - E_i$	$(O_i - E_i)^2/E_i$
57	54·3	2·7	0·134
203	210·3	−7·3	0·253
383	407·1	−24·1	1·427
525	525·4	−0·4	0·000
532	508·6	23·4	1·077
408	393·8	14·2	0·512
273	254·1	18·9	1·406
139	140·6	−1·6	0·018
45	68·0	−23·0	7·779
27	29·3	−2·3	0·181
10	11·3	−1·3	0·150
6	5·8	0·2	0·007

$-0·6 \qquad \chi^2 = 12·944$

$\Sigma(O_i - E_i)$ is not exactly zero here because of round-off in the E_i's, making their sum 2608·6 instead of 2608.

To assess the significance of the value of χ^2, it is necessary to know the number of d.f. involved in its make-up. This will be the next step.

FRAME 49

We now need to explore the concept of degrees of freedom rather more thoroughly than before.   Take first the case of a variance estimate based on a sample of size n.   In the first programme of this Unit you have seen that, there being n terms in $\Sigma(x - \bar{x})^2$ and one constraint on the values of $x - \bar{x}$ (a sum of zero), the number of d.f. in the estimate is n − 1, i.e.

number of terms in the sum   number of constraints to which
used to calculate s^2 −   these terms are subject

Next recall the goodness-of-fit test, made in this programme on the results from an experiment with a die.   The number of d.f. then obtained for χ^2 was 6 − 1, i.e.

number of terms summed   number of constraints to which
to give χ^2 −   these terms are subject

The one constraint was caused by ΣO_i and ΣE_i both having the same value.

In the present example, the sum giving χ^2 has 12 components and, as with the die results, there is a constraint caused by the O_i's and the E_i's having the

FRAME 49   (continued)

same totals.   However, now there is a second restriction because the E_i's have been made to have something else in common with the O_i's.   Can you say what it is?   If it is not immediately evident, think back to how the E_i's were calculated (look back to FRAME 47 if you need to be reminded of the details).

****

49A

The values of E_i were calculated from a Poisson distribution having the same mean as the data itself.   Thus the O_i's and the E_i's give distributions with the same mean.

FRAME 50

There are thus 2 constraints, reducing the number of d.f. in X^2 to $12 - 2 = 10$.   Decide whether the value of $12 \cdot 94$ obtained for X^2 shows a significant difference between the two sets of frequencies, at the 5% testing level.

****

50A

The 5% critical value of X^2 for $\nu = 10$ is $18 \cdot 31$.   Thus the difference between the two sets of frequencies can reasonably be attributed to chance and the Poisson distribution would be regarded as fitting the data satisfactorily. (Following the improvements made in counting equipment since the days of Rutherford's experiment, even closer agreement with the Poisson model has been shown by more recent data.)

FRAME 51

In the next example, the goodness of fit of a normal model will be tested.   The data on lives (in hours) of 80 lamps, which were grouped into a frequency table in Unit 1, will be used.   The normal model that will be considered is that with the same mean ($1225 \cdot 5$) and s.d. (346) as the grouped data.   To remind yourself of how the expected frequencies given by this model would be obtained, calculate the frequency that would be given for the interval whose true end-points are $1400 \cdot 5$ and $1600 \cdot 5$.   In arriving at your answer you will need to use the total 80;   what other quantities obtained from the data figure in your calculations?

****

51A

$80 \times 0 \cdot 1672 \simeq 13 \cdot 4$

The mean and s.d.

FRAME 52

The complete set of frequencies given by the normal model are shown on the next page, together with the observed frequencies.

Life (hours)	Observed Frequency	Expected Frequency
< 200·5	0	0·1
200·5 – 400·5	1	0·6
400·5 – 600·5	2	2·1
600·5 – 800·5	5	5·9
800·5 – 1000·5	12	11·8
1000·5 – 1200·5	17	17·1
1200·5 – 1400·5	20	17·8
1400·5 – 1600·5	12	13·4
1600·5 – 1800·5	7	7·3
1800·5 – 2000·5	3	2·9
2000·5 – 2200·5	1	0·8
> 2200·5	0	0·2
	80	80·0

First combine adjacent groups where necessary to avoid $E_i < 5$ and then calculate χ^2 as before.

****

52A

O_i	E_i	$O_i - E_i$	$(O_i - E_i)^2/E_i$
8	8·7	–0·7	0·056
12	11·8	0·2	0·003
17	17·1	–0·1	0·001
20	17·8	2·2	0·272
12	13·4	–1·4	0·146
11	11·2	–0·2	0·004
80	80·0	0·0	$\chi^2 = 0·482$

FRAME 53

To assess the significance of this value of χ^2, the number of d.f. must be known.   There were 6 terms in the sum and, as you noted earlier, the values of O_i and E_i were made to have the same total and to give distributions with the same mean and s.d.   There were thus 3 constraints imposed and the required number of d.f. is therefore $6 - 3 = 3$.   By referring to TABLE 5 decide whether to reject, at the 5% level, the N.H. that lives are normally distributed.

****

53A

For $\nu = 3$, the 5% critical value of χ^2 is 7·81 so the value obtained is far from being large enough to justify the rejection of the normal model.

FRAME 54

In goodness-of-fit tests an unusually large value of χ^2 represents a lack of agreement between data and theory, and casts doubt on the suitability of the theory.   An unusually small value of χ^2, on the other hand, would represent a quite remarkable agreement between data and theory and raises suspicions about the data.   Having decided that 0·482 is not unusually large, we might now ask

FRAME 54   (continued)

if it is unusually small.   As a guide to the answer, complete the following
statement by referring to TABLE 5.

For $\nu = 3$,   there is a 95% chance of χ^2 being greater than .... and
hence a 5% chance of χ^2 being less than ....

****

54A

$0 \cdot 35, \quad 0 \cdot 35$

FRAME 55

Thus you see that, in this example, χ^2 would have to be less than $0 \cdot 35$ to be
unusually small if "unusually" is defined as "having a probability of less than
5%".   Hence the value of $0 \cdot 482$ is not, at this level, significantly small.
But suppose that 10% were substituted for 5% in the definition of "unusually"?
How would you then view a value of $0 \cdot 482$ for χ^2?

****

55A

There is a 90% chance of χ^2 *being greater than* $0 \cdot 58$ *and hence a 10% chance
of being less than* $0 \cdot 58$.   *The chance of getting a value as small as* $0 \cdot 482$ *is
therefore between 5 and 10%, so although the closeness of the agreement
between the two sets of frequencies is not unusual enough to be significant at
the 5% level, it comes near to being so.   Thus you might feel slightly
suspicious about the data.   We have to confess that, on this occasion, your
suspicions would be justified.   The data was a figment of the authors'
imagination and was chosen to give a roughly symmetric distribution.*

FRAME 56

The general rule for finding the number of degrees of freedom when using a χ^2
goodness-of-fit test may now be stated as:

Number of degrees of freedom	=	Number of terms which are summed to give χ^2	−	Number of quantities obtained from the observations and used to calculate the expected frequencies

In the test on the results from the die experiment, only one quantity, the total
of 60, was obtained from the data and used in calculating the E_i's.   In
fitting a Poisson distribution to the Rutherford–Geiger data, two such
quantities, the total and the mean, were used.   In the last example, where a
normal distribution was fitted to the lamp data, there were 3 quantities – the
total, the mean and the s.d. – obtained from the data and used in calculating
the E_i's.

In the next example you will be asked to work out for yourself the number of
d.f. involved in the calculation of χ^2.

FRAME 57

The data in the following table was obtained from tests made on 250 nylon bars
which had been moulded under similar conditions from the same batch of moulding
powder.   Each bar was subjected to a test at 5 places along its length to see
whether it would break under a particular applied force.   The number of breaks
which occurred was recorded for each bar.

Number of breaks	0	1	2	3	4	5
Number of bars	141	62	31	14	1	1

The aim of the investigation was to discover whether brittleness was randomly
distributed throughout the bars or whether it was concentrated in particular
bars.   If the former were the case, the probability of a break occurring would
be the same at every test.   Then, when a bar is tested at 5 points, at each
point there is a two-way outcome - break or no break - and the probability p
of a break is the same at each of the 5 points.   Under these circumstances
what deduction immediately follows about the distribution of x, the number of
points at which a bar breaks?

****

57A

*Binomial with n = 5.   The terms in the expansion of $(q + p)^5$, where
q = 1 - p, will give the probabilities of 0, 1, 2, ... 5 breaks occurring.*

FRAME 58

To work out the theoretical frequencies that this model would give, it will be
necessary to have a value for p.   As a large number of trials were carried
out, a reasonable estimate of p can be obtained from the data.   Breaks
occurred at 175 of the 1250 test points, so p can be estimated as
175/1250 = 0·14.   Write down the formula for P(x), the probability of a bar
breaking at x points.   How would you deduce a formula for expected frequency,
i.e. number of bars out of 250 which will, on average, break at x points?

****

58A

$$P(x) = {}^5C_x \ 0 \cdot 86^{5-x} \ 0 \cdot 14^x \qquad \textit{Expected frequency} = 250 \ P(x)$$

FRAME 59

The values of P(x) for x = 0, 1, 2, ...5 are given below, together with the
expected frequencies.   (You may wish to refer back to FRAMES 25-27 on pages
94-95, in which the fitting of this binomial model was discussed at greater
length.)

x	0	1	2	3	4	5
P(x)	0·4704	0·3829	0·1247	0·0203	0·0017	0·0001
Expected frequency	117·6	95·7	31·2	5·1	0·4	0·0

Now apply a χ^2-test to see whether there is a significant difference between
these frequencies and those which were observed.   If you decide that there is,
say at which level.

****

O_i	E_i	$O_i - E_i$	$(O_i - E_i)^2/E_i$
141	117·6	23·4	4·656
62	95·7	−33·7	11·867
31	31·2	−0·2	0·001
16	5·5	10·5	20·045

$$\chi^2 = 36 \cdot 569$$

In calculating the E_i's, the value of 0·14 for p and the total of 250 were used.

$$\therefore \quad \nu = 4 - 2 = 2$$

From tables, it is seen that χ^2 exceeds the 5% and 1%, and even the 0·1%, critical values.

Note: There is therefore very strong evidence indeed that the results are not consistent with the hypothesis of a binomial model and one would conclude that the probability of a break at a test point is not the same for all the bars. If you compare the observed and expected frequencies, you will see that there were more bars with zero breaks than expected and also a higher number of bars with 3 or more breaks than expected. This could be explained by some bars being tough throughout and not breaking at any point, whereas other bars were brittle throughout and thus tended to break repeatedly.

FRAME 60

Contingency Tables

Suppose that a particular dimension of a machine-made article is required to be within specified lower and upper tolerance limits. The articles, when checked for size by the use of limit ("go" and "no-go") gauges, will fall into one of three categories – undersize, within tolerances and oversize. The table below shows the number of articles in each of these three categories produced during a period of time by each of the four machines A, B, C, D which manufacture them.

Machine \ Size	Undersize	Within tolerances	Oversize	Totals
A	6	162	8	176
B	15	136	9	160
C	11	223	6	240
D	18	199	7	224
Totals	50	720	30	800

You will see that there were 6 items from Machine A which were undersize, 15 from Machine B which were undersize, and so on. Adding up the columns gives the sub-totals which show how the 800 articles were distributed among the size categories (50 undersize, etc.) and adding along the rows gives the sub-totals which show the number of articles produced by each machine (176 by Machine A, etc.).

Check your comprehension of the table by answering the following questions:

(i) State how many articles were (a) produced by Machine D and within the tolerances, (b) produced by Machine D, (c) within the tolerances.

(ii) State the proportion of the 800 articles that were (a) undersize, (b) produced by Machine A.

****

(i)   *(a) 199*   *(b) 224*   *(c) 720*
(ii) *(a) 50/800 = 0·0625*   *(b) 176/800 = 0·22*

The figures given in the table in the previous frame are all frequencies. A
table of frequency data arising, as this one does, from a classification with
respect to two attributes (in this case, machine and size) is called a
CONTINGENCY TABLE.   You will notice that in the present example there are 4
rows, deriving from the classification according to machine, and 3 columns,
from the classification according to size.   This is a 4 × 3 contingency
table (4 rows × 3 columns).   Obviously, had the same data been arranged with 3
rows for the size categories and 4 columns corresponding to the different
machines, it would have been a 3 × 4 contingency table.   How many rows and
columns do you think an m × n contingency table has?

              ****

m rows × n columns

We now consider the question of whether the machines differ among themselves in
meeting the tolerance limits placed on the dimension of the product.   Does one
machine produce more undersize items than the others, or fewer oversize items,
or less articles which are not within the tolerances?   Or do all machines, in
the long run, produce the same proportion of articles in each of the size
categories?

A decision on whether there is any difference between the machines can be based
on a significance test.   The null hypothesis to be tested is that there is no
difference between the machines.   We then have to see whether, if this
hypothesis were true, the observed differences as shown by the data can be
reasonably explained as the effect of chance variation.   If not, then the
hypothesis will be rejected in favour of the alternative – that there is a
difference between the machines.

From the N.H. it would follow that, for instance, the proportion of undersize
items produced is the same for each machine.   You have already noted that, in
the sample of 800, the proportion of undersize items was 50/800.   Taking this
as an estimate of the proportion of undersize items produced overall would give
(50/800) × 176, i.e. 11, as the expected number of undersize items out of the
total of 176 produced by Machine A.   By similar reasoning, the expected
number of "within tolerances" items out of a total of 176 would be
(720/800) × 176, i.e. 158·4, and the expected number of oversize items would
be (30/800) × 176, i.e. 6·6.

The total number of articles produced by Machine B was 160.   Find the expected
number in each size category, by similar reasoning to that just used for
Machine A.

              ****

Expected number of undersize items   *= (50/800) × 160 = 10*
Expected number of "within tolerances" items = (720/800) × 160 = 144
Expected number of oversize items   = (30/800) × 160 = 6

Continuing in this way gives the set of expected frequencies shown here in brackets below the observed frequencies.

Size Machine	Undersize	Within tolerances	Oversize	Totals
A	6 (11)	162 (158·4)	8 (6·6)	176
B	15 (10)	136 (144)	9 (6)	160
C	11 (15)	223 (216)	6 (9)	240
D	18 (14)	199 (201·6)	7 (8·4)	224
Totals	50	720	30	800

You will now see that the problem is one of comparing a set of observed

O	E	O − E	$(O-E)^2/E$
6	11	−5	2·273
162	158·4	3·6	0·082
8	6·6	1·4	0·297
15	10	5	2·500
136	144	−8	0·444
9	6	3	1·500
11	15	−4	1·067
223	216	7	0·227
6	9	−3	1·000
18	14	4	1·143
199	201·6	−2·6	0·034
7	8·4	−1·4	0·233
800	800·0	0·0	10·80

frequencies with the corresponding theoretical frequencies given by a hypothesis. You already know that a χ^2-test can be used in making such a comparison. The calculation of the test statistic proceeds along the familiar lines (for simplicity, the suffix i for O and E is now omitted).

What do you now need to know if you are to use the χ^2 table to judge whether a value of 10·80 is unusually high?

****

The number of degrees of freedom on which this χ^2 is based.

As has been explained before, the number of d.f. in χ^2 is the number of its components (i.e. terms in the sum) which are free to vary independently of one another. Now the terms which form the sum are obtained from the values of O − E and you have already noticed, in the goodness-of-fit tests, that $\Sigma(O - E) = 0$. This is clearly also the case in the present example but there are further constraints on the values of O − E, as is shown by displaying them in the lay-out of the contingency table on the next page.

Size / Machine	Undersize	Within tolerances	Oversize	Totals
A	-5	3·6	1·4	?
B	5	-8	3	?
C	-4	7	-3	?
D	4	-2·6	-1·4	?
Totals	?	?	?	0

Add the rows and columns.   What do you notice about the sub-totals thus obtained?   Is this feature special to this particular example or would it have happened if we had started with a different contingency table?

****

64A

They are all zero.   This will always happen - if you examine the basis on which the E's were calculated you will see that it ensured that their sub-totals were the same as for the O's.   Obviously if $\Sigma O = \Sigma E$ then $\Sigma(O - E) = 0$.

FRAME 65

Having established that the sub-totals must all be zero, let us now find how many of the values of $O - E$ can vary independently of one another.   If another 800 articles had been measured, a different set of observed frequencies would have been recorded, resulting in a different set of values of $O - E$. Imagine what such a set of values could be.   Starting with the top row, you could give your imagination free rein when writing down the first two values but the third will then have been fixed because of the requirement that the row must add to zero.

Size / Machine	Undersize	Within tolerances	Oversize	Totals
A	FREE	FREE	FIXED	0
B				0
C				0
D				0
Totals	0	0	0	0

Continue in this way, saying whether each value is FREE or FIXED.   Work along each row from left to right, starting with the 2nd row and moving down the table ending with the 4th row.

****

65A

A	*FREE*	*FREE*	*FIXED*
B	*FREE*	*FREE*	*FIXED*
C	*FREE*	*FREE*	*FIXED*
D	*FIXED*	*FIXED*	*FIXED*

The values are fixed in the last row because the column totals must add to zero.

Thus only 6 of the O - E values are free to vary independently and the appropriate χ^2 has therefore 6 d.f. (The order in which the values are considered is immaterial. We chose one that is systematic and shows clearly what is happening, but any other order would still give you only 6 FREE's. Try it out for yourself, if you have doubts.)

By referring to TABLE 5, assess the significance of the value of 10·80 which has been obtained for χ^2 in the present test.

****

66A

Not significant at the 5% level. (It is, however, just significant at the 10% level, suggesting somewhat faint evidence of a difference between the machines.)

FRAME 67

It is a simple matter to obtain a general formula for the number of d.f. in χ^2, when working with a contingency table. In the problem just solved, the contingency table had 4 rows and 3 columns. Looking at the FREE's in 65A, you will see that there are $(4 - 1)$ rows of them and $(3 - 1)$ columns, giving $(4 - 1)(3 - 1)$ degrees of freedom. If the contingency table had m rows and n columns, what then would be the number of d.f. in χ^2?

****

67A

$(m - 1)(n - 1)$ degrees of freedom for an $m \times n$ contingency table.

FRAME 68

The following data might have arisen from an investigation into the effectiveness of a vaccine in combating an infectious disease. For each member of a sample of 120 people who have contracted the disease, it is recorded whether or not they had been inoculated with the vaccine during the last 12 months and the severity of their attack is placed in one of 3 grades.

	Severe	Medium	Mild
Vaccinated	2	8	30
Not vaccinated	22	28	30

This is another example of a contingency table. Is it 2×3 or 3×2?

****

68A

2×3, as there are 2 rows and 3 columns.

FRAME 69

A χ^2-test applied to this table can provide the answer to the question: Is there real evidence of an association between recent vaccination and severity of attack? To test the N.H. that there is no such association, expected frequencies based on this hypothesis will be required. First see if you can calculate these frequencies.

****

The expected frequencies are shown in brackets below the observed ones.

	Severe	Medium	Mild	Totals
Vaccinated	2 (8)	8 (12)	30 (20)	40
Not vaccinated	22 (16)	28 (24)	30 (40)	80
Totals	24	36	60	120

*You could have obtained the frequencies in the first row either by multiplying
40 in turn by 24/120, 36/120 and 60/120, or by multiplying each of the totals
24, 36 and 60 by 40/120.   Obviously either approach leads to the same answer
in the end.   If you recall the rule of multiplication for independent
probabilities (dealt with in Unit 1) you will realise that this is what is being
used.   The figures in the table give 40/120 for P(victim has been vaccinated
recently) and 24/120 for P(victim has a severe attack).   Thus, if the severity
of attack is independent of vaccination, the probability that a victim has been*

vaccinated recently and has a severe attack is $\frac{40}{120} \times \frac{24}{120}$ and the expected

number of people in this category is therefore $\frac{40}{120} \times \frac{24}{120} \times 120$,   i.e. $\frac{40 \times 24}{120}$,

which is what you will have obtained more directly.

Now calculate X^2 and decide whether or not you would reject the N.H.

****

$X^2 = 16 \cdot 25$ $\nu = (2 - 1)(3 - 1) = 2$

*For 2 d.f. the 0·1% critical value of X^2 is 13·82, so a value of 16·25 is
highly significant.   At any of the usual significance levels the N.H. would be
rejected in favour of the A.H. that there is an association between vaccination
and severity of attack.   If you compare the observed and expected frequencies
in 69A you will see that the vaccinated people suffer less and the others suffer
more than would have been expected on average if the N.H. were true.   Thus there
is strong evidence that the vaccine, even when it does not prevent the infection,
still reduces the risk of a severe attack.*

The 2 × 2 table

As was said when introducing the use of X^2 for comparing observed and expected
frequencies, the assumption of a X^2-distribution for $\Sigma(O - E)^2/E$ is an
approximation and, for it to be reasonably good, no E should be too small, the
condition E ≮ 5 being commonly accepted.   This can be relaxed slightly if the
number of terms in the summation is large enough, but such would not be the case
in a 2 × 2 classification.   When the number of observations in a 2 × 2
table is small enough to affect the adequacy of the X^2 approximation, Fisher's
exact test can be used.   This will not be described in detail in this text.
Briefly, it calculates the probability of the observed set of frequencies, or

FRAME 71   (continued)

more extreme results, occurring.   By 'more extreme results' is meant sets of
frequencies which depart even further from the expected ones than those observed.
Such sets of frequencies can be listed and their exact probabilities calculated.
No complication of this kind, however, arises in the following problem and you
should be able to go ahead and solve it.

Of 100 new cars purchased at the same time by a car hire company, 50 are model
A and 50 are model B.   After a period of time has elapsed, during which all
cars have been in use, an inspection is made.   The table shows, for each type
of model, the number of cars in which rusting
of the bodywork is found.   Use χ^2 to decide
whether there is evidence of a real difference
between the finish of these two models of car.

	Rust	No rust
Model A	15	35
Model B	23	27

****

71A

*The usual calculations give 2·72 which is less than 3·84, the 5% critical
value of χ^2 with 1 d.f.   This leads to the conclusion that there is not
evidence of a real difference between the finish of models A and B.*

*NOTE: Did you notice that $|O - E|$ was the same for each cell in the table?
Thus the value of χ^2 can be written as $4^2\left(\dfrac{1}{19} + \dfrac{1}{31} + \dfrac{1}{19} + \dfrac{1}{31}\right).$*

FRAME 72

This problem appeared in a slightly different guise in Misc. Ex. 12 of the
previous programme – perhaps you recognised it.   The statistic then on which
your solution was based was the standard normal variate.   That solution and the
present one are not unconnected.   You will recall that, for 1 d.f., χ^2 is
simply the square of a single standard normal variate and thus we are now using
u^2 where before we used u.   It is easily seen that the values obtained using
the two test statistics are related in this way.   In the answer to Misc. Ex. 12
the exact value of $|u|$ was $\dfrac{40}{\sqrt{19 \times 31}}$ and the exact value obtained for χ^2 in
the last frame was $\dfrac{40^2}{19 \times 31}$.

FRAME 73

Whether using χ^2 for $\Sigma(O - E)^2/E$, or the normal distribution as a substitute
for the binomial, the approximation being made replaces a discrete variate by a
continuous one.   You have already been made aware of this in the case of the
normal approximation to the binomial and seen how to take account of it by
making a continuity correction.   In the case of χ^2 itself, you saw, when it
was introduced, that it represents the sum of squares of normal variates, which
are continuous.   However, in $\Sigma(O - E)^2/E$, the O's are observed frequencies
and are therefore essentially discrete.   It is in situations where there is
only 1 d.f., as in a 2×2 table, that the need to take account of this arises
and you may then find Yates' continuity correction applied when a value for χ^2
is calculated.   This entails adding 0·5 to O when O < E, and subtracting

$0 \cdot 5$ from O when $O > E$.   The effect of this is to reduce the difference
between O and E by $0 \cdot 5$, thus replacing the original $(O - E)^2$ by
$(|O - E| - 0 \cdot 5)^2$ in the summation to give X^2.   Recent investigations have
shown, though, that in some types of problem this correction overcompensates.
If used in the problem in FRAME 71, would it have affected the conclusion?

****

73A

*No.   The effect of the correction is to reduce the value of X^2, which was
already below the critical value, still further.   In the expression for X^2 in
71A, Yates' continuity correction would cause the 4 to be replaced by $3 \cdot 5$.*

FRAME 74

A Computer Example

The arithmetic required in the solution of problems in this text has been kept
to manageable levels, and by yourself going through a procedure such as
significance testing, step by step, you should have been helped to an
understanding of the basis of that procedure.   In the practical situation, the
solution of problems may be aided by the use of standard computer programs.
For instance, the NAG (Numerical Algorithms Group) library includes a subroutine
for dealing with contingency tables.   It calculates X^2, except when the table
is 2×2 and the number of observations below a specified value, in which case
the probabilities required for Fisher's exact test are found.

In the example shown on the next page a program for testing the difference
between two sample means is being used, through a terminal linked to a distant
computer.   The program incorporates an F-test for a common population variance
and the data is from the following problem:

The values obtained by a group of students for the maximum efficiency (expressed
as a percentage) of a model water turbine in a university engineering laboratory
were: $66 \cdot 5$ $65 \cdot 4$ $68 \cdot 2$ $68 \cdot 6$ $66 \cdot 9$ $68 \cdot 8$

Results obtained at a time when operating conditions were slightly different
yielded the following figures for maximum efficiency (again, %):
    $64 \cdot 9$ $64 \cdot 0$ $66 \cdot 9$ $65 \cdot 8$ $63 \cdot 4$

Is there evidence that the change in conditions has affected the efficiency?

After typing a reference to the program required and then the instruction RUN,
the user is asked for various items of information as the execution of the
program proceeds.   Where a question mark appears at the beginning of a line,
the teletype halts and waits for the user to make the necessary response, which
appears on the same line.   In working out the F value, the computer selects
the larger of the two variance estimates and divides it by the smaller.   As
this program is used for teaching purposes it calls on the user to look up the F
and t tables, but a program designed for a different purpose might not require
this.   Assuming that the value of F must reach at least the 5% significance
level if the hypothesis of a common variance is to be rejected, was the user
correct in responding YES at that point and, if so, what should the final answer
be?

FRAME 74   (continued)

```
RUN
INPUT THE NUMBER OF DATA IN THE FIRST SAMPLE.
?6

INPUT DATA OF FIRST SAMPLE.
?66.5, 65.4, 68.2, 68.6, 66.9, 68.8

INPUT THE NUMBER OF DATA IN THE SECOND SAMPLE.
?5

INPUT DATA OF SECOND SAMPLE.
?64.9, 64.0, 66.9, 65.8, 63.4

FIRST SAMPLE:

SAMPLE MEAN      SAMPLE ESTIMATE OF VARIANCE
 67.4              1.82

SECOND SAMPLE:

SAMPLE MEAN      SAMPLE ESTIMATE OF VARIANCE
 65                1.955

F VALUE = 1.074  WITH 4 DEGREES OF FREEDOM IN THE NUMERATOR
AND 5 DEGREES OF FREEDOM IN THE DENOMINATOR.

CONSULT F TABLES TO SEE WHETHER THIS F VALUE ALLOWS
US TO ASSUME A COMMON VARIANCE FOR THE TWO POPULATIONS.
IF IT DOES, TYPE...YES...IF NOT, TYPE.....NO
?YES
THE POOLED ESTIMATE OF POPULATION VARIANCE IS NOW 1.88

THE DIFFERENCE OF SAMPLE MEANS IS 2.4

THE T VALUE IN THIS CASE IS 2.891 WITH 9 DEGREES OF FREEDOM.
CONSULT T TABLES.   IS THIS T VALUE LARGE ENOUGH TO
SUGGEST THAT THE POPULATIONS HAVE DIFFERENT MEAN VALUES?
IF SO, AT WHAT SIGNIFICANCE LEVEL?

DONE
```

```
                 **************************************************
```
74A

Yes, as the value of F_5^4 would have to be at least $7 \cdot 39$ to be significant at the 5% level.   As $|t| > 2 \cdot 26$ but $< 3 \cdot 25$, the means are significantly different at the 5% level, but not at the 1%.

FRAME 75

Miscellaneous Examples

In this frame a collection of miscellaneous examples is given for you to try. Questions 14 and 25 are more mathematical and you may omit them if you wish. Answers are supplied in FRAME 76, together with such working as is considered helpful.

1. Some discussion in the previous programme centred round an investigation
    into whether a drug affects the blood glucose level of diabetic rats.   The
    point was made that the experiment would be best planned to make paired
    comparisons by recording the level in each rat before and after the drug
    had been administered.   Suppose this to have been done with 6 rats, with
    the following results (in mg/ml):

Rat	1	2	3	4	5	6
Before (x_B)	2·21	2·02	1·76	2·13	1·75	1·89
After (x_A)	2·00	2·04	1·47	1·73	1·83	1·67

The choice between a one-sided and a two-sided test must be guided by the
particular circumstances surrounding the investigation.   Three
possibilities may be envisaged:

  (i)   The data have been collected by a research student in a university
        biochemistry department who is studying the metabolism of diabetic
        rats and is interested in whether the drug has any effect either
        way on their blood glucose.

  (ii) The data result from trials of a new drug.   A lowering of the
        blood glucose level would indicate that the drug has been successful.
        If a significant decrease is not shown, research on the drug will be
        abandoned, it then being immaterial whether the level is raised or
        unaltered.

  (iii) The drug has been shown to meet the need for which it is intended
        (which is not the treatment of diabetes) and is now being tested to
        see whether it could, in some cases, have undesirable side effects.
        A significant increase in the blood glucose level of treated rats
        would point to the existence of such side effects when diabetes is
        present.

What conclusion should be reached in each of these three situations if the
above data were obtained?

2. A large urban passenger transport authority uses tens of thousands of
    light bulbs annually.   Its present purchasing contract is for a brand of
    bulb which has been shown to have a mean length of life of 1200 hours and
    a standard deviation of 105 hours.   When another make becomes available
    at a much lower price, the authority decides that it will change to buying
    these cheaper bulbs provided that they do not have a mean life less than
    1200 hours.   When life-tested, 25 of them are found to have a mean
    length of life of 1170 hours.   In the event that the cheaper bulbs are
    as good as the more expensive ones, the authority is prepared to take a 5%
    risk of not correctly detecting that this is so and mistakenly continuing
    with the present contract.   Having fixed this level of risk, should the
    authority continue with their present contract?   (Assume that the standard
    deviation of the lives of the cheaper bulbs is the same as for the bulbs at
    present being supplied.)

3. The average daily amount of scrap from a particular manufacturing process
    is 25·5 kg with s.d. 1·6 kg.   A modification is suggested in an attempt
    to reduce this amount.   During a 10-day trial period, the weight (kg)
    of scrap produced each day was as follows: 24·5, 25·0, 26·1, 22·8,
    25·0, 21·9, 23·5, 25·2, 22·0, 23·0.   From the nature of the
    modification, no change in the day-to-day variability of the amount of scrap

FRAME 75   (continued)

is anticipated, but you could check this assumption for yourself by a
suitable test.   A first glance at the figures suggests that the
modification is effective.   Does a significance test confirm this?

4.   You are familiar with a confidence interval, defined by two limits which
have a stated probability of containing the true value of the parameter.
In some situations it may be more informative to give only a lower bound
above which you are, say, 95% confident that the true value lies, or in
other cases an upper bound below which, with 95% confidence, you can say
it lies.   Give the 95% confidence upper bound for the mean daily amount
of scrap produced by the modified process in the previous question.

5.   In FRAME 2 it was stated that a statistical test would confirm the
hypothesis that variation in yield was unaffected by the presence of the
additive.   Verify this statement.

6.   In Misc. Ex. 10 on page 220 you were told to assume that the variation in
blood glucose level from rat to rat was the same for treated and untreated
rats.   Show that the data (given in FRAME 1 on page 188) supported that
assumption.

7.   Check the assumption, made in Misc. Ex. 13 on page 220, that the variation
in the results of single-thread strength tests is the same for both types
of yarn.

8.   In a traverse survey replicate measurements of one of the angles were made.
The readings were: $43^{\circ}51'10''$, $43^{\circ}50'20''$, $43^{\circ}51'0''$, $43^{\circ}50'30''$,
$43^{\circ}50'20''$, $43^{\circ}50'30''$, $43^{\circ}50'50''$.

Find 95% confidence limits for σ^2, the population variance of such
readings, using (i) F, (ii) χ^2.   Deduce 95% confidence limits for σ.

9.   It is known from long experience that, for a particular chemical component,
determinations made with a mass spectrometer have a variance of $0 \cdot 24$.   An
analyst who is new to the job makes a series of 25 determinations with the
spectrometer and they give an unbiased estimate of variance of $0 \cdot 32$.   Has
the analyst made a contribution to the variation of results, over and above
that inherent in the use of the instrument, i.e. is the variance estimate
of $0 \cdot 32$ significantly larger than the $0 \cdot 24$ value?

10.   A spring manufacturer will change to a new supplier of wire if there is
sufficient evidence that the wire from this source is more uniform in
diameter than that used in the present production of springs.   What
decision would you recommend on the basis of the following data, resulting
from random measurements of diameter made on each type of wire?

	Present wire	New wire
Number of measurements	11	15
Sum of squares of deviations from sample mean i.e. $\Sigma(x - \bar{x})^2$	$15 \cdot 20$	$6 \cdot 72$

11.   In the operation of battery-powered electrical equipment in may be cheaper
to replace all batteries together, at fixed intervals, than to replace each
battery individually when it fails.   Suppose that this is the case if the
s.d. of battery lifetimes is less than 10 hours, and that tests on 12

batteries of a type being considered for use in the equipment give $s = 6$, where s^2 is the unbiased estimate of the variance of the population of battery lives (recorded in hours).   The decision as to whether or not to use these batteries is to be made by testing the N.H. $\sigma^2 = 100$ against the A.H. $\sigma^2 < 100$.   To what conclusion does this test lead?

12. With some measuring techniques the precision is the same irrespective of the size of the measurement being made.   With others the larger the quantity being measured, the larger the error is likely to be.   From what is known about it, the latter is thought to be the case with a spectro-chemical method for determining the amount of iron in zirconium.   The method was used to determine the amount of iron, in p.p.m., in two samples of zirconium with different iron content.   Ten observations were made on each sample and the sum of squares, i.e. $\Sigma(x - \bar{x})^2$, calculated for each set of 10 observations.   The results are given below.

Sample 1   (lower iron content): $\Sigma(x_1 - \bar{x}_1)^2 = 8100$
Sample 2   (higher iron content): $\Sigma(x_2 - \bar{x}_2)^2 = 72\,900$

Do these data give real support to the assertion that the error of measurement is greater for high iron contents than for low ones?

13. A flour bleaching agent has, in the past, been ground in a hammer-mill. It is proposed that the grinding be done in an air-attrition mill as this produces a much finer particle with, therefore, a higher bleaching effect. After being ground the bleach is fed into a flour stream through a volumetric feeder and it is essential that the flow rate should fluctuate as little as possible.

The initial problem is to discover whether the change of milling technique would increase the variability of the feed rate.   For test purposes a feeder is operated first with hammer-ground and then with air-ground powder. In each case the amount of feed (in grams) passing through in a 1-minute interval is recorded for 5 such intervals.   The variance estimate calculated from the 5 observations on the hammer-ground powder is $0\cdot04$, that obtained from the 5 observations when the finer air-ground powder is used is $1\cdot95$.   Show that this provides strong evidence that the flow rate is more variable when the finer powder is used.

Trials are next carried out with a small amount of magnesium carbonate added to the air-ground powder, to see if this will make it flow as uniformly as the hammer-ground powder.   The feeder is operated under the same conditions as before.   Three separate trials are made, with $\frac{1}{2}$%, 1% and 5% addition of magnesium carbonate, and the variance estimates given by each set of 5 observations are respectively $0\cdot33$, $0\cdot15$ and $0\cdot28$. Is there any amount of additive for which the variability of the feed rate is not significantly higher than for the hammer-ground powder?

14. The probability density function for $F_{\nu_2}^{\nu_1}$ is given by

$$p(F) = \frac{cF^{(\nu_1-2)/2}}{(\nu_2 + \nu_1 F)^{(\nu_1+\nu_2)/2}}$$

where the value of c depends on ν_1 and ν_2 and is such as to make the total area under the curve equal to 1.   For $\nu_1 > 2$, the probability

curves have the same general features as are exhibited by the curves shown
in FRAME 14, i.e. $p(F) = 0$ when $F = 0$, $p(F)$ then increases to a
maximum and then $p(F) \to 0$ as F increases.   How do the curves for
$\nu_1 = 1$ and $\nu_1 = 2$ differ from this general pattern?

15. Often in a civil engineering project, one of the primary factors to be
     considered is the load-bearing capacity of the relevant bedrock, while an
     important criterion in the economic operation of a quarry is the crushing
     strength of the rock found there.   To measure the load-bearing capacity or
     crushing strength in such cases, a borehole may be sunk and samples of the
     rock strata removed and brought to a rock mechanics laboratory to be tested.
     The procedure then is to drill the rock into smaller cores, usually 25 mm
     diameter, to be crushed on a compression testing machine.   If, in preparing
     a core for testing, the diamond saw is out-of-true or the core is not
     correctly aligned in its clamp, the ends of the core will not be cut
     squarely to its axis.   To investigate whether this affects the results of
     the crushing tests, an experiment was conducted with 50 mm high cores, all
     oven-dried and from the same batch of limestone. 10 of them were cut with
     zero-sloped ends (i.e. end faces perpendicular to the axis) and 5 were cut
     with one end having a set amount of slope (which was, in fact, reckoned to
     be the minimum extent of slope which would be readily noticeable as being
     out-of-true).   The compressive strengths (in kN) were as follows:

     Standard specimens (both ends perpendicular to axis): 53·1, 78·8, 54·4,
     51·3, 75·0, 57·3, 60·2, 63·9, 67·0, 45·0.

     One end out-of-true: 37·0, 27·8, 32·3, 28·3, 31·1.

     Is there evidence that the condition of the ends affects the test results?
     A further set of 6 cores (same size, batch of limestone etc. as before)
     were cut with one end out-of-true but this time the amount of slope was
     only two thirds of what it was for the previous sample of 5.   The values
     of compressive strength (x kN) then obtained gave $\bar{x} = 57\cdot3$,
     $\Sigma(x - \bar{x})^2 = 862\cdot42$.   Compare these results with those given for the
     standard specimens.

     (This was part of an investigation by P.J. Cotter, a final year
     undergraduate student in the Department of Civil Engineering, Loughborough
     University of Technology.)

16. The table shows the number of piston-ring failures which occurred on each
     of 5 steam-driven compressors over a period of years.

Compressor Number	1	2	3	4	5
Number of failures	42	35	31	48	44

     Assuming that the compressors had equal use during the period, is there
     evidence of a real difference between the compressors with respect to
     piston-ring failure?

17. When examining the crystals which had formed during an experiment a
     research chemist classified them, on an arbitrary scale, as 53 large, 48
     medium and 9 small.   According to his theory the ratios
     large : medium : small should be 6 : 4 : 1.   As a result of this
     experiment, should he reject his theory?

18. In Misc. Ex. 5 on page 113 you found the theoretical frequencies given by
     a Poisson distribution with the same mean as the observed distribution
     shown there.   Test the goodness of fit of the Poisson model.

19. In Misc. Ex. 7 on page 97 you calculated the theoretical distribution
     given by a binomial model.   Test the goodness of fit of this model.

20. In FRAME 21 on page 126 you began the task of finding the theoretical
     frequencies given by an exponential model when fitted to data on the time
     gaps between vehicles. Find the theoretical frequencies given by this model
     for the remaining groups and test the agreement with the observed
     frequencies.

     (Don't forget time gaps > 30.   This category isn't shown in the data as
     the observed frequency was zero.   Nevertheless, the expected frequency
     may be non-zero.)

21. A chemical manufacturer requires an especially high grade of raw material
     for a certain process.   On average a proportion p of the available raw
     material is of this standard.   If x is the number of cartons of raw
     material which need to be tested in order to discover the first high grade
     carton derive the probability density function of x.

     In a series of trials the number of cartons tested in order to find the
     first high grade carton is as follows:

Number of cartons tested	1	2	3	4	5	6	7	8	9
Frequency	42	21	13	11	4	4	2	2	1

     On the assumption that the proportion p of high grade material is constant
     these results should fit a distribution of the above type.   Estimate p
     and test this assumption by means of the χ^2 test of goodness of fit.   (L.U.)

     (HINT: You may find it helpful to refer back to Misc. Ex. 14 on page 98.)

22. The blood groups of 200 hospital patients were recorded.   The table
     shows the number of patients of each sex having blood of group O, A, B and
     AB.   Use a significance test to
     judge whether there is evidence
     of a difference between men and
     women patients in general, as
     far as blood groups are
     concerned.

Group / Sex	O	A	B	AB
Men	52	36	7	5
Women	36	44	13	7

23. A geologist collects 120 hand-specimen-sized pieces of limestone from a
     particular area.   A qualitative assessment of the texture of each specimen
     is made by classifying it
     as either fine-grained,
     medium-grained or
     coarse-grained.   The
     colour is also assessed,
     using the categories light,
     medium and dark.   Would
     the data shown in the
     table support the

Colour / Texture	Light	Medium	Dark
Fine	4	20	8
Medium	5	23	12
Coarse	21	23	4

     hypothesis that, for the limestone in this area, colour is independent of
     texture?

24.

	Defective	Satisfactory
Before	18	108
After	4	64

The table shows the number of defective and satisfactory articles in two samples, one taken before and one after the introduction of a modification to the process of manufacture.   Do the data provide strong evidence that the modification affects the quality of the output?   (L.U.)

25.   It was noted in the answer to FRAME 70 that, for the 2 × 2 table under consideration, $|0 - E|$ was the same for each cell in the table.   A little thought should show you that this will happen in any 2 × 2 table. Find the value of $(0 - E)^2$ common to every cell in a 2 × 2 table with cell frequencies a, b, c, d as shown. Ignoring Yates' correction, deduce the following formula which is sometimes quoted for a 2 × 2 table:

a	b
c	d

$$\chi^2 = \frac{n(ad - bc)^2}{(a + b)(a + c)(b + d)(c + d)} \quad \text{where } n \text{ is the total}$$

number of observations, i.e.   a + b + c + d.

Answers to Miscellaneous Examples

1.   If $d = x_A - x_B$, $\bar{d} = -0\cdot17$, $\Sigma(d - \bar{d})^2 = 0\cdot17$, $t = -2\cdot26$

   (i)   N.H.: $\mu_d = 0$,   A.H. $\mu_d \neq 0$, $|t| < 2\cdot57$.   No sig. effect at 5% level.

   (ii)   N.H.: $\mu_d = 0$,   A.H. $\mu_d < 0$, $t < -2\cdot02$ but $\nless -3\cdot36$.   Decrease sig. at 5%, but not 1% level.

   (iii)   N.H.: $\mu_d = 0$,   A.H. $\mu_d > 0$.   No need to proceed further, as a negative value of $\bar{d}$ cannot possibly provide evidence of an increase in blood glucose.

2.   N.H.: $\mu = 1200$,   A.H.: $\mu < 1200$,   where μ = mean life of cheaper bulbs,   u = -1·43.   For 5% significance,   u < -1·64   would be required, so the decision is in favour of the cheaper bulbs.

3.   To check, at the 5% level, that the variance is unchanged, find σ^2/s^2 and compare with the value of F_9^∞ given by TABLE 4 for P = 2·5.   Or you could find $9s^2/\sigma^2$ and see whether it is in the acceptance interval bounded by the values of χ^2 with 9 d.f. given by TABLE 5 for P = 97·5 and   P = 2·5.

   N.H.: $\mu = 25\cdot5$ A.H.: $\mu < 25\cdot5$,   where μ = mean daily amount of scrap from modified process.   u = -3·16, showing a sig. reduction at the 1% level.

4.   We can be 95% confident that the mean daily amount of scrap is less than 23·9 + 1·64 × 1·6/√10   i.e.   24·7 kg.

5. $F_4^\infty = \dfrac{12\cdot25}{10\cdot7} < 8\cdot26$ Not sig. at 5% level.

6. $F_5^5 \simeq 1 \cdot 22 < 7 \cdot 15$ Not sig. at 5% level.

7. $F_4^6 \simeq 1 \cdot 45 < 9 \cdot 20$ Not sig. at 5% level.

8. Calculations are simplified if you subtract, say, $43°50'$ from all readings
    and then work in seconds. (i) Using F_∞^6 and F_6^∞ with $P = 2 \cdot 5$, 95%
    confidence limits for σ^2 are $s^2/2 \cdot 41$ and $4 \cdot 85 s^2$, i.e. 166 and 1940
    to 3 sig. figs. (ii) Using χ^2 with 6 d.f. and $P = 97 \cdot 5$ and $2 \cdot 5$,
    there is a 95% chance that $2400/\sigma^2$ is between $1 \cdot 24$ and $14 \cdot 45$ i.e.
    that σ^2 is between 166 and 1940.   There is thus a 95% chance that
    $12 \cdot 9 < \sigma < 44 \cdot 0$.

9. $F_\infty^{24} = 1 \cdot \dot{3} < 1 \cdot 52$ Not sig. at 5% level, i.e. analyst's inexperience has
    not contributed to the variation of results.

10. $F_{14}^{10} = 3 \cdot \dot{1}6 > 2 \cdot 60$ but $< 3 \cdot 94$.   If the risk of making a change, when the
    new supplier's wire is not more uniform, has only to be less than 5%, then
    the manufacturer should change to the new source of supply, but if this risk
    must be less than 1% the evidence of greater uniformity is not strong
    enough to support a decision to change supplier.

11. $F_{11}^\infty = 2 \cdot \dot{7} > 2 \cdot 40$ but $< 3 \cdot 60$.   If testing at the 5% level, the N.H. would
    be rejected in favour of the A.H. and the batteries would be accepted but
    if stronger evidence that $\sigma < 10$ is required, in the form of a 1% level,
    then the batteries would not be acceptable.

12. $F_9^9 = 9$ Although the 5% critical value of F_9^9 is not given in the table
    it is obviously between $3 \cdot 23$ and $3 \cdot 14$, the values given for F_9^8 and F_9^{10}
    respectively.   Similarly the 1% critical value of F_9^9 is between $5 \cdot 47$
    and $5 \cdot 26$.   Thus the value obtained here is significant at the 1% level,
    supporting the assertion that the error is greater for higher iron contents.

13. $F_4^4 = 48 \cdot 75$, sig. at 1% level.
    Yes, 1% of additive gives $F_4^4 = 3 \cdot 75$, not sig. at 5% level.

14. $\nu_1 = 1$: $p(F) = \dfrac{c}{F^{\frac{1}{2}}(\nu_2 + F)^{(1 + \nu_2)/2}}$, $p(F) \to \infty$ as $F \to 0$,

    as with curve shown for χ^2 with $\nu = 1$ in FRAME 35.

    $\nu_1 = 2$: $p(F) = \dfrac{c}{(\nu_2 + 2F)^{1 + \nu_2/2}}$, $p(F) = \dfrac{c}{\nu_2^{1 + \nu_2/2}}$ when $F = 0$.   You will

    get an idea of what the curve looks like if you refer back to that shown
    for χ^2 with $\nu = 2$ in FRAME 35.

15. $F_4^9 = 8 \cdot 32$, not sig. at 5% level, so a common variance can be assumed.
    $t = 5 \cdot 87 > 3 \cdot 01$, so sig. at 1% level, i.e. condition of ends has affected
    results.
    $F_9^5 = 1 \cdot 51$, not sig. at 5% level, hence a common variance.
    $t = 0 \cdot 55 < 2 \cdot 14$, so not sig. at 5% level, i.e. results not affected by
    this amount of slope.

16. No difference between compressors would mean a uniform probability
     distribution with each expected frequency of failures equal to 40.
     χ^2 = 4·75 < 9·49, the 5% critical value for 4 d.f.   No sig. difference
     at 5% level.

17. Theory gives expected frequencies 60, 40 and 10 for large, medium and
     small crystals respectively. χ^2 = 2·52.   For 2 d.f., 5% critical value
     of χ^2 = 5·99, so no grounds for rejecting theory.

18. Combining first two groups and also last four gives expected frequencies:
     13·8, 12·3, 10·3, 6·4, 5·2. χ^2 = 0·40, ν = 5 - 2 = 3   Not sig. at 5%
     level, confirming that Poisson model gives a good fit (almost, but not quite,
     good enough to arouse suspicion).

19. χ^2 = 0·687, ν = 5 - 2 = 3   Not sig. at 5% level, so binomial model fits
     data satisfactorily.

20. Combining groups just enough to avoid E < 5, but allowing 4·8, values
     of E are 46·8, 35·9, 27·5, 21·0, 16·1, 12·3, 9·5, 7·2, 5·5, 7·5, 5·9,
     4·8, giving χ^2 = 12·00, ν = 12 - 2 = 10   Not sig. at 5% level, so
     fit is satisfactory.

21. p = 0·4.   Expected frequencies given by geometric distribution with same
     mean (= 1/p) are 40·0, 24·0, 14·4, 8·6, 5·2, 7·8, combining frequencies
     for 6 or more cartons to avoid E < 5. χ^2 = 1·74, ν = 6 - 2 = 4
     Not sig. at 5% level, so assumption would not be rejected.

22. χ^2 = 5·84, ν = 3   No sig. difference, at 5% level, between blood groups
     of men and women patients.   (Some of the probabilities associated with
     this problem were discussed in FRAME 50 on page 68.)

23. χ^2 = 17·73, ν = 4   Hypothesis that colour and texture are independent
     would be rejected at 1% level.   Examining the major contributions to χ^2
     suggests that light colour tends to accompany coarse texture.

24. No. χ^2 = 3·1, which for 1 d.f. is not sig. at 5% level.

25. $(ad - bc)^2/n^2$.

Nonparametric (Distribution-free) Tests

Introduction

In the previous two programmes you have been introduced to tests concerned with
hypotheses about parameters (e.g. means in the case of t-tests and variances in
the case of F-tests) where the underlying theory rests on an assumption that the
samples are taken from a normal population.

The tests that you will meet in this programme represent a more recent
development in statistical thinking and are usually said to be NONPARAMETRIC or
DISTRIBUTION-FREE.   Strictly speaking these two terms are not synonymous and
neither, in fact, provides an entirely satisfactory description of the category
of tests to which they are applied.   Nevertheless it is common practice to use
them interchangeably when referring to this area of statistics and we shall do
likewise in this text.

The tests are distribution-free in so far as they do not specify a particular
form, e.g. normal, for the distribution from which the samples are taken, but
they may impose lesser restrictions (such as continuity and symmetry).   The
brief coverage given here is intended only to serve as an introduction and to
give you a glimpse of how such features as signs, ranks and runs can be
employed in testing hypotheses.

Sign Tests

The approach here is based on observations being represented by either a plus
sign or a minus sign, as is illustrated by the following example.

Suppose that 4 minutes is claimed to be the median time taken by a factory's
machine operators to complete a particular task which they carry out many times
a day.   At 7 randomly chosen points in time an operator (also picked at random
on each occasion) was observed and the time taken to complete the task was
recorded, the results (in minutes) being:

$$3 \cdot 5 \qquad 3 \cdot 2 \qquad 3 \cdot 9 \qquad 4 \cdot 8 \qquad 3 \cdot 8 \qquad 3 \cdot 4 \qquad 3 \cdot 7$$

Do these figures cast doubt on the claimed median time?

The question implies that a two-sided significance test is required.   In
accordance with the usual procedure we begin by stating:

$$\text{N.H.: Median time} = 4 \text{ minutes}$$
$$\text{A.H.: Median time} \neq 4 \text{ minutes}$$

Each observation is now considered in relation to the supposed median.   If
greater, the observation is designated by a plus sign, if less by a minus sign,
giving in this case

$$- \quad - \quad - \quad + \quad - \quad - \quad -$$

Now, by its very definition, a median has a 50% chance of being exceeded.
Thus, if the N.H. is true, the chance of getting a + is $\frac{1}{2}$ and the chance of
getting a - is $\frac{1}{2}$.   We have to decide whether the result obtained above is
sufficiently unusual to cast doubt on the hypothesis.   What would be the

probability of getting so few +'s, i.e. of getting only 0 or 1 +, from 7 observations?   (Refer back to FRAME 6 page 190 if you are wondering why this probability is needed.   The situation there is very similar.)

****

2A

Using the binomial distribution with p = ½, n = 7
P(0) + P(1) = 8/128 = 0•0625

FRAME 3

As this is a two-sided test the other extreme must also be taken into account. What is the probability of getting only 1 - or none, i.e. 6 or more +'s?

****

3A

The same, i.e.   8/128 or 0•0625

FRAME 4

It is now seen, therefore, that the probability of 6 or more signs being the same is 2 × 0•0625 i.e. 12•5%.   Thus, even if a 10% significance level were chosen, the N.H. would not be rejected.

If all 7 times had been less than 4 minutes, would there then have been sufficient grounds for rejecting the N.H. at (i) the 5% significance level, (ii) the 1% significance level?

****

4A

On the basis of the N.H.,   P(7 -'s or 7 +'s) = 1/64 ≃ 0•0156.

(i) As this probability is less than 5%, the N.H. would be rejected at that level.

(ii) The N.H. would not, however, be rejected at the 1% level.   There is, in fact, no result that would be significant at this level if only 7 times are recorded.   Hence, if a 1% level were chosen, at least 8 times would have to be recorded.

FRAME 5

You may have wondered what we would have done if there had been a recorded time of 4•0 minutes.   Well, time is a continuous variate and a value recorded as 4•0 could, in reality, have been anywhere between 3•95 and 4•05.   As there is no way of knowing which side of 4•0 it fell on, such an observation would have to be discarded and the test made on the remaining 6.

In dealing with only 7 observations we were able to calculate the required probabilities quite easily but obviously these calculations could be more tedious for larger samples.   As has been mentioned before, binomial distribution tables are available; also, if the number of observations is large enough, the normal distribution can be used as an approximation.

Now answer these questions:

(i)   Suppose that, in the data in FRAME 2, the fourth recorded time had been
      4·0 instead of 4·8.   Would the N.H. then have been rejected at the 5%
      significance level?

(ii) If 36 times had been recorded, how few or how many +'s would lead to the
      rejection of the N.H. at the 5% level?   (Use a normal approximation.)

      ****

5A

(i)   *P(6 -'s or 6 +'s) = 2/64 = 0·031 25.   Hence the N.H. would be rejected
      at the 5% level.*

(ii) *Using the normal distribution with mean 18 (= np) and s.d. 3 (= $\sqrt{npq}$),
      the rejection region would be that outside 18 ± 1·96 × 3.   This
      corresponds to the number of +'s being < 12 or > 24.   Putting it
      another way, this means fewer than 12 signs of one kind.   (12 is not
      included as on a continuous scale it can correspond to a value as high as
      12·5.)*

FRAME 6

You have now seen how a sign test can be used to decide whether a population
median has a particular value.   A similar test can be applied to data which
consists of matched pairs.   The following table shows the marks awarded by each
of two judges A and B to 6 contestants for the title of "Craft Apprentice of
the Year":

Contestant	1	2	3	4	5	6
Judge A	75	70	42	55	81	66
Judge B	67	51	43	45	84	59

If we wanted to decide whether, in the long run, the marks of one judge are more
often than not higher than those of the other, we could do so by applying a sign
test to the difference between each pair of marks.   The N.H. to be tested would
then, in effect, be: That these differences are from a population with a median
of zero.   Thus when a difference is > 0, it would be designated +, and when
it is < 0, it would be designated -, as shown below:

Difference (A − B)	+8	+19	−1	+10	−3	+7
Sign	+	+	−	+	−	+

Find the probability that, out of 6 signs, the number which are the same is 2
or less.   Hence decide whether the N.H. should be rejected at the 5%
significance level.

      ****

6A

P(2 or fewer -'s) = P(0) + P(1) + P(2) = 22/64 = 11/32
P(2 or fewer +'s) = 11/32
P(2 or fewer signs the same) = 11/16 = 0·6875
Obviously the N.H. should not be rejected.

You will notice that, in applying the sign test in this example, we only took account of whether or not Judge A's mark was higher than Judge B's.   The test would therefore still be applicable when a comparison between members of a pair is to be made but quantitative assessment is difficult.   For instance, suppose that two methods of anodising aluminium are to be compared with regard to the general appearance (brightness, lack of blemishes etc.) of the end product. Whilst it might be difficult to measure these qualities in numerical terms, it would not be so difficult to decide which specimen of a pair had the more pleasing appearance.   A + sign could then be given to a pair in which Method 1 was judged superior, and a - sign where Method 2 was preferred.   If out of 40 pairs judged, 25 showed Method 1 superior, 11 showed Method 2 superior and the remaining 4 were ties (i.e. no discernible difference between the two), what conclusion would you come to?

****

7A

Discarding the 4 ties, there are 25 +'s and 11 -'s from 36 pairs.   From your answer to (ii) in FRAME 5 you will see that this is significant at the 5% level i.e. the N.H. of no difference between the methods would be rejected.

FRAME 8

The Wilcoxon Signed Rank Test for matched pairs

In the example comparing anodising methods, each pair of specimens was categorised as + or - according as Method 1 or Method 2 was judged to give the better result.   This showed the sign test to advantage in that it made the most of what limited information was available.   In the example about the judges, however, more information was available than was made use of by the sign test, which takes no account of whether the differences are marginal or not. For instance, a difference of +19 is recorded as + and a difference of −1 as −, without any regard for the fact that the difference in one direction is very much greater than it is in the other.

The test that will now be described still uses the signs of the differences but it also takes into account their relative size by assigning a RANK to each. This ranking is done by considering the differences arranged in ascending order of absolute magnitude (thus +3, for example, would be placed lower than −10). Then rank 1 is assigned to the smallest, 2 to the next smallest and so on. Looking at the differences in the judges' scoring, shown in FRAME 6, you will see that −1 is the smallest in magnitude and it is therefore given a rank of 1. Then −3, being the next smallest in magnitude, is ranked 2.   Continue with assigning ranks in this way.

****

8A

Difference (A − B)	+8	+19	−1	+10	−3	+7
Rank	4	6	1	5	2	3

FRAME 9

The thought may have crossed your mind that, although it did not happen here, the situation could arise when two or more differences have the same absolute magnitude.   What ranks should then be assigned to these differences?   The answer is quite simple.   Suppose, for instance, that Judge A had awarded

Contestant 1 a mark of 74, instead of 75.   The difference would then be +7, instead of +8, thus creating a tie with the difference at the end of the row. The ranks 3 and 4 are shared between the two, i.e. 3·5 each, as shown below:

Difference (A - B)	+7	+19	-1	+10	-3	+7
Rank	3·5	6	1	5	2	3·5

Now suppose that Judge A's mark for Contestant 1 was 77.   What would be the ranks in that case?

****

9A

Difference (A - B)	+10	+19	-1	+10	-3	+7
Rank	4·5	6	1	4·5	2	3

FRAME 10

Returning to the original data, as ranked in answer frame 8A, the signs of the differences are now considered in conjunction with their rank.   Rearranging in rank order we have:

Rank of difference	1	2	3	4	5	6
Sign of difference	-	-	+	+	+	+

We now take into account not only how many -'s there are (as was done in the sign test) but how they rank in magnitude.   This is done by calculating the RANK SUM.   For the - signs this is 1 + 2, for the + signs it is 3 + 4 + 5 + 6.   It is more convenient to work with the smaller sum, which in this case is for the - signs.   Denoting this sum by T, we have T = 1 + 2 = 3.

The question is then one of whether or not a value of T as small as this would be reasonably likely if there were no real difference between the two standards of judging.   The various ways in which T $\leqslant$ 3 could arise can be listed quite easily.   They are:

Rank	1	2	3	4	5	6	
	+	+	+	+	+	+	T = 0
	-	+	+	+	+	+	T = 1
	+	-	+	+	+	+	T = 2
	+	+	-	+	+	+	T = 3
	-	-	+	+	+	+	T = 3

These 5 sign combinations are the only ones giving T $\leqslant$ 3.   There are, of course, many other possible combinations but for them T > 3.   Bearing in mind that each of the 6 ranks can be associated with either a + or a -, can you say what the total number of possibilities is?

****

10A

$2 \times 2 \times 2 \times 2 \times 2 \times 2 = 2^6$

FRAME 11

If the N.H. is true, all these ways are equally likely.   Hence, when T is the sum of ranks associated with - signs, $P(T \leqslant 3) = \frac{5}{2^6} = \frac{5}{64}$.   Alternatively it could be argued that if, for each sign, $P(+) = \frac{1}{2}$ and $P(-) = \frac{1}{2}$, then

FRAME 11   (continued)

each combination of 6 signs will have a probability of $(\frac{1}{2})^6$. Thus the probability of one or other of the 5 combinations occurring is $5(\frac{1}{2})^6$.

Now, as we are looking for a difference between judges either way (A marking higher than B or B marking higher than A), the probability of getting such a small rank sum as 3 from + signs must also be taken into account. Remember that, if the hypothesis is rejected because of an unusually small T from − signs, it would also have been rejected if an equally small T had been obtained from + signs. Can you state the value that $P(T \leqslant 3)$ would have if T were the sum of ranks associated with + signs?

****

11A

The same as for the sum of ranks associated with − signs, i.e. 5/64.

FRAME 12

The probability of getting such a small rank sum as 3, from either + or − signs, is therefore $2 \times 5/64 = 5/32 \simeq 0.156$. Is there a difference between the two judges at the 5% level of significance? Compare the present conclusion with that reached using the simpler sign test in your answer to FRAME 6.

****

12A

No, as $0.156 > 0.05$. Although the conclusion finally reached is actually the same as that arrived at previously, you will notice that this time we are much nearer to 5% significance than before. With another set of data the two tests could lead to different decisions.

FRAME 13

By referring back to the sign combinations giving various values of T, shown in FRAME 10, find $P(T \leqslant 2)$ and $P(T \leqslant 1)$ where T is the rank sum associated with either + or −. Hence decide how small a value of T would be required to show a significant difference between the judges at the 5% level.

****

13A

$P(T \leqslant 2) = 2 \times 3/64 \simeq 0.094$ $P(T \leqslant 1) = 2 \times 2/64 \simeq 0.062$

In neither of these cases has a probability less than 0.05 been reached. However, $P(T = 0) = 2 \times 1/64 \simeq 0.031$ and thus $T = 0$ (which would occur when Judge A's marks were either always higher or always lower than Judge B's) would show a significant difference if the level of risk has been set at 5%. (Note that the 1% level could not be attained with only 6 pairs of observations.)

FRAME 14

It is hoped that, by working out for yourself the critical value of T required for a given level of significance, you have gained an insight into the basis of the test. However, it would be laborious to have to go through this procedure every time such a test is made and critical values of T for the usual significance levels are available for a range of values of n, the number of pairs of observations. It can be shown that the distribution of T has

$$\text{mean} = n(n + 1)/4 \qquad \text{and} \qquad \text{variance} = n(n + 1)(2n + 1)/24 \qquad (14.1)$$

and that when n is sufficiently large (> 25, say) the distribution is
approximately normal.

The derivation of the formulae (14.1) does not require any really advanced
mathematics but it may be more instructive for you just to verify them for a
particular value of n.   You established that, when n = 6, there are 2^6 , i.e.
64, possible ways in which a sign could be associated with each rank and just 5
of these were listed in FRAME 10.   To list all 64 would be a time-consuming
task but for n = 3 the number of such possibilities would be only 2^3 , i.e. 8,
and it should not take you long to write all these down.   You will then be able
to deduce the probability distribution for T and calculate its mean and
variance.   Try it.

****

Rank	1	2	3	T^*		T	$P(T)$
	+	+	+	0		0	1/8
	−	+	+	1		1	1/8
	+	−	+	2		2	1/8
	+	+	−	3		3	2/8
	−	−	+	3		4	1/8
	+	−	−	5		5	1/8
	−	+	−	4		6	1/8
	−	−	−	6			

* T is taken here as the
rank sum associated
with − signs, but
if you took + signs
instead you should still
end up with the same
distribution for T.

$Mean = \Sigma TP(T) = 3$

$Variance = \Sigma(T - 3)^2 P(T)$ or $\Sigma T^2 P(T) - 3^2$
            $= 28/8$ or $100/8 - 9$
            $= 3 \cdot 5$

Putting n = 3 in (14.1) gives the same
answers.

The Mann-Whitney Test

The Wilcoxon signed rank test may be regarded as a nonparametric analogue of the
t-test which you used for paired comparisons in the second programme of this
Unit.   In that programme you also saw how a t-test could be used to judge the
significance of a difference between the means of two independent samples, where
the data had not been obtained on a paired basis.   It is to the latter type of
t-test that the test which will now be introduced corresponds in distribution-
free methods.

As an illustration, let us return to the time taken by a machine operator to
perform a particular task.   Suppose that a comparison is to be made between
left-handed and right-handed operators, to see whether either is faster than the
other.   If times (in minutes) are recorded for 4 left-handed operators and 5
right-handed operators, then a sample of 4 times will have to be compared with
a sample of 5 times.   Here are three sets of results that might occur:

Left-handed	3·2	3·4	3·5	3·3		} (15.1)
Right-handed	3·7	4·8	3·9	3·8	4·1	

Left-handed	4·0	3·9	3·8	4·5		} (15.2)
Right-handed	3·2	3·5	3·4	3·3	3·6	

FRAME 15   (continued)

Left-handed	3·2	3·7	3·5	4·0		(15.3)
Right-handed	3·4	3·3	4·5	3·0	3·8	

Look carefully at each set of data and state whether, at first sight, it suggests
that there might be a difference between the two categories of operator.   (The
accent is on the phrase 'at first sight'.   As you know by now, differences
shown by data must be judged in the light of the probability of their chance
occurrence to see whether they are really significant.   Here you are just being
asked for first impressions.)

****

15A

*(15.1) suggests that left-handed operators may be faster, as their recorded
times are all shorter than any of those recorded for the right-handed operators.*

*(15.2) suggests that right-handed operators may be faster, their times all
being shorter than any recorded for the left-handed operators.*

(15.3) does not seem to show any difference between the two categories.

FRAME 16

Let us now see how the observations in one set appear if all 9 are jointly
arranged in order, from the smallest to the largest.   Using L (for left-handed)
and R (for right-handed) to indicate to which sample each observation belongs,
this gives, for (15.1),

3·2	3·3	3·4	3·5	3·7	3·8	3·9	4·1	4·8
L	L	L	L	R	R	R	R	R

Repeat this procedure for (15.2) and (15.3).

****

16A

(15.2)	*3·2*	*3·3*	*3·4*	*3·5*	*3·6*	*3·8*	*3·9*	*4·0*	*4·5*
	R	*R*	*R*	*R*	*R*	*L*	*L*	*L*	*L*
(15.3)	*3·0*	*3·2*	*3·3*	*3·4*	*3·5*	*3·7*	*3·8*	*4·0*	*4·5*
	R	*L*	*R*	*R*	*L*	*L*	*R*	*L*	*R*

FRAME 17

Obviously observed times in one sample being less than those in the other can be
translated into L's preceding R's or R's preceding L's.   Admittedly (15.1)
and (15.2) are extreme cases in that all the L's precede all the R's or vice
versa, but it should now be obvious that if the data is to provide evidence of a
real difference between the times of left-handed and right-handed operators there
must be at least a preponderance of L's preceding R's or vice versa.   To
assess whether such a preponderance, or even the extreme case of (15.1) or
(15.2), could reasonably have happened by chance or whether it is significant at
a selected level, a probability distribution is needed.   In the Mann-Whitney
test this distribution is that of U, whose value, for the data in (15.1) would
be defined as follows:

For each L, count the number of R's which precede it, then total these numbers.

Thus, for the first L, number of preceding R's = 0
         for the second L, number of preceding R's = 0 etc.

and finally U = 0 + 0 + 0 + 0 = 0

Associated with this is the statistic U' which, in this case, would be the corresponding sum when the L's preceding each R are counted and added together.

Thus, for the first R, number of preceding L's = 4
           for the second R, number of preceding L's = 4 etc.

and finally U' = 4 + 4 + 4 + 4 + 4 = 20

Note that U + U' = 20 = 4 × 5 i.e. product of sample sizes.

Now find U and U', as defined above, for the data in (15.2) and (15.3) and in each case check that U + U' = 20.

****

17A

(15.2)   *U = 5 + 5 + 5 + 5 = 20   U' = 0 + 0 + 0 + 0 + 0 = 0*
(15.3)   *U = 1 + 3 + 3 + 4 = 11   U' = 0 + 1 + 1 + 3 + 4 = 9*

FRAME 18

If the N.H. of no difference in the speeds of left-handed and right-handed operators is put forward, the probability of such an extreme case as (15.1) or (15.2) occurring is easily found. On the basis of the N.H. all sequences of 4 L's and 5 R's would be equally likely. The total number of them is the number of ways of selecting 4 places out of 9 for the L's to occupy (or 5 places out of 9 for the R's) i.e. $^9C_4$ (or $^9C_5$).

Now $^9C_4 (= {}^9C_5) = \dfrac{9!}{4!5!} = 126$. As there is only one arrangement in which all L's precede all R's, the probability of this happening, which is the probability that U = 0 as in (15.1), is 1/126. For a two-sided test, all R's being less than all L's would give equal cause for rejecting the N.H. The probability of either happening is $\dfrac{1}{126} + \dfrac{1}{126} = \dfrac{1}{53} \approx 0 \cdot 019$.

   (i)   Will the data in (15.1) therefore lead to the rejection of the N.H. that there is no difference between the speeds of left-handed and right-handed operators when it is tested against the A.H. that there is a difference and a 5% significance level has been chosen?
  (ii)   What if the same test were applied to the data in (15.2)?
 (iii)   Would either of your answers be altered by the choice of a 1% significance level?

****

18A

(i)   Yes.
(ii) The N.H. would be rejected, as for (15.1).
(iii) Yes, in neither case would the N.H. be rejected if a 1% significance level were chosen. (Note, therefore, that with such sample sizes there are no results which could show a significant difference at the 1% level. If this level is chosen, more times must be recorded.)

FRAME 19

To judge the significance of values of U other than those obtained for the data in (15.1) and (15.2), it would be necessary to know more about the probability distribution of U. We can investigate this distribution for ourselves, much as we did for T earlier. This will involve listing all the possible sequences. For 4 L's and 5 R's there are 126 such sequences so, as the general idea can

FRAME 19   (continued)

be illustrated just as well with smaller samples, let us look instead at the distribution of U when there are 2 L's and 3 R's.   Can you say how many possibilities will have to be enumerated in that case?

****

19A

$^5C_2$ or $^5C_3$ = 10

FRAME 20

One of these 10 possibilities is LLRRR, another is LRLRR.   Complete the list.   Then for each of the 10, find the value of U by adding up the number of R's which precede each L, and the value of U' by adding up the number of L's which precede each R, as was done in FRAME 17.

****

20A

					U	U'							U	U'
L	L	R	R	R		0	6		R	L	R	L	R	3	3
L	R	L	R	R		1	5		R	L	R	R	L	4	2
L	R	R	L	R		2	4		R	R	L	L	R	4	2
L	R	R	R	L		3	3		R	R	L	R	L	5	1
R	L	L	R	R		2	4		R	R	R	L	L	6	0

Did you notice that in every case, U + U' = 6 = 2 × 3 = product of sample sizes?

FRAME 21

The probability distribution for U is readily deduced to be that shown on the right.   Note the symmetry of the distribution.   Also check that the same distribution applies to U'.

Is there any value of U that would lead to the difference between the two samples being judged significant at the 5% level?

U	P(U)
0	0·1
1	0·1
2	0·2
3	0·2
4	0·2
5	0·1
6	0·1

****

21A

No.   With these sample sizes (2 and 3) there is no value of U which would be sufficiently unusual.

FRAME 22

This exercise has shown you how the distribution of U for given sample sizes can be obtained, but it would be troublesome to have to derive the appropriate distribution every time you required to know whether a value of U was significant or not.   It is also unnecessary, as tables of the critical values of U for standard significance levels and various combinations of sample sizes are available and can be found in most books which deal with nonparametric tests at greater length than this text.

When dealing with the operators' times, U was found by adding the number of R's preceding each L and U' by adding the number of L's preceding each R but

which of these sums is specified as U and which as U' is a purely arbitrary
affair and you have already seen that they both have the same probability
distribution.   In practice, U is usually taken to be the smaller of the two
sums as this will then entail less counting and totalling.   The tables will
then tell you how small a value of U must be in order to be significant at the
required level.

For instance, for sample sizes of 4 and 5, tables show that a value of $U \leqslant 1$
would be required for a difference between left-handed and right-handed
operators to be significant at the 5% level.   Returning to the sets of
operators' times arranged in FRAME 16 and 16A, in the case of (15.1) we would
obviously choose to count the R's preceding each L, giving U = 0 which
therefore shows a significant difference, as we decided in our earlier
investigations.   With (15.2), on the other hand, we would obviously prefer to
count the L's preceding each R, giving again U = 0 and showing a significant
difference.   It is not obvious, just by looking at (15.3), which alternative
will give the smaller sum.   From your answer in 17A, however, you know that it
is 9.   Does this indicate a significant difference between the two samples at
the 5% level?

****

22A

*No, as U = 9 is not in the rejection region $U \leqslant 1$.   This confirms our first
impressions on looking at the data.*

FRAME 23

In data such as (15.3), where it is not immediately obvious which counting
procedure will lead to the smaller U, you can just make a guess.   Then, when
you have calculated a value for U, you will know whether you have guessed
correctly.   How?

****

23A

*It has been noticed that the sum of the two U's is always equal to the product
of the sample sizes, which in the case of (15.3) is 4 × 5.   Thus, if you
decided to count the L's preceding the R's, you would get U = 9 and know
that to be the smaller sum because the other must be 20 - 9, i.e. 11.   If,
on the other hand, you were to count the R's preceding the L's, which would
give U = 11, you would know at once that you had guessed wrong and that the
smaller value is 20 - 11, i.e. 9.*

FRAME 24

The next example will give you the chance to put this into practice.   It will
also serve to illustrate another point.   In the previous example the actual
times taken by the operators did not enter into the final analysis, it was only
their position in rank order that was relevant.   Thus the Mann-Whitney test
is applicable to data where the observations can only be made on a ranked basis,
as in the following example:

A geologist carried out a simple experiment to see if flint in one area was, on
the whole, of the same hardness as flint in another area.

5 pieces of flint were collected from area A and 6 pieces from area B, each
piece being marked to show its area of origin.   Facilities for making actual
hardness measurements were not available but the geologist was able to rank the

FRAME 24   (continued)

11 pieces in order of hardness.   To do this he compared them two at a time, by rubbing the two pieces against each other and then judging the piece sustaining less damage to be the harder of the two.   By repeatedly following this procedure all 11 pieces were ultimately placed in order from softest to hardest.   Their areas of origin were then seen to be

A   A   A   B   A   B   B   B   A   B   B

From tables, it can be found that for sample sizes of 5 and 6 the rejection region for U, when testing at the 5% level on a two-sided basis, is U ≤ 3. Should the geologist reject the hypothesis that the hardness of the flints is the same for areas A and B?

****

24A

Counting the B's preceding A's gives U = 0 + 0 + 0 + 1 + 4 = 5.   As the product of sample sizes is 30, this U is clearly the smaller sum.   As the data has not given U ≤ 3, the hypothesis should not be rejected.   If you gave yourself the harder task of counting the A's preceding B's, you will have obtained U = 3 + 4 + 4 + 4 + 5 + 5 = 25 and then realised that the smaller sum is 30 − 25 = 5.

FRAME 25

It can be shown that in the general case, where the sample sizes are n_1 and n_2, the distribution of U has

$$\text{mean} = \frac{n_1 n_2}{2} \quad \text{and} \quad \text{variance} = \frac{n_1 n_2 (n_1 + n_2 + 1)}{12} \qquad (25.1)$$

The derivation of these formulae will not be given here but you are invited to check them for yourself in the case of the distribution of U found in FRAME 21.

If n_1 and n_2 are sufficiently large (both ≥ 8, say) the distribution of U can be approximated closely by the normal distribution with the same mean and variance.   For sample sizes of 9 and 15 what will this approximation give for the critical value of U at the 5% significance level if the test is, as before, a two-sided one and the practice of choosing U to be the smaller of the two sums is continued?

****

25A

Taking $n_1 = 9$, $n_2 = 15$ (or $n_1 = 15$, $n_2 = 9$,   which will produce exactly the same result),   mean(U) = 67·5,   s.d.(U) = $15\sqrt{5}/2$

TABLE 2 tells us that if u is N(0, 1),   P(u < −1·96) = 2·5%

Hence P(U < 67·5 − 1·96 × $15\sqrt{5}/2$) = 5%,   allowing for U being either of the two sums.   This gives U ≤ 34 for the rejection region corresponding to a 5% significance level requirement (which agrees exactly with the figure given by tables for the critical value of U).

FRAME 26

Instead of the counting procedure so far used to obtain a value of U, it is possible to employ a formula involving a rank sum.   Taking as an example the data (15.1), ranks can be assigned to the observations when arranged in order as in FRAME 16.

Time	3·2	3·3	3·4	3·5	3·7	3·8	3·9	4·1	4·8
Sample	L	L	L	L	R	R	R	R	R
Rank	1	2	3	4	5	6	7	8	9

The sum of the ranks assigned to one of the samples must first be found.
Suppose we take the smaller sample, the L's.   Denoting the rank sum by R_1,
we have $R_1 = 1 + 2 + 3 + 4 = 10$.

It can be shown that the value of U, the total number of R's preceding L's,
is given by the formula

$$U = R_1 - \frac{n_1(n_1 + 1)}{2} \tag{26.1}$$

where n_1 is the size of the sample on which R_1 is based.   Here $n_1 = 4$,
whence $U = 10 - 10 = 0$.

Correspondingly, the value of U', which in this case is the number of L's
preceding R's, is given by the formula

$$U' = R_2 - \frac{n_2(n_2 + 1)}{2} \tag{26.2}$$

where R_2 is the sum of ranks for the other sample and n_2 is the size of the
sample on which R_2 is based.   You already know what the value of U' should
be for the present example.   Check that (26.2) does, in fact, give that value.

****

26A

$n_2 = 5$ $R_2 = 5 + 6 + 7 + 8 + 9 = 35$ $U' = 20$

FRAME 27

Looking at (26.1) you will see that, for given n_1, there is a simple linear
relationship between U and R_1, of the form $U = R_1$ - constant.   It represents
a change of origin such as you have sometimes used in the coding of data.   The
WILCOXON RANK SUM TEST, which makes R_1 instead of U the basis of the test, is
therefore equivalent to the Mann-Whitney test.   The mean and variance of U
were given in (25.1).   See if you can deduce the mean and variance of the
distribution of R_1, as given by (26.1).

****

27A

$$R_1 = U + \frac{n_1(n_1 + 1)}{2}$$

$$\therefore \quad mean(R_1) = mean(U) + \frac{n_1(n_1 + 1)}{2} = \frac{n_1(n_1 + n_2 + 1)}{2}$$

$$and \quad var(R_1) = var(U) = \frac{n_1 n_2(n_1 + n_2 + 1)}{12}$$

FRAME 28

Run Tests

In an earlier programme in this Unit, results obtained by repeatedly tossing a
coin were subjected to a significance test to decide whether the coin was fair.
However, the only aspect of the data that was considered was the total number of

FRAME 28   (continued)

heads that occurred in, say, 20 tosses.   No account was taken of the sequence
in which "heads" and "tails" occurred, and, on that basis, 10 heads in 20
tosses would provide no evidence of irregularity in either the coin or its
tossing.   Suppose we now look at the order in which the 10 heads and 10 tails
were recorded.   Three possibilities are listed below.

  (i)   T H T H T H T H T H T H T H T H T H T H
 (ii)   T H H H T H T T T T H H T H T T H H H T
(iii)   T T T T T T T T T T H H H H H H H H H H

Which of these results would arouse your suspicions that heads and tails were
not equally likely at each toss?

                 ****

                                                                          28A

(i)   and   (iii)

*(i)   suggests very strongly that the results of successive tosses were not
        independent, the result of each toss being dependent on what result
        preceded it.*

*(iii) suggests that the probability of getting a head during the earlier trials
        was not the same as in the later trials.*

FRAME 29

Of course, (i) and (iii) are extreme cases, specially chosen to make our point.
To assist in detecting a time trend or lack of independence when they are less
obvious, a test based on the number of runs can be applied.   In a sequence of
two symbols, e.g. H and T, a RUN is defined as a succession of symbols of one
kind which are followed and preceded by symbols of the other kind (or by no
symbols, as at the beginning and end of the sequence).   For (i), (ii) and (iii),
each run is indicated by underlining, and the total number of runs, r,   then
given.

  (i)   T H T H T H T H T H T H T H T H T H T H   r = 20

 (ii)   T H H H T H T T T T H H T H T T H H H T   r = 11

(iii)   T T T T T T T T T T H H H H H H H H H H   r = 2

Clearly the results which alert our suspicions that the sequence of T's and H's
is not a purely random one are those in which the number of runs is either
exceptionally high, as in (i), or exceptionally low, as in (iii).   To know how
exceptional a particular value of r is, a knowledge of its probability
distribution is required.   It can be shown that, if n_1 is the number of
observations of one type and n_2 is the number of the other type, then the
distribution of r is one with

$$\text{mean} = \frac{2n_1 n_2}{n_1 + n_2} + 1 \qquad \text{and} \qquad \text{variance} = \frac{2n_1 n_2 (2n_1 n_2 - n_1 - n_2)}{(n_1 + n_2)^2 (n_1 + n_2 - 1)}$$

Some critical values of r, corresponding to the usual significance levels, are
available from tables.   If n_1 and n_2 are both large enough, the distribution
is closely approximated by the normal distribution with the same mean and
variance.   Use this approximation to find the range of values of r for which,
testing on a two-sided basis at the 5% significance level, you would reject the
hypothesis that a sequence containing 10 H's and 10 T's is a random one.

                 ****

$n_1 = n_2 = 10,$ *mean = 11,*   *variance = 90/19.*

r would have to be outside the range $11 \pm 1 \cdot 96\sqrt{90/19}$ *i.e.* $6 \cdot 7$ *to* $15 \cdot 3.$
As r *will be an integer, this means* $r \leqslant 6$ *or* $\geqslant 16.$

*Note that, as anticipated, the sequences in (i) and (iii) would therefore lead
to the rejection of the hypothesis.   The sequence in (ii), though, would not.*

Flight-test results in a missile development programme are classified as either
"success" or "failure", denoted here by S and F respectively.   In 30
consecutive flight tests the results, in time order, were as follows:

$$F\ F\ S\ F\ F\ F\ S\ S\ F\ F\ S\ S\ S\ F\ F\ S\ S\ S\ S\ S\ F\ S\ S\ S\ F\ S\ S\ S\ S\ F\ S$$

To answer such questions as whether there was a tendency for a failure to be
followed by a success or whether the chance of success had improved or
deteriorated during the course of the programme, it would be helpful to know
whether the sequence of F's and S's can reasonably be regarded as a random
one.   Investigate this by means of a runs test, using a normal approximation.
(We should perhaps emphasise what is meant by a random sequence, in case this
has not become clear to you.   In the coin tossing it meant that the result of
any toss was independent of the result of any other toss and the probability of
a "head" occurring was the same every time.   In the present example it means
that the result of any trial is independent of the result of any other trial
and the probability of success is the same at every trial.)

$$\text{***}$$

There are $18\,S's,$ $12\,F's$ *and* 14 *runs.*

Taking $n_1 = 18$ *and* $n_2 = 12$ *(or the other way round, it doesn't make any
difference) gives, for the distribution of* $r,$ *mean = 15·4 and s.d.* $\simeq 2 \cdot 58.$
*It is obvious that, if the normal approximation is used, the observed value of
14 gives* $|u| < 1 \cdot 96.$ *Thus, working with a 5% significance level, the
hypothesis of a random sequence would be accepted.*

Advantages and Disadvantages

The advantages of nonparametric techniques over their parametric counterparts
are that:

   They are encumbered by fewer restrictive assumptions.

   They are easier to apply in that they require less involved calculations
   (though in the present age of computers and calculators this is less important
   than it was previously).

   They are based on relatively simple ideas.   Thus you have been able to obtain
   for yourself distributions of T and U, for instance, whereas the derivation
   of the t-distribution has remained to some extent shrouded in mystery.   The
   more a scientist or engineer understands of the theory behind a statistical
   method the less likely is he to employ that method in a situation where its
   usage would be incorrect or inadvisable.

FRAME 31   (continued)

They can offer ways of dealing with data on an ordinal scale, i.e. where it is possible to state that one observation is greater or less than another whereas quantitative measurement is difficult.   For this reason they have been found particularly valuable in the behavioural sciences.

On the other hand, when the assumptions required by parametric tests hold, the nonparametric tests are less efficient, being less likely to detect a false hypothesis.

FRAME 32

Miscellaneous Examples

In this frame a collection of miscellaneous examples is given for you to try. Answers are provided in FRAME 33, together with such working as is considered helpful.

1.   In FRAME 21 on page 195 you were asked to decide whether the values 1247, 1254, 1250, 1253 (in $^{\circ}$C), obtained by a metallurgist in repeated determinations of the melting point of manganese showed evidence of bias when compared with the published value of 1246°C.   You also investigated, in the same way, the results obtained by another metallurgist, which were 1261, 1268, 1264, 1267.   What, in each case, would be the conclusion reached by using a sign test?   Make a comparison with the conclusions to which a t-test led.

2.   Use (i) a sign test, (ii) Wilcoxon's signed rank test, to decide whether the data on % yields in FRAME 22 on page 196 provides evidence of a difference between the two processes.   Compare your answers with that previously obtained by a t-test.

3.   Misc. Ex. 16 on page 221 gives data on the heart rates of the crews on some of the Apollo space flights.   If the Apollo 15 LMP is ignored, so that the data can be treated as paired, would a sign test show a significant difference between pre-flight and 1st post-flight heart rates?   Would the Wilcoxon signed rank test lead to the same conclusion?

4.   Tables show that, when 24 pairs of observations are being compared by means of a Wilcoxon signed rank test, the difference between them is significant at the 5% level if $T \leqslant 81$, where T is whichever of the two rank sums is the smaller.   At the 1% level the corresponding requirement is $T \leqslant 61$.   How close to these critical values are those obtained by using the normal distribution as an approximation?

5.   To compare two pump designs from the point of view of wear and corrosion, 5 pumps of each design were made and put on trial, under similar conditions, for the same period of time.   The condition of each pump was then assessed on a scale from 0 to 15, the lower the score the poorer being the condition, i.e. the greater the degree of wear and corrosion. The assessments were:

| Design A: | 11, | 14, | 3, | 10, | 8 |
| Design B: | 6, | 1, | 7, | 4, | 9 |

Use the Mann-Whitney procedure to test the hypothesis of no difference between the two designs.   (Tables show that where both samples are of size 5, the rejection region for U, for 5% significance on a two-sided basis, is $U \leqslant 2$.)

6. In an experiment 25 mentally sub-normal patients with behaviour disorders
    were randomly divided into two groups. Those in one group (A) were
    treated with a tranquilliser over a period of time during which those in
    the other group (B) were given inert tablets as a control.   The object
    was to see whether the tranquilliser was effective in improving the
    behaviour of such patients.   At the end of the period of treatment all the
    patients were rated on the Claridge Excitability Rating scale, on which the
    highest score corresponds to the most disturbed behaviour.   To judge the
    effectiveness of the tranquilliser, therefore, the hypothesis that there
    is no difference between the scores of the two groups has to be tested
    against the alternative that group A have lower scores.   (Note that a
    one-sided test is appropriate here, as we are looking to the tranquilliser
    to improve a patient's behaviour.)   The scores were as follows:

    A: 82,   69,   76, 118, 100, 174, 185,   46,   41,   71, 135, 116
    B: 84, 141, 224,   72, 154, 218,   91, 137, 209, 111, 238, 147, 193

    To what decision would the Mann-Whitney test lead in this case?   (Assume
    that the sample sizes are large enough for the distribution of U to be
    taken as normal.)

7. A meteorologist studying a 90-day record of precipitation classifies each
    day as W (wet, with 0·25 mm of rain or more) or D (dry, with less than
    0·25 mm of rain).   The sequence thus obtained is:

    W W D D W W D D D D D D W W W W D D D D D D W D D D W W W D D D D D W W
    D D D D D D W W W W D D D W D D D D D D W W W W D D D D D D D W W D D D D
    W W D D D D D W D D D W W W D D D D D

    Test the hypothesis that the sequence is random.

8. A run test can be applied to a sequence of numerical data by classifying
    each observation as a (above the median) or b (below the median), any
    observation equal to the median being omitted.   This could be done with
    the following measurements of the diameters (in mm) of 38 successive
    shafts turned on an automatic lathe: 6·32, 6·38, 6·25, 6·43, 6·32, 6·27,
    6·43, 6·27, 6·40, 6·32, 6·25, 6·38, 6·43, 6·27, 6·35, 6·45, 6·40, 6·30,
    6·34, 6·22, 6·38, 6·55, 6·17, 6·38, 6·27, 6·43, 6·35, 6·40, 6·17, 6·48,
    6·27, 6·34, 6·50, 6·27, 6·38, 6·33, 6·55, 6·63.

    Check that the median is 6·35.   Then show the data as a sequence of a's
    and b's and test this sequence for randomness.

9. The sequence to which a run test can be applied is not necessarily one of
    time, it can be one of position.   An example of this could occur when, in
    describing a series of finely laminated shales with regard to colour, a
    geologist uses the terms light (L) and dark (D).   Progressing up a section,
    the observed sequence of light and dark laminae might then be, say,
    L D L D D L L D L L L L D.   Is this a random arrangement of L's and D's?
    (The values of n_1 and n_2 here are rather small for the use of the normal
    approximation for the distribution of r.   However, tables are available
    from which it can be found that for $n_1 = 8$, $n_2 = 5$, r must be $\leqslant 3$ or
    $\geqslant 11$ to be significant at the 5% level, when testing on a two-sided basis.)

Answers to Miscellaneous Examples

1. For both sets of data, each observation > 1246, giving $4 +$'s.
    $P(4 +$'s or $4 -$'s$) = 0 \cdot 125$.   Thus sign test does not show evidence of
    bias, at the 5% level, in either case.   Note that it (i) takes no
    account of the fact that the second metallurgist's values are further away
    from 1246 than the first, (ii) would never show a sig. difference at
    the 5% level with a sample size of only 4 (but don't forget the t-test
    might be invalid for such a small sample if $\bar{x}$ can't be assumed to be
    normally distributed).   Whereas t-test compares means, sign test only does
    so if distribution of observations is symmetrical.

2. (i) and (ii)   No sig. difference at 5% level.   (Refer back to the
    treatment of the judges' marks in FRAMES 6-12, if you had difficulty.)
    Note that these tests retain the N.H. while the t-test rejected it.

3. $P(11 +$'s or $11 -$'s$) = 1/1024 < 0 \cdot 001$ Sign test shows sig. difference
    at $0 \cdot 1$% level. $P(T = 0$ for either $+$'s or $-$'s$) = 1/1024$.   As all
    differences are in the same direction, giving ranks to the signs has no
    effect here and the conclusion is exactly the same as for the sign test.

4. For 5%: $150 - 1 \cdot 96 \times 35 = 81 \cdot 4$ gives $T \leqslant 80$, but very nearly $T \leqslant 81$.
    For 1%: $150 - 2 \cdot 58 \times 35 = 59 \cdot 7$ gives $T \leqslant 59$.

    Only in a few cases would using the approximation affect the decision made.

5. $U = 5$.   The hypothesis would not be rejected at the 5% level.

6. $U = 33$, from counting B's preceding A's.   Taking U as $N(78, \quad 338)$,
    $u = \dfrac{32 \cdot 5 - 78}{13\sqrt{2}} = -2 \cdot 47$ Sig. at 1% level, showing Group A's behaviour to
    be less disturbed than B's.   Thus tranquilliser
    is effective.

7. $r = 26$, $n_1 = 30$, $n_2 = 60$, $u = -3 \cdot 7$ Sig. at $0 \cdot 1$% level.
    There is an apparent tendency for wet days to follow wet days, as is the
    case when weather is primarily influenced by frontal systems.

8. b a b a b b a b a b b a a b a a b b b a a b a b a a b a b b a b a b a a
    $r = 26$, $n_1 = n_2 = 18$, $u = 2 \cdot 54$ Sig. at 5% level, nearly at 1%.

    NOTE: There are more runs than would be expected in a random sequence.
    This suggests that the setting of the lathe was being frequently adjusted,
    possibly after each shaft was turned to compensate for a discrepancy from
    the nominal diameter (which was, in fact, $6 \cdot 35$ mm).   Had there been a
    significantly <u>small</u> number of runs, this could indicate either a general
    increase or a general decrease in diameters over the period of time.   If
    an increase, for instance, there would be a tendency for the b's to occur
    mostly at the beginning of the sequence and the a's at the end.

9. $r = 8$ Not sig. at 5% level.   The arrangement would be accepted as
    random.

Quality Control and Acceptance Sampling

Introduction

Some variation in the quality of a manufactured product is inevitable.   For
instance, light bulbs coming off a production line will differ slightly from one
to another and will not all last for the same length of time.   In spinning,
uniformity of the yarn being spun may be aimed for but will not be achieved.
Screw blanks produced from hexagon bar by an automatic machine will not all have
exactly the same dimensions.   The amount of an impurity present in the output
of a refining process will vary over a period of time.

Where mass production is involved and 100% inspection is not feasible,
statistical methods can be applied in monitoring the quality of the product.
This programme will describe quality assurance techniques appropriate to:

(1) Controlling the manufacturing process so as to maintain the quality of the
     product at the level required.

(2) The assessment of the quality of batches of the finished product by the
     consumer to whom they are supplied.

It is to (1) that your attention will first be directed;   then (2) will be
dealt with later under the heading of Acceptance Sampling.

Control Charts

The variation in the product of a repetitive manufacturing process, which is
unavoidable and cannot be removed, may be said to be due to non-assignable
causes.   When subject only to this chance variation the process is said to be
in a state of statistical control.   The dimension of the screw blank, or
whatever aspect of the quality of a product is being considered, will then be
a random variable whose distribution (and therefore mean and variance) will
remain unchanged while the state of statistical control continues.   However,
the distribution will be affected if, say, the setting of the machine changes
or a part becomes worn.   The process is then said to have gone out of control.
The quality control techniques that will now be outlined help the manufacturer
to identify such assignable causes of variation and hence remove them (by
resetting the machine or replacing the part).

Which of the alternatives offered correctly completes the following statement?
If all the assignable causes of variation have been removed, a process is said
to be   in a state of statistical control   .
         out of control

       ****

in a state of statistical control.

To detect when an assignable cause of variation is creeping in and causing a
process to go out of control, samples of the product are taken at regular
intervals and tested.   The choice of the size of sample will depend on the
particular circumstances - the larger the sample the more reliable the

FRAME 3   (continued)

information that it gives, but the longer it takes to test the items and provide
that information, and the greater the cost involved.   So it is a matter of
striking a balance between the two.

A simple, effective and widely used device for analysing and interpreting the
data obtained from the samples taken is the SHEWHART CONTROL CHART.   Where the
quality of each item in the sample is assessed quantitatively (e.g. weight,
dimension, moisture content) two such charts are useful:

(1)   A control chart for keeping a check on the <u>average</u> quality of the product.
       The usual form of chart for this is one on which the <u>sample means</u> are
       plotted, i.e. an $\bar{x}$-chart.

(2)   A control chart for keeping a check on the <u>variability</u> of product quality.
       To meet this need, the <u>sample ranges</u> are usually plotted on what can
       therefore be called an $\bar{R}$-chart, if R is the notation for range.   The ease
       and speed with which the range can be calculated have led to it being
       preferred to other measures of spread such as the standard deviation.

In some situations the quality of the product is determined by whether or not it
possesses a particular attribute, e.g. whether an explosive fires or doesn't
fire, whether a soldered joint makes electrical contact or not, whether a
product has a dimension which is passed by go/no-go gauges or not.   Each item
in the sample can, in this case, be classified as either defective or not
defective, and an appropriate control chart would be one based on either the
number of defectives, or the fraction defective, in the sample.

All the control charts mentioned above are based on the same general principles,
which will now be explained with reference to the control chart for means.
Dealing with sample means will require a knowledge of their sampling
distribution, which you learned about in the first programme of this Unit.   The
same notation will be used here, i.e.

Population mean μ Population variance σ^2
Sample size n   Sample mean $\bar{x}$

If all possible samples of size n are considered, a distribution of $\bar{x}$ results.
What are the mean, variance and standard deviation of this distribution?   What
can be said of it when the distribution of x is normal?   What approximation
is often used when x is not normally distributed?

****

3A

Mean = μ Variance = σ^2/n s.d. = $\sigma/\sqrt{n}$

*If the distribution of the variate x is normal, so also is the distribution of
$\bar{x}$.   Because of the Central Limit Theorem, the normal model often gives a
reasonable approximation for the distribution of $\bar{x}$ when x itself is not
normally distributed.*

FRAME 4

On the assumption that $\bar{x}$ is $N(\mu, \sigma^2/n)$, fill in the gaps in the following
statements:

(i)   The probability of a sample mean $\bar{x}$ falling outside the limits $\mu \pm 3\sigma/\sqrt{n}$
       is ....

(ii)   There is a 1 in 40 chance of a sample mean $\bar{x}$ exceeding ....

(iii) There is a 1 in 40 chance of a sample mean $\bar{x}$ being less than ....

 (iv) There is a 5% chance of a sample mean $\bar{x}$ falling outside the limits
       $\mu \pm$ ....

  (v) There is a 0·1% chance of a sample mean $\bar{x}$ exceeding ....

 (vi) There is a 0·1% chance of a sample mean $\bar{x}$ being less than ....

(vii) 99·8% of samples will have a mean $\bar{x}$ within the limits $\mu \pm$ ....

        ****

4A

(i)   About 0·3%   (ii) $\mu + 1·96\sigma/\sqrt{n}$ (iii) $\mu - 1·96\sigma/\sqrt{n}$

(iv) $1·96\sigma/\sqrt{n}$ (v) $\mu + 3·09\sigma/\sqrt{n}$ (vi) $\mu - 3·09\sigma/\sqrt{n}$

(vii) $3·09\sigma/\sqrt{n}$

FRAME 5

The diagram shows the basic type of control chart originally proposed by
W.A. Shewhart, of the Bell Telephone Company of America, and described in
"The Economic Control of Quality of a Manufactured Product" in 1931.

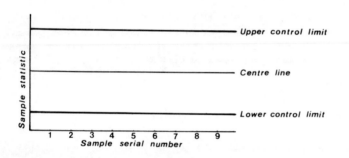

In the case of an
$\bar{x}$-chart, the sample
statistic is the
sample mean;   in an
R-chart, it is the
sample range.   The
chart is set up at the
start with a
horizontal centre line
and a pair of parallel
control lines.   The
centre line corresponds
to the value taken by
the population
parameter when the
process is in statistical control.   In a control chart for means this is the
process mean, i.e. the population mean μ.   The control lines are placed
symmetrically with regard to the centre line.   For an $\bar{x}$-chart, Shewhart
suggested that their distance from the centre line should be 3 × s.d. of the
distribution of $\bar{x}$.   They are sometimes loosely referred to as "three-sigma
limits", a term which may confuse you, because if the symbol σ is used for the
population s.d., the distance of each control line from the centre line is
actually .... Fill in the gap, taking the sample size as n.

        ****

5A

*$3\sigma/\sqrt{n}$.   The distance would be 3σ if $n = 1$,   i.e. individual observations
were being considered instead of sample means.*

FRAME 6

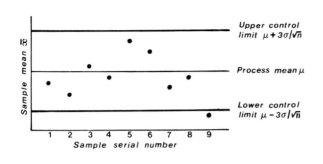

On this control chart for means, therefore, the centre line would be drawn in the position corresponding to μ on the vertical scale, and the control lines at μ ± 3σ/√n. As samples are taken, their means are plotted in time order, as shown. If the process is in control and therefore the process mean is μ, and if the distribution of sample means can be taken as normal, what is the probability of a point being (i) inside the band between the two control lines, (ii) outside this band?

****

6A

(i) 99·7%   (ii) 0·3%

_____

FRAME 7

Thus the chance of a point falling outside the control band (i.e. above the upper limit or below the lower one) is very remote while the process remains in control.   Therefore, if such a point occurs, it gives a strong indication that the process mean has shifted, the process is out of control and rectifying action (e.g. stopping production and resetting the machine) needs to be taken. In the chart in FRAME 6, did any point indicate that the process was out of control, and, if so, which?

****

7A

The point representing Sample 9, for which the mean was below the lower control limit.

_____

FRAME 8

A slightly more elaborate version of the original Shewhart control chart was recommended in a British Standard in 1935 and gained general acceptance in Britain.   In this form of chart there are two pairs of control lines - the inner (warning) limits and the outer (action) limits.   On an $\bar{x}$-chart, the inner limits are placed at μ ± 1·96σ/√n and the outer ones at μ ± 3·09σ/√n. Thus if the process is in control and the sample means are normally distributed, there is only a 1 in 20, or 5%, chance of a sample mean falling outside the warning limits and a 1 in 500, or 0·2%, chance of one falling outside the action limits.

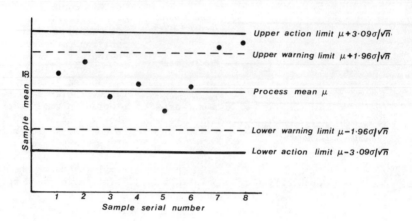

With a factor of 3·09 instead of 3, the outer limits differ little from those
in the basic Shewhart chart and are used in the same way.   That is, a point
outside them is a clear indication that the process is out of control and
action is called for.   The inner limits are included to increase the chart's
sensitivity to a change in the production process.   A point falling outside
these limits acts as a warning that all may not be well.   It suggests that
samples should be taken more frequently, but is insufficient justification for
halting the process as 5% of points would be expected to fall outside these
limits when the process is in control.   Two successive points outside the same
warning limit (as with samples 7 and 8) would, however, usually be taken to be
good evidence that action is needed.   If this practice is adopted, and $\bar{x}$ is
normally distributed, what is the probability of two successive points outside
the same warning limit causing the process to be halted unnecessarily?

****

8A

If the process is in control and $\bar{x}$ is $N(\mu, \sigma^2/n)$

$P(2$ successive points above upper warning limit$) = \dfrac{1}{40} \times \dfrac{1}{40} = 0·025 \times 0·025$
$= 0·000\,625$

$P(2$ successive points below lower warning limit$) = 0·000\,625$

$P(either$ of these occurs$) = 0·000\,625 + 0·000\,625 = 0·001\,25$ or 1 in 800

Alternatively: $P(point$ outside warning limits$) = \dfrac{1}{20}$,

$P(next$ point outside same warning limit$) = \dfrac{1}{40}$, $P(both$ happen$) = \dfrac{1}{20} \times \dfrac{1}{40} = \dfrac{1}{800}$

FRAME 9

The choice of position for control limits is an arbitrary one, based on
tradition and experience.   There is no reason why, in a particular situation,
different limits from those suggested here should not be chosen.   The
governing considerations are practical and economic.   The wider apart the
control limits, the less the risk of a "false alarm" but the greater the risk

of an assignable cause of variation going undetected.   It is a matter of
balancing one risk against the other.

If you are familiar with significance tests, you may have noticed the similarity
between the considerations which influence the choice of control limits and those
which influence the choice of significance level.   It may also have occurred
to you that the control chart in FRAME 8, for instance, is a graphical
representation of a two-sided test of the hypothesis that the population mean
is μ, with the inner control limits corresponding to a 5% significance level
and the outer limits to a 0·2% level.   You may even have wondered what the
control chart does that could not have been achieved by a significance test.
One answer is that it does more than show whether an individual point is outside
the limits or not – the sequential plot of sample means (or ranges or whatever)
gives a pictorial record which may help in understanding the past performance of
the process and may reveal a trend or systematic pattern.   Also, once the
control lines have been drawn on the chart, the actual recording of the results
on it requires no special mathematical skill and can be done on the spot.
This is an advantage, as remedial action needs to be immediate and it is
therefore preferable not to have to send the data elsewhere for analysis.

FRAME 10

To set up a control chart for means, it is necessary to know the values of the
process mean and s.d. when the process is in a state of statistical control,
i.e. to know the values of μ and σ.   If this information is not already
available, the usual practice is to obtain estimates of μ and σ from the first
samples taken after the process has "settled down" and, as far as is known,
assignable causes of variation have been removed.   If, say, 20 samples of
size 5 have been taken this would usually be considered an adequate basis for
estimates.   The value of μ is then taken as that of the overall mean $\bar{\bar{x}}$ which,
while being the mean of all the 100 observations, may be more conveniently
found from being also the mean of the 20 values of $\bar{x}$.   For estimating σ, the
method which requires the least amount of calculation uses sample ranges.   The
symbol adopted here for sample range will be R, but you will sometimes find w
used, as in the British Standards on the subject.

Consider two populations, one having a larger s.d. than the other.   If
numerous samples of size n were taken from each population, for which set of
samples do you think the values of R would, on average, be higher?

             ****

10A

The samples from the population with the higher s.d.

FRAME 11

Investigation of the relationship between the sampling distribution of R and
the population s.d. σ has shown that $a_n \bar{R}$ can be used to estimate σ, where $\bar{R}$
is the mean of the sample ranges which have been obtained and the factor a_n
depends only on the sample size n.   Values of a_n are available in tables
(or you may find d_n given, in which case $a_n = 1/d_n$).   Estimating σ in this
way is not recommended for larger samples, say, for $n > 12$ (not a serious
drawback in quality control as samples are usually smaller than that, anyway)
and works to best advantage when the distribution of observations is normal.

The setting up of an $\bar{x}$ chart for controlling the diameter of glass tubing produced by an automatic machine will now be used as an illustration.   Samples of 5 pieces were taken and measured.   For the 1st sample, the measurements (in mm) which resulted were: 6·19   6·27   6·25   6·20   6·22

Write down the values of $\bar{x}$ and R for this sample.

****

11A

$\bar{x}$ = 6·226   R = 6·27 - 6·19 = 0·08

FRAME 12

The values of $\bar{x}$ and R obtained from the first 20 samples were:

Sample	1	2	3	4	5	6	7	8	9	10
Mean $\bar{x}$	6·226	6·220	6·178	6·236	6·220	6·246	6·214	6·208	6·194	6·268
Range R	0·08	0·15	0·13	0·09	0·14	0·05	0·14	0·09	0·13	0·11

Sample	11	12	13	14	15	16	17	18	19	20
Mean $\bar{x}$	6·240	6·240	6·188	6·218	6·198	6·226	6·242	6·226	6·260	6·232
Range R	0·14	0·12	0·11	0·19	0·20	0·08	0·12	0·15	0·09	0·19

Find the grand (overall) mean $\bar{\bar{x}}$ and the mean range $\bar{R}$.

****

12A

$\bar{\bar{x}} = \dfrac{\Sigma\bar{x}}{20} = 6\cdot224$ $\bar{R} = \dfrac{\Sigma R}{20} = 0\cdot125$

FRAME 13

For a sample size of 5, the value of a_n = 0·430.   The estimate of σ given by $\bar{R}$ is therefore 0·430 × 0·125 = 0·053 75.   Taking σ to have this value and μ to have the value of $\bar{\bar{x}}$, find where to place the inner and outer control limits as defined in FRAME 8.

****

13A

Inner (warning) limits: 6·224 ± 1·96 × 0·053 75/$\sqrt{5}$ = 6·224 ± 0·047
                                                      i.e.   6·177 and 6·271

Outer (action) limits: 6·224 ± 3·09 × 0·053 75/$\sqrt{5}$ = 6·224 ± 0·074
                                                      i.e.   6·150 and 6·298

FRAME 14

Now prepare an $\bar{x}$ chart for this process, with the control lines drawn as shown in FRAME 8.   (We suggest you start the vertical scale at 6·10.)   Then plot the points representing the means of samples 1 - 20.   By so doing you will be able to check that the process was, in fact, in control during this initial period and that the observations have therefore formed a sound basis for the calculation of the limits.   (When a range chart is drawn for this data, with the values of R for samples 1 - 20 plotted, none of the points is outside the warning limits, thus showing no evidence of σ changing during the period.)

****

                                                                               14A

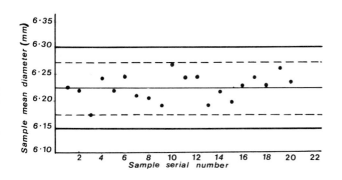

*As all points are
within the warning
limits, the process may
be assumed to be in
statistical control.
(Had this not been the
case, procedures exist
for dealing with the
situation but we shall
not go into details
here.)*

                                                                         FRAME 15

The next 10 sample means were as follows:

Sample	21	22	23	24	25	26	27	28	29	30
Mean $\overline{x}$	6·259	6·248	6·240	6·272	6·303	6·226	6·179	6·235	6·219	6·245

When the ranges of these samples were plotted on the R-chart, none fell outside
the warning limits. However, at one point, the $\overline{x}$-chart gave a strong
indication of a shift in the process mean and corrective action had to be taken.
When did this occur?

        ****

                                                                               15A

After sample 25.

                                                                         FRAME 16

Process Capability

The limits on a control chart are not, of course, to be confused with the limits
which may be imposed by a specification. In the case of the glass tubing, for
instance, such a specification might be a requirement that the diameter be
between 6·0 and 6·4 mm, i.e. 6·2 ± 0·2 mm. The specification limits, note,
refer to individual items, not to sample means. Now if the process mean and
s.d. are μ and σ respectively, and individual measurements are normally
distributed, the statistical tolerance interval to which the process is
working (sometimes referred to as the natural limits of the process) could be
given as μ ± 3·09σ, or more simply as μ ± 3σ. The proportion outside the
interval μ ± 3·09σ would be only 0·2%; for the interval μ ± 3σ the
proportion would be 0·3%. We will opt for simplicity, for the time being, and

FRAME 16   (continued)

adopt $\mu \pm 3\sigma$.   Then if the specification limits coincide with these natural
process limits, 99·7% of items will conform with the specification - a
situation that would usually be regarded as satisfactory.   Thus a process in
statistical control with a particular dimension (in mm) having mean 1 and
s.d. 0·001 would meet specification limits 1 ± 0·003 for this dimension.
Comment on the capability of the process in meeting each of the following
specifications: (i) 1 ± 0·001, (ii) 1 ± 0·004.

****

16A

(i)   *Items from this process would not be satisfactory as about 32% of them*
       would have a dimension outside the specified tolerance.
(ii) *The process would be even more adequate for this specification than for*
       1 ± 0·003.

FRAME 17

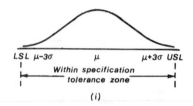

(i)

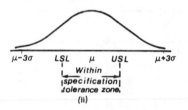

(ii)

In diagrams (i) and (ii) the upper and lower specification limits are denoted by
USL and LSL respectively.   Clearly the requirements of the specification will
be met if its limits are, as in (i), outside the natural limits of the process
but if its limits are inside, as in (ii), more than 0·3% of items will be
defective.   A measure of the process capability is given by the ratio
$\dfrac{USL - LSL}{\sigma}$.   If this ratio is .... than 6, i.e. USL - LSL is ....
than 6σ, then wherever the process mean is situated, more than 0·3% of
defectives will occur.   Which of the alternatives, "less" or "greater",
correctly fills each gap in the preceding sentence?

****

17A

less, less.

FRAME 18

Obviously if the ratio >6, i.e. USL - LSL > 6σ, the precision of the process
is adequate for the specification provided that the mean can be set as required.
Returning to the production of glass tubing, for which a control chart was set
up in FRAME 14, would you consider this process able to meet a specification
for diameter of (i) 6·20 ± 0·25 mm,   (ii) 6·20 ± 0·05 mm?   If in either case
you answer "No", say whether a resetting of the machine to alter μ could
result in the specification being adequately met.   State any assumptions made
in arriving at your answers to these questions.

****

Taking μ = 6·224 *and* σ = 0·05375, *and the statistical tolerance interval of the process to then be* 6·224 ± 3 × 0·05375, *i.e.* 6·063 *to* 6·385, *it is seen that (i) is met but not (ii).* *As* 6σ ≃ 0·32 *and in (ii)* USL − LSL = 0·10, *i.e.* < 6σ, *this specification could not be satisfactorily met wherever* μ *was placed.* *The answers assume a normal distribution for tube diameters.*

Note: The values of μ *and* σ *used here are, you will recall, only estimates, and from earlier work you will know that such estimates can be more informative if confidence limits are given.* *If* μ *and* σ *are known, it can be stated (with 100% confidence) that the interval* μ ± 3σ *contains* 99·7% *of the population. If* μ *and* σ *have to be estimated an interval can be given which we are, say, 95% confident contains* 99·7% *of observations.* *The determination of an interval along these lines is treated in* BS 2846 : Part 3 : 1975, *which is identical with the International Standard ISO 3207.* *In this particular example, the answers to (i) and (ii) would still have been the same had we made allowance for estimates being used for* μ *and* σ.

If the ratio $\dfrac{USL - LSL}{\sigma}$ is much greater than 6, the specification tolerances can be met easily − one might almost say that the process is too good for the specification. The process need not then be so tightly controlled and modified control limits can be used. The following exercise will show you one way which has been recommended for drawing up limits of this kind.

For given LSL, USL and σ:

(i)   What is the highest value to which the process mean could be allowed to rise if not more than 0·1% of items are to have measurements exceeding USL?

(ii)   What is the lowest value to which the process mean could be allowed to fall if not more than 0·1% of items are to have measurements below LSL?

(iii) On an $\bar{x}$-chart for samples of size n, where would the upper (warning and action) limits be placed to signal an increase in the process mean from the value found in (i)?

(iv) On an $\bar{x}$-chart for samples of size n, where would the lower control limits be placed to signal a decrease in the process mean from the value found in (ii)?

    ****

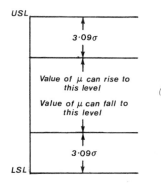

(i)   USL − 3·09σ (ii)   LSL + 3·09σ

    The answers to (i) and (ii) are illustrated in the diagram on the left.

(iii) *Warning:* USL − 3·09σ + 1·96$\sigma/\sqrt{n}$

       Action: USL − 3·09σ + 3·09$\sigma/\sqrt{n}$

(iv) *Warning:* LSL + 3·09σ − 1·96$\sigma/\sqrt{n}$

       Action: LSL + 3·09σ − 3·09$\sigma/\sqrt{n}$

Note: An $\bar{x}$-chart is set up with upper and lower controls as found in (iii) and (iv) respectively, and operated in the same way as with ordinary limits. These modified limits allow some latitude in the value of the process mean. The concept is simple, but open to criticism. To meet this, alternative modified limits have been proposed. We shall not give details here but suggest that, if you are interested, you refer to the specialist literature on quality control.

FRAME 20

Average Run Length

If a point falls outside the action limits on an $\bar{x}$-chart, it is almost certain that the process mean has shifted, but it does not follow that, if a point falls inside the action limits, the process mean has not shifted. We shall now consider the question of how swiftly the action limits reveal a change that has taken place. Obviously this will depend on how <u>great</u> a change has taken place. The larger the change the more likely it is that a sample mean will fall outside the action limits. Suppose the process mean suddenly changes from μ by an amount $3 \cdot 09\sigma/\sqrt{n}$. What is the probability that the first sample (size n) taken after the change will have a mean falling outside the action limits, i.e. $\mu \pm 3 \cdot 09\sigma/\sqrt{n}$?

****

20A

$\frac{1}{2}$. *If, say, the process mean has increased to $\mu + 3 \cdot 09\sigma/\sqrt{n}$, then this will be the mean of the distribution of $\bar{x}$, which can usually be assumed normal and therefore symmetrical. Hence there is an equal chance of $\bar{x}$ being above $\mu + 3 \cdot 09\sigma/\sqrt{n}$ (i.e. beyond the action limit) or below it. (The chance of $\bar{x}$ falling below the lower action limit is negligible.)*

FRAME 21

There is therefore a 1 in 2 chance of the change being detected when only 1 sample has been taken. What is the chance that the number of samples taken before the change is detected is (i) 2, (ii) 3, (iii) r?

****

21A

$P(2\ samples\ taken) = P(1st\ sample\ mean\ inside) \times P(2nd\ sample\ mean\ outside)$
$$= \frac{1}{2} \times \frac{1}{2} = \frac{1}{4}$$

$P(3\ samples\ taken) = \frac{1}{2} \times \frac{1}{2} \times \frac{1}{2} = \frac{1}{8}$ $P(r\ samples\ taken) = \left(\frac{1}{2}\right)^r$

FRAME 22

Now find the average number of samples that will be taken before the change is detected by the action limits. This is known as the AVERAGE RUN LENGTH (ARL).

HINT: You will find the binomial expansion $(1 - a)^{-2} = 1 + 2a + 3a^2 + \ldots$
        useful.

****

Evaluating $\Sigma x P(x)$ with $x = 1, 2, 3, \ldots\ldots\ldots$ gives

$$1 \times \frac{1}{2} + 2 \times \left(\frac{1}{2}\right)^2 + 3 \times \left(\frac{1}{2}\right)^3 + \ldots\ldots = \frac{1}{2}\left\{1 + 2 \times \frac{1}{2} + 3 \times \left(\frac{1}{2}\right)^2 + \ldots\ldots\right\}$$

$$= \frac{1}{2}\left(1 - \frac{1}{2}\right)^{-2} = \frac{1}{2} \cdot \frac{1}{\frac{1}{2}} = 2$$

If you compare this with Misc. Ex. 14 on page 98 of Unit 1, where the mean of a geometric distribution was found to be $1/p$, you will see that the same distribution applies to run lengths, with $p = \frac{1}{2}$ in this particular example.

FRAME 23

In this case, then, the change would be revealed after, on average, 2 samples had been taken. This is a reasonably quick response, but the change was, after all, a large one. Suppose that instead the change had been only $\sigma/\sqrt{n}$, e.g. to $\mu + \sigma/\sqrt{n}$. What then would be the chance of a sample mean falling outside the action limits, i.e. what is $P(\overline{x} > \mu + 3\cdot09\sigma/\sqrt{n})$?

****

23A

$$P(u > 2\cdot09) = 0\cdot0183, \quad \text{where} \quad u = \frac{\overline{x} - (\mu + \sigma/\sqrt{n})}{\sigma/\sqrt{n}} \quad \text{and } u \text{ is } N(0, 1).$$

FRAME 24

You can easily see what the ARL will be in this case, if you imagine $\frac{1}{2}$ in your answer in 22A being replaced by $0\cdot0183$, i.e. $p = 0\cdot0183$ instead of $p = \frac{1}{2}$. This will give an ARL of $1/0\cdot0183 \simeq 55$, so there would, on average, be quite a lengthy delay before the signal for corrective action is given. This delay is reduced by adopting the additional rule of taking action when two consecutive points fall outside the same warning limit, but a better way of improving the detection rate is to construct the type of chart that will now be described.

FRAME 25

Cumulative Sum Charts

The failure of the Shewhart chart to react quickly to a small change in process performance is caused by its reliance on only one point, the current one, with no account being taken of previous observations. That is the reason for the suggested improvement that has just been mentioned, i.e. considering also the previous point and taking action if both points fall outside the same warning limit. Another modification rules that a run of points on one side of the central line should also be taken as a signal for action. A method that takes account of all the previous samples, besides the current one, does so by using a CUMULATIVE SUM, often abbreviated to CUSUM.

As with the Shewhart-type chart, we shall concentrate on the control of the process mean. Let successive sample means be denoted by $\overline{x}_1, \overline{x}_2, \overline{x}_3, \ldots\ldots$ and $S_1, S_2, S_3, \ldots\ldots$ be the corresponding cumulative sums of their deviations from some reference value, k. Then,

$$S_1 = \overline{x}_1 - k \qquad\qquad S_2 = (\overline{x}_1 - k) + (\overline{x}_2 - k) = S_1 + (\overline{x}_2 - k)$$
$$S_3 = (\overline{x}_1 - k) + (\overline{x}_2 - k) + (\overline{x}_3 - k) = S_2 + (\overline{x}_3 - k)$$

Write down S_r in terms of S_{r-1}.

****

25A

$$S_r = S_{r-1} + (\overline{x}_r - k)$$

FRAME 26

We shall take k equal to μ, the process mean.   Then

$$S_1 = \overline{x}_1 - \mu \qquad\qquad S_2 = (\overline{x}_1 - \mu) + (\overline{x}_2 - \mu) \quad \text{etc.}$$

Now, if the distribution of individual observations x has mean μ, then, assuming each sample to have been randomly selected so that $\overline{x}_1$, $\overline{x}_2$, etc. are random variables, what follows about the mean of the distribution of (i) $\overline{x}_1$, (ii) $\overline{x}_2$, (iii) $\overline{x}_r$, (iv) $\overline{x}_r - \mu$, (v) S_r ?

****

26A

(i)   Mean = μ,   (ii)   Mean = μ,   (iii)   Mean = μ,   (iv)   Mean = 0
(v)   Mean = Mean($\overline{x}_1 - \mu$) + Mean($\overline{x}_2 - \mu$) + ... + Mean($\overline{x}_r - \mu$) = 0 + 0 + ... + 0
                                                                                          = 0

FRAME 27

Thus, through random fluctuations, some of the values of $\overline{x}_1 - \mu$, $\overline{x}_2 - \mu$, $\overline{x}_3 - \mu$, etc. will be positive and some will be negative, but their expected (i.e. average) value is zero, and so also is that of each of the cumulative sums S_1, S_2, S_3, ...   Hence if these sums are plotted consecutively the points will hover about a horizontal line through zero.   Now suppose that after, say, the 10th sample has been taken the process goes out of control and the mean increases to $\mu + \delta$.   From the 11th sample onwards, i.e. for $r \geqslant 11$, what will be the mean of the distribution of (i) $\overline{x}_r$, (ii) $\overline{x}_r - \mu$?

****

27A

(i) $\mu + \delta$ (ii) δ

FRAME 28

Hence each S_r after the change will show an average increase of δ over the preceding sum, i.e. S_{r-1}, and the path of their plots will follow a linear trend with an upward slope.   If, on the other hand, the process mean had decreased to $\mu - \delta$ after the 10th sample had been taken, subsequent values of $\overline{x}_r - \mu$ would have an average value of $-\delta$.   Hence each S_r after the change will show an average decrease of δ below the preceding sum, i.e. S_{r-1}.

FRAME 28   (continued)

Will the path of their plots follow a linear trend   (i) with an upward slope,
(ii) in a horizontal direction or   (iii) with a downward slope?

****

28A

(iii)

FRAME 29

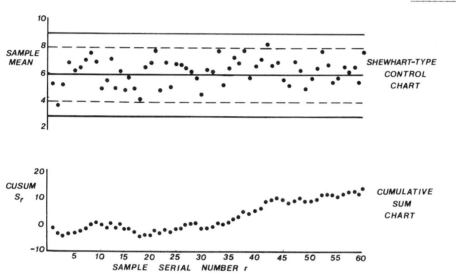

The diagram illustrates how a cumulative sum chart reacts to a change in
population mean.   For the first sequence of 30 samples, $\bar{x}$ is N(6, 1)   and
for the second sequence of 30, $\bar{x}$ is N(6·5, 1),   all the samples (of size 4)
having been drawn randomly from a population in which $\sigma = 2$ but with the
value of μ increasing from 6 to 6·5 after the 30th sample.   So that you can
compare the two techniques, a Shewhart-type control chart based on $\mu = 6$ is
shown above the cusum chart based on deviations from the same μ.   The control
lines on the upper chart have as yet given no signal of a shift in mean – there
is no point outside the action limits nor are there two consecutive points
beyond the same warning limit.   The cusum chart, on the other hand, is already
showing a sustained upward trend.   There are two further advantages of the
cusum chart which you can now see for yourself.   One is that, by noticing
where the change of slope occurs, you get some indication of when the change in
mean took place and this knowledge greatly assists in tracing its cause.   In
the chart shown in the diagram, for instance, the upward trend appears to begin
at, or soon after, $r = 30$ and thus suggests that that was when the change in
mean took place.   The other advantage is that from the slope of the path an
estimate of the size of the change can be made.   You have already seen that,
if there is an increase of δ, the mean value of each $\bar{x} - \mu$ in the long run
is δ.   Thus in the present situation the chart could suggest taking the
average value of $\bar{x} - \mu$ over the last 30 samples as an estimate of δ.   This
estimate would be $\{(\bar{x}_{31} - \mu) + (\bar{x}_{32} - \mu) + \ldots\ldots + (\bar{x}_{60} - \mu)\}/30$.   Express
this in terms of S_{30} and S_{60}.

****

$(S_{60} - S_{30})/30$

FRAME 30

For this data, the value of S_{30} was $-0 \cdot 98$ and the value of S_{60} was $14 \cdot 06$,

giving $\dfrac{S_{60} - S_{30}}{30} = \dfrac{15 \cdot 04}{30} \simeq 0 \cdot 5$.   Obviously if the change in slope were judged
to take place after, say, the 29th or 32nd samples (as might be the case when
relying on a visual appraisal) slightly different estimates would be obtained.

The appearance of a sloping path on the chart is influenced by the scales chosen
for the axes.   The recommended practice is that, taking the horizontal distance
between plotted points as 1 unit, the same distance on the vertical scale
should represent approximately $2 \times$ standard deviation of whatever is being
investigated.   In the case of a chart for sample means this would be $2\sigma/\sqrt{n}$.
What is the value of $\sigma/\sqrt{n}$ for the data plotted in the previous frame?

****

30A

1

FRAME 31

In the chart in FRAME 29, therefore, 1 unit on the horizontal scale corresponds
to 2 units on the vertical scale.   With most data the value of $2\sigma/\sqrt{n}$ would
not work out so nicely and then a rounded value is used.

The problem remains of how to decide just when a change of slope can be
ascribed to random variation and when it is sufficiently sustained to justify
a conclusion that the process mean has altered.   A method that provides a
basis for a clearcut decision, as did the control lines on the Shewhart chart,
is to be preferred to a subjective judgment made by eye.   Such a method will
now be described.

FRAME 32

Decision Rule using a V-mask

With the Shewhart control chart you have seen how lines drawn on the chart can
form the basis of deciding whether or not the process has gone out of control.
For cusum charts, the use in a similar way of two lines in the shape of a V was
put forward by G.A. Barnard in 1959.   The position of the two lines changes as
successive points are plotted, so a V-mask, which can be
placed over the chart and moved along it, is used.   A
convenient form of mask can be made from transparent paper
or perspex.   Two lines forming a V are drawn, as shown,
and the point A marked at a distance d from the vertex O.
The two arms of the V make equal angles θ with the line
AO.   Diagrams (i) - (iii) illustrate the way in which
the V-mask is used.   As each point is plotted the mask is
superimposed with A on the current point and AO parallel
to the horizontal axis.   If, as in (i), all the previous
points are within the arms of the V (however far produced)
the process is considered to be in statistical control.   As soon as a point
falls outside this area, as in (ii) and (iii), a change in mean is signalled as
having occurred at around that time.

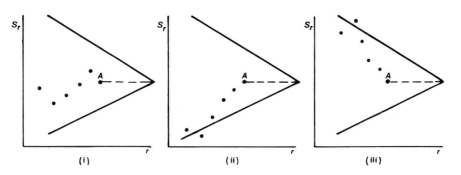

Which of (ii) and (iii) signals (a) an increase,   (b) a decrease, in the mean
level at which the process is operating?

****

32A

(ii)   (a)   i.e. a point falling below the lower arm signals an increase.
(iii) (b)   i.e. a point above the upper arm signals a decrease.

FRAME 33

Obviously the shape of a particular V-mask will depend on the values chosen
for d and θ.   In the Shewhart chart, the further apart the control lines are,
the less is the risk of a false alarm but the greater the risk of a change
passing unnoticed.   The arguments that apply to the choice of d and θ are
similar to those which apply to the choice of position for the control lines,
and also, incidentally, to the choice of significance levels in hypothesis
testing.   Will increasing the value of θ increase or decrease the risk of a
false alarm?

****

33A

Decrease.

FRAME 34

If the standard scaling mentioned in FRAME 30 is used, it can be shown that
$\theta = 30^{\circ}$ and d = 2 (measured in the units of the horizontal scale) make the
chance of a false alarm 1 in 500 i.e. the same as for the outer control limits
on a Shewhart chart.   However, a change of $\sigma/\sqrt{n}$ in μ would be signalled
when, on average, 18 sample means had been recorded after the change took place.
This represents a better speed of detection than the corresponding figure of 55
obtained for the Shewhart action limits in FRAME 24.   Note, though, that the
cusum chart does not give such an improvement in the speed of detection for
larger changes in μ.   If you recall that in FRAME 23 it was noted that a
change of $3 \cdot 09\sigma/\sqrt{n}$ would be revealed by the Shewhart control limits after, on
average, 2 samples had been taken, you will see why - there is then less scope
for improvement.   Where only relatively large changes are of concern, the
Shewhart-type chart may be preferred because of its simplicity.

Example

The following exercise will give you an opportunity to use a V-mask yourself and to test your understanding of what has been said about control charts in this text.

Sample	1	2	3	4	5	6	7	8	9	10	11
$\bar{x}$	11·23	10·10	9·23	9·97	10·51	9·08	8·36	10·77	9·42	10·95	10·66

Sample	12	13	14	15	16	17	18	19	20	21	22
$\bar{x}$	12·31	9·40	11·30	12·83	11·68	11·63	11·44	12·48	9·95	12·10	11·45

The table shows a sequence of values of $\bar{x}$, the means of successive samples of size 5. The data, like that plotted in FRAME 29, has been generated for demonstration purposes and thus it is known that the population variance throughout is 5. To begin with the population mean was 10.

(i) Where would the inner and outer control limits be placed on an $\bar{x}$-chart designed to signal a shift in the value of μ from 10? Would any of the points fall outside these limits? (This can be answered without actually drawing the chart.)

(ii) Plot the cusum chart for the data. Taking 1 cm as unit on the horizontal scale is suggested as suitable. Does the chart give you the impression that the mean has changed? If so, when does it seem that the change occurred?

(iii) Construct a V-mask, with θ = 30° and d = 2 (this will be 2 cm if you adopted the suggested scale). A piece of tracing paper is ideal for this purpose. Then move the V-mask along the cusum path with the point A placed in turn over each point plotted, in time sequence. Does the V-mask signal a change in the value of μ, and, if so, when?

(iv) If you think that there was a change in μ, which of the following new values do you find the most plausible: 8·5, 10·5, 11·5?

****

35A

(i) $\sigma/\sqrt{n}$ = 1 whence: Warning limits at 8·04 and 11·96, action limits at 6·91 and 13·09. The means for samples 12, 15, 19 and 21 are above the upper warning limit, but none is outside the action limits (nor are there two consecutive points outside the same warning limit).

(ii) If you calculated the cusums correctly you should have S_{22} = 16·85. The path of the last 10 or 11 points shows a pronounced upward trend, suggesting that an increase in μ took place around the time when the 11th and 12th samples were taken.

(iii) When A is on point 17, points 13 and 14 are below the lower arms of the V, thus giving a strong indication that μ had increased by the time sample 13 was taken.

(iv) 11·5. When the alert was given at sample 17, estimate of change = $(S_{17} - S_{12})/5 \approx 1·4$.

(In actual fact the population mean was increased by 1·5 after the 10th sample.)

Acceptance Sampling

You have now seen how, while manufacture is proceeding, charts can be used to
indicate where corrective action is needed to maintain a uniform quality of
product.   We shall now consider the assessment of the quality of a product by
the consumer wishing to see whether it is satisfactory from his point of view.
As a manufacturer is, in turn, also a consumer, such an assessment may
similarly be required with regard to the supply of the raw materials from which
the product is made.

Where the system of manufacture is one of mass production, the product is
usually supplied to the consumer in what is termed a LOT or BATCH.   The
question then arises: How is the consumer to decide whether a particular lot is
of an acceptable standard?   In precision engineering it is not uncommon for
every item in it to be inspected but there are many situations where, for
various reasons, 100% inspection is not feasible.   One reason might be that
the cost of inspection would be too high.   Another might be that inspection
involves a destructive test, as in determining the blowing time of a fuse,
where the fuse is destroyed by the test.   Similarly, in roadway construction,
if the whole of a batch of rolled-asphalt wearing course (a bituminous mixture
used in surfacing) were to be analysed for its constituents, there would be
none left for laying on the road, apart from the cost of carrying out the
analysis.   In such situations the decision as to the acceptability of the
product must be based on a sample taken from the batch and that is what is
meant by ACCEPTANCE SAMPLING.   The remainder of this programme will acquaint
you with some of the basic ideas involved.

For the sake of simplicity we shall only deal with acceptance sampling plans
which apply where inspection simply classifies an item as defective or not
defective, e.g. whether the blowing time of a fuse is less than a specified
value, rather than what the time actually is.   The proportion, p, of
defectives which a batch contains can then be used to describe its quality.

If the consumer agrees that a small proportion, p_0, say, of defective items in
a batch is permissible, then the ideal arrangement would be one in which
(a) all batches in which the actual proportion of defectives does not exceed
the agreed value p_0 are accepted (this will be fair to the producer), and
(b) all batches in which the actual proportion of defectives exceeds p_0 are
rejected (this will be fair to the consumer).   If P_a denotes the probability
of accepting a batch in which the actual proportion of defectives is p, this
arrangement can be restated as

$$\begin{cases} P_a = 1 & \text{for } p \leqslant p_0 \\ P_a = \ldots.. & \text{for } p > p_0 \end{cases}$$

Can you fill the gap in the second statement?

```
****************************************************
```

$P_a = 0 \quad for \quad p > p_0$

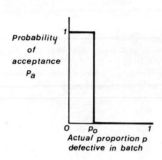

Probability of acceptance P_a

Actual proportion p defective in batch

The graph of P_a against p, shown on the left, represents the OPERATING CHARACTERISTIC (OC) CURVE for this scheme. Unfortunately, although ideal from the point of view of the end result, in that all satisfactory batches are accepted and all unsatisfactory batches are rejected, such a scheme is rendered impracticable by the amount of inspection it would require. Which of the following numbers of items, taken from a batch of size N, would always assure you of achieving this ideal: pN, $(1 - p)N$, N?

****

38A

N

FRAME 39

As only 100% inspection will always guarantee 100% correctness in assessing the quality of a batch, the most that we can look for in an acceptance sampling plan is that the probability of acceptance should be <u>high</u> for batches of <u>good</u> quality and <u>low</u> for batches of <u>poor</u> quality. This would mean the OC curve being as near to the ideal as is possible within the limitations of the amount of inspection that can be carried out. A statistical approach to the problem will enable us to calculate, for a particular plan, just what those probabilities are, so that both producer and consumer know exactly what risks they are taking.

The simplest type of plan is a SINGLE SAMPLING SCHEME. An example of this would be: Take a sample of 10 items from the batch. Inspect each item. Accept the batch if there is no more than 1 defective item in the sample, otherwise reject it. What then is the value of P_a when (i) p = 0, (ii) p = 1?

****

39A

(i) $P_a = 1$.   *If there are no defective items in the batch, there cannot possibly be any in the sample and the batch is certain to be accepted.*

(ii) $P_a = 0$.   *If all the items in the batch are defective, then all the items in the sample must be defective so there is no possibility of the batch being accepted.*

FRAME 40

We will now find P_a in terms of p generally for this scheme, in which the condition for acceptance is that there should not be more than 1 defective in a sample of 10 items. It will be assumed that the batch size is so large, relative to the sample size, that when each item is selected for the sample the probability of a defective can be taken as having the constant value p. The binomial model then applies. State, in terms of p , the probability that, in a sample of 10 items, the number of defectives will be (i) 0, (ii) 1.

FRAME 40   (continued)

Deduce an expression for P_a in terms of p.   Check that it gives the values
of P_a for p = 0 and p = 1 already found.

****

40A

(i) *P(0) = (1 − p)¹⁰*   *(ii)* *P(1) = 10p(1 − p)⁹*

P_a = *P(0) + P(1) = (1 + 9p)(1 − p)⁹*   *(40A.1)*

FRAME 41

The table gives, for the particular plan under discussion, the values of P_a for
various values of p.   These can be found from (40A.1) quite easily with the
aid of a calculator or they can be looked up directly in tables of the binomial
distribution.

p	0	0·05	0·10	0·15	0·20	0·30	0·40	0·50	0·60	1
P_a	1	0·9139	0·7361	0·5443	0·3758	0·1493	0·0464	0·0107	0·0017	0

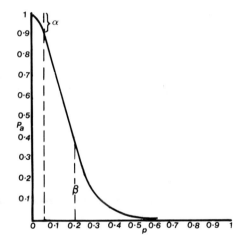

The OC curve for this acceptance
criterion is shown on the left.

    (i)   What is the chance of a batch
in which 10% of items are
defective being (a) accepted,
(b) rejected?

   (ii)   What is the risk of accepting a
batch in which 20% of items
are defective?

 (iii)   What is the risk of rejecting a
batch in which 5% of items are
defective?

  (iv)   Which of risks (ii) and (iii)
is represented by α in the
diagram and which by β?

****

41A

(i) *(a) 0·7361* *(b) 0·2639*   *(ii)* *0·3758*   *(iii)* *0·0861*
(iv) *α represents (iii) and β represents (ii).*

FRAME 42

A sampling plan such as that just described is defined by two parameters, the
size of the sample, n, and the maximum allowable number of defectives, c, often
called the ACCEPTANCE NUMBER.   The general form of procedure may be summarised
thus:

FRAME 42   (continued)

Take a sample of n items from the batch

Find, by inspection, the number of defectives, r, in the sample

```
        ┌──────────────────────────────┐
      r ≤ c                           r > c
      ACCEPT                          REJECT
```

What were the values of n and c in the particular scheme whose OC curve was drawn in the previous frame?

****

42A

n = 10   c = 1

FRAME 43

Suppose that producer and consumer agree on p = 0·05 as representing an acceptable quality of product.   Reference to the table in FRAME 41 shows that, if the (n = 10, c = 1) scheme were used, about 91% of batches in which p = 0·05 would be accepted.   Bearing in mind that 100% is unattainable, this might seem reasonable.   However, if you look at the chances of acceptance for higher values of p, you will see that it would be very unsatisfactory from the consumer's standpoint.   The chance of a batch containing 10% defectives (i.e. for which p = 0·10) being accepted would be about 74% and nearly 38% of batches containing 20% defectives (p = 0·20) would be accepted.

It might be thought that allowing only 1 defective in a sample of 10 would be suitable for an agreed quality level of p = 0·10.   However, if you refer to the table in FRAME 41 again, you will see that the scheme would please neither producer nor consumer.   The producer could complain that about 26% of batches which are up to standard (i.e. in which p = 0·10) would be rejected.   Worse still, about 9% of batches with p = 0·05, and so of <u>better</u> quality than required, would also be rejected.   The consumer could complain that the chance of accepting a batch with quality as poor as p = 0·20 is far too high. Comparing the performance of the plan in the case of an agreed quality level of p = 0·10 with the previous situation discussed when the agreed level was p = 0·05, would you say that it is (i) better for the producer but worse for the consumer, (ii) better for the consumer but worse for the producer, or (iii) worse for both producer and consumer?

****

43A

(ii)

FRAME 44

To satisfy both producer and consumer, values of n and c must be chosen so that the risks of (a) batches of good quality being rejected, and (b) batches of poor quality being accepted, are both sufficiently low.   The risk of (a) is known as PRODUCER'S RISK and that of (b) as CONSUMER'S RISK.   Obviously 'good' and 'poor' quality and 'sufficiently low risk' would need to be defined.   This can be done by specifying the values of p_1, α, p_2 and β, where α is the risk of rejection of a batch in which the proportion of defectives is p_1 and β is the

risk of acceptance of a batch in which the proportion of defectives is p_2.
The producer will then be assured that, for a batch in which the proportion of
defectives does not exceed p_1, the risk of rejection will not be greater than
α.   At the same time the consumer will know that, for a batch in which the
proportion of defectives is as high as p_2, the risk of acceptance will not
exceed β.   The proportion p_1 is called the ACCEPTABLE QUALITY LEVEL (AQL)
and α, being the risk that a batch of this quality will be rejected, is the
producer's risk. p_2 is called the LIMITING QUALITY (LQ) or, if given as a
percentage, the LOT TOLERANCE PERCENT DEFECTIVE

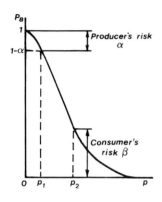

(LTPD), and β, being the risk that a batch of this
quality will be accepted, is the consumer's risk.
The diagram shows p_1, α, p_2 and β in relation to an
OC curve.   By referring to the table in FRAME 41,
state, for the (n = 10, c = 1)   acceptance plan,

(i)   the values of α and β corresponding to
       $p_1 = 0 \cdot 1$ and $p_2 = 0 \cdot 15$,

(ii)   the values of p_1 and p_2 for which the
       producer's risk is about 9% and the consumer's
       risk is about 5%.

****

44A

(i) $\alpha = 0 \cdot 2639$, $\beta = 0 \cdot 5443$ *(ii)* $p_1 = 0 \cdot 05$, $p_2 = 0 \cdot 4$

As was noted earlier, this (n = 10, c = 1) scheme would lead quite often to
the acceptance of batches of too low a quality to be tolerated, one would think,
by the consumer.   Taking   c = 0,   instead of   c = 1,   would improve matters
from the consumer's point of view, but make things worse for the producer.   To
make the OC curve nearer to the ideal it would be necessary to increase the
value of n, but this is a relatively uneconomic way of achieving a better OC.
An alternative way is offered by a DOUBLE SAMPLING SCHEME.   In this type of
plan a sample is taken initially which would be large enough to deal with a
batch of either very inferior quality or very good quality.   A second sample
is then taken (or, in other words, the original sample size is increased) only
if the first result is not sufficiently decisive.   A typical scheme is
summarised in the diagram on the next page.

The plan is defined by the values of n_1, n_2, c_1, c_2 and c_3,   just as a single
sampling plan is defined by the values of   n and c.   What are the values of
n_1, n_2, c_1, c_2, c_3 in the double sampling scheme described below?

Take a first sample of 10.   If 0 or 1 defectives are found, accept the
batch;   if 3 or more defectives are found, reject the batch;   otherwise take a
second sample, this time of 20 items.   If in the combined sample of 30 items,
less than 4 defectives are found, accept the batch, otherwise reject it.

Take a sample of n_1 items from the batch

Find, by inspection, the number of defectives, r_1, in this sample

| $r_1 \leqslant c_1$ | $c_1 < r_1 \leqslant c_2$ | $r_1 > c_2$ |
| ACCEPT | | REJECT |

Take another n_2 items from the batch

Find, by inspection, the number of defectives, r_2, in this 2nd sample

| $r_1 + r_2 \leqslant c_3$ | $r_1 + r_2 > c_3$ |
| ACCEPT | REJECT |

****

45A

$n_1 = 10, \quad n_2 = 20, \quad c_1 = 1, \quad c_2 = 2, \quad c_3 = 3$

FRAME 46

If the proportion of defectives in a batch arriving for inspection is p (what may be described as the incoming quality) state the probability that this sampling scheme will result in (i) the batch being accepted at the first stage, (ii) a second sample being taken, (iii) a decision being reached at the first stage, (iv) the first sample result being inconclusive and the combined samples then leading to acceptance, (v) the batch being accepted. Assume, as we have done previously, that the batch size is large enough for the binomial model to be used.

****

46A

(i) $(1 + 9p)(1 - p)^9$ *(ii)* $45p^2(1 - p)^8$ *(iii)* $1 - 45p^2(1 - p)^8$
(iv) $P(r_1 = 2) \times P(r_2 \leqslant 1) = 45p^2(1 + 19p)(1 - p)^{27}$
(v) *The sum of (i) and (iv)*

FRAME 47

For $p = 0 \cdot 10$, the answer (iii) has the value $0 \cdot 8063$. This represents the proportion of occasions on which a batch containing 10% defectives would be either accepted or rejected when a sample of only 10 items had been inspected. Answer (ii) has the value $0 \cdot 1937$, which is the proportion of occasions when a sample of 30 items would have to be taken from such a batch before a decision could be reached. For batches with 10% defectives, therefore, the expected (i.e. average) number of items that this scheme would require to be examined is $0 \cdot 8063 \times 10 + 0 \cdot 1937 \times 30 = 13 \cdot 87$. This is the AVERAGE SAMPLE NUMBER (ASN) which this scheme requires for this incoming batch quality. Give a formula for the ASN required by the scheme for batches in which the proportion of defectives is p. Check that it gives the values you would anticipate for $p = 0$ and $p = 1$.

****

$\{1 - 45p^2(1 - p)^8\} \times 10 + 45p^2(1 - p)^8 \times 30 = 10\{1 + 90p^2(1 - p)^8\}$

If $p = 0$, i.e. there are no defectives in the batch, no defectives will be found in the first sample and the batch is bound to be accepted at that stage. Hence the number of items inspected is always 10, and therefore ASN = 10. Similarly, if $p = 1$, i.e. all items are defective, the batch is bound to be rejected at the first stage and again ASN = 10.

Now use differentiation to find the value of p for which the ASN is a maximum and hence sketch the curve showing the relation between ASN and p. If you need a refresher on how to do this, refer to "Differentiation and its Applications" in Mathematics for Engineers and Scientists Vol. 1. Alternatively, if you prefer to avoid differentiation, you could calculate the ASN for a few values of p and use those points to make a sketch of the curve.

****

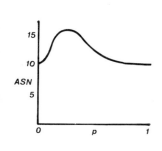

$\dfrac{d}{dp}\left[10\{1 + 90p^2(1 - p)^8\}\right] = 1800p(1 - p)^7(1 - 5p)$

ASN has maximum value 16·04 when $p = 0·2$.

Note: ASN curves for other schemes have the same general shape but the maximum point occurs in different positions. For $p = 0$ and $p = 1$ the ASN is always n_1, the size of the 1st sample, and thus for values of p near to 0 and 1 the ASN is always near to n_1. This agrees with the statement made in FRAME 45 that it would often be possible to classify batches of very poor or very good quality on the basis of the initial sample.

By sampling in two stages and only proceeding to the second stage if it is deemed advisable, there is greater economy in the number of items requiring inspection than with an equivalent single sampling plan. This idea can be taken further, with more than two stages in the plan, double sampling being just a particular case of the more general concept of multiple sampling. The ultimate extension of the idea is found in SEQUENTIAL SAMPLING. In this, items are drawn from the batch one by one. After each is taken, a decision is made either to accept the batch or to reject it or to take another item. Thus the sample size n gradually increases until a decision to accept or reject is reached. At each stage the total number of defectives, r, so far obtained is viewed in relation to the current value of n; if r is sufficiently low the batch is accepted, if sufficiently high, the batch is rejected. For a plan giving producer's risk α and consumer's risk β corresponding to batch qualities p_1 and p_2 respectively, it can be shown that the decision rule should be:

Accept if $r < sn - h_1$; reject if $r > sn + h_2$, continue sampling if

$sn - h_1 < r < sn + h_2$ where $s = \dfrac{1}{D} \log \dfrac{1 - p_1}{1 - p_2}$, $h_1 = \dfrac{1}{D} \log \dfrac{1 - \alpha}{\beta}$,

$h_2 = \dfrac{1}{D} \log \dfrac{1 - \beta}{\alpha}$, D being $\log \dfrac{p_2(1 - p_1)}{p_1(1 - p_2)}$. The base of logarithms is immaterial provided that the same base is used throughout.

If we choose $p_1 = 0.05$, $\alpha = 0.05$, $p_2 = 0.15$, $\beta = 0.10$ we get $s = 0.092$, $h_1 = 1.861$ and $h_2 = 2.389$. Thus the decision rule will be:

Accept if $r < 0.092n - 1.861$, reject if $r > 0.092n + 2.389$, otherwise continue.

When $n = 1$ this becomes: Accept if $r < -1.769$, reject if $r > 2.481$, otherwise continue. As r (the total number of defectives to date) cannot ever be negative, the batch could never be accepted after only 1 item has been inspected, nor could it be rejected as at that stage the value of r must be either 0 or 1 so $r > 2.481$ is impossible. Is there any possibility of sampling being halted when (i) $n = 2$, (ii) $n = 3$?   What is the minimum number of items that would have to be inspected before a batch could be accepted?

****

(i) $n = 2$ gives: Accept if $r < -1.677$, reject if $r > 2.573$.   Both are impossible, so sampling would always continue.   (ii) $n = 3$ gives: Accept if $r < -1.585$, reject if $r > 2.665$.   Thus if the first 3 items were all defective, the batch would be rejected and sampling would halt.   At least 21 items must be taken for the "accept" decision to be possible.   When $n = 21$, the condition for it is $r < 0.071$ and thus the batch would be accepted if $r = 0$.

Denoting the result "defective" by d and "not defective" by g, the following sequence was recorded when a sequential sampling plan was being used:

$$g \; g \; d \; g \; g \; g \; g \; g \; d \; g \; g \; g \; g \; d \; g \; g \; g \; d \; g \; g \; g \; g \; g \; d \; g \; g \; g \; g \; d \; g$$

When should it have been stopped if the particular scheme defined in the previous frame had been adopted and what decision would have been made?

****

When $n = 3 - 8$, $r = 1$; when $n = 9 - 13$, $r = 2$; when $n = 14 - 17$, $r = 3$; when $n = 18 - 20$, $r = 4$.   Nowhere is the value of r large enough to lead to rejection and it has already been shown that acceptance is impossible for $n < 21$.   For $n = 21 - 23$, $r = 4$ and sampling continues.   When $n = 24$, $r = 5 > 4.597$, the batch is rejected and sampling stops.

The procedure can be displayed graphically.   The critical value of r required for acceptance rises steadily as n increases and its graph against n is a straight line with, in the general case, gradient s.   The same is true of the critical value of r required for rejection and thus the two critical levels can be represented by a pair of parallel lines as in diagram (i), shown on the next page.   As long as r remains between the lines, sampling continues.   If it falls below the lower line the batch is accepted, if it rises above the upper line the batch is rejected.   The solution to the problem in the previous frame is shown in diagram (ii) in this way.

Now find the values of s, h_1 and h_2 for a sequential sampling plan to meet the requirements of a producer who will agree to only a 5% risk of having

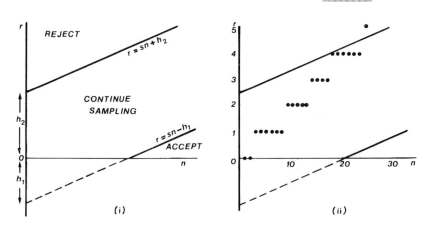

(i)   (ii)

batches with 10% defective rejected, and a consumer who is prepared to take
only a 10% risk of accepting batches of quality as poor as 30% defective.
Hence write down the equations of the decision lines and draw them on a graph
which allows for $n \leqslant 18$.   Then record the following results until you arrive
at the point when, with this plan, a decision is reached:

$$g \; g \; g \; g \; g \; g \; g \; g \; d \; g \; g \; g \; g \; g \; g \; g \; g \; g \; d \; g$$

****

51A

$p_1 = 0 \cdot 10$, $\alpha = 0 \cdot 05$, $p_2 = 0 \cdot 30$, $\beta = 0 \cdot 10$,   *giving* $s = 0 \cdot 186$, $h_1 = 1 \cdot 668$,
$h_2 = 2 \cdot 141$.   *Acceptance line is* $r = 0 \cdot 186n - 1 \cdot 668$,   *rejection line is*
$r = 0 \cdot 186n + 2 \cdot 141$.   *Stop at 15th point, which falls in acceptance region.*

FRAME 52

Analogy with Hypothesis Testing

Your attention has already been drawn to the fact that the Shewhart control
chart is really a graphical representation of a series of significance tests,
with the control lines corresponding to the chosen significance level.   In
acceptance sampling, too, a hypothesis is, in effect, being tested.   In
deciding whether or not to accept a batch we are testing the hypothesis that the
quality is up to standard against the alternative that it isn't.   The risk of
rejecting the hypothesis when, in fact, it is correct was described, in
significance testing terms, as the risk α of a Type 1 error.   In acceptance
sampling it is the risk of rejecting a batch when, in fact, it is up to standard,
i.e. the producer's risk α.   Similarly the consumer's risk β of accepting a
batch which is not up to standard corresponds to the risk β of a Type 2 error
which, in significance testing, occurs when a $\begin{array}{c}\text{true}\\\text{false}\end{array}$ hypothesis is $\begin{array}{c}\text{accepted}\\\text{rejected}\end{array}$.
Choose the correct words here.

****

52A

. . . . *when a false hypothesis is accepted.*

In significance testing it was pointed out that while, in our tests of
hypotheses such as $\mu = \mu_0$ or $p = p_0$, it was possible to specify the value
of α (the significance level), the value of β depended on the actual value
of μ or p and was therefore, perforce, unknown. The test of a population
proportion is the one which identifies most closely with the acceptance
procedures described in this programme, so let us concentrate on that. In
FRAMES 39 - 41 we considered taking a sample of 10 items from a batch.
Suppose this to be done to test the N.H. $p = 0 \cdot 05$ against the A.H. $p > 0 \cdot 05$,
and the N.H. is to be rejected if 2 or more defectives occur in the sample.
Then the risk of a Type 1 error, being the probability of 2 or more defectives
occurring when $p = 0 \cdot 05$, is known. It is $1 - P(0) - P(1)$, which you can
see from the table in FRAME 41 is $1 - 0 \cdot 9139$, i.e. about 9%. This would be
the significance level α. The probability β of a Type 2 error, i.e. of
retaining the N.H. $p = 0 \cdot 05$ when, in fact, it is incorrect, will depend on p
and the function defining it is what we called P_a. Thus the OC curve shows

the risk β of a Type 2 error for various values of p. The power function of
the test is $1 - \beta$, i.e. the probability of rejecting a false hypothesis.
Clearly it is also a function of p, and its graph, the power curve, is really
the OC curve seen from a different angle. In the acceptance sampling
procedures discussed in this programme, the consumer's risk has been defined as
the value of β for a particular value of p, which we called p_2.

Miscellaneous Examples

In this frame a collection of miscellaneous examples is given for you to try.
Answers are supplied in FRAME 55, together with such working as is considered
helpful.

1.   The following data refer to a controlled operation on a machine. Samples
     of four were taken at intervals and the dimension of a specific diameter
     in millimetres above or below 300 mm is recorded for each item in each
     of twelve samples:

Sample 1	2	3	4	5	6	7	8	9	10	11	12
22	-2	-12	-6	2	-10	-16	-2	-16	2	-8	0
2	6	-6	-6	-2	-4	-4	-2	-2	-2	6	6
12	14	-8	2	8	8	-10	0	0	6	2	0
0	6	-16	-10	2	-2	-2	4	10	8	12	24

     Calculate the grand mean and the mean range $\overline{w}$ of the samples and, using
     the estimate $\sigma = a_n \overline{w}$ for the standard deviation with $a_n = 0 \cdot 486$,
     calculate inner (95%) and outer (99·8%) controls for the sample means.

     Draw up a quality control chart for means of samples of four and on it
     plot the means of the above 12 samples and of a further 18 samples as
     follows:

Sample 13	14	15	16	17	18	19	20	21
14	-6	2	10	6	-2	14	16	4
-4	-12	6	12	0	-4	-6	-6	-10
-20	-4	-8	16	14	-2	12	12	2
0	2	-12	0	10	-2	12	-10	-14

Sample	22	23	24	25	26	27	28	29	30
	-8	-8	4	2	0	-8	10	4	24
	-14	-2	0	-2	4	12	0	0	-2
	-4	2	-10	-8	8	18	-6	16	12
	8	22	14	14	18	2	16	14	14

Discuss the desirability of an adjustment to the machine after the 19th sample and after the 30th sample.

Calculate tolerance limits to which the machine appears to be capable of working and, for tolerances 270 to 330 mm, insert a line on the chart showing the allowable width of control limits.   (L.U.)

(Note: Interpret 'allowable width of control limits' as referring to the outer controls.)

2.   A quality control scheme is in operation for a process producing ball-bearings.   It has been established that when the process is under control the average diameter of the bearings is 1 cm with a standard deviation of 0·003 cm.   Samples of 9 bearings are taken every hour and the diameters measured.   Draw a control chart to be used for recording the average diameter of each sample, inserting 95% inner control limits and 99% outer control limits.

The average diameters, in cm, of ten successive samples are 1·0006, 0·9997, 0·9992, 1·0012, 1·0008, 1·0012, 1·0018, 1·0016, 1·0020 and 1·0022. Plot these points on your chart and comment briefly on what conclusions you draw.

If the process goes out of control so that the average diameter changes to 1·001 cm, the standard deviation remaining the same, calculate the probability that the average diameter of a single sample of 9 bearings would be such as to lead to the process being investigated.   Calculate the probability of the process being investigated if samples of 25 bearings have been taken throughout.   (L.U.)

3.   The use of control charts is not confined to monitoring the quality of a product being manufactured.   They have also found application in the laboratory, where they can be used in maintaining the accuracy and precision of analytical methods and measuring instruments.   An example of this occurs in the control of radio-assay counting equipment.   Suppose that the performance of a low geometry alpha counter is to be checked routinely by recording 10 1-minute counts on a standard known to have a mean counting rate of 12 960 counts per minute, and then plotting the mean of each 10 counts on a control chart with μ = 12 960.   In this situation a false alarm is less of a nuisance than is usually the case with a manufacturing process so the action limits can allow a 1% risk of it happening.   Assuming that recorded counts follow a Poisson distribution, use a suitable approximation to find where the action limits should be placed.

4.   As well as being used in quality control, cusum techniques find application in "post-mortem" investigations, i.e. in searching through a set of past data, recorded in time sequence, to see when changes in mean level, if any, occurred.   When that is done, one is not looking for a change from some particular target level, but just for a change.   Thus,

in calculating the cusums, the reference value from which deviations are taken is the overall mean of the observations.   The table shows the daily yields obtained at a chemical plant.

Day	1	2	3	4	5	6	7	8	9	10	11	12	13	14	15	16	17
Yield	89	85	90	89	91	86	90	86	90	89	87	89	90	87	92	86	90

Day	18	19	20	21	22	23	24	25	26	27	28	29	30	31	32	33	34
Yield	91	89	86	92	94	91	89	93	92	94	93	92	91	94	90	93	89

Day	35	36	37	38	39	40	41	42	43	44	45	46	47	48	49	50
Yield	91	89	92	90	90	91	87	91	88	93	92	89	90	89	90	89

Obtain the mean of the 50 observations and take it as the reference value k when calculating the cusums S_1, S_2, ... S_{50}, where $S_1 = 89 - k$, etc.   (You will, of course, be dealing here with individual observations when forming the cusums, instead of sample means as previously, but the principle is the same.)   Can you forecast what S_{50} will be?   Plot the cusum graph (we recommend scales such that the same distance represents 1 unit on the horizontal axis and 2 units on the vertical axis) and just from looking at it, suggest what was happening to the mean level of yield during the 50-day period.

5.   Sketch the OC curve for the following scheme: A single item is taken at random from the batch and inspected.   If it is defective, the batch is rejected; otherwise, the batch is accepted.

6.   Rejection of a batch does not necessarily mean that it is scrapped.   In the case of rolled asphalt, for instance, removal of the material from the site would be very costly for the supplier and the roadway constructor may therefore agree to take material judged by the sampling plan to be of "reject" quality, but at a lower price.   Another possibility, in situations where the testing of the product is not destructive, is offered by a rectification plan.   Under this arrangement a rejected lot is subjected to 100% inspection and all defectives in it are replaced. Suppose this plan is adopted for lots of size N (large in relation to the sample size) in which p is the proportion of defectives on arrival for inspection, and P_a is the probability of a lot being accepted.   In outgoing lots, what will be (i) the expected (i.e. average) number of defectives, (ii) the expected proportion of defectives, known as the average outgoing quality (AOQ)?

7.   A company purchases large lots of items using the single sampling plan for which n = 4, c = 0.   (i) Find the probability of acceptance of a lot in terms of the proportion of defective items which it contains.   (ii) What is the probability of (a) a lot containing 50% defectives being accepted, (b) a lot containing 10% defectives being rejected?   (iii) Estimate the AQL p_1 corresponding to a producer's risk of 5% and the LTPD, i.e. p_2 expressed as a percentage, corresponding to a consumer's risk of 10%.

FRAME 54   (continued)

(iv) If rectification is agreed on, find an expression for the average
outgoing quality in terms of the incoming quality p.   Find the value
of p for which the AOQ has its highest value, known as the <u>average
outgoing quality limit</u> (AOQL), and sketch the curve of AOQ against p.

8.   An accountant checks large batches of bills for errors by a single
      sampling plan in which 50 bills are taken at random and checked
      individually.   If no more than 1 bill is found to be in error, the batch
      is passed.   Otherwise all bills in the batch have to be checked
      individually.   If the proportion of incorrect bills in a batch is p,
      find (i) the probability, given by the binomial model, that the batch
      will be passed, (ii) the expected proportion of incorrect bills in a
      passed batch, (iii) the approximation to your answer to (ii) given by the
      appropriate Poisson model when p is sufficiently small.

9.   A double sampling plan for dealing with a large batch of pieces is as
      follows.   Take a first sample of 10 pieces; if no defective is found,
      pass the batch; if 2 or more defectives are found, reject the batch;
      otherwise take a second sample, this time of 15 pieces.   If not more
      than 1 defective is found in this second sample, pass the batch;
      otherwise reject it.   (i) What are the values here of n_1, n_2, c_1, c_2, c_3
      as defined in the plan in FRAME 45?   (ii) Find, for a batch in which the
      proportion of defective pieces is p, (a) the probability of the batch
      being accepted (base your answer on the binomial model), (b) the ASN.
      What value of p maximises the ASN?   (iii) If $p = 0 \cdot 01$, use a suitable
      approximation to the binomial model used in (ii) to evaluate the
      probability of the first sample leading immediately to (a) acceptance,
      (b) rejection.

10.   A Road Research Laboratory Report (LR 276) suggests an acceptance
      procedure for rolled asphalt based on comparison with a "Standard Job"
      which defines, in statistical terms, a reasonable standard of quality as
      far as both client and producer are concerned.   When a sample is taken
      from a batch of material and its composition determined, the results are
      assessed in relation to those which would be obtained from a "Standard Job".
      For the latter, limits can be found outside which only 10% of results
      would occur; in the acceptance sampling procedure a result outside
      these 10% limits classifies the sample as defective.

      (i) Suppose that 4 samples are taken and the acceptance criterion is
      that not more than 1 should be defective. What is the probability of a
      batch of the same quality as the "Standard Job" being accepted?
      (ii) Suppose that, in the case of rolled asphalt wearing course, samples
      from the "Standard Job" would give, when analysed for % stone content,
      results which are $N(30, 2^2)$.   What are the limits (symmetrically placed
      with respect to the mean) outside which only 10% of results would occur?
      (iii) For a batch of material for which sample analyses of % stone content
      are $N(32, 2^2)$, what is the probability of getting a result outside the
      10% limits found in (ii) and hence classified as defective?   Deduce the
      probability of such a batch being accepted under the (n = 4, c = 1)
      scheme mentioned in (i).

11.   Find the equations of the decision lines for a sequential sampling plan to
      meet the requirements: $p_1 = 0 \cdot 10$, $\alpha = 0 \cdot 05$, $p_2 = 0 \cdot 30$, $\beta = 0 \cdot 20$.   The
      table on the next page gives the acceptance numbers c_n for n up to 24.

Check these entries and explain why there is no entry for n = 1 - 6.
Complete the table by finding the corresponding values of the rejection
number d_n (i.e. the minimum number of defectives which leads to
rejection).

n	1 - 2	3 - 5	6	7 - 10	11	12 - 15	16	17 - 21	22	23 - 24
c_n	-	-	-	0	0	1	1	2	2	3
d_n										

Questions 12 and 13 are rather more mathematical and you may wish to omit them.

12.   In a sequential sampling scheme there is an initial score of N.   Articles
are drawn from a large batch successively and tested, a unit being added
to the score if the test is satisfactory and a penalty N - 1 being
subtracted from the score if it is unsatisfactory.   The batch is accepted
if the score reaches 2N and rejected if the score reaches zero.   There
is no limit to the number that may be examined.   Show that if p is the
proportion of defective articles in the batch the chance P of the batch
being accepted is given by

$$P = \frac{(1 - p)^N}{1 - Np(1 - p)^{N-1}}$$

If multiple sampling is used in which up to three samples may be taken,
the sample size in each case being N, the (cumulative) acceptance numbers
of defectives 0, 1, 2 and the rejection numbers 2, 3, 3 respectively
in the three samples, show that

$$P = (1 - p)^N\{1 + [Np(1 - p)^{N-1}] + [Np(1 - p)^{N-1}]^2\} \qquad \text{(L.U.)}$$

Note: The sequential scheme is an example of Barnard's Handicap system,
in which a "handicap" H and "penalty" b are chosen.   The "score" S is
then set equal to H and as testing proceeds 1 is added to S when the
item is not defective and b is subtracted when it is.   If S becomes
equal to 2H, the batch is accepted; S $\leqslant$ 0 leads to rejection.

13.   Find, in terms of p and N, the average number sampled in the multiple
sampling scheme described in Qu. 12.

Answers to Miscellaneous Examples

1.   Continuing to take 300 as reference value: Grand mean = 1/3, $\bar{w}$ = 15·6.
Inner limits −7·13 and 7·80, outer limits −11·43 and 12·10.
Adjustment not advised after 19th sample.   As 29th and 30th sample means
are both outside same warning limit, with 30th almost outside action limit,
adjustment then advisable.

Taking μ and σ as having the values estimated, 99·7% of diameters would
be inside the limits 277 and 323 mm, or if you use μ ± 3·09σ
(i.e. 99·8% inside) the limits are 277 and 324 mm.   For modified
control limits as in (iii) and (iv) in FRAME 19, the line should extend

from 281·8 to 318·2 mm (i.e. from −18·2 to +18·2 if you used 300 as a reference value on your chart).

2. 95% inner limits 0·9980 and 1·0020, 99% outer limits 0·9974 and 1·0026. Both 9th and 10th points are outside same inner limit, giving strong indication that process mean has shifted.   0·057.   0·180.

3. Poisson model gives $\sigma^2 = \mu = 12\,960$.   Normal approximation gives limits at $12\,960 \pm 2\cdot58 \times 36$, i.e. 12 867 and 13 053.

4. Mean = 90. S_{50} = sum of deviations from mean = 0.   For the first 20 days the plant appears to have been giving a mean yield lower than 90, then a change occurs and the level of yield rises above 90 until about day 32 or 33, after which it is around 90.

Note: With a more sophisticated approach these impressions could be put to the test.   If then judged significant, the follow up would be to try and relate the changes in yield with changes in the plant operating conditions.

5. The straight line joining the point $p = 0$, $P_a = 1$ to the point $p = 1$, $P_a = 0$; its equation is $P_a = 1 - p$.

6. (i) $P_a \times pN + (1 - P_a) \times 0 = P_a pN$ (ii) $P_a p$

7. (i) $(1 - p)^4$ (ii) (a) 0·0625   (b) 0·3439   (iii) 0·013, 43·8% (iv) $p(1 - p)^4$ Maximum when $p = 0\cdot2$, AOQL = 0·08192.

8. (i) $(1 + 49p)(1 - p)^{49}$ (ii) $p(1 + 49p)(1 - p)^{49}$ (iii) Using Poisson approximation with $\mu = 50p$ gives $p(1 + 50p)e^{-50p}$.

9.   (i) $n_1 = 10$, $n_2 = 15$, $c_1 = 0$, $c_2 = 1$, $c_3 = 2$. (ii) (a) $(1 - p)^{10} + 10p(1 - p)^{23}(1 + 14p)$ (b) $10\{1 + 15p(1 - p)^9\}$, $p = 0\cdot1$. (iii) (a) $e^{-0\cdot1} = 0\cdot905$ (b) $1 - 1\cdot1e^{-0\cdot1} = 0\cdot0047$.

10.   (i) $0\cdot9^4 + 4 \times 0\cdot9^3 \times 0\cdot1 \simeq 0\cdot948$ (ii) $30 \pm 1\cdot64 \times 2$, i.e. 26·72 and 33·28. (iii) 0·265,   0·712.

11. Acceptance line: $r = 0\cdot186n - 1\cdot154$.   Rejection line: $r = 0\cdot186n + 2\cdot054$. n must be at least 7 before the condition $r < 0\cdot186n - 1\cdot154$ can be satisfied.   −, 3, 4, 4, 5, 5, 6, 6, 7, 7.

12. In the sequential scheme acceptance can only occur after N, 2N, 3N, ... trials.   Respective probabilities are $(1 - p)^N$, $Np(1 - p)^{2N-1}$, $N^2 p^2 (1 - p)^{3N-2}$, ...   Summing to infinity gives required result. In the multiple scheme, probabilities of being accepted after 1, 2, 3 samples have been taken are respectively $(1 - p)^N$, $Np(1 - p)^{N-1}(1 - p)^N$ and $\{Np(1 - p)^{N-1}\}^2 (1 - p)^N$.   Adding gives required result.

13. $N\left[1 + Np(1 - p)^{N-1} + \{Np(1 - p)^{N-1}\}^2\right]$

UNIT 2—Revision Examples

1. Suppose it has been established that, in repeated titrations of 5·00 ml of 0·1M HCl (an acid) with 0·1M NaOH (an alkali), the results are normally distributed, the mean being 5·00 ml of alkali, and the standard deviation 0·04 ml.

    (i) In what proportion of such titrations would the volume of alkali be expected to exceed 4·95 ml?

    (ii) If 4 titrations are made and the mean volume of alkali used is calculated, this mean will obviously vary from one set of 4 titrations to another. What can be said about its distribution? What proportion of such means will be greater than 5·03 ml?

    (iii) Suppose that, in 4 replicate titrations of 5·00 ml of HCl with NaOH, the mean volume of alkali used was 5·06 ml. If you knew the acid to be 0·1M HCl would you reject a claim that the NaOH was of the same concentration? Base your answer on a 5% level of significance and then say whether it would be different if a 1% level were chosen.

2. The life (in hours) of an item is normally distributed with mean 1000 and variance 2000. A sample of 5 items is then tested.

    (i) What is the probability that the sample mean life exceeds 1050 hours?

    (ii) What is the probability that the sample variance exceeds 4800?

    (C.E.I.)

    (NOTE: In this example, interpret 'sample variance' as meaning what in this text has been called 'sample estimate of population variance' and denoted by s^2.)

3. An American building code bases its definition of the compressive strength of concrete on the ultimate strength of test cylinders of specified dimensions when subjected to unconfined axial compression after having been cured for 28 days under standard laboratory moist conditions. Past experience of test results from a wide variety of projects has shown that the strengths of test cylinders made from the same quality of concrete are distributed normally. When design calculations have been based on a specified compressive strength f_c', the code requires of the concrete to be used in the structure that

    (i) there is a probability of less than 1 in 10 that a random individual test cylinder will give a strength result less than f_c',

    (ii) there is a probability of less than 1 in 100 that the mean strength of 3 test cylinders will be less than f_c',

    (iii) there is a probability of less than 1 in 100 that the strength of an individual test cylinder will be more than $3·5\,N\,mm^{-2}$ below f_c'.

    Taking μ and σ as the mean and s.d. respectively of the strengths of test cylinders made from the concrete, find, in terms of f_c' and σ, the minimum value that μ must have for criterion (ii) to be met. With this value for μ, what proportion of individual strength test results would fall

below f'_c?   Deduce that criterion (i) will always be met if (ii) is.
Find, in terms of f'_c and σ, the minimum value of μ required to satisfy
(iii).

4.   Tests made on 9 tyres of a certain make, selected at random from the
     output of the factory, gave the number of km (x) for which each tyre
     lasted.   Taking these 9 values of x and using a calculator it was
     found that $\Sigma x = 324\,000$ and $\Sigma(x - \bar{x})^2 = 46\,080\,000$.   Find 95%
     confidence limits for the average number of km for which tyres of this
     make will last.

5.   In replicate determinations by acetylation of the percentage x by weight
     of the hydroxyl group in an alcohol, the following results were obtained:
     28·6, 30·0, 31·1, 30·5, 29·6, 28·4.   Test the hypothesis that the alcohol
     is n-propyl alcohol, for which the hydroxyl group is 28·3% of the total
     weight.

6.   Components manufactured under an old process are known to have reliability
     such that exactly half fail before they have been in use for 500 hours,
     and half survive 500 hours use, so that

$$\Pr\{\text{life} < 500 \text{ hours}\} = \tfrac{1}{2}$$

     In a trial of a new manufacturing process a random sample of size 10 is
     taken and placed on trial, the trial lasting for 500 hours.   Of the 10
     components 9 survive the trial.   Show how a statistical test can be
     constructed to discover if the new process has different properties from
     the old one, and report on your conclusions from this data.

     Discuss critically the appropriateness of this particular experiment in
     assessing the qualities of the new process.   (L.U.)

7.   An electrical property of two samples of a dielectric is measured in
     arbitrary units with the following results:

Sample A	8·3	8·3	8·1	8·1	8·2		
Sample B	7·9	8·1	8·0	7·9	8·2	7·9	8·0

     Is the difference between the means of the two samples significant at the
     5% level?   (L.U.)

8.   Two methods, gravimetric and spectrophotometric, are available for
     assessing the phosphate content of a certain substance.   It was suspected
     that the two techniques do not give consistent results and to test this, 9
     samples of the substance were taken randomly.   Each sample was divided
     into two parts, one part being then subjected to the gravimetric method of
     analysis and the other to the spectrophotometric method.   Which half was
     subjected to which method was decided on a random basis.   The table shows
     the phosphate content determinations, in convenient units:

Sample	1	2	3	4	5	6	7	8	9
Spectrophotometric method	58·4	65·9	51·3	56·1	74·4	82·4	40·1	87·3	84·8
Gravimetric method	55·7	62·5	49·0	55·5	75·4	79·6	38·4	86·8	82·5

From these results it can be estimated that the spectrophotometric method
gives values which are, on average, 1·7 units higher than those obtained
by the other method.   It would, however, be more informative to give
confidence limits for the overall mean difference between the two methods.
What would these limits be, for 95% confidence?

9.   An important consideration in selecting magnetic tape for computer use
      is the amount of wear the tape produces in the read-write heads.   An
      investigation was carried out to see whether two brands of tape, "Alpha"
      and "Beta", differ in this respect.   In laboratory wear tests continuous
      20-metre loops of tape were driven at a constant speed of 1 metre per
      second, with tension accurately controlled.   The measure of head wear
      was the weight loss (in milligrams) produced during a 1-hour continuous
      run on a precision metal disc used to simulate the recording head.   The
      weight losses observed for a random sample of 5 loops of "Alpha" tape
      were:

            0·04   0·06   0·05   0·08   0·07

      and the weight losses observed for a random sample of 5 loops of "Beta"
      tape were:
                  0·07   0·09   0·08   0·09   0·07

      A variance ratio test shows that neither brand is more variable than the
      other as regards weight loss.   Use a suitable test to decide, at the 1%
      significance level, whether there is evidence that one brand of tape
      produces more head wear than the other.

10.   Using a method which was new to him, a chemist made 6 determinations of
      the percentage of an impurity in samples of a material, giving the
      following results:

            8·0   7·2   8·6   8·4   7·8   8·0   % impurity.

      Later, when more experienced in the technique, he again made 6 analyses
      of samples of the same material, and the results were:

            8·2   7·9   7·5   8·5   8·1   8·4   % impurity.

      Is there evidence that experience has increased the precision of his
      analyses?

11.   A method developed for calculating the lift coefficient C_L on an aerofoil
      predicts a value of 1·80, for a particular incidence angle.   When a
      model of the aerofoil was constructed and tested at the same incidence
      angle and flow conditions (Reynold's number etc.) the following 5
      observations were obtained for C_L: 1·75, 1·71, 1·81, 1·74, 1·79.   Is
      there reasonable agreement between theory and observation?   Another theory
      predicts a value of 1·82 for C_L.   How does this compare with the
      experimental results?

12.   In an experiment to discover what blood alcohol concentration is lethal to
      rats, progressively larger amounts of alcohol were injected into each rat
      (previously fasted) and the blood alcohol level was determined as soon as
      respiratory failure occurred.   From observations made in this way on
      over 200 rats, the distribution of lethal blood alcohol concentrations
      (in mg/ml) was found to be satisfactorily fitted by a normal model with

mean 9·30 and s.d. 0·16.   A new drug, purported to be an antidote to alcohol, was tested by pre-treating 4 randomly chosen rats with it and then subjecting each to the alcohol infusion just described.   The mean of the 4 lethal concentrations was found to be 9·49.   What would be the probability of a sample mean as high as this occurring in 4 untreated rats?   From the results of the test would you conclude that the drug is effective?

13.   Two manufacturers produce steel wire.   Eight drums of wire from manufacturer A and seven from B are tested for tensile strength, the results being given below in suitably coded units.

| A | 60 | 42 | 69 | 63 | 55 | 28 | 32 | 43 |
| B | 81 | 29 | 21 | 18 | 69 | 31 | 24 | |

Given that, for A, $60^2 + 42^2 + \ldots + 43^2 = 20\,776$ and, for B, $81^2 + 29^2 + \ldots + 24^2 = 14\,465$,

(i)   test the hypothesis that both sets of observations are subject to the same variance σ^2,

(ii)   form an estimate of this common variance σ^2,

(iii) test the hypothesis that both sets of observations are from populations with the same mean, μ,

(iv)   obtain a 95% confidence interval for μ.

State clearly any assumptions that you make.   (L.U.)

14.   At present a dairy uses glass bottles as milk containers but is considering changing to paper cartons.   This would be more economical in the long term provided that the change does not result in a short term loss of more than 15% of customers.   When 204 randomly selected customers are asked how they would react to such a change, only 162 say that they would find paper cartons acceptable.   What should the dairy decide if, in the event of changing to cartons, they are prepared to take up to a 5% risk of losing more than 15% of customers in the short term?

15.   When checking a batch of a solution which is to be used as a reactant in a chemical process, 9 determinations of its pH are made, giving:

8·34   8·29   8·34   8·32   8·30   8·33   8·32   8·29   8·35

For solutions of this type the method of determination used is known to give measurements which are approximately normally distributed (about the actual pH of the solution) with a s.d. of 0·02.   If the reactant is required to have a pH of 8·30, should this batch be rejected?

16.   One hundred ball bearings are taken from a consignment and their diameters measured.   The results are given below in a grouped frequency table.

Diameter (mm)	4·81–4·85	4·86–4·90	4·91–4·95	4·96–5·00	5·01–5·05
Frequency	5	12	18	23	20

Diameter (mm)	5·06–5·10	5·11–5·15	5·16–5·20
Frequency	12	7	3

By suitably coding the data, or otherwise;

(i)   Estimate the sample mean.

(ii) Estimate the sample standard deviation.

(iii) Test the hypothesis that the consignment of ball bearings has a mean diameter of 5·00 mm against the alternative that it is less.

(iv) Give a 95% confidence interval for the standard deviation of the consignment.

State any assumptions that you make.   (L.U.)

17. A specification for concrete requires that the mix be designed to have a stated mean strength, the figure given for this being based on an assumption that the s.d. of results from test cubes made from the mix is 6 N mm^{-2}. If, however, the contractor can produce satisfactory evidence that the method of controlling the concrete he is to provide will give a lower s.d., a correspondingly lower design mean strength can be accepted.

Suppose that the compressive strength results (in N mm^{-2}) obtained from 8 test cubes, made from concrete mixed by the contractor, were:

26·2   29·0   32·4   31·9   33·4   29·6   30·0   28·3

Would you consider that they provide satisfactory evidence of σ being less than 6?

18. Two drugs were tested on 8 cats for their ability to slow the heart, drug B being tested on the same cats as had been used for tests with drug A. The resulting heart rate changes were:

Cat	1	2	3	4	5	6	7	8
Drug A	-20	-14	-36	-28	-8	-20	-7	+1
Drug B	-14	-12	-22	-28	+10	0	-8	+22

(i) Use a t-test to decide whether the two drugs differ in the mean reduction in heart rate which they achieve.

(ii) If the number of pairs of observations in a Wilcoxon signed ranks test is 7, find $P(T = 0)$, $P(T = 1)$ and $P(T \leqslant 1)$ when T is the rank sum associated with (a) + signs, (b) - signs. Deduce the probability of getting a rank sum less than or equal to 1, from either + or - signs.

Use a Wilcoxon signed ranks test to compare the effectiveness of drugs A and B. (Cat 4 will have to be omitted from the analysis as the difference, being zero, is neither + or -.)

19. The percentages of a substance found in six random samples taken from a large quantity of metal were

4·21   4·57   4·60   4·55   4·32   4·60

Find 95% fiducial limits for the mean percentage of the substance in the metal.

Subsequently a further seven random samples were taken from a similar quantity of a second metal giving percentages

4·40   4·60   4·80   4·85   4·70   4·45   4·55

Use the variance ratio test to compare the variability of the two metals
and the t-test to compare the mean percentages of the substance in the
metals.   Comment on the results of the tests.   (L.U.)

(NOTE: For 'fiducial limits' read 'confidence limits'.)

20.   For viscose fibres, Young's modulus in extension can be taken as
      $11 \cdot 62 \text{ kN mm}^{-2}$.   It is a commonly held view that, because of anisotropy,
      the effective Young's modulus in bending is greater than that in extension.
      To see whether this is borne out by experimental results, the modulus in
      bending was determined for 8 fibres.   The values (in kN mm^{-2}) were:

      18·02   11·84   14·73   8·61   17·55   10·30   8·26   14·69

      Do these results provide real evidence of a modulus in bending higher than
      11·62?

21.   In 4 determinations of the percentage of silicon dioxide in a given
      sample of B.C.S. 308 an analyst obtained the following results by the
      molybdenum-blue method: 4·38, 4·44, 4·23, 4·35.   Obtain 95% confidence
      limits, based on these results, for the actual percentage of silicon
      dioxide present in the sample.

      In looking for a method of analysis giving less variation in results, the
      analyst also made 5 determinations of the percentage of silicon dioxide
      in the sample by the quinoline molybdosilicate method.   These gave a
      value of 0·0036 as an unbiased estimate of the variance of such
      determinations.   As this is less than half the variance estimate given
      by results obtained using the molybdenum-blue method, a possible
      conclusion is that the molybdosilicate method is more precise (i.e. there
      is less variation in its results).   Apply a suitable statistical test to
      decide whether this conclusion is a sound one.

22.   From each of two batches, A and B, of steel rods delivered by a
      manufacturer, a random sample of six was chosen and these rods were tested
      to destruction.   The breaking loads on the rods in newtons were as
      follows:

      | Batch A | 895 | 1021 | 1105 | 900 | 1024 | 950 |
      | Batch B | 1024 | 1120 | 1100 | 1020 | 1025 | 990 |

      (i)   Use the variance ratio test to discuss whether the two batches may
             be assumed to belong to normal populations with the same variance.

      (ii)   Use the t-test to compare the average breaking loads of the batches.

      (iii) If the acceptable mean breaking load for the rods was 1050 newtons,
             can the whole consignment of rods be accepted?   (L.U.)

23.   A new method (A) of heat treatment for steel components is tested against
      the old method (B).   At each of ten production periods two components are
      taken close together in time and, independently for each period, one is
      randomly chosen to receive treatment A and the other treatment B.

      The treated components are then tested for breaking strength, with the
      following results:

Period	1	2	3	4	5	6	7	8	9	10
A	10·1	9·7	14·8	11·2	13·1	14·2	13·3	8·2	11·2	10·4
B	10·9	10·4	13·2	10·6	11·2	12·4	12·7	8·7	9·1	9·9

It has been suggested that treatment A would increase the breaking strengths.   Do you consider that the data support this conjecture?   Give an appropriate lower confidence bound for the increase in strength under treatment A.   State any assumptions you make in your analysis.   (L.U.)

24.   The frequencies of daily failures of a machine are given in the following table:

Number of failures per day	0	1	2	3	4	5	6
Frequency	51	111	37	37	8	4	2

On the assumption of a constant failure rate these results should fit a Poisson distribution.   Find this distribution and use a χ^2-test to examine the assumption that the failure rate is constant.   (L.U.)

25.   In a genetical experiment, pure-breeding red-flowered antirrhinums were crossed with a pure-breeding white-flowered variety.   The first generation (what geneticists call the F_1) all had pink flowers.   They were allowed to interpollinate randomly and this produced a second (F_2) generation consisting of 154 plants with red flowers, 306 with pink flowers and 140 with white flowers.   Test whether these results are in agreement with Mendelian theory, which predicts the ratio 1 red : 2 pink : 1 white   for the F_2 generation.

26.   A manufacturer of cough medicine for children, looking at ways of disguising its unpleasant taste, tried out four different flavouring agents A, B, C, D.   When one of the flavoured mixtures was given to a child, it was recorded as being either "Acceptable" or "Not acceptable". The table shows, for each flavour, the number of children giving each of these two responses.

Do the flavouring agents differ significantly in their acceptability?

	A	B	C	D
Acceptable	15	12	20	13
Not acceptable	21	28	17	24

27.   The probability density of χ^2 with ν degrees of freedom being given by

$$f(\chi^2) = \frac{1}{2\Gamma(\nu/2)} \left(\tfrac{1}{2} \chi^2 \right)^{(\nu-2)/2} e^{-\chi^2/2}, \qquad 0 \leqslant \chi^2 \leqslant \infty,$$

show, without using the table of χ^2, that if $\nu = 4$ the chance of χ^2 exceeding the value 9·5 is approximately 5 per cent.

Five similar machines produce the following numbers of defective articles in the periods stated:

Machine	A (1 hour)	B (1 hour)	C (2 hours)	D (2 hours)	E (3 hours)
Defectives	12	16	37	20	50

Use the χ^2-test to compare the performance of the machines.   (L.U.)

(NOTE: The first part of this question requires integration by parts and some readers may wish to omit it.   It also requires the value of $\Gamma(\nu/2)$ when $\nu = 4$, i.e. the value of $\Gamma(2)$, which is 1.)

28. The following figures refer to the accidents on a certain road during the two-year period before and the two-year period after the introduction of the "Clearway" system of the complete prohibition of stopping on the carriageway.

Type of accident	Before	After
Fatal	12	13
Injury	108	117
Non-injury	180	70
Total	300	200

In looking for possible effects of making the road a "Clearway", it can be shown that there has been a significant decrease in the total number of accidents occurring. But has there been a change in the severity of the accidents? Use an appropriate test to arrive at your answer to this question.

29. In a study of the growth of daisy (Bellis perennis) and ribwort (Plantago lanceolata) plants in a large area of lawn, a circular frame was thrown randomly 200 times. At each throw, the presence or absence of each species in the area ringed was noted. The results are shown in the table. Is there evidence of an association between the presence of one species and the presence of the other?

	Daisy	No daisy
Ribwort	29	51
No ribwort	76	44

30. The number of dust particles in a small part of a volume of gas was counted on 143 occasions with the following results:

Number of particles	0	1	2	3	4	5	>5
Frequency	34	46	38	19	4	2	0

Test the goodness of fit of a Poisson distribution to the data. Why is it reasonable to expect a Poisson distribution to arise in this situation? (L.U.)

31. In tests made by a consumer organisation on two types of flare, the Supaflash and the Britalite, the following burning times (in minutes) were recorded for 12 flares of each make.

Supaflash | 20·9 19·3 19·6 23·3 21·2 22·4 14·2 16·5 16·7 17·3 15·2 21·4
Britalite | 15·9 15·5 17·4 18·0 13·9 15·6 15·8 13·4 10·1 24·3 15·7 16·4

Use a Mann-Whitney test to decide whether the two types of flare differ in the times for which they burn. Does a t-test lead to the same conclusion? (For the Supaflash times, $\Sigma x = 228 \cdot 0$, $\Sigma x^2 = 4428 \cdot 62$. For the Britalite times, $\Sigma x = 192 \cdot 0$, $\Sigma x^2 = 3193 \cdot 54$.)

32. During a 41-day production period in a cement plant, daily test cubes were taken and their compressive strengths (in $N\,mm^{-2}$) recorded. The sequence of results was: 43·1, 42·5, 46·6, 41·0, 45·3, 42·5, 43·0, 46·0, 45·6, 49·0, 48·2, 47·0, 43·3, 45·4, 41·5, 43·8, 44·3, 48·8, 48·7, 46·4, 47·6, 47·9, 43·1, 43·3, 44·2, 41·5, 46·6, 44·3, 48·1, 48·2, 46·3, 42·0, 44·7, 40·9, 44·3, 45·9, 46·6, 49·2, 49·7, 43·6, 46·8.

Check that the median is 45·4. Test the sequence for randomness by considering runs above and below the median.

33.   When a row of antirrhinum plants was inspected for rust, each plant was
      classified as either healthy (H) or infected (I).   The sequence in the
      row was: H I I I I H H H H H H H H I I I H I I I H I H H H H.   Test for
      randomness.

34.   A chemical plant produces acid in a continuous process.   Samples of the
      product are taken at regular intervals and their specific gravity is
      measured.   It may be assumed that these observations are from a normal
      population with mean $1 \cdot 18$ and variance $0 \cdot 025$.   After every five
      observations the average value of the specific gravity is obtained and
      plotted on a quality control chart.

      Draw a two-sided control chart for this process which has inner control
      lines containing 95% of the sample means and outer control lines
      containing $99 \cdot 5\%$ of the sample means.   Twelve such successive means are
      given below.   Plot them on your chart and comment briefly on your
      findings.

      $1 \cdot 29$ $1 \cdot 08$ $1 \cdot 16$ $1 \cdot 18$ $1 \cdot 18$ $1 \cdot 25$ $1 \cdot 28$ $1 \cdot 22$ $1 \cdot 35$ $1 \cdot 13$ $1 \cdot 38$ $1 \cdot 41$

      If the process mean falls to $1 \cdot 15$ what is the probability that a sample
      mean will fall below the lower inner control line?   For what value of
      the process mean is the probability that a sample mean will fall below the
      lower outer control line equal to $0 \cdot 95$?   (L.U.)

35.   Concrete for which there is a probability p (i.e. 100p%) that a test
      cube made from it will give a compressive strength test result below a
      specified strength L, is said to be "100p% defective to L".   If a
      specification requires that 40 cubes be made and tested and that not
      more than 2 results should fall below the specified strength L, give an
      expression for the probability of a concrete that is $2 \cdot 5\%$ defective to L
      complying with this requirement.   Then evaluate this probability by
      using a suitable approximation to the binomial model.

36.   A large batch of items is to be tested by the following double sampling
      scheme.   In the first sample 20 items are taken and the scheme is:
      if no defective items are found, pass the batch; if 2 or more defective
      items are found, reject the batch; if 1 defective item is found, take
      a second sample.

      In a second sample 40 items are taken and the scheme is: if no or one
      defective item is found, pass the batch.   Otherwise reject the batch.

      (i)   Obtain an expression for the probability of accepting a batch in
            which the true proportion defective is p.   Also obtain an
            approximate evaluation of this probability when p = $0 \cdot 05$.   Define
            Operating Characteristic and sketch the OC curve for this scheme.

      (ii) Obtain an expression for the average sampling number for the scheme
            when the true proportion defective is p.   Sketch the graph of
            the ASN as a function of p.   What value of p maximises the
            ASN?   (L.U.)

37.   At Swinburne College of Technology, Melbourne, a comparative study of two
      methods of teaching mathematics was made in 1975.   Of first year
      engineering students, some were taught in the traditional way and the
      others by a trial system based on programmed learning.   The table shows,

for each group, the number of students who, at the end of the second semester, were awarded grades ranging from H_1 (first class honours) to N (fail).

Method \ Grade	H_1	H_{2A}	H_{2B}	H_3	P_1	P_2	N
Trial	2	3	12	19	109	9	31
Traditional	3	3	10	11	33	7	44

Test the hypothesis that grading is independent of method of teaching.

ANSWERS

1. (i) 0·8944   (ii) N(5·00, 0·02²), 0·0688
    (iii) u = 3·0.   Claim rejected at 5% level, also at 1%.

2. (i) 0·0062   (ii) 0·05 approx.

3. f'_c + 1·345σ.   About 0·09. f'_c - 3·5 + 2·33σ

4. 34 150 and 37 850 km approx.

5. $|t|$ = 3·24 > 2·57.   Hypothesis rejected at 5% level.

6. P(such an extreme result) = 11/512 ≈ 0·02.   Difference sig. at 5% level.

7. F^6_4 = 1·3̇, not sig. at 5% level so pooled variance estimate can be used, giving $|t|$ = 3·12 > 2·23.   Difference between means sig. at 5% level.

8. 0·62 and 2·78.

9. $|t|$ = 2·39 < 3·36.   Not sig. at 1% level.

10. F^5_5 = 1·82 < 5·05.   No sig. increase in precision at 5% level.

11. $|t|$ = 2·24 < 2·78.   Not sig. at 5% level, so agreement is reasonable.
     $|t|$ = 3·35 > 2·78.   Sig. difference between theory and results, at 5% level.

12. P(u > 2·375) ≈ 0·009 < 0·01.   Yes, at 1% sig. level.

13. (i) F^6_7 = 2·84 < 5·12. Hypothesis accepted at 5% level.   (ii) 5386/13
     (iii) $|t|$ = 0·95 < 2·16.   Hypothesis accepted at 5% level.
     (iv) 33·1 and 55·5

14. u ≈ 2·2 > 1·64.   Change to paper cartons should not be made.

15. u = 3 > 2·58.   At 1% sig. level, batch would be rejected.

16.   (i) 4·99   (ii) 0·085   (iii) t = -1·18 ≮ -1·66.   Or as sample
      is large, you could use u = -1·18 ≮ -1·64.   Either leads to
      retention of hypothesis at 5% level.
      (iv) 1·49 to 1·97.

17. F_7^∞ = 6·41 > 5·65.   Or, using χ^2 with 7 d.f., $\frac{\Sigma (x - \bar{x})^2}{36}$ = 1·09 < 1·24.
      Either leads to the conclusion σ < 6, at the 1% sig. level.

18.   (i) $|t|$ = 3·05 > 2·36 but < 3·50.   Difference sig. at 5% level,
      but not 1%.
      (ii) (a) 1/128, 1/128, 1/64.   (b) 1/128, 1/128, 1/64.   1/32 = 0·031 25.
      Difference sig. at 5% level, but not 1%.

19.   4·30 and 4·65. F_5^6 = 1·04 < 6·98.   No sig. difference in variability,
      at 5% level. $|t|$ = 1·56 < 2·20.   No sig. difference between mean
      percentages, at 5% level.

20.   t = 1·02 < 1·89.   Not sig. at 5% level.

21.   4·21 and 4·49. F_4^3 = 2·1̇6 < 6·59.   Not sig. at 5% level, so conclusion
      of greater precision would not be sound.

22.   (i) F_5^5 = 2·57 < 7·15.   Not sig. at 5% level.   Same variance may be
      assumed.
      (ii) t = 1·62 < 2·23.   Difference between means not sig. at 5% level.
      (iii) t = 1·68 < 2·20.   Not sig. at 5% level so consignment can be
      accepted.

23.   t = 2·019 > 1·83.   Sig. increase, at 5% level.   95% lower confidence
      bound = 0·07.

24.
Number of failures	0	1	2	3	4	5	6	7 or more
Expected frequency	59·2	85·3	61·4	29·5	10·6	3·1	0·7	0·2

Combining last 4 frequencies leads to χ^2 = 20·51, ν = 3.   Sig. at
0·1% level.   Very good grounds for rejecting assumption of constant
failure rate.

25. χ^2 = 0·89 < 5·99.   Not sig. at 5% level, showing agreement with theory.

26. χ^2 = 5·12 < 7·81.   No sig. difference at 5% level.

27. $\int_{9\cdot5}^\infty \frac{1}{4} \chi^2 e^{-\chi^2/2} \, d(\chi^2)$ = 0·0497; χ^2 = 6·19 < 9·49,   no sig. difference in

performance.

28. χ^2 = 30·0 > 13·82.   At 0·1% level, sig. change in severity of accidents.

29. χ^2 = 14·12 > 10·83.   Evidence of association, sig. at 0·1% level.

30. χ^2 = 1·34 < 7·81.   Not sig. at 5% level.   Satisfactory fit.

31.   U = 34.   Sig at 5% level (using normal approximation).
      t = 2·33 > 2·07.   Sig. at 5% level.

32. 14 runs.   Sig. at 5% level (using normal approximation).

33. 9 runs.   Hypothesis of randomness not rejected, at 5% level (using normal approximation).

34. Inner control lines: 1·04 and 1·32.   Outer control lines: 0·98 and 1·38.   11th point above upper inner control line and 12th above upper outer control line firmly indicate that the process is now out of control. About 6%.   0·84.

35. $0·975^{40} + 40 \times 0·975^{39} \times 0·025 + 780 \times 0·975^{38} \times 0·025^2$.   Poisson approximation gives $2·5e^{-1} = 0·920$.

36. (i) $(1 - p)^{20} + 20p(1 - p)^{58}(1 + 39p)$.   Poisson approximation gives $e^{-1}(1 + 3e^{-2}) \simeq 0·517$.   The OC is the function of p which represents the probability of accepting a batch in which the true proportion defective is p.   For this scheme the curve shows the OC decreasing from 1 when p = 0 to 0 when p = 1, with zero slope at both these points.
     (ii) $20\{1 + 40p(1 - p)^{19}\}$.   ASN = 20 when p = 0 and p = 1. Maximum value $\simeq 35·1$, occurs when p = 0·05.

37. If H_1 and H_{2A} are merged, only 1 out of 12 expected frequencies is <5 and this may be considered allowable.   Then $\chi^2 = 28·89 > 20·52$. Sig. at 0·1% level.   Merging H_1, H_{2A} and H_{2B}, so that no E_i is <5, leads to the same conclusion, as $\chi^2 = 28·63 > 18·47$.   (These answers are based on exact values of E_i.   If you rounded off E_i to 1 d.p. the value of your χ^2 test statistic will not be correct to 2 d.p., only to the nearest integer.   However, $\chi^2 = 29$ still leads to the same decision.)

UNIT 3
VARIANCE ANALYSIS,
CORRELATION and REGRESSION

This Unit comprises three programmes:

    (a)   Analysis of Variance

    (b)   Correlation

    (c)   Regression

Before reading these programmes, it is necessary that you are familiar with the
following

Prerequisites

For (a):   Sampling distribution of the mean.
            t-distribution.
            F-test.

For (b):   t-distribution.
            Ideas of significance testing and confidence intervals.

For (c):   Correlation.
            For FRAMES 30-41, F-test.   It is also preferable to have followed (a).
            For FRAMES 42-52, t-distribution, idea of confidence intervals.

Analysis of Variance

Comparison of Several Means

In Unit 2 you learned how to decide whether the means of two samples differed significantly. Two examples will now be described in which a comparison between several means is required.

(1) Four different rubber compounds A, B, C, D were tested for tensile strength. In each test a rectangular specimen was prepared and pulled in a longitudinal direction. This was done for 4 specimens of each compound, giving the following results (in $N\,mm^{-2}$):

A	B	C	D
22·1	22·1	23·8	21·9
20·7	23·0	24·2	23·4
22·9	21·9	24·1	22·6
21·5	21·8	23·1	22·9

(2) Samples of water were drawn off from a source of supply at different times and 5 determinations of iron content made on each sample, using the same method throughout. The results (in ppm) were as follows:

Sample 1	10·3	9·8	10·9	11·4	10·1
Sample 2	10·9	9·8	10·0	10·3	10·5
Sample 3	10·3	11·4	10·8	10·6	10·9
Sample 4	10·7	11·3	11·2	10·8	11·0

(Here the sample values are in rows, instead of in columns as in (1). The difference is merely in presentation so don't try to read any special meaning into it.)

In investigations producing data of this nature, there are various questions which may need to be answered. We shall begin by considering the question which in (1) would be "Do the rubber compounds differ from one another in their tensile strengths?" and in (2) would be "Is there variation in the iron content of this water supply from time to time?"

The most obvious start towards obtaining an answer would seem to be: in (1), finding the mean tensile strength of specimens of each rubber compound, and in (2), finding the mean determination of iron content for each sample of water. This gives:

For the rubber compounds: $\bar{x}_A = 21·8$, $\bar{x}_B = 22·2$, $\bar{x}_C = 23·8$, $\bar{x}_D = 22·7$.

For the water data: $\bar{x}_1 = 10·5$, $\bar{x}_2 = 10·3$, $\bar{x}_3 = 10·8$, $\bar{x}_4 = 11·0$.

As by now you will be well aware, the fact that these sample means differ among themselves does not necessarily mean that the compounds differ in their tensile strengths or that changes in the iron content of the water are occurring with time. A glance at the data shows that there is variation in the observations even when made on the same rubber compound or on the same water sample. This variation can presumably be attributed to testing error. The question is therefore whether the variation among sample means can be explained by this testing error or whether there is another component caused by differing tensile strengths in (1) or differing iron contents in (2).   In analysing the variation to see whether this component exists, we shall use the variance as the measure of variation and hence the approach adopted is called ANALYSIS OF VARIANCE.   It will be assumed that the variation due to testing error is in (1) the same for one rubber compound as for another, and in (2) the same for all water samples.   When the same test procedure is used throughout this is not an unreasonable assumption.

<u>FRAME 3</u>

For demonstration purposes we shall use the especially simple set of data shown here.   Sample means have been calculated, also the grand mean of all the 20 observations.

Sample 1	Sample 2	Sample 3	Sample 4
x_1	x_2	x_3	x_4
5	3	4	1
7	4	3	3
6	1	7	3
9	3	6	1
3	4	5	2

Sample totals $T_1 = 30$ $T_2 = 15$ $T_3 = 25$ $T_4 = 10$

Sample means $\overline{x}_1 = 6$ $\overline{x}_2 = 3$ $\overline{x}_3 = 5$ $\overline{x}_4 = 2$

Total number of observations   N = 20

Grand total   T = 80   Grand mean $\overline{\overline{x}} = 80/20 = 4$

If these samples were all from the same population, its variance σ^2 (which would be due to the testing error referred to in the previous frame) could be estimated in three ways.

First, an estimate could be obtained from the entire 20 observations.   Working from first principles, this would involve taking the squares of the deviations from the grand mean $\overline{\overline{x}}$, as shown below.

$(5 - 4)^2 = 1$	$(3 - 4)^2 = 1$	$(4 - 4)^2 = 0$	$(1 - 4)^2 = 9$
$(7 - 4)^2 = 9$	$(4 - 4)^2 = 0$	$(3 - 4)^2 = 1$	$(3 - 4)^2 = 1$
$(6 - 4)^2 = 4$	$(1 - 4)^2 = 9$	$(7 - 4)^2 = 9$	$(3 - 4)^2 = 1$
$(9 - 4)^2 = 25$	$(3 - 4)^2 = 1$	$(6 - 4)^2 = 4$	$(1 - 4)^2 = 9$
$(3 - 4)^2 = 1$	$(4 - 4)^2 = 0$	$(5 - 4)^2 = 1$	$(2 - 4)^2 = 4$

Summing gives $\Sigma(x - \overline{\overline{x}})^2 = 90$.   What is the number of degrees of freedom in this sum and how would you now obtain an estimate of σ^2?

****

3A

20 - 1 = 19 d.f.   Estimate of $\sigma^2 = 90/19$

Secondly, we could look at the variation within each sample and consider the squares of the deviations from the sample mean.   These are:

$(x_1 - \overline{x}_1)^2$	$(x_2 - \overline{x}_2)^2$	$(x_3 - \overline{x}_3)^2$	$(x_4 - \overline{x}_4)^2$
$(5 - 6)^2 = 1$	$(3 - 3)^2 = 0$	$(4 - 5)^2 = 1$	$(1 - 2)^2 = 1$
$(7 - 6)^2 = 1$	$(4 - 3)^2 = 1$	$(3 - 5)^2 = 4$	$(3 - 2)^2 = 1$
$(6 - 6)^2 = 0$	$(1 - 3)^2 = 4$	$(7 - 5)^2 = 4$	$(3 - 2)^2 = 1$
$(9 - 6)^2 = 9$	$(3 - 3)^2 = 0$	$(6 - 5)^2 = 1$	$(1 - 2)^2 = 1$
$(3 - 6)^2 = 9$	$(4 - 3)^2 = 1$	$(5 - 5)^2 = 0$	$(2 - 2)^2 = 0$

Now, in Unit 2 you used $\dfrac{\Sigma(x_1 - \overline{x}_1)^2 + \Sigma(x_2 - \overline{x}_2)^2}{(n_1 - 1) + (n_2 - 1)}$ to obtain an estimate of a

common variance from two samples of n_1, n_2 items respectively, the denominator representing the number of d.f. in the numerator ($n_1 - 1$ d.f. in the first sum and $n_2 - 1$ d.f. in the second).   This formula can be extended to any number of samples.   If there are 4, the numerator will be $\Sigma(x_1 - \overline{x}_1)^2 + \Sigma(x_2 - \overline{x}_2)^2 + \Sigma(x_3 - \overline{x}_3)^2 + \Sigma(x_4 - \overline{x}_4)^2$.   Find the value this sum of squares takes in the present example, and the number of d.f. in it. Hence find an estimate of σ^2 by dividing the sum of squares by the number of d.f.

****

$\Sigma(x_1 - \overline{x}_1)^2 + \Sigma(x_2 - \overline{x}_2)^2 + \Sigma(x_3 - \overline{x}_3)^2 + \Sigma(x_4 - \overline{x}_4)^2 = 20 + 6 + 10 + 4 = 40$

There are 4 d.f. in each Σ, giving $4 + 4 + 4 + 4$, i.e. 16, altogether. Estimate of $\sigma^2 = 40/16 = 2\cdot5$.

The method just used for estimating σ^2 does not depend on the samples being from populations with the same mean, only on the samples being from populations with the same variance.   We now come to the last of the three methods and this does rely on the hypothesis that the samples are all from the same population (hence a common mean as well as variance).   If that is the case, how is the variance of the distribution of sample means $\overline{x}$ related to the population variance σ^2 when the sample size is 5, as in the present example?

****

$\overline{x}$ will be distributed with variance $\sigma^2/5$.

Now if $\overline{x}_1$, $\overline{x}_2$, $\overline{x}_3$, $\overline{x}_4$ are 4 values of $\overline{x}$ which themselves have a mean $\overline{\overline{x}}$, an estimate of $\mathrm{var}(\overline{x})$ can be found from them.   Can you see how?

****

$\dfrac{1}{3}\Sigma(\overline{x} - \overline{\overline{x}})^2$, *i.e.* $\dfrac{(\overline{x}_1 - \overline{\overline{x}})^2 + (\overline{x}_2 - \overline{\overline{x}})^2 + (\overline{x}_3 - \overline{\overline{x}})^2 + (\overline{x}_4 - \overline{\overline{x}})^2}{3}$ (6A.1)

will give an unbiased estimate of $\mathrm{var}(\overline{x})$.   This is equivalent to using

$\frac{1}{n-1} \Sigma (x - \overline{x})^2$ *to estimate var(x),   only now we have $\overline{x}$ instead of x, and therefore $\overline{\overline{x}}$ instead of $\overline{x}$.*

It follows that (6A.1) could be used to give an estimate of $\sigma^2/5$. Deduce a formula for estimating σ^2 and state the number of d.f.

****

$5\{(\overline{x}_1 - \overline{\overline{x}})^2 + (\overline{x}_2 - \overline{\overline{x}})^2 + (\overline{x}_3 - \overline{\overline{x}})^2 + (\overline{x}_4 - \overline{\overline{x}})^2\}/3$ *(7A.1)*

Number of d.f. = 4 - 1 = 3

Now use (7A.1) to obtain an estimate of σ^2 for the data which we are now working on.

****

Estimate of $\sigma^2 = 5\{(6-4)^2 + (3-4)^2 + (5-4)^2 + (2-4)^2\}/3 = 50/3$

Each of the three variance estimates was a ratio, the numerator of which involved a sum of squares of deviations. In the first we were considering the variation of all the observations as a whole about the grand mean and the numerator is therefore described as the TOTAL SUM OF SQUARES. In the second we were considering the variation of the observations within the samples about their own sample means, resulting in what may be termed the WITHIN SAMPLES SUM OF SQUARES. In the third case the variation between the sample means was under consideration, giving rise to a numerator called the BETWEEN SAMPLES SUM OF SQUARES. To check that you are quite clear about this terminology, write down the values for these three sums of squares obtained in FRAMES 3-8.

****

Total: 90   Within samples: 40   Between samples: 50

As has already been pointed out, the "within samples" variation estimates σ^2 whether or not there is a difference between the means of the populations from which the samples were taken. In the case of the rubber compounds, for instance, it will estimate the testing error variance whether or not there is any real difference between the tensile strengths of compounds A, B, C and D. To answer the question "Can the difference between sample means be reasonably attributed to the variation caused by the test procedure?" we therefore compare the variance estimate obtained from the "between samples" sum of squares with that obtained from the "within samples" sum of squares.

The comparison is on a one-sided basis, because the question is really: Is the "between samples" variance estimate significantly greater than the "within

FRAME 10   (continued)

samples" estimate?   If we answer "No", we are saying that the variation between samples is attributable to the test procedure.   If our answer is "Yes", we are saying that there is another source of variation besides that of the test procedure, e.g. the rubber compounds differ with respect to tensile strength or the iron content of the water supply varied over a period of time.

For the data being used for demonstration, the variance estimates to be compared are:

$$\text{Within samples:} \quad 40/16 \quad \text{based on} \quad 16 \ \text{d.f.}$$
$$\text{Between samples:} \quad 50/3 \quad \text{based on} \quad 3 \ \text{d.f.}$$

To test the hypothesis that these are both estimates of the same population variance σ^2, will you use (i) an F-test with $\nu_1 = 16$, $\nu_2 = 3$, (ii) an F-test with $\nu_1 = 3$, $\nu_2 = 16$, (iii) a t-test with $\nu = 19$, (iv) a χ^2-test with $\nu = 16$?

****

10A

(ii)

FRAME 11

The variance ratio to consider is $F_{16}^{3} = \dfrac{50/3}{40/16} = 6 \cdot \dot{6}$.   Is this significant at (i) the 5% level, (ii) the 1% level?

****

11A

From TABLE 4 it is seen that the value of F_{16}^{3} exceeds both the 5% and 1% critical values, which are 3·24 and 5·29 respectively, and thus is significant at both levels.   In other words, there is quite strong evidence that the samples are not all from populations with the same mean - if they were, the chance of sample means varying as much as these do would be less than 1%.

FRAME 12

It is usual to set out in an analysis of variance (ANOVA) table the various quantities which are calculated in this kind of investigation.   For the present data it would look like this:

Source of variation	Sum of squares	Degrees of freedom	Variance estimate
Between samples Within samples	50 40	3 16	50/3 40/16
Total	90	19	

The term MEAN SQUARE is often applied to a variance estimate obtained here, as you see, by dividing a sum of squares by the appropriate number of d.f.   A quick glance at (i) the sum of squares column, and (ii) the degrees of freedom column, in the table, should bring to your notice a relationship between the entries in each case.   What is it?

****

In (i) 50 + 40 = 90 and in (ii) 3 + 16 = 19.   Thus in both cases the "total"
entry is the sum of the "between" and "within" entries.

It remains to be seen whether the relationships which you have just noticed have
occurred because of a special set of data or whether they apply to the general
case.   Meanwhile we will be on the look-out for the same thing happening with
the next set of data.

The following braking distances (in m) for a car travelling at 65 km/h were
recorded in tests on randomly chosen tyres of four different brands A, B, C, D.

Brand A:	22	24	25	25
Brand B:	31	29	30	26
Brand C:	20	21	19	24
Brand D:	25	24	29	26

The data analysed in the preceding frames consisted of 4 samples of 5
observations each.   The tyre data is similar in form, the only difference
being that there are now 4 observations in each sample instead of 5.   You
are going to be asked to find the three sums of squares, by squaring the
appropriate deviations and adding, as was done for the previous data.   Later
you will find that there are ways of reducing the computation.   However, the
analysis of variance technique is one in which it is all too easy to follow a
set procedure without any real appreciation of the reasoning behind it, so
working through another example from first principles should prove a
worthwhile exercise.   The data is fictitious and the numbers carefully chosen
to make the arithmetic simple.

As a first step, find the mean braking distance for each brand of tyre
(i.e. $\bar{x}_A$, $\bar{x}_B$, $\bar{x}_C$, $\bar{x}_D$) and for all the tyres as a whole (i.e. the overall
mean $\bar{\bar{x}}$).

****

$\bar{x}_A = 24$ $\bar{x}_B = 29$ $\bar{x}_C = 21$ $\bar{x}_D = 26$ $\bar{\bar{x}} = 25$

By following the same procedure as before, find the "total", "within samples"
and "between samples" (i.e. between brands) sums of squares.   Also write down
the number of d.f. in each sum.   Is there the same relationship as before
between (i) the three sums of squares, (ii) their corresponding d.f.?

****

Total sum of squares = 184, obtained by summing the squares of the deviations
of each of the 16 observations from their mean 25.
Number of d.f. = 16 - 1 = 15.

Within samples sum of squares = 6 + 14 + 14 + 14 = 48, obtained from
$\Sigma(x_A - \bar{x}_A)^2 + \Sigma(x_B - \bar{x}_B)^2 + \Sigma(x_C - \bar{x}_C)^2 + \Sigma(x_D - \bar{x}_D)^2$, *i.e. by considering the*
variation of the observations within a sample about their own sample mean.
Number of d.f. = 3 + 3 + 3 + 3 = 12.

ANALYSIS OF VARIANCE

14A   (continued)

Between samples sum of squares = 4(1 + 16 + 16 + 1) = 136.   The sum inside the brackets is $(\bar{x}_A - \bar{\bar{x}})^2 + (\bar{x}_B - \bar{\bar{x}})^2 + (\bar{x}_C - \bar{\bar{x}})^2 + (\bar{x}_D - \bar{\bar{x}})^2$, i.e. we are looking at how the sample means vary about the overall mean.   If there is no difference between the brands of tyre this sum, when divided by its number of d.f., would estimate var($\bar{x}$), not var(x), i.e. $\sigma^2/4$, not σ^2.   The factor 4 must therefore be introduced (like the factor 5 in the previous example) to obtain an estimate of σ^2 for comparison with that obtained from the "within samples" sum of squares.   Note that the 4 comes from the sample size, not the number of samples.   Number of d.f. = 3.

If your answers were correct you will have noticed that (i) 136 + 48 = 184 and (ii) 3 + 12 = 15, and hence the same relationships exist as before.

FRAME 15

Now set out the analysis of variance table for this data, along the lines shown in FRAME 12.   Then use an F-test to test the hypothesis that there is no difference between the braking distances required by the 4 brands of tyre. Give the answers that would result from choosing significance levels of 5% and 1% respectively.

****

15A

Source of variation	*Sum of squares*	*Degrees of freedom*	*Variance estimate*
Between samples	*136*	*3*	*45·$\dot{3}$*
Within samples	*48*	*12*	*4*
Total	*184*	*15*	

$F^3_{12} = 11\cdot\dot{3}$

Significant at both 5% and 1% levels.

The hypothesis of no difference, i.e. the null hypothesis, would therefore be rejected.

FRAME 16

It is hoped that you have now gained an insight into what the various entries in the analysis of variance table represent and why they are being considered. The next step is to look at ways in which the calculations leading to the sums of squares can be reduced and simplified.

First, find the three sums of squares for the data shown on the right by using their definitions i.e. taking the appropriate deviations, squaring etc. The necessary means are given and only very simple arithmetic is required.

	Sample 1	Sample 2	Sample 3	Sample 4
	2	11	0	5
	4	9	1	4
	5	10	-1	9
	5	6	4	6
	$\bar{x}_1 = 4$	$\bar{x}_2 = 9$	$\bar{x}_3 = 1$	$\bar{x}_4 = 6$

Grand mean $\bar{\bar{x}} = 5$

****

Total: 184   Within samples: 48   Between samples: 136

Perhaps you have already noticed that you have seen these answers before.   Can you explain why they are exactly the same as those obtained for the tyre data?

****

The data in FRAME 16 can be obtained by subtracting 20 from each braking distance in the tyre data.   The means are correspondingly 20 less than those which you found in response to FRAME 13.   Now, if $x' = x - 20$ and $\bar{x}' = \bar{x} - 2($ obviously $x' - \bar{x}' = x - \bar{x}$.   Hence all the deviations obtained in calculating the sums of squares for the data in FRAME 16 are exactly the same as those obtained for the tyre data earlier.

The upshot of this is that, before computing the entries for an analysis of variance table, you can reduce the numbers to a more manageable size by subtracting a convenient amount (in this case 20) from all the observations. You do not subsequently need to take this into account as it has no effect on the sums of squares or variance estimates.   This is not really a new discovery for you, only a reminder of what you learned about coding in the first programme of Unit 1.   You saw then that $\Sigma(x - \bar{x})^2$, and hence var(x), were unaffected by a change of origin.

Mention of coding may have reminded you that it can involve a change of unit. No advantage would be gained from such a change in the case of the tyre data analysis, but with some other sets of data it could simplify calculations.   If that were so, and all observations were divided by 10, say, what would be the effect on (i) the variance estimates, (ii) the F-ratio?

****

(i)   Dividing the observations by 10 would divide the variance estimates by 100.   (If in doubt, refer back to FRAME 65 on page 35 of Unit 1, noting that the result obtained there can also be expressed as $var(x') = var(x)/h^2$.)

(ii) The F-ratio would be unaffected as both numerator and denominator would have been divided by 100.

You have already, on two occasions, found the three sums of squares to have related values such that

$$\text{Total sum of squares} = \text{Between samples sum of squares} + \text{Within samples sum of squares}$$

It will now be shown that this relationship is a general one and did not simply occur because of fortuitous data.   We shall then be able to make use of it by deducing the third sum from the two which prove to be the most convenient to calculate.

To proceed to a general result, it will be necessary to introduce a general form of notation.   For k samples, each of size n, this will be as follows:

						Totals	Means
Sample 1	x_{11}	x_{12}	$\cdots$	x_{1j}	$\cdots$ x_{1n}	T_1	$\bar{x}_1$
Sample 2	x_{21}	x_{22}	$\cdots$	x_{2j}	$\cdots$ x_{2n}	T_2	$\bar{x}_2$
$\vdots$							
Sample i	x_{i1}	x_{i2}	$\cdots$	x_{ij}	$\cdots$ x_{in}	T_i	$\bar{x}_i$
$\vdots$							
Sample k	x_{k1}	x_{k2}	$\cdots$	x_{kj}	$\cdots$ x_{kn}	T_k	$\bar{x}_k$

Total number of observations = N   Overall total = T   Overall mean = $\bar{\bar{x}}$

You will see that:

x_{ij} is the jth observation in the ith sample

T_i, the sum of the observations in the ith sample = $x_{i1} + x_{i2} + \ldots + x_{in}$

which may be expressed as $\displaystyle\sum_{j=1}^{n} x_{ij}$

and $\bar{x}_i$, the mean of the ith sample = T_i/n

(i)   What values are taken by (a) i, (b) j?

(ii)   Express (a) N in terms of n and k,   (b) the overall total T in terms
       of the sample totals.

       ****

19A

(i)   (a) $i = 1, 2, \ldots k$ (b) $j = 1, 2, \ldots n$

(ii) (a) Total number of observations N = Number per sample $\times$ Number of samples
          = nk

      (b) $T = T_1 + T_2 + \ldots + T_k$ which can be written $\displaystyle\sum_{i=1}^{k} T_i$.

FRAME 20

Having established the notation we can now proceed to find expressions for the
three sums of squares.   Look at the following expressions (i), (ii) and (iii),
and decide which of the deviations (a), (b) and (c) each represents.   Also name
the sum of squares to which each is relevant.

(i) $\bar{x}_i - \bar{\bar{x}}$ (ii) $x_{ij} - \bar{\bar{x}}$ (iii) $x_{ij} - \bar{x}_i$

(a)   The deviation of an individual observation (the jth in the ith sample) from
      the overall mean.

(b)   The deviation of the ith sample mean from the overall mean.

(c)   The deviation of an individual observation (the jth) in the ith sample from
      the mean of that sample.

       ****

(i) (b) Between samples.   (ii) (a) Total.   (iii) (c) Within samples.

For the within samples sum of squares, deviations from $\bar{x}_i$ of each observation
in the ith sample are required, i.e. $x_{ij} - \bar{x}_i$ has to be found for
$j = 1, 2, \ldots\ldots n$. These deviations then have to be squared and added, giving
$\sum_{j=1}^{n} (x_{ij} - \bar{x}_i)^2$.   This sum has to be found for each sample, i.e. for
$i = 1, 2, \ldots\ldots k$ and the sums added together giving
$\sum_{j=1}^{n} (x_{1j} - \bar{x}_1)^2 + \sum_{j=1}^{n} (x_{2j} - \bar{x}_2)^2 + \ldots\ldots + \sum_{j=1}^{n} (x_{kj} - \bar{x}_k)^2$, which may be
expressed more compactly as $\sum_{i=1}^{k} \left\{ \sum_{j=1}^{n} (x_{ij} - \bar{x}_i)^2 \right\}$, or simply as
$\sum_{i=1}^{k} \sum_{j=1}^{n} (x_{ij} - \bar{x}_i)^2$.   This is the within samples sum of squares.   What is the

number of d.f. in it?

****

There are $n - 1$ d.f. in $\sum_{j=1}^{n} (x_{ij} - \bar{x}_i)^2$.   As k such sums go to make up the
within samples sum of squares, the number of d.f. is $k(n - 1)$.

Now choose from expressions (i) - (iv), the one that is correct for (a) the
between samples sum of squares, (b) the total sum of squares, stating in each
case the number of d.f.

(i) $n \sum_{i=1}^{k} (\bar{x}_i - \bar{\bar{x}})^2$ (ii) $k \sum_{i=1}^{n} (\bar{x}_i - \bar{\bar{x}})^2$ (iii) $\sum_{j=1}^{n} (x_{ij} - \bar{\bar{x}})^2$

(iv) $\sum_{i=1}^{k} \sum_{j=1}^{n} (x_{ij} - \bar{\bar{x}})^2$

****

(a) (i) $k - 1$ d.f.   If you made a wrong choice, go back and read FRAMES 5-7
again.   The numerator of (7A.1) is the between samples sum of squares
with $n = 5$ and $k = 4$.

(b) (iv) $N - 1$ d.f.   If you made a wrong choice, go back and read FRAME 3
again.   There $\bar{\bar{x}} = 4$ and the values set out at the end of the frame
are those of $(x_{ij} - \bar{\bar{x}})^2$.   Summing for each sample and then over all
samples leads to the total sum of squares which is 90.

Setting out the results in tabular form:

Source of variation	Sum of squares	Degrees of freedom
Between samples	$n \sum\limits_{i=1}^{k} (\bar{x}_i - \bar{\bar{x}})^2$	$k - 1$
Within samples	$\sum\limits_{i=1}^{k} \sum\limits_{j=1}^{n} (x_{ij} - \bar{x}_i)^2$	$k(n - 1)$
Total	$\sum\limits_{i=1}^{k} \sum\limits_{j=1}^{n} (x_{ij} - \bar{\bar{x}})^2$	$N - 1$

Clearly $k - 1 + k(n - 1) = kn - 1 = N - 1$, so the additive relationship between the d.f., previously found to exist in particular examples, is quickly established in the general case. To do the same for the sums of squares will take a little longer.

The deviation of an individual observation from the overall mean can be split up thus:

$$x_{ij} - \bar{\bar{x}} = (x_{ij} - \bar{x}_i) + (\bar{x}_i - \bar{\bar{x}})$$

i.e. $\quad \dfrac{\text{deviation from}}{\text{overall mean}} = \dfrac{\text{deviation from}}{\text{sample mean}} + \dfrac{\text{deviation of sample}}{\text{mean from overall mean}}$

Squaring, we get

$$(x_{ij} - \bar{\bar{x}})^2 = (x_{ij} - \bar{x}_i)^2 + 2(x_{ij} - \bar{x}_i)(\bar{x}_i - \bar{\bar{x}}) + (\bar{x}_i - \bar{\bar{x}})^2$$

Summing over all the observations in the ith sample gives

$$\sum_{j=1}^{n} (x_{ij} - \bar{\bar{x}})^2 = \sum_{j=1}^{n} (x_{ij} - \bar{x}_i)^2 + 2(\bar{x}_i - \bar{\bar{x}}) \sum_{j=1}^{n} (x_{ij} - \bar{x}_i) + n(\bar{x}_i - \bar{\bar{x}})^2 \quad (23.1)$$

One of the terms on the R.H.S. of (23.1) is zero.   Which one?

****

23A

The second term, because $\sum\limits_{j=1}^{n} (x_{ij} - \bar{x}_i)$, which is the sum of the deviations of all the observations in the ith sample from their mean, is zero. You learned of this property of a mean – that the sum of the deviations of all the observations from it is always zero – in the first programme of Unit 1.

(23.1) thus becomes $\quad \sum\limits_{j=1}^{n} (x_{ij} - \bar{\bar{x}})^2 = \sum\limits_{j=1}^{n} (x_{ij} - \bar{x}_i)^2 + n(\bar{x}_i - \bar{\bar{x}})^2$

Then summing over all k samples leads to

$$\sum_{i=1}^{k} \sum_{j=1}^{n} (x_{ij} - \bar{\bar{x}})^2 = \sum_{i=1}^{k} \sum_{j=1}^{n} (x_{ij} - \bar{x}_i)^2 + n \sum_{i=1}^{k} (\bar{x}_i - \bar{\bar{x}})^2 \qquad (24.1)$$

| TOTAL SUM | WITHIN SAMPLES | BETWEEN SAMPLES |
| OF SQUARES | SUM OF SQUARES | SUM OF SQUARES |

We have now established this important and fundamental relationship, which partitions the total, overall variation into two component parts. It is hoped that evaluating the sums of squares by taking deviations, squaring and adding, as was done in earlier frames, has helped to emphasise what each represents. However, the figures for which this was done were artificial, having been carefully chosen to give simple arithmetic. With real data, more cumbersome calculations would be encountered; it is most unlikely that the sample means, for instance, would work out exactly to nice convenient values like 6 and 3. Now, if you recall your introduction to variance in Unit 1, you will remember that whereas it was originally defined in terms of $\sum_{i=1}^{n} (x_i - \bar{x})^2$, which we have usually abbreviated to $\Sigma(x - \bar{x})^2$, a formula was subsequently derived which did not necessitate taking deviations from the mean $\bar{x}$. Which of the following gives $\Sigma(x - \bar{x})^2$?

(i) $\Sigma x^2 + (\Sigma x)^2/n$ (ii) $\Sigma x^2 - n(\Sigma x)^2$ (iii) $\Sigma x^2 - (\Sigma x)^2/n$

****

24A

(iii) i.e. $\Sigma(x - \bar{x})^2 = \Sigma x^2 - (\Sigma x)^2/n$ *(24A.1)*

This result can be applied to the sums of squares involved in the present analysis of variance to give alternative formulae leading to more convenient computation. Let us first consider the total sum of squares, which consists of the sum of squares of the deviations of N values of x from their mean $\bar{\bar{x}}$. For simplicity the notation will henceforth be abbreviated to $\sum_{i} \sum_{j} (x_{ij} - \bar{\bar{x}})^2$, indicating that the summation is to be taken over all i's and j's, and hence over all x_{ij}'s. Applying (24A.1) gives

$$\sum_{i} \sum_{j} (x_{ij} - \bar{\bar{x}})^2 = \sum_{i} \sum_{j} x_{ij}^2 - \left(\sum_{i} \sum_{j} x_{ij} \right)^2 / N \qquad (25.1).$$

Note the difference in meaning between $\sum_{i} \sum_{j} x_{ij}^2$ and $\left(\sum_{i} \sum_{j} x_{ij} \right)^2$. In the former all the x's are squared and then the squares are added. In the latter all the x's are added and then their sum is squared. What letter was assigned in FRAME 19 to the quantity represented by $\sum_{i} \sum_{j} x_{ij}$?

****

25A

T, it being the sum of all the observations.

(25.1) can therefore be rewritten as

$$\sum_i \sum_j (x_{ij} - \bar{\bar{x}})^2 = \sum_i \sum_j x_{ij}^2 - T^2/N \qquad (26.1)$$

Taking next the between samples sum of squares, this requires $\sum_{i=1}^{k} (\bar{x}_i - \bar{\bar{x}})^2$,

henceforth abbreviated to $\sum_i (\bar{x}_i - \bar{\bar{x}})^2$. Applying (24A.1) gives

$$\sum_i (\bar{x}_i - \bar{\bar{x}})^2 = \sum_i \bar{x}_i^2 - (\sum_i \bar{x}_i)^2/k$$

As $\bar{x}_i = T_i/n$, this can be restated as

$$\sum_i (\bar{x}_i - \bar{\bar{x}})^2 = \sum_i (T_i/n)^2 - (\sum_i T_i/n)^2/k$$

$$= \frac{1}{n^2} \sum_i T_i^2 - \frac{1}{n^2 k} (\sum_i T_i)^2$$

What letter has been assigned to denote $\sum_i T_i$?

Distinguish between $\sum_i T_i^2$ and $(\sum_i T_i)^2$, by explaining how each would be calculated.

****

26A

T.

$\sum_i T_i^2$ *is the sum of the squares of the sample totals, i.e. each sample total is squared and then the squares are added.*

$(\sum_i T_i)^2$ *is the square of the sum of the sample totals i.e. the sample totals are added, giving T, and then squared, giving T^2.*

Thus $\sum_i (\bar{x}_i - \bar{\bar{x}})^2 = \frac{1}{n^2} \sum_i T_i^2 - \frac{1}{n^2 k} T^2$ and the between samples sum of squares is

given by $n \sum_i (\bar{x}_i - \bar{\bar{x}})^2 = \frac{1}{n} \sum_i T_i^2 - \frac{1}{nk} T^2 = \frac{1}{n} \sum_i T_i^2 - \frac{T^2}{N}$ \qquad (27.1)

The term T^2/N, which is subtracted in both (26.1) and (27.1), is sometimes referred to as the correction factor.

Having calculated two of the three sums of squares, the third can be found by subtraction using (24.1). The table in FRAME 23 can now be restated in the form which is used for computational purposes.

Source of variation	Sum of squares	Degrees of freedom
Between samples	$\frac{1}{n} \sum_i T_i^2 - \frac{T^2}{N}$	$k - 1$
Within samples	By subtraction	By subtraction
Total	$\sum_i \sum_j x_{ij}^2 - \frac{T^2}{N}$	$N - 1$

To ensure that you understand how to apply these formulae, try them out on the data shown in FRAME 3.   First write down the values of n, k and N.   Then find $\sum_i T_i^2$, $\sum_i \sum_j x_{ij}^2$ and the correction factor T^2/N, and hence complete the calculations outlined in the above table.

****

$n = 5 \qquad k = 4 \qquad N = 20$

$\sum_i T_i^2 = T_1^2 + T_2^2 + T_3^2 + T_4^2 = 30^2 + 15^2 + 25^2 + 10^2 = 1850$

For Sample 1, $\sum_j x_{1j}^2 = 5^2 + 7^2 + 6^2 + 9^2 + 3^2 = 200$.   For Sample 2,

$\sum_j x_{2j}^2 = 3^2 + 4^2 + 1^2 + 3^2 + 4^2 = 51$, and so on, giving

$\sum_i \sum_j x_{ij}^2 = 200 + 51 + 135 + 24 = 410$

$T = T_1 + T_2 + T_3 + T_4 = 80 \qquad$ Correction factor $T^2/N = 320$

Between samples sum of squares = 1850/5 − 320 = 50 with 4 − 1 = 3 d.f.
Total sum of squares = 410 − 320 = 90 with   20 − 1 = 19 d.f.
Within samples sum of squares = 90 − 50 = 40 with 19 − 3 = 16 d.f.
Note the agreement between these results and those previously obtained and set out in the table in FRAME 12.

Now that you understand the basis on which questions such as those posed in FRAME 1 can be answered and now that you have been shown how the calculations can most conveniently be carried out, we can proceed to the solution of the problems outlined in that frame.

The calculations for (1) are set out on the next page, displaying a lay-out which you may find it helpful to follow when solving similar problems.   All observations have had 22 subtracted from them − you will recall that this does not affect the sums of squares.   The figures in brackets are the values of x_{ij}^2.

FRAME 28   (continued)

					T_i	$T_i^{\,2}$	$\sum\limits_j x_{ij}^{\,2}$
A	0·1(0·01)	-1·3(1·69)	0·9(0·81)	-0·5(0·25)	-0·8	0·64	2·76
B	0·1(0·01)	1·0(1·00)	-0·1(0·01)	-0·2(0·04)	0·8	0·64	1·06
C	1·8(3·24)	2·2(4·84)	2·1(4·41)	1·1(1·21)	7·2	51·84	13·70
D	-0·1(0·01)	1·4(1·96)	0·6(0·36)	0·9(0·81)	2·8	7·84	3·14
				Totals	10·0	60·96	20·66

Correction factor = $10·0^2/16$ = 6·25
Between samples (i.e. compounds) sum of squares = 60·96/4 - 6·25 = 8·99
Total sum of squares = 20·66 - 6·25 = 14·41

Source of variation	Sum of squares	Degrees of freedom	Variance estimate
Between samples	8·99	3	2·996̇
Within samples	5·42	12	0·4516
Total	14·41	15	

$$F_{12}^{3} = \frac{2·99\dot{6}}{0·451\dot{6}} \approx 6·63$$

With this analysis before you, give your answer to the question "Do the rubber compounds differ from one another in their tensile strengths?"

****

28A

The value of F_{12}^{3} exceeds the 1% critical value (5·95). It would be concluded that the rubber compounds do differ from one another, the risk of coming to such a conclusion when there is no real difference being less than 1%. Employing the usual phraseology, the answer to the question is "Yes, at the 1% significance level".

FRAME 29

Having seen the solution to (1), you should have no difficulty in carrying out a similar analysis for (2) and hence answering the question "Is the iron content of this water supply different at different times?" Try it! (We suggest you first subtract 10 from all the observations to reduce the numbers involved.)

****

29A

						T_i	$T_i^{\,2}$	$\sum\limits_j x_{ij}^{\,2}$
1	0·3(0·09)	-0·2(0·04)	0·9(0·81)	1·4(1·96)	0·1(0·01)	2·5	6·25	2·91
2	0·9(0·81)	-0·2(0·04)	0·0(0·00)	0·3(0·09)	0·5(0·25)	1·5	2·25	1·19
3	0·3(0·09)	1·4(1·96)	0·8(0·64)	0·6(0·36)	0·9(0·81)	4·0	16·00	3·86
4	0·7(0·49)	1·3(1·69)	1·2(1·44)	0·8(0·64)	1·0(1·00)	5·0	25·00	5·26
					Totals	13·0	49·50	13·22

Correction factor = $13 \cdot 0^2/20 = 8 \cdot 45$
Between samples sum of squares = $49 \cdot 50/5 - 8 \cdot 45 = 1 \cdot 45$
Total sum of squares = $13 \cdot 22 - 8 \cdot 45 = 4 \cdot 77$

Source of variation	*Sum of squares*	*Degrees of freedom*	*Variance estimate*
Between samples	*$1 \cdot 45$*	*3*	*$0 \cdot 48\dot{3}$*
Within samples	*$3 \cdot 32$*	*16*	*$0 \cdot 2075$*
Total	*$4 \cdot 77$*	*19*	

$F_{16}^{3} \simeq 2 \cdot 33 < 3 \cdot 24.$ *Not sig. at 5% level.   Thus no real evidence of*
variation in iron content is provided by the data.

Where a significant difference has been found between the means as a whole, the question of how they differ may arise.   In the case of the rubber compounds, for instance, is there one that is really stronger than all the others or one that is really weaker than all the others?

Making individual comparisons between pairs of sample means suggests the use of Student's t.   It may, in fact, have crossed your mind at the start of this programme that questions such as those posed in FRAME 1 could be answered by performing a series of t-tests on each pair of sample means.   This procedure would have two snags.   First, if 3 samples were to be tested in pairs the number of tests required would be $^3C_2$, i.e. 3;   for 4 samples the number of tests would be $^4C_2$, i.e. 6, for 5 it would be $^5C_2$, i.e. 10, and so on. The clumsiness of this approach is in contrast with the elegance of the analysis of variance technique.   The second, and more serious objection, concerns the overall significance level.   Suppose the 5% level is chosen for each test. Then when there is no difference between the two population means, the probability of wrongly concluding that a difference exists is $0 \cdot 05$ (the risk, you will recall, of a Type 1 error).   Now if the results of the tests are independent of one another, the risk of this happening at least once in 3 tests would be $1 - 0 \cdot 95^3 \simeq 0 \cdot 14$,   representing an overall significance level of about 14%.   On the same basis, what would the overall significance level be for (i) 6 tests, (ii) 10 tests?

****

(i) $1 - 0 \cdot 95^6 \simeq 0 \cdot 26.$ *(Thus, when making a comparison of 4 samples from the same population, there would be a 26% chance of deciding that a difference between their means exists, i.e. of making a Type 1 error.)*

(ii) $1 - 0 \cdot 95^{10} \simeq 0 \cdot 40.$ *(This would be the risk of a Type 1 error for 5 samples.)*

These significance levels have been calculated on the basis of the results of each t-test being independent of one another but that is not wholly true.   Thus, even if one were to reduce the overall risk of a Type 1 error by, say, choosing a 1% level for each t-test, there would still be some difficulty in assessing exactly what that overall risk would be.   The ANOVA technique therefore offers

a more satisfactory way of making an overall test.   However, when that indicates
the existence of significant differences, there could be an argument for using
a form of t-test as a follow-up.   The data on rubber compounds will be used as
an illustration, the F-test having shown a significant difference between them.
Placing their means in order of magnitude, we have

$$\overline{x}_A \qquad \overline{x}_B \qquad \overline{x}_D \qquad \overline{x}_C$$

$$21\cdot8 \qquad 22\cdot2 \qquad 22\cdot7 \qquad 23\cdot8$$

Adjacent means can now be compared to see whether they differ significantly.
As they are all based on samples of the same size, this can be done by
calculating the LEAST SIGNIFICANT DIFFERENCE (LSD).   To understand the basis
of this, first consider two samples, each of size n, being taken from a
population with mean μ and variance σ^2.   If the sample means are denoted
by $\overline{x}_1$ and $\overline{x}_2$, what are the mean and variance of the distribution of $\overline{x}_1 - \overline{x}_2$?

****

31A

$$Mean = \mu - \mu = 0 \qquad Variance = var(\overline{x}_1) + var(\overline{x}_2) = \frac{\sigma^2}{n} + \frac{\sigma^2}{n} = \frac{2\sigma^2}{n}$$

FRAME 32

As usual it will be taken that the distributions of $\overline{x}_1$ and $\overline{x}_2$, and therefore
of $\overline{x}_1 - \overline{x}_2$, can be assumed normal.   Hence $\overline{x}_1 - \overline{x}_2$ is $N(0, \frac{2\sigma^2}{n})$ and
$\dfrac{\overline{x}_1 - \overline{x}_2}{\sigma\sqrt{2/n}}$ is $N(0, 1)$.   If s^2 is an estimate of σ^2 based on ν d.f., what
can be said of the distribution of $\dfrac{\overline{x}_1 - \overline{x}_2}{s\sqrt{2/n}}$?

****

32A

It will be a t-distribution with ν d.f.

FRAME 33

In the usual t-test for comparing the means of two samples, the estimate of the
common variance is based on the observations in the two samples.   In the case
of the rubber compound data a better estimate is available, based on all 4
samples.   What value has been obtained for it and what is the number of d.f.?

****

33A

$0\cdot451\overset{.}{6}$, obtained from the within samples sum of squares, with 12 d.f.

FRAME 34

The sample size, n, is 4 (not to be confused with the number of compounds).
Thus, if there were no difference between the tensile strengths of the compounds,
for any pair of sample means we could say that $\dfrac{\overline{x}_1 - \overline{x}_2}{\sqrt{0\cdot451\overset{.}{6}/2}}$ follows a

t-distribution with 12 d.f.   Can you now say what value $|\overline{x}_1 - \overline{x}_2|$ would have to exceed to be significant at the 5% level?

****

34A

$$\sqrt{0 \cdot 451\dot{6}/2} \times 2 \cdot 18 \simeq 1 \cdot 04$$

FRAME 35

With the least significant difference now calculated as 1·04, we look at the means set out in FRAME 31 and see that $\overline{x}_C$ exceeds $\overline{x}_D$, and hence $\overline{x}_A$ and $\overline{x}_B$, by more than the LSD.   This suggests that compound C has a higher tensile strength than any of the other compounds.   The differences between A, B and D, however, are less than the LSD, suggesting that there is little to choose between these three compounds.

The tendency of comparisons between individual means to classify too many differences as significant is reduced by only proceeding with it if the F-test gives a significant result, and by only making comparisons between means which are adjacent when placed in order of magnitude (selecting for comparison the highest and lowest of a set of, say, 5 means increases the likelihood of the difference being significant).   Another safeguard is provided when the nature of the experiment fixes in advance which means should be compared - you will meet an example of this in Qu. 4 of the Miscellaneous Examples at the end of this programme.   The advantage of the LSD method is its simplicity.   Other methods have been developed (e.g. Duncan, Scheffé) which better control the overall risk of a Type 1 error but they are not so simple and will not be discussed here.

FRAME 36

Underlying Assumptions and Model

One assumption on which the foregoing procedures are based, that of a common variance σ^2 for the populations from whence the samples come, has already been brought to your attention.   Another assumption, that these populations are normal, is implicit in the use of the F-test.   Fortunately, violations of these assumptions are not serious unless they are very marked and when that happens the situation can sometimes be remedied by first transforming the data, e.g. by taking logarithms.

Analysing the variation in the observations under scrutiny is helped by the formulation of a model which embodies the various assumptions made.   To familiarise you with the idea of a model, we will begin by considering a random variable x whose values arise from the repeated measurement of a quantity whose true value is μ.   Any value of x can be expressed in the form

$$x = \mu + e$$

where e (which can be either positive or negative) represents the error in measurement.   This very simple model shows that it is the presence of the random error e that causes x to vary randomly.   If the measurement is without bias, the mean of the distribution of x is μ.   What does this imply about the mean of the distribution of e?   If, moreover, x is $N(\mu, \sigma^2)$, what can be said about the distribution of e?

****

Mean = 0.   e is N(0, σ²).

We can now apply a similar idea to the type of situation described earlier in
this programme, where several samples or groups are being compared.   If the ith
sample is from a population whose mean is μ_i, then any observation in that
sample can be represented by

$$x_{ij} = \mu_i + e_{ij} \qquad (37.1)$$

where the e_{ij}'s are from a population whose mean is 0.   The analysis of
variance procedure which we have used assumes that, for all samples, the e_{ij}'s
are independent of one another and are all $N(0, \sigma^2)$.

The breaking down of x_{ij} into component parts, as in (37.1), can be extended
further by expressing each μ_i in the form $\mu + \alpha_i$, i.e. $\mu_1 = \mu + \alpha_1$,
$\mu_2 = \mu + \alpha_2$, etc., where μ is the overall mean.   The α's may then be said
to represent the "effects" attributable to the different brands of tyre or rubber
compounds or times at which the water was drawn off.

(37.1) can now be rewritten as $x_{ij} = \mu + \alpha_i + e_{ij}$ (37.2)

Observations in the ith sample will all have the same value of α_i but, in
general, different values of e_{ij}.   In the tyre data in FRAME 13 there is one
sample in which it happened, by chance, that two values of e_{ij} were the same.
Can you spot where this occurred?

****

*In the braking distances recorded for Brand A, the two 25's result from e_{ij}
taking the same value in each case.*

It can now be seen that in the use of an F-test for the comparison of means, the
hypothesis being tested was $\mu_1 = \mu_2 = \ldots = \mu_i = \ldots = \mu_k = \mu$.   Restate
this hypothesis in terms of the α's.

****

$\alpha_1 = \alpha_2 = \ldots = \alpha_i = \ldots = \alpha_k = 0.$ *That is, which brand of tyre is being
used has no effect on the braking distance, or which rubber compound is being
tested has no effect on the tensile strength, or the time when the water is
drawn off has no effect on the iron content.*

Extension to Two-way Classification

So far, in this programme, we have only looked at problems where one possible
source of variation, apart from random error, was being considered.   In the data

on braking distances, for instance, the one factor under investigation was the
brand of tyre;   in the water sample analyses, it was the time at which the water
was drawn off.   The experimental design was that of a ONE-WAY CLASSIFICATION,
leading to ONE-WAY ANALYSIS OF VARIANCE.

Let us now suppose that, in the tyre tests, four different cars were used with
each brand of tyre being tested on each car.   The data would then be in a
form such as:

	Car 1	Car 2	Car 3	Car 4
Brand A	22	24	25	25
Brand B	31	29	30	26
Brand C	20	21	19	24
Brand D	25	24	29	26

Similarly, in the case of the water analyses, the 5 determinations made on each
sample might have been made by 5 different analysts, with results classified
thus:

	Analyst A	Analyst B	Analyst C	Analyst D	Analyst E
Sample 1	10·3	9·8	10·9	11·4	10·1
Sample 2	10·9	9·8	10·0	10·3	10·5
Sample 3	10·3	11·4	10·8	10·6	10·9
Sample 4	10·7	11·3	11·2	10·8	11·0

In these examples, an observation is classified according to two characteristics.
In the case of the braking distances these two characteristics are tyre brand
and car, for the iron content determinations they are water sample and analyst.
The experimental design now involves a TWO-WAY CLASSIFICATION.

(In both of the above sets of data the same figures as before are being used to
save unnecessary arithmetic.   Lest this be misinterpreted, it should be made
clear that the experiments from which the present data arise have been planned
quite differently from the previous ones, in that there is now a requirement
that each tyre brand be tested on each of the 4 cars and each water sample be
analysed by each of the 5 analysts.)

This new development will require an extension of the model put forward in
(37.2), with an additional term to allow for the effect of the second factor,
as in

$$x_{ij} = \mu + \alpha_i + \beta_j + e_{ij} \qquad (40.1)$$

In the tyre experiment, x_{ij} would be the braking distance recorded with the
ith brand of tyre on the jth car, α_i representing "tyre effect" and β_j "car
effect".   In the water experiment, x_{ij} would be the iron content in the ith
sample as determined by the jth analyst.   Which of α_i and β_j then represents
"sample effect" and which "analyst effect"?

        ****

α_i represents "sample effect" and β_j represents "analyst effect".

With the braking distances recorded on a two-way basis (car and tyre brand) there are now two questions that can be answered.   As with the previous one-way analysis, the question of whether there is a difference between tyre brands can be considered - in effect, this involves testing the hypothesis: $\alpha_i = 0$ for all i.   Now the question of whether there is a difference between cars can also be considered, the corresponding hypothesis under test being that $\beta_j = 0$ for all j.   The TWO-WAY ANALYSIS OF VARIANCE procedure that will now be described neatly combines the tests of these two hypotheses.   It is along similar lines to the one-way analysis but goes further with the breakdown of the total sum of squares.

If we are to proceed to general results, we shall require a form of notation which covers any two-way classification.   The data can be thought of as being set out in rows and columns, as in the examples in FRAME 39.   If x_{ij} is used to denote the observation in the ith row and jth column, and there are r rows and c columns, the notation can be summarised thus:

	Column 1	Column 2	Column j	Column c
Row 1	x_{11}	x_{12}	x_{1j}	x_{1c}
Row 2	x_{21}	x_{22}	x_{2j}	x_{2c}
Row i	x_{i1}	x_{i2}	x_{ij}	x_{ic}
Row r	x_{r1}	x_{r2}	x_{rj}	x_{rc}

State the values of r and c for each set of data in FRAME 39, as there set out.

****

41A

For the braking distances: $r = 4$, $c = 4$.
For the water analyses: $r = 4$, $c = 5$.

You will recall that, in the one-way analysis of variance, the total sum of squares was partitioned into two sums as:

Total SS = Between samples SS + Within samples SS

where SS is an abbreviation for "sum of squares".

Only one of these sums of squares led to an estimate of σ^2, the variance common to the populations from which the samples were taken, regardless of whether those populations have equal means or not.   Which one?

****

42A

The within samples SS. (Refer back to FRAME 5 if you did not answer correctly.)

As the within samples sum of squares leads to an estimate of σ^2, the variance attributable to the experimental error represented in the model by the e_{ij} term, it is sometimes referred to as the Error Sum of Squares. In dealing with the braking distances you saw that, on the basis of the N.H. of no difference between the brands of tyre, the between samples (i.e. brands) sum of squares would also lead to an estimate of σ^2.   When you found that estimate to be significantly larger than the other one, you decided that the variation among the brand sample means was too great to be explained by experimental error and therefore rejected the N.H.

All this suggests that, to test the hypothesis of no difference between cars, we should also consider the variation of car means about the overall mean and see if that is too great to be explained by experimental error.   To do this along similar lines to the "between brands" comparison would require a "between cars" sum of squares from which a variance estimate can be obtained.   With this in view, we split up the deviation of any individual observation x_{ij} from the overall mean $\bar{\bar{x}}$ thus:

$$x_{ij} - \bar{\bar{x}} = (\bar{x}_i - \bar{\bar{x}}) + (\bar{x}_j - \bar{\bar{x}}) + (x_{ij} - \bar{x}_i - \bar{x}_j + \bar{\bar{x}}) \qquad (43.1)$$

where $\bar{x}_i$ is the mean braking distance for the ith tyre brand (row) and $\bar{x}_j$ is that for the jth car (column).   (This notation may not satisfy those who demand mathematical rigour but will, we feel, be adequate for present purposes.) You may like to compare (43.1) with the partitioning of $x_{ij} - \bar{x}$ in FRAME 23.

Squaring and summing over all observations leads, in the general case of r rows and c columns, to

$$\sum_{i=1}^{r} \sum_{j=1}^{c} (x_{ij} - \bar{\bar{x}})^2 = c \sum_{i=1}^{r} (\bar{x}_i - \bar{\bar{x}})^2 + r \sum_{j=1}^{c} (\bar{x}_j - \bar{\bar{x}})^2$$

$$+ \sum_{i=1}^{r} \sum_{j=1}^{c} (x_{ij} - \bar{x}_i - \bar{x}_j + \bar{\bar{x}})^2 \qquad (43.2)$$

The derivation of this result is similar to that shown in FRAMES 23 and 24 for the corresponding one-way result but is more lengthy because of more terms on the R.H.S.   It is therefore omitted here but if your curiosity is aroused you should have no difficulty in working your way through it if you follow the previous procedure.   The sum on the L.H.S. is already familiar to you as the total sum of squares.   What is the number of d.f. involved in it   (i) in terms of N, the total number of observations,   (ii) in terms of r and c?

****

(i) N - 1   (ii) rc - 1

In the one-way analysis, the between samples sum of squares was $n \sum_{i=1}^{k} (\bar{x}_i - \bar{\bar{x}})^2$, which can be expressed as

FRAME 44   (continued)

Number in sample $\times$ Σ(sample mean - overall mean)^2, the summation being over all samples.   The number of d.f. involved was k - 1,   i.e. 1 less than the number of samples.

In the present situation, think first of the <u>rows</u> as being the samples and hence identify which of the terms on the R.H.S. of (43.2) is the between rows sum of squares.   Then think of the columns as being samples and identify which of the other terms is the between <u>columns</u> sum of squares.   Also state the number of d.f. involved in each case.

****

44A

$$c \sum_{i=1}^{r} (\overline{x}_i - \overline{\overline{x}})^2 = \textit{Number in row} \times \Sigma(\textit{row mean - overall mean})^2, \quad \textit{the summation}$$

being over all rows.   Hence it is the between rows SS.   Number of d.f. = r - 1, i.e. 1 less than the number of rows.

Similarly $r \sum_{j=1}^{c} (\overline{x}_j - \overline{\overline{x}})^2$ *is the between columns SS, with c - 1 d.f.*

FRAME 45

It can be shown that the remaining sum on the R.H.S. of (43.2), when divided by its number of d.f., estimates σ^2.   Thus it corresponds to the within samples sum of squares in the one-way analysis but the description "error sum of squares" is now more appropriate.   Even better, perhaps, as a general description, is the term "residual sum of squares".   The term e_{ij} in the model has been attributed to experimental error, which, no doubt, suggested in your mind errors made by the experimenter in taking readings etc.   That would, indeed, often be the explanation of the variation.   There could also, however, be other causes which one would not regard as error and it is therefore more correct to think of e_{ij} as representing the residual variation which cannot be accounted for by the other factors under consideration (such as tyre brand, type of rubber compound etc.).

The d.f. of the sums in (43.2) have the same additive property as had the corresponding sums in the one-way analysis of variance.   The complete ANOVA table for a two-way classification is therefore

Source of variation	Sum of squares	Degrees of freedom
Between rows	$c \sum_{i=1}^{r} (\overline{x}_i - \overline{\overline{x}})^2$	$r - 1$
Between columns	$r \sum_{j=1}^{c} (\overline{x}_j - \overline{\overline{x}})^2$	$c - 1$
Residual (error)	$\sum_{i=1}^{r} \sum_{j=1}^{c} (x_{ij} - \overline{x}_i - \overline{x}_j + \overline{\overline{x}})^2$	$(r - 1)(c - 1)$
Total	$\sum_{i=1}^{r} \sum_{j=1}^{c} (x_{ij} - \overline{\overline{x}})^2$	$N - 1$, i.e. $rc - 1$

It is left to you to check the additive relation between the d.f. before
proceeding to the next frame.

As with the one-way analysis, the form in which the sums of squares are first
derived is not necessarily the most suitable for computational purposes.   The
total sum of squares can again be expressed as $\sum_i \sum_j x_{ij}^2 - T^2/N$, where T is

the total of all the observations.   The formula for the between samples sum of

squares was $\frac{1}{n} \sum_i T_i^2 - \frac{T^2}{N}$, which can be restated as

$\frac{1}{\text{number in sample}} \times \Sigma(\text{sample total})^2$ - correction factor, the summation being
over all samples.

We shall now use T_i to denote a row total and T_j to denote a column total.

Thinking of a row as being a sample, the between rows sum of squares is seen to

be $\frac{1}{\text{number in row}} \times \Sigma(\text{row total})^2$ - correction factor, the summation being over

all rows, i.e. $\frac{1}{c} \sum_i T_i^2 - \frac{T^2}{N}$.   Now think of a column as being a sample, and

deduce an expression for the between columns sum of squares in terms of the T_j's.

****

$\frac{1}{\text{number in column}} \times \Sigma(\text{column total})^2$ - correction factor, the summation being

over all columns, i.e. $\frac{1}{r} \sum_j T_j^2 - \frac{T^2}{N}$.

Restating the two-way ANOVA table in a form suitable for computational purposes:

Source of variation	Sum of squares	Degrees of freedom
Between rows	$\frac{1}{c} \sum_i T_i^2 - T^2/N$	r - 1
Between columns	$\frac{1}{r} \sum_j T_j^2 - T^2/N$	c - 1
Residual (error)	By subtraction	By subtraction
Total	$\sum_i \sum_j x_{ij}^2 - T^2/N$	N - 1

To test for a significant difference between rows or between columns, the
appropriate variance estimates are calculated and F-tests applied, as in the
one-way analysis.   The data on braking distances in FRAME 39 will be used as an

illustration, with 20 subtracted from each observation to reduce the numbers in the arithmetic.   (As you know, this does not affect the values of the sums of squares.)

The following lay-out of the calculations is an extended version of that used for the one-way analysis:

	Car 1	Car 2	Car 3	Car 4	T_i	T_i^2	$\sum_j x_{ij}^2$
Brand A	2(4)	4(16)	5(25)	5(25)	16	256	70
Brand B	11(121)	9(81)	10(100)	6(36)	36	1296	338
Brand C	0(0)	1(1)	-1(1)	4(16)	4	16	18
Brand D	5(25)	4(16)	9(81)	6(36)	24	576	158
T_j	18	18	23	21	80	2144	584
T_j^2	324	324	529	441	1618		
$\sum_i x_{ij}^2$	150	114	207	113	584		

Correction factor = $80^2/16$ = 400
Total SS = 584 - 400 = 184
Between brands (rows) SS = 2144/4 - 400 = 136
Between cars (columns) SS = 1618/4 - 400 = 4·5

In this example there are both 4 rows and 4 columns.   In the between brands SS, does the denominator 4 in 2144/4 come from the number of rows (brands) or the number of columns (cars)?

****

47A

The number of columns, i.e. c = 4

The ANOVA table is:

Source of variation	Sum of squares	Degrees of freedom	Variance estimate
Between brands	136	3	45·3̇
Between cars	4·5	3	1·5̇
Residual	43·5	9	4·83̇
Total	184	15	

To decide whether the between brands variance estimate is significantly greater than that representing the residual variation, an F-test is used.

We have $F_9^3 = \dfrac{45\cdot\dot{3}}{4\cdot8\dot{3}} \simeq 9\cdot38$.   What conclusion would you draw?

****

As this value of $F_9^3 > 6 \cdot 99$, *it would be concluded, that at the 1% level, the mean braking distance is not the same for each tyre brand population.*

To reject the hypothesis of 'no difference between cars', it would be necessary to show the between cars variance estimate to be significantly higher than the residual estimate.   As $1 \cdot 5 < 4 \cdot 8\dot{3}$, there is no possibility of showing this here, so the hypothesis is retained, i.e. we can find no real evidence of braking distances varying from car to car.   If instead of $1 \cdot 5$, a value $> 4 \cdot 8\dot{3}$ had been obtained, the usual F-test would have followed.   Describe in words the ratio that would then have been calculated.

****

Between cars variance estimate/Residual variance estimate.

Now draw up a two-way ANOVA table for the water data in FRAME 39 and test (i) the hypothesis that there was no difference in the iron content of the water supply at the times when the samples were drawn off,   (ii) the hypothesis that no analyst shows a bias with respect to any other, i.e. no analyst tends to produce readings higher (or lower) than the others.   (If you first subtract 10 from all observations, it will simplify the arithmetic and you can make use of the calculations already done for the one-way analysis in answering FRAME 29.)

****

Source of variation	Sum of squares	Degrees of freedom	Variance estimate
Between samples	1·45	3	0·48$\dot{3}$
Between analysts	0·15	4	0·0375
Residual	3·17	12	0·2642
Total	4·77	19	

(i) $F_{12}^3 = 0 \cdot 48\dot{3}/0 \cdot 2642 \simeq 1 \cdot 83$.   *Not sig. at 5% level.   Hypothesis retained.*

(ii)   *As* $0 \cdot 0375 < 0 \cdot 2642$, *F-test not required.   Hypothesis retained.*

In this example, arranging for each analyst to test each water sample has led to data classified on a two-way basis and two hypotheses - (i) concerning iron contents and (ii) concerning analysts - could then be tested.   But suppose only the iron content to be of interest and thus only one hypothesis, (i), to be under test.   Then, if circumstances do not permit all determinations to be made by the same analyst, there could still be an advantage in planning the experiment along the present lines and thus making an allowance for an analyst-to-analyst contribution to the variation of results.   As things have turned out in this particular case, there appears to be no difference between the analysts.   Thus, whether or not such a difference is allowed for at the outset, the same conclusion is likely to be reached, as has happened here – in both 50A (two-way classification) and 29A (one-way classification) you have found no significant difference between iron contents.   Had analyst-to-analyst variation existed, however, the two approaches could well have led to different conclusions.   In the next two frames you will see how the difference in approach can affect the decision reached.

Suppose that 18 discs, taken from steel ingots, were randomly divided into 3 groups and each group subjected to a different form of heat treatment.   The yield point (in $MN\,m^{-2}$) was then determined for each treated specimen, with the following results:

Treatment A:	292	273	347	310	301	349
Treatment B:	345	308	344	317	351	345
Treatment C:	356	332	339	355	320	326

Subtracting 320 from each value and forming the usual totals to prepare for a one-way analysis gives:

							T_i	T_i^2	$\sum_j x_{ij}^2$
A:	-28	-47	27	-10	-19	29	-48	2304	5024
B:	25	-12	24	-3	31	25	90	8100	2940
C:	36	12	19	35	0	6	108	11 664	3062
Totals							150	22 068	11 026

Form the ANOVA table and decide whether there is evidence of the heat treatments affecting the yield points differently.

****

Source of variation	Sum of squares	Degrees of freedom	Variance estimate
Between treatments	2428	2	1214
Within treatments	7348	15	489·86
Total	9776	17	

$F_{15}^{2} \simeq 2 \cdot 48$, which is not large enough to be significant at the 5% level. Thus there is no real evidence of differences between the heat treatments.

In making the F-test you are comparing the between treatments variation with the within treatments variation.   The latter could be attributable to testing error but as discs were taken from more than one ingot, the variation between ingots could also be a contributory factor.   That could so swell the within treatments variation of results as to cause a difference between treatments to remain undetected.   This is not the first time that we have encountered this kind of problem.   You may find it helpful to go back to the programme Tests of Significance (1) in Unit 2 and read again FRAME 22 on page 196.   In the examples cited there, it was seen that, to avoid variations from rat to rat obscuring any effect the drug may have had and to avoid batch-to-batch variation obscuring a difference between the two processes, a "paired comparison" experimental design was advisable.   For the two chemical processes this involved raw material from each batch being used in trials with each process.   If, in the present problem, only two heat treatments were to be compared, a suitable paired design would be to prepare two discs from each ingot and then subject one of the pair to one treatment and one to the other.   The procedure described below is the obvious extension to this when a comparison between three heat treatments is to be made.

From each of 6 ingots, 3 discs were prepared.   Of each set of 3 discs, one disc was subjected to heat treatment A, one to B and the other to C - the allocation of disc to treatment being made on a random basis.   Yield points (in $MN\,m^{-2}$) for the treated specimens were as follows:

Treatment	Ingot 1	Ingot 2	Ingot 3	Ingot 4	Ingot 5	Ingot 6
A	347	292	301	273	310	349
B	344	308	345	317	345	351
C	356	332	355	320	339	326

Draw up the two-way ANOVA table for this data.   Does it confirm that there is a significant "ingot effect"?   What conclusion is now reached about whether the heat treatments affect the yield point differently?

(If you look carefully at this data you will see that the observations for each treatment are the same as in the previous frame.   This has been done so that you can make use of the previous calculations, and also so that you can compare the two approaches.)

****

53A

Source of variation	Sum of squares	Degrees of freedom	Variance estimate
Between treatments	2428	2	1214
Between ingots	4765·$\dot{3}$	5	953·0$\dot{6}$
Residual	2582·$\dot{6}$	10	258·2$\dot{6}$
Total	9776	17	

$F_{10}^{5} = 3·69 > 3·33.$ *Sig. at 5% level, i.e. showing a significant ingot effect.*

$F_{10}^{2} = 4·70 > 4·10.$ *Sig. at 5% level, i.e. showing a significant difference between heat treatment effects.*

A Computer Program

We have demonstrated the ANOVA technique on sets of data specially chosen to give simple calculations.   The tedium of more cumbersome calculations can be avoided by getting a computer to do them for you.   The program shown on the next page is for one-way analysis of variance and is written in 1900 FORTRAN (similar to FORTRAN IV).   If you are sufficiently familiar with FORTRAN to be

able to follow this program, you should not find it too difficult to progress
to writing a program for two-way analysis.   You could then test it on the
examples for which we have already worked out the answers.   If you are not
familiar with FORTRAN, read on, because you should still be able to answer the
question at the end of the frame.

```
      MASTER ONEWAYANOVA
      DIMENSION X(8,12),T(8)
C THIS PROGRAM CALCULATES THE ANOVA TABLE FOR K SAMPLES EACH OF SIZE N.
C K MUST NOT EXCEED 8 AND N MUST NOT EXCEED 12.
      READ(1,1)N,K
    1 FORMAT(2IO)
C THE VALUES OF N AND K HAVE NOW BEEN READ IN.
      DO 3 I=1,K
    3 READ(1,2)(X(I,J),J=1,N)
    2 FORMAT(8FO.O)
C ALL OBSERVATIONS ARE NOW STORED IN THE ARRAY X, THE JTH OBSERVATION IN
C THE ITH SAMPLE BEING STORED AS X(I,J).
      SUMXSQ,GRANDT,SUMTSQ=O.
      DO 5 I=1,K
      T(I)=O.
      DO 4 J=1,N
      T(I)=T(I)+X(I,J)
    4 SUMXSQ=SUMXSQ+X(I,J)*X(I,J)
      GRANDT=GRANDT+T(I)
    5 SUMTSQ=SUMTSQ+T(I)*T(I)
C THE SAMPLE TOTALS ARE NOW STORED IN THE ARRAY T, T(I) BEING THE TOTAL
C FOR THE ITH SAMPLE.  GRANDT IS THE GRAND TOTAL.   SUMXSQ IS THE SUM OF
C THE SQUARES OF THE X(I,J)'S.   SUMTSQ IS THE SUM OF THE SQUARES OF THE
C SAMPLE TOTALS.
      NTOT=K*N
C NTOT IS THE TOTAL NUMBER OF OBSERVATIONS.
      CF=GRANDT*GRANDT/NTOT
C CF IS THE CORRECTION FACTOR.
      BETWEENSS=SUMTSQ/N-CF
      TOTALSS=SUMXSQ-CF
      WITHINSS=TOTALSS-BETWEENSS
C THE THREE SUMS OF SQUARES HAVE NOW BEEN CALCULATED.
      NDFB=K-1
      NDFT=NTOT-1
      NDFW=NDFT-NDFB
C THE CORRESPONDING DEGREES OF FREEDOM HAVE NOW BEEN FOUND.
      BETWEENMS=BETWEENSS/NDFB
      WITHINMS=WITHINSS/NDFW
      F=BETWEENMS/WITHINMS
      WRITE(2,6)BETWEENSS,NDFB,BETWEENMS,WITHINSS,NDFW,WITHINMS,TOTALSS,
     1NDFT,F,NDFB,NDFW
    6 FORMAT(' SOURCE',18X,'SUM',8X,'DF',5X,'VARIANCE ESTIMATE'/
     1' BETWEEN SAMPLES',6X,F9.3,4X,I3,8X,F10.4/' WITHIN SAMPLES',7X,
     2F9.3,4X,I3,8X,F10.4/' TOTAL',15X,F10.3,4X,I3/' F = ',F6.3,' WITH',
     3I3,' DF IN NUMERATOR AND',I3,' DF IN DENOMINATOR')
      STOP
      END
      FINISH
```

FRAME 54   (continued)

This program was used to analyse the results of an investigation designed to
discover whether the variation in quality, from batch to batch, of an
intermediate product (H-acid) is such as to affect the yield of a dyestuff
(Naphthalene Black 12B)
prepared from it.   A
sample of the
intermediate product was
taken from each of 6
batches, and 5
preparations of the
dyestuff made in the
laboratory from each
sample.   The table shows
the determinations of the equivalent yield of each preparation as grams of
standard colour, for samples 1 - 6.

1	2	3	4	5	6
1440	1620	1540	1560	1490	1580
1480	1640	1470	1510	1560	1520
1450	1510	1590	1600	1490	1440
1460	1630	1440	1550	1560	1440
1520	1590	1450	1600	1540	1540

The lay-out of the data on the cards was as shown below, with the values of n
and k on the first card, the yields for Sample 1 on the next card, and so on.

```
5 6
1440.      1480.      1450.      1460.      1520.
1620.      1640.      1510.      1630.      1590.
1540.      1470.      1590.      1440.      1450.
1560.      1510.      1600.      1550.      1600.
1490.      1560.      1490.      1560.      1540.
1580.      1520.      1440.      1440.      1540.
```

The output was as follows:

```
SOURCE               SUM        DF     VARIANCE ESTIMATE
BETWEEN SAMPLES    55150.000     5        11030.0000
WITHIN SAMPLES     58080.000    24         2420.0000
TOTAL             113230.000    29
F = 4.558 WITH 5 DF IN NUMERATOR AND 24 DF IN DENOMINATOR
```

Is there evidence that different batches of H-acid give different yields of
dyestuff?

                 ****

                                                                        54A

Yes, at the 1% level of significance, as the 1% critical value of F_{24}^{5} is 3.90

FRAME 55

Further Developments

This introduction to analysis of variance has given you only the merest glimpse
of what can be achieved by it.   A brief mention of some further possible
developments may help to give you some idea of its full potential.

We have concentrated on the use of the ANOVA technique, with F-test, in
answering such questions as whether different rubber compounds have different
tensile strengths or whether the iron content of a water supply was different
at different times.   From the variance analysis, however, more information can
be extracted than the establishment, or otherwise, of significant differences.
In a one-way classification, for instance, it may not only be relevant to know
that a sample-to-sample variation exists, but also to know how great the

variation is or to have some estimate of the effect denoted by α_i in the model.

It is then necessary to decide which of two types of model is appropriate. With the car tyres the comparison concerned just the four brands for which braking distances had been recorded and what is known as the FIXED EFFECTS model is called for.   With the water samples, on the other hand, the concern may have been with the iron content at all times during the period of investigation. The times at which water was drawn off would then have constituted a random sample from the population of all possible times and the RANDOM EFFECTS model is appropriate.   However, if only the four particular times at which water was drawn off were of interest, the fixed effects model would apply.

Not only can further information be extracted from the simple experimental designs used in this programme, but also more complicated designs exist.   In the two-way classification, for instance, we considered only the case where one observation was made on each combination of tyre brand and car, or of analyst and sample.   If, however, there was replication, with two or more observations made on each combination, it would be possible to look for INTERACTION.   What is meant by this can be explained with reference to the braking distances. The model (40.1) would assume "tyre effect" and "car effect" to be independent of one another.   But Brand B tyres might show the poorest performance for cars as a whole, and Car 3 the poorest for tyres as a whole, yet the combination of Brand B tyres with Car 3 be remarkably successful;   that is, there might be a tyre brand-car interaction.   To investigate this, the analysis would need to be based on a more intricate model than (40.1).

Miscellaneous Examples

In this frame a collection of miscellaneous examples is given for you to try. Answers are supplied in FRAME 57, together with such working as is considered helpful.

1.   In a consumer association's laboratory, socks are tested for shrinkage by treatment in a wash wheel which takes 4 socks at a time.   In an experiment to discover whether the treatment of socks in the machine differs from run to run, 20 socks were divided randomly into 5 groups. (The socks were as alike as possible - same manufacturer, same yarn, etc. - but inevitably there would be small variations from one to another.) The % shrinkage in length after treatment was measured with the following results:

Run 1	Run 2	Run 3	Run 4	Run 5
7·4	2·5	6·6	7·9	6·7
6·7	5·9	6·3	2·7	7·3
9·3	1·4	4·5	3·4	5·1
5·8	4·6	6·2	7·6	8·1

Draw up the ANOVA table for this data.   Is there evidence of a difference in treatment between runs?

2.   The following data resulted from a project carried out by a civil engineering student, to which reference has already been made in Misc. Ex. 15 on page 265.   All the limestone cores in these crushing tests were 25 mm in diameter and 25 mm high, with end faces perpendicular to the axis, and the same compression testing machine was used throughout.   Six of the cores were tested in their natural state, as cut from the rock.

Another six were saturated for 7 weeks in water kept at room temperature
before being tested.   The remaining six were dried in an electric oven
at a temperature of 105°C for 24 hours prior to test.   The compressive
strengths (in kN) were as follows:

Natural (as cut):	60·6	65·1	96·9	57·9	85·6	82·7
Saturated:	72·8	82·7	59·8	61·8	57·1	91·8
Dried:	75·2	64·8	82·9	64·3	70·2	54·8

Estimate the variance of the testing error assuming that it is the same
whatever the moisture content.   Is there evidence that the moisture
content of a limestone core affects its compressive strength?

3.   In the examples of one-way analysis so far considered in this programme,
all samples have contained the same number of observations, n.   That is
the ideal experimental design but circumstances do not always permit it.
Fortunately very little modification to the formulae for the sums of
squares is required to accommodate unequal sample sizes.   The total sum
of squares is calculated in much the same way as before.   The between
samples sum of squares, which was previously $\frac{1}{n} \Sigma T_i^2 - \frac{T^2}{N}$, i.e.

$$\Sigma \frac{T_i^2}{n} - \frac{T^2}{N} , \text{ is now } \Sigma \frac{T_i^2}{n_i} - \frac{T^2}{N} , \text{ i.e. } \frac{T_1^2}{n_1} + \frac{T_2^2}{n_2} + \cdots + \frac{T_k^2}{n_k} - \frac{T^2}{N} ,$$

where n_1, n_2, ... n_k are the sample sizes.   The following example
gives you an opportunity to try this out for yourself.

It is planned to study the effect of NaCN (sodium cyanide) on the
uptake of an amino acid by preparations of the intestine taken from a
species of fish.   More preparations will be required than can be obtained
from a single fish, so a preliminary investigation is carried out to see
whether the use of different fish will introduce an extra source of
variation into the results.   Of the three fish selected for these trials,
two yielded 5 intestinal preparations but the other gave only 4.   The
values recorded for the uptake of the amino acid during a fixed interval
of time were (in μmol g^{-1} dry weight):

						Σx	Σx^2
Fish 1	2·35	2·03	2·12	2·51	2·14	11·15	25·0175
Fish 2	2·01	1·97	1·79	2·03	2·10	9·90	19·6560
Fish 3	1·62	1·96	1·35	1·53		6·46	10·6294

To assist you in your calculations the sum of the observations and of their
squares is shown for each sample.   Complete the analysis of variance and
decide whether there is a significant difference between fishes.

4.   In an investigation into the effect of light on the reproduction of a
type of seaweed, a long period of darkness was interrupted by a short
period of illumination.   Tests were made using light of 5 different
wavelengths, and there were 10 tests for each wavelength.   Which lot of
seaweed was subjected to which wavelength was determined randomly.   At
the end of each test a measure of the production of spores was recorded.
Past experience having shown that a lognormal model applies (i.e. log x
is normally distributed) the analysis of variance is applied to the
logarithms of the observations.   The results gave:

FRAME 56   (continued)

Colour	Blue	Green	Yellow	Red	Far-red
$\Sigma(\log x)$	42·731	42·796	42·272	39·641	42·523
$\Sigma(\log x)^2$	182·620	183·251	178·771	157·985	180·908

Is there evidence that the various light treatments differ in their effect
on spore production?   Theory suggests that the reaction to red light will
be different from reaction to light of other wavelengths.   Use the LSD to
judge whether the red light mean (of the transformed variable) differs
significantly from the other treatment means.

5.   Having applied analysis of variance, combined with an F-test, to data
consisting of three or more samples, you may be interested to see what
happens when the same technique is applied to two samples.   Try it out
on the pH data, details of which were given in FRAME 36 on page 203, and
see whether you arrive at the same conclusion as was reached then.   Note
that the F-value you obtain is the square of the t-value previously
obtained and show that this relationship still holds in the more general
case of two samples each of size n.

6.   The following table gives the productivity (measured in suitable units
against some standard) of three shifts in a given industrial plant over a
period of one week.

Shift	Mon.	Tues.	Wed.	Thurs.	Fri.
First shift	6	11	9	15	8
Second shift	-2	15	10	8	0
Third shift	-12	7	-9	8	1

Are there significant differences in productivity (a) from shift to
shift,   (b) from day to day?   (C.E.I.)

7.   Four methods (A, B, C, D) of analysis are available for determining the
percentage of a particular constituent in a given sample of material.
Three different analysts (Tom, Dick,

	A	B	C	D
Tom	65	72	64	63
Dick	65	76	67	64
Harry	63	72	65	68

Harry) each do one analysis by each
method, obtaining the percentages
shown.   Do the results show
significant differences   (i) between
analysts,   (ii) between methods?

8.   There is a choice of four types of machine A, B, C, D to use for making
a particular product.   During a trial period, three 1-hour intervals
during the operation of each
machine were randomly chosen
for recording output, with
the results (in suitable
units) as shown here.   Test
the hypothesis that there

Observation	A	B	C	D
1	30	38	36	25
2	38	31	25	28
3	31	42	35	28

was no difference between the four types of machine in their mean rate of
output.

9.   Four possible display arrangements of instruments on a control panel were
tried out by simulating an emergency and noting the reaction times (in
tenths of a second) required by the operator to correct the situation.
Each of 5 operators did one test with each display, in random order, with

the following results:

		Operator			
Display	1	2	3	4	5
A	10	8	11	10	11
B	15	11	12	11	15
C	10	5	8	8	14
D	13	12	13	15	16

Is there evidence that   (i) the display arrangement affects reaction times, (ii) the operators differ in their quickness of response?   What alteration would be needed in the experimental design if a possible interaction between operator and display is to be investigated?

10.   Eight metal strips are each cut into six portions, each set of six portions then being distributed randomly between six machines in order that measures of tensile strength can be made.

If the average tensile strengths recorded by the six machines are   103, 101, 102, 105, 103 and 104 units respectively, and the residual mean square yielded by the analysis of variance is 2, is there any reason to believe the machines are essentially different?   (C.E.I.)

11.   Determinations were made of the yield of a chemical using two catalytic methods.   A number of batches of raw material were used, the two methods being used on material from each batch.

An analysis of variance of the percentage yields is given below with some entries missing.

Source of variation	Degrees of freedom	Sums of squares
Between methods		27·8703
Among batches		829·4400
Error	24	
Total	49	995·5503

(a)   Complete the analysis of variance table.
(b)   How many batches were used in the investigation?
(c)   Is there a significant difference between methods?
(d)   What would be the effect on the significance of the between methods comparison if it had not been possible to separate the sum of squares due to batches from the error sum of squares?   (L.U.)

Answers to Miscellaneous Examples

1. | Source | SS | d.f. | Var.est. |
|---|---|---|---|
| Between runs | 33·04 | 4 | 8·26 |
| Within runs | 48·88 | 15 | 3·2586 |
| Total | 81·92 | 19 | |

$F_{15}^{4} = 2·53$.   Not sig. at 5%. Socks do not appear to be treated differently in different runs.

2.   179·92.   Between moisture contents SS = 56·94.   As this is < 179·92, no F-test is required and it can be stated that there is no evidence of compressive strength being affected by moisture content.

3.   C.F. $= 27 \cdot 51^2/14$ Total SS $= 55 \cdot 3029 - $ C.F.

Between fishes   SS $= \dfrac{11 \cdot 15^2}{5} + \dfrac{9 \cdot 90^2}{5} + \dfrac{6 \cdot 46^2}{4} - $ C.F.

Source	SS	d.f.	Var.est.	
Between fishes	0·842 25	2	0·421 125	$F^2_{11} = 11 \cdot 48$
Between preparations within fishes	0·403 50	11	0·036 682	Difference between fishes sig. at 1% level.
Total	1·245 75	13		

4. $F^4_{45} = 7 \cdot 00$.   Difference between treatments sig. at 1% level (and even
at 0·1%).   For 5% significance, LSD $= 0 \cdot 143$.   Red light mean (3·9641)
differs from other means by more than this, thus confirming theory.
For 1% significance, LSD $= 0 \cdot 191$.   Red light mean still differs from
other means by more than this, giving theory even stronger confirmation.

5. $F^1_{16} = 9$.   Sig. at 1% level, as before.

6.   (a) $F^2_8 = 6 \cdot 31$.   Sig. at 5%.   (b) $F^4_8 = 4 \cdot 07$.   Sig. at 5%.

7.   (i) $F^2_6 = 1$.   Not sig. at 5%.   (ii) $F^3_6 = 13 \cdot 5$.   Sig. at 1%.

8. $F^3_8 = 2 \cdot 2\dot{5}$.   No sig. difference between machines at 5% level.

9.   (i) $F^3_{12} = 12 \cdot 45$.   Sig. at 1%.   (ii) $F^4_{12} = 6 \cdot 39$.   Sig. at 1%.
To investigate the possibility of interaction between operator and display
it would be necessary to replicate observations on each combination of
the two.

10. $F^5_{35} = 8$.   Sig. at 1% (also at 0·1%).   Very good reason to believe
machines different.

11. (a)

Source of variation	Degrees of freedom	Sum of squares	Variance estimate
Between methods	1	27·8703	27·8703
Between batches	24	829·4400	34·5600
Error	24	138·2400	5·7600
Total	49	995·5503	

(b) 25   (c) $F^1_{24} = 4 \cdot 84 > 4 \cdot 26$.   Sig. at 5%.   (d) Error SS would
be 967·6800.

$F^1_{48} = \dfrac{27 \cdot 8703}{20 \cdot 1600} \simeq 1 \cdot 38$.   Not sig. at 5%.   The table in (a) shows strong
evidence of a difference between batches ($F^{24}_{24} = 6$).   Inability to isolate
this source of variation obscures the between methods effect.

Correlation

Scatter Diagrams

Up till now, this course has concentrated on statistical methods which apply to data involving one variable only, which we have usually called x. Thus x might be the trace amount of chromium found in a specimen of shale or it might be the height of a man. However, the geologist may have measured not only the amount of chromium but also the amount of nickel, so that for each specimen there are two variables whose values have been recorded. Similarly, the weight of each man, as well as his height, might be included in the data being looked at by the human biologist. In such cases there are pairs of measurements of two variables, which we will call x and y. Now the geologist may be interested in whether the amount of chromium in a shale specimen is related to the amount of nickel in it, while the biologist, having good reason to expect weight and height to be related, may seek confirmation of this and wish to assess how close this relationship is. This programme will consider how to decide whether two such variables are related and how to measure the closeness of the relationship, if it exists.

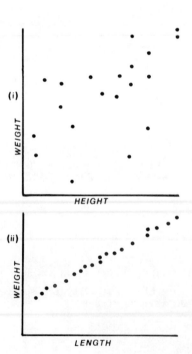

As a first step in looking for a possible relationship between two variables x and y, a SCATTER DIAGRAM may be drawn. In this, each pair of observations is represented by a point with coordinates (x, y) with respect to two axes at right angles to one another. If the heights and weights of 20 men had been recorded the scatter diagram might appear as in (i). On the other hand, if the lengths and weights of 20 pieces of 1 mm diameter copper wire were recorded, the scatter diagram shown in (ii) might be obtained. The points might not lie exactly on a straight line but would be near to doing so.

No doubt you will find that what these diagrams show agrees with what you already know of these pairs of variables. For instance, which of the following predictions would you feel able to make with complete confidence?

(1) A man whose height is 1·80 m will weigh more than a man whose height is 1·65 m.

(2) Men of height 1·80 m will be found, on average, to weigh more than men of height 1·65 m.

(3) A 1·80 m length of 1 mm diameter copper wire will weigh more than a 1·65 m length of the same wire.

****

2A

(2) and (3) but not (1), as a fat man who is 1·65m tall could weigh more than
a slim man who is 1·80 m tall.

FRAME 3

In the case of the copper wire (assumed uniform) it is an elementary physical
fact that the weight of a piece of the wire is proportional to its length and
that there is therefore a straight line relationship between the two variables,
weight and length.   If pairs of measurements do not lie exactly on a straight
line when plotted, the cause lies solely in errors in measuring.   Theoretically,
at any rate, there is a FUNCTIONAL RELATIONSHIP between weight and length.
This means that specifying the weight completely determines the length, or,
alternatively, specifying the length completely determines the weight.   No such
functional relationship exists between the weight and height of a man - it is not
possible, for instance, to predict a man's weight from his height.   Taller men
do, admittedly, tend to weigh more than shorter ones and the scatter diagram
suggests that this trend is linear.   This time, though, it is not errors in
measurement that are the main cause of the scatter of the points about a possible
trend line, but the presence of other factors besides height which influence a
man's weight.   It can be said that there is complete correlation between the
two variables, length and weight, when we are dealing with 1 mm diameter copper
wire but there is a lesser degree of correlation between a man's height and
weight.

Now look at the three diagrams shown here.   Then read (a), (b) and (c) and
pair each with the diagram that you think it describes.

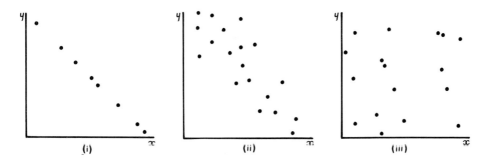

(a)   There is no relationship at all between x and y.

(b)   There is a functional relationship between x and y, i.e. the value of x
       completely determines the value of y and vice versa.   This relationship
       is linear and is such that y decreases as x increases.

(c)   The value of one variable is related to some extent with the value of the
       other, the general trend being a linear one as in the case of men's
       heights and weights.   In the present example, however, as one variable
       increases the tendency is for the other to decrease, and thus in this
       respect differs from the relationship between a man's height and weight.

                    ****

3A

(a) (iii),   (b) (i),   (c) (ii)

The Correlation Coefficient

You have now seen that the relationship between two variables can be non-existent, or complete, or somewhere in between.   Also, if a relationship exists, it may be such that high values of one variable go with high values of the other, or with low values, depending on the nature of the relationship.   As a measure of the extent of a relationship, the CORRELATION COEFFICIENT may be used.   For a sample of pairs of observations of x and y, the value r of this coefficient (the Pearson product moment correlation coefficient, to give it its full title) is given by the formula

$$r = \frac{\Sigma(x - \bar{x})(y - \bar{y})}{\sqrt{\Sigma(x - \bar{x})^2 \Sigma(y - \bar{y})^2}} \qquad (4.1)$$

You will gain an insight into the origin of this formula when you learn about regression, in the next programme in this Unit.   In the meantime we can find out what values are taken by r for various sets of data and see how it acts as a measure of correlation.

First let us consider the 9 pairs of values of x and y shown in columns (1) and (2) in the table.   If plotted they all lie exactly on a straight line (you may like to verify this).   That is to say, there is a functional relationship betweeen them, which is linear and is, in fact, y = x/2, as you can easily check for yourself.   The calculation of r is set out in the table below.

(1) x	(2) y	(3) $x - \bar{x}$	(4) $y - \bar{y}$	(3) × (3) $(x - \bar{x})^2$	(4) × (4) $(y - \bar{y})^2$	(3) × (4) $(x - \bar{x})(y - \bar{y})$
0	0	-12	-6	144	36	72
4	2	-8	-4	64	16	32
6	3	-6	-3	36	9	18
8	4	-4	-2	16	4	8
12	6	0	0	0	0	0
14	7	2	1	4	1	2
16	8	4	2	16	4	8
22	11	10	5	100	25	50
26	13	14	7	196	49	98
108	54	0	0	576	144	288

$\bar{x} = 12 \qquad \bar{y} = 6$

Substituting the values of the appropriate Σ's in (4.1) gives $r = \dfrac{288}{\sqrt{576 \times 144}}$

$= 1$

Now calculate the value of r corresponding to the following 9 pairs of values of x and y, which are also functionally related.   (Perhaps you can say what the relationship is.   If you can't, it doesn't matter, just check the equation when you meet it in the answer frame.)

x	0	4	6	8	12	14	16	22	26
y	13	11	10	9	7	6	5	2	0

****

5A

$\Sigma(x - \bar{x})^2 = 576$, as before. $\bar{y} = 7$, $\Sigma(y - \bar{y})^2 = 144$, $\Sigma(x - \bar{x})(y - \bar{y}) = -288$

$r = \dfrac{-288}{\sqrt{576 \times 144}} = -1$

The points all lie on a straight line - its equation is $y = 13 - \frac{1}{2}x$.

FRAME 6

Notice that in both these examples, where there is complete correlation between
the two variables, the magnitude of r is 1.   In the first example, where the
line has a positive slope i.e. y increases as x increases, r is positive.
In the second example, where the line has a negative slope i.e. y decreases
as x increases, r is negative.   From the calculations you will see that the
sign of r is the same as the sign of $\Sigma(x - \bar{x})(y - \bar{y})$.   Looking back at the
steps leading up to this sum, it is apparent from columns (3) and (4) in the
previous frame that negative values of $x - \bar{x}$ were always paired with negative
values of $y - \bar{y}$, and positive values of $x - \bar{x}$ with positive values of $y - \bar{y}$.
Thus each product $(x - \bar{x})(y - \bar{y})$ was positive and their sum, consequently, was
positive too.   Now look at your calculations in the second example.   What do
you notice about the signs of $x - \bar{x}$ and $y - \bar{y}$?

****

6A

Always opposite.   Hence each product $(x - \bar{x})(y - \bar{y})$ is negative and their
sum is negative in consequence.

FRAME 7

A little thought will show that what has just been noticed about the sign of
$\Sigma(x - \bar{x})(y - \bar{y})$ could have been anticipated before the actual calculations were
carried out.   The points for the first set of data
in FRAME 5 are plotted here.   Lines are drawn
through the point $(\bar{x}, \bar{y})$ parallel to the x- and
y-axes.   These lines divide the area into 4
quadrants, numbered as shown.

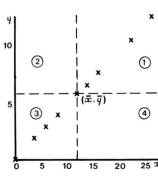

For any point (x, y) in quadrant ①, $x > \bar{x}$
and $y > \bar{y}$.   Hence both $x - \bar{x}$ and $y - \bar{y}$ are
positive and $(x - \bar{x})(y - \bar{y})$ is positive.   Now
take each of the quadrants ②–④ in turn, and
state, for any point (x, y) in that quadrant, the
signs of $x - \bar{x}$, $y - \bar{y}$ and $(x - \bar{x})(y - \bar{y})$
respectively.

****

7A

	$x - \bar{x}$	$y - \bar{y}$	$(x - \bar{x})(y - \bar{y})$
②	−	+	−
③	−	−	+
④	+	−	−

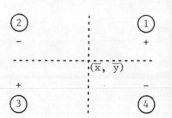

The sign of $(x - \bar{x})(y - \bar{y})$ for points in each of the 4 quadrants is shown in the diagram on the right.

Where a straight line relationship exists between x and y, such that above average y's go with above average x's and below average y's go with below average x's, <u>all</u> points will lie in quadrants ① and ③. Hence $\Sigma(x - \bar{x})(y - \bar{y})$ must be positive, as was found to be the case for the points plotted in the previous frame.

If the straight line relationship is such that y decreases as x increases, then <u>all</u> points will lie in quadrants ② and ④, making $\Sigma(x - \bar{x})(y - \bar{y})$ negative, as you found in your answer to FRAME 5.

Where there is not actually a functional relationship, but there is a tendency for high values of y to go with high values of x, <u>most</u> points will be in quadrants ① and ③. Hence $\Sigma(x - \bar{x})(y - \bar{y})$ will be positive, even though some values of $(x - \bar{x})(y - \bar{y})$ may be negative. Similarly if the tendency is for low values of y to go with high values of x, <u>most</u> points will be in quadrants .... and .... and $\Sigma(x - \bar{x})(y - \bar{y})$ will be .... Can you fill in the gaps in the last sentence?

****

8A

②, ④, *negative.*

FRAME 9

If x and y are not related in any way at all, points will fall with equal likelihood in each of the 4 quadrants. Thus the + terms and − terms in $\Sigma(x - \bar{x})(y - \bar{y})$ will tend to cancel each other out when added, and if this happens the overall sum is zero.

Now consider the following values of x paired in turn with each row of values of y and draw a scatter diagram for each set of pairs. For one set $\Sigma(x - \bar{x})(y - \bar{y})$, and hence r, is positive; for another, negative; and for the other, zero. See if you can identify which is which by looking at each diagram. (You may find it helpful to draw lines through $(\bar{x}, \bar{y})$ as in the diagrams in FRAMES 7 and 8.) Then find out whether your identification was correct, by calculating r for each set of data.

		0	4	6	8	12	14	16	22	26
	x									
(i)	y	4	3	8	6	7	13	2	11	0
(ii)	y	11	13	8	4	7	6	3	2	0
(iii)	y	0	2	4	3	7	6	8	11	13

To save extra calculations, the values of x and y have been chosen to be the same as in the table in FRAME 5, so $\bar{x} = 12$, $\bar{y} = 6$, $\Sigma(x - \bar{x})^2 = 576$ and

FRAME 9   (continued)

$\Sigma(y - \overline{y})^2 = 144.$ They are, however, paired differently so you will need to calculate $\Sigma(x - \overline{x})(y - \overline{y})$ in each case.

****

9A

(i)   r = 0   (ii)   r = -0·889   (iii)   r = +0·986

FRAME 10

It has now been noted that the correlation coefficient can range in magnitude from 0 to 1.   You have seen that if the two variables are not related at all, r = 0,   and that if there is a complete functional relationship, which is linear, $|r| = 1$.   The sign of the coefficient is positive if the two variables tend to increase together, negative if one tends to decrease as the other increases. In general, then,

$$-1 \leqslant r \leqslant +1$$

It should be pointed out that while a complete lack of any relationship at all between values of x and values of y entails a correlation coefficient of zero, the converse is not true.   The correlation coefficient measures only the extent to which the variables are related <u>linearly</u>.   If it is zero, it does not follow that there is no kind of relationship at all.   The following data will serve to illustrate this for you.   Plot the points and also calculate the value of r.

x	0	1	2	3	4	5	6
y	10	5	2	1	2	5	10

****

10A

r = 0,   but the points are not scattered about indiscriminately.   In fact, they all lie on a parabola, x and y being connected by the functional relationship
$y = x^2 - 6x + 10.$

FRAME 11

The question of how the units in which x and y are measured affects the value of r will now be considered.   Take the case of x being a man's height in metres and y his weight in kilograms, and suppose r to have been calculated from observations recorded in these units.   If the heights were converted to cm (i.e. the x's multiplied by 100) what effect would that have on (i) the values of $x - \overline{x}$, $(x - \overline{x})^2$ and $(x - \overline{x})(y - \overline{y})$,   (ii) the value of $\Sigma(x - \overline{x})^2$ and of $\Sigma(x - \overline{x})(y - \overline{y})$.   Deduce the effect on r.   Then consider how the value of r would be affected if the weights were converted to grams (i.e. the y's multiplied by 1000).

****

11A

(i)   Every $x - \overline{x}$ would be multiplied by 100, every $(x - \overline{x})^2$ by 100^2 and every $(x - \overline{x})(y - \overline{y})$ by 100.   (ii) $\Sigma(x - \overline{x})^2$ would be multiplied by 100^2 and $\Sigma(x - \overline{x})(y - \overline{y})$ by 100.

As the numerator and denominator of (4.1) would both be multiplied by the same factor of 100, the change of units for x would have no effect on the value of r.   Obviously changing the units in which y is measured would not have any effect either.

Thus the value of the correlation coefficient is independent of the units in which the two variables are measured, as indeed it must be, for the extent to which height and weight are related is a matter of human biology and is not influenced by the choice of units for the measurements.

Alternative formula for calculating r

The denominator of (4.1) contains $\Sigma(x - \bar{x})^2$ and $\Sigma(y - \bar{y})^2$ and you know that these sums are involved when calculating estimates of the variances of x and y respectively.   The numerator is associated in a similar way with what is called the covariance of x and y.

In Unit 1 it was shown that $\Sigma(x - \bar{x})^2 = \Sigma x^2 - \dfrac{1}{n}(\Sigma x)^2$

$$\text{and}\quad \Sigma(y - \bar{y})^2 = \Sigma y^2 - \frac{1}{n}(\Sigma y)^2$$

n being the number of observations in each case, and you have seen that from a computational point of view this alternative formula may be more convenient. A similar alternative exists for $\Sigma(x - \bar{x})(y - \bar{y})$.   It can be shown that, for n pairs of observations,

$$\Sigma(x - \bar{x})(y - \bar{y}) = \Sigma xy - \frac{1}{n}\Sigma x \, \Sigma y \qquad (12.1)$$

The derivation of this result begins by expanding $(x - \bar{x})(y - \bar{y})$ as $xy - \bar{x}y - \bar{y}x + \bar{x}\,\bar{y}$ and then summing each term in this expansion.   You may like to try to derive (12.1) in this way.

****

$$\Sigma(x - \bar{x})(y - \bar{y}) = \Sigma xy - \bar{x}\,\Sigma y - \bar{y}\,\Sigma x + n\bar{x}\bar{y}$$
$$= \Sigma xy - n\bar{x}\bar{y} - n\bar{x}\bar{y} + n\bar{x}\bar{y}$$
$$= \Sigma xy - n\bar{x}\bar{y}$$
$$= \Sigma xy - \frac{1}{n}\Sigma x \, \Sigma y$$

The formula for r can therefore be restated as

$$r = \frac{\Sigma xy - \dfrac{1}{n}\Sigma x \, \Sigma y}{\sqrt{\{\Sigma x^2 - \dfrac{1}{n}(\Sigma x)^2\}\{\Sigma y^2 - \dfrac{1}{n}(\Sigma y)^2\}}}$$

or, multiplying numerator and denominator by n, as

$$r = \frac{n\Sigma xy - \Sigma x \, \Sigma y}{\sqrt{\{n\Sigma x^2 - (\Sigma x)^2\}\{n\Sigma y^2 - (\Sigma y)^2\}}} \qquad (13.1)$$

Check that, using this formula, the same value is obtained for r in (iii) in FRAME 9 as was then found with the original formula.

****

13A

*Substituting n = 9,   Σx = 108,   Σy = 54,   Σx² = 1872,   Σy² = 468,   Σxy = 932,
leads to   r = 0·986,   as before.*

FRAME 14

Bivariate Frequency Table

In Unit 1 you saw how, when dealing with observations of one variable, it may be
helpful to form a frequency table if the amount of data is too large to handle
conveniently otherwise.   This idea can be extended to BIVARIATE data, i.e. to
paired observations of two variables, as is illustrated by the table shown here,
in which measurements of height and weight for 50 men have been classified
according to suitably chosen intervals.   There were, for instance, 16 men
whose height was in the category 180 – 184 cm and, of them, 7 had a weight in
the category 65·5 – 70·4 kg.   How many men were there whose weight was in the
60·5 – 65·4 kg group, and how many of these had a height in the 175 – 179 cm
group?   Is it possible that one of the men measured was 165cm tall and

Height x (cm)

	160-164	165-169	170-174	175-179	180-184	185-189	190-194	f_y
80·5-85·4							1	1
75·5-80·4			1		3	3	2	9
70·5-75·4					2			2
65·5-70·4		2	1	3	7			13
60·5-65·4		1	2	5	1	1		10
55·5-60·4	2	1	4	1	2			10
50·5-55·4	1		2		1			4
45·5-50·4			1					1
f_x	3	4	11	9	16	4	3	50

Weight y (kg) is the left label.

weighed 56·9 kg?   Is it possible that two of the men had these measurements?

****

14A

10, 5.   Yes.   No.

FRAME 15

The sub-totals f_x shown on the bottom row represent the frequency distribution
of the men's heights.   What frequency distribution is represented by the
sub-totals f_y shown in the extreme right-hand column?

****

15A

The frequency distribution of the men's weights.

FRAME 16

Looking at the general pattern of the frequencies in the various cells in the
table conveys a similar impression to that given by the scatter diagram for men's
heights and weights in FRAME 2.   The empty cells, meaning zero frequency, in

the top left-hand and bottom right-hand corners of the table correspond to the
empty spaces in the equivalent parts of the scatter diagram.   As you would
expect, the table indicates a tendency for tall men to weigh more than shorter
ones.

For the purpose of calculating the coefficient of correlation between height
and weight from data in this form, all observations in a group are taken to have
the values of x and y at the middle of their respective intervals, as was done
with frequency distributions for a single variate.   What are the mid-points of
the intervals for (i) x,   (ii) y?

****

16A

(i)   162,   167,   172,   177,   182,   187,   192.
(ii) 47·95, 52·95, 57·95, 62·95, 67·95, 72·95, 77·95, 82·95.

FRAME 17

The 7 men referred to in FRAME 14 would thus all be taken to have a height of
182 cm and a weight of 67·95 kg.   In finding the various sums required for r
you would have to take the frequencies into account in much the same way that
you did when finding the mean and standard deviation of a frequency distribution
in Unit 1.   To find the sum corresponding to Σx, the frequencies f_x would be
used, giving

$3 \times 162 + 4 \times 167 + 11 \times 172 + 9 \times 177 + 16 \times 182 + 4 \times 187 + 3 \times 192 = 8875$

If this is then divided by 50, what will the answer represent?

****

17A

The mean height $\bar{x}$ of the 50 men.

FRAME 18

How would you find the sum corresponding to Σy?   (You are not being asked to
actually evaluate it.)   If this sum is divided by 50, what will the answer
represent?

****

18A

Using the frequencies f_y, calculate
$1 \times 47·95 + 4 \times 52·95 + 10 \times 57·95 + \ldots + 1 \times 82·95$.   The mean weight $\bar{y}$ of the
50 men.

FRAME 19

Now that you have some idea of how to deal with a bivariate frequency table we
will not proceed here with the calculation of r.   If you were told that its
value was either (i) −0·918, (ii) 0·627 or (iii) 0·045, which answer would
you be inclined to accept as correct?

****

(i) can be ruled out because r is clearly not negative, and (iii) seems too small considering the obvious trend shown in the table. (ii) is, in fact, the correct value.

Interpreting a value of r

When a value of r is calculated from n pairs of observations, it measures the degree of correlation between the two variables for those n pairs. However, one would usually be trying to look beyond the immediate data. For instance, it would probably not just be a question of establishing a correlation between height and weight for the 20 or 50 men who had been measured, but of establishing such a correlation for <u>all</u> men. As with many situations described in Unit 2, the problem is one of sample and population. It is the sample that we know about but the population that we <u>want</u> to know about. Following the convention of using Greek letters for population parameters, the value of the correlation coefficient in the population is customarily denoted by ρ. Different samples from the same population may well yield different values of r, and those values of r will generally differ from ρ. There is therefore a need for caution in making conclusions about ρ from a value of r. Some guidance in this will now be given.

Populations are usually large, often infinite, but the number of points that can be shown in a scatter diagram is limited. However, with some imagination on your part, diagram (i) can serve to represent a population in which x and y are uncorrelated, i.e. $\rho = 0$.

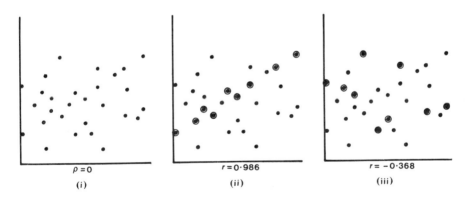

$\rho = 0$ r = 0·986   r = −0·368

(i)   (ii)   (iii)

In diagrams (ii) and (iii), two possible samples from this population are indicated by the ringed points, in (ii) giving r = 0·986 and in (iii) giving r = −0·368. Obviously there are many other samples that could arise from this population, giving values of r from −1 to +1. Hence obtaining a non-zero value of r from a set of observations does not, of itself, mean that a correlation between the two variables has been established. However, for samples taken from a population with $\rho = 0$, while all values of r within the range −1 to +1 are <u>possible</u> they are not equally <u>probable</u>. To get a value of r near to ±1, a relatively unusual sample is required with the points closely following a straight line, as in diagram (ii).   Values of r nearer to 0, on the other hand, can be obtained from a wide variety of samples and are thus more likely to occur.

We have been looking at the likelihood of various values of r occurring when $\rho = 0$.   This will now enable us to see how to deal with the reverse situation, which is the one that happens in practice, where a value of r has been found and you want to decide whether it is likely that $\rho = 0$.   As a value of r as far away from zero as $0 \cdot 986$ is unlikely to occur when $\rho = 0$, we can argue that getting $r = 0 \cdot 986$ means that it is unlikely that $\rho = 0$.   Similarly, if a value of r as near to zero as $-0 \cdot 368$ is quite likely if $\rho = 0$, we can reason that getting $r = -0 \cdot 368$ means that $\rho = 0$ is quite ....   Which of the words "likely" and "unlikely" would you choose for completing this sentence?

****

21A

likely

FRAME 22

The previous frame has outlined, in general terms, one aspect of the interpretation of r.   It has shown you why, having obtained a value of r which indicates a degree of correlation in the sample, you should ask the question: "Is this really evidence of an association between the two variables generally, or could this value of r happen quite easily by chance when there is no such association, i.e. $\rho = 0$?"   Putting the question another way: "Is the value of r statistically significant?"   The answer is provided by a significance test, along the lines now familiar to you.   The hypothesis that $\rho = 0$ is put forward and the value of r examined in the event of that hypothesis being true.   If $|r|$ is large enough to be classified as "unlikely", we would then reject the hypothesis and decide that there is evidence of a correlation existing generally between the two variables.   Notice that we are considering only whether there is a significant correlation, without regard to whether it is positive or negative; in other words, the test is two-sided. Stating this in the usual way:

NULL HYPOTHESIS: $\rho = 0$
ALTERNATIVE HYPOTHESIS: $\rho \neq 0$

The next step is to decide whether the value of r falls into the "unlikely" category.   As you know by now, what is classified as "unlikely" depends on what significance level has been chosen.   Suppose, for the sake of argument, that this level of risk has been fixed at 5%.   You will then need to know what value of $|r|$ has only a 5% chance of being exceeded if $\rho = 0$.   What that critical value of $|r|$ is will depend on how r varies from sample to sample, i.e. on the sampling distribution of r.   Do you think that this distribution will be affected by the sample size n?   (Ask yourself whether the high value of r given by the sample of size 9 in diagram (ii) in the previous frame would be just as likely to occur if 18 points had been ringed at random. Then consider whether or not a large sample is more likely to give you a better idea of what ρ really is than a smaller sample.)

****

Getting 18 randomly selected points which show such a strong linear trend will be even less likely than getting 9 points which do so. The larger n is, the more information you have about the population. So the answer is yes, it seems reasonable that there will be different sampling distributions of r for different sample sizes.

FRAME 23

It can be shown that, if $\rho = 0$, the distribution of $\dfrac{r}{\sqrt{1 - r^2}} \sqrt{n - 2}$ is a

t-distribution with $(n - 2)$ d.f. This result is based on both variables x and y being normally distributed and is an approximation otherwise. If r is found from a sample of 9 pairs of observations the acceptance and rejection regions corresponding to a chosen significance level could be deduced from the distribution with 7 d.f. For this distribution, there is a 5% chance of $|t|$ being greater than .... and a 1% chance of $|t|$ being greater than .... Fill in the gaps.

****

2·36, 3·50 (obtained by reference to TABLE 3).

FRAME 24

Hence, if $\rho = 0$, there is a 5% chance that

$\left| \dfrac{r\sqrt{7}}{\sqrt{1 - r^2}} \right| > 2 \cdot 36$,   i.e. that $\dfrac{7r^2}{1 - r^2} > 2 \cdot 36^2$ or $7r^2 > 5 \cdot 57(1 - r^2)$

which leads to $r^2 > 0 \cdot 4431$,   i.e. $|r| > 0 \cdot 666$.

A value of $r < -0 \cdot 666$ or $> +0 \cdot 666$ would therefore be judged significant at the 5% level. The ranges of r for which the N.H. $\rho = 0$ is accepted or rejected may be summarised thus:

-1	-0·666	0	+0·666	+1

←REJECT→ ←————————   ACCEPT   ————————→ ← REJECT→

Thus, on this basis, a sample of 9 pairs of observations giving $r = 0 \cdot 986$ would be regarded as evidence of a correlation in the population, but a sample giving $r = -0 \cdot 368$ would not.

Now use your other answer in 23A to find the range of values of r that would be considered significant at the 1% level. Would $r = 0 \cdot 986$ still be regarded as evidence of a correlation existing in the population, at this level of significance?

****

$\dfrac{7r^2}{1 - r^2} > 3 \cdot 50^2$ *leads to* $|r| > 0 \cdot 798$, *i.e.* $r < -0 \cdot 798$ *or* $r > +0 \cdot 798$.

As $r = 0 \cdot 986$ *falls into this category, it would be regarded as evidence of a correlation existing in the population.*

For your convenience, TABLE 6 is provided to save you the bother of working out from the t-table the critical value of $|r|$ each time you require it. The table gives the values of $|r|$ which, if $\rho = 0$, have a 10%, 5%, 1% or 0·1% chance of being exceeded. The number of degrees of freedom is the same as you used for the t-distribution, i.e. $\nu = n - 2$. The values in the table have been obtained in just the same way that the values 0·666 and 0·798 were obtained in the previous frame. Check that the table gives these as the 5% and 1% critical values for a sample of 9 pairs of observations. Then use the table to decide whether $r = 0·627$, when given by the measurements made on 50 men as mentioned earlier in the programme, signifies a correlation between weight and height for men in general.

****

$\nu = 48$, which is between the values 45 and 50 given in TABLE 6. Thus the 0·1% critical value of $|r|$ is obviously between 0·465 and 0·443, showing that $r = 0·627$ is much too high a value to be ascribed to chance happening but signifies a correlation between weight and height.

You should now be able to work through the procedure required for deciding whether the following data provide evidence of a correlation between the amounts of chromium and nickel present in shale. The figures are the trace amounts (in p.p.m.) of each element found in each of 6 specimens.

Specimen	A	B	C	D	E	F
Chromium	200	245	190	220	230	235
Nickel	130	165	95	140	135	145

Calculate r, using (4.1) and assess its significance.

****

x	y	$x - \bar{x}$	$y - \bar{y}$	$(x - \bar{x})^2$	$(y - \bar{y})^2$	$(x - \bar{x})(y - \bar{y})$
200	*130*	*-20*	*-5*	*400*	*25*	*100*
245	*165*	*25*	*30*	*625*	*900*	*750*
190	*95*	*-30*	*-40*	*900*	*1600*	*1200*
220	*140*	*0*	*5*	*0*	*25*	*0*
230	*135*	*10*	*0*	*100*	*0*	*0*
235	*145*	*15*	*10*	*225*	*100*	*150*
1320	*810*	*0*	*0*	*2250*	*2650*	*2200*

$\bar{x} = 220$, $\bar{y} = 135$; $r = 0·901 > 0·811$ and hence sig. at 5% level.

However, if we want to be more sure of the existence of a correlation, then moving to the 1% level we find that 0·901 is not large enough to be significant. Notice that whereas a value of 0·627 for r showed strong evidence of correlation when obtained from a sample of size 50, it would provide no evidence whatsoever in the present situation where the sample size is only 6. The smaller the sample, the larger r needs to be to provide evidence of correlation.

An assessment of what a value of r tells us about the population can also be
made by obtaining a confidence interval for ρ.   An easy way of doing this is
to use charts given in Biometrika Tables for Statisticians, Vol 1.   One just
reads off the 95% and 99% confidence limits for ρ corresponding to sample
size and value of r.   In this way, both 95% and 99% confidence intervals
were estimated for ρ for   (i) the height and weight of men, based on the 50
observations which gave r = 0·627,   (ii) the amounts of chromium and nickel in
shale, based on the 6 observations which gave r = 0·901.   Look at the
following 4 intervals and decide which were found for (i) and which for (ii),
distinguishing in each case between 95% and 99% limits.   You don't need the
charts for this!

(a)   0·30 and 0·98   (b)   0·33 and 0·80   (c)   0·44 and 0·77
(d)   −0·07 and 0·99

                   ****

 *(i)   95% (c),   99% (b).   These could not apply to (ii) as they don't contain
        0·901.   Note also that neither contains zero, in agreement with our
        decision to reject   ρ = 0   at both 5% and 1% levels.*

*(ii)   95% (a),   99% (d).   Note that (d) contains zero, agreeing therefore with
        our decision that   ρ = 0   could not be rejected at the 1% level.*

A word of warning now of the danger of drawing wrong conclusions when a
significant correlation has been established.   Remember that a positive value
of ρ only means a tendency for high values of x to go with high values of y;
it does not follow that high values of x cause high values of y, or vice versa.
Similarly, a negative value of ρ means only that high values of x tend to go
with low values of y.   For an explanation of why the two variables are
associated it is necessary to look beyond correlation theory to the
circumstances surrounding them.   In the case of a man's height and weight, it
is obvious that his weight will depend on his body measurements, of which
height is one, and that therefore height is a causal factor (there are others,
of course) in determining weight.   A significant correlation, in this case,
supports what we would expect to find and will give a measure of the extent to
which height influences weight.   One can, however, cite many examples where it
would be quite ludicrous to deduce a causal relationship from a significant
correlation.   In "How to lie with statistics" Darrell Huff quotes the fact
that a high positive correlation has been established between annual figures,
over a period of years, for the salaries of Presbyterian ministers in
Massachusetts (who were presumably preaching the evils of drink) and the price
of rum in Havana.   It would obviously be preposterous to conclude that the
ministers get a pay rise because the price of rum has increased, or that the
price of rum in Havana is influenced by the ministers' salaries.   A much more
credible explanation is that both salaries and price have been affected by
inflation and thus when one rises, so does the other.

The real danger of drawing false conclusions, however, lies in situations where
the conclusion is a plausible one.   There could, for instance, be a temptation
to say that the establishment of a positive correlation between the incidence of
lung cancer and the number of cigarettes smoked proves that cigarette smoking

is a cause of the disease.   As you should now appreciate, it is not quite as simple as that and it is only after research into the effect of tobacco smoke on lung tissue, and so on, that a causal link is now considered to be established.

Rank Correlation

In illustrative examples you have seen the use of the correlation coefficient when applied to data concerning men's heights and weights, and amounts of chromium and nickel, all of which can be measured in well-defined units.   You cannot so easily measure the skill of a craftsman, or how nice (or nasty!) a cough medicine tastes, or how ill a hospital patient is.   In such cases it may, however, be feasible to assign an order of ranking, e.g. it can be said of a group of craftsmen who is the best, the next best, and so on, and different cough medicines can be listed in order of preference.   We shall now consider how to measure the correlation between two sets of ranks.   The following example will serve as an illustration:

Nine apprentices were given an intelligence test and were also ranked by their supervisor according to their job performance.   The results are given below.

Apprentice	A	B	C	D	E	F	G	H	I
Rank in test	4	2	6	8	1	9	7	5	3
Rank on job	5	1	6	7	4	8	9	3	2

The rank 1 is assigned to the apprentice with the highest rating, rank 2 to the next highest, and so on.   Thus on the basis of the intelligence test, E had the highest rating and F the lowest.   Who were rated highest and lowest on the basis of their performance on the job?

****

B highest,   G lowest.

The question now to be considered is whether there is any correlation between an apprentice's ability, as rated by the intelligence test, and his standard of job performance.   An answer could be obtained by treating the ranks in the same way as measured observations were treated, i.e. calculating a value of r, the product moment correlation coefficient for the sample.   We suggest you do this now.   Taking the ranking in the test as x and that on the job as y, you will probably find it easiest to calculate Σx, Σy, Σx^2, Σy^2 and Σxy, and then use (13.1)

****

$\Sigma x = \Sigma y = 45$ $\Sigma x^2 = \Sigma y^2 = 285$ $\Sigma xy = 274$ $r = 441/540 = 0 \cdot 816$

It will possibly have occurred to you that when the x's and y's are ranks there is something special about them.   For any 9 pairs of ranks, the values of x will always be 1, 2, ... 9, and the values of y always 1, 2, ... 9. More generally, if the number of pairs is n, the x-values will always be

FRAME 31   (continued)

1, 2, ...n and the y-values 1, 2, ...n.   From this it follows that the
product moment correlation coefficient takes a specially simple form when
applied to ranks.   This form expresses the coefficient in terms of the
difference in ranks for each pair and is known as SPEARMAN'S RANK CORRELATION
COEFFICIENT, having been introduced by C.E. Spearman, a British psychologist, in
1906.   Denoting it by r_s, and each difference in ranks by d, the formula is

$$r_s = 1 - \frac{6\Sigma d^2}{n(n^2 - 1)} \qquad (31.1)$$

If you would like to see the derivation of this formula you can find it in the
APPENDIX at the end of this programme.

The values of d and d^2 for the apprentice data are shown below (it does not
matter which way the difference is taken).

Apprentice	A	B	C	D	E	F	G	H	I
d	-1	1	0	1	-3	1	-2	2	1
d^2	1	1	0	1	9	1	4	4	1

$\Sigma d^2 = 22$ and $r_s = 1 - \frac{6 \times 22}{9 \times 80} = 0 \cdot 81\dot{6}$, as you found in 30A.

Now use (31.1) to find r_s for each of the following two sets of data, (i) and
(ii), that might have resulted from ranking the apprentices.

	Apprentice	A	B	C	D	E	F	G	H	I
(i)	Rank in test	1	2	3	4	5	6	7	8	9
	Rank on job	1	2	3	4	5	6	7	8	9
(ii)	Rank in test	1	2	3	4	5	6	7	8	9
	Rank on job	9	8	7	6	5	4	3	2	1

****

31A

(i) $r_s = 1$ *(ii)* $r_s = -1$ *Note that (i) represents complete agreement
and (ii) the other extreme, i.e. a complete reversal of ranking.*

FRAME 32

The sampling distribution of r_s is known and tables are available giving the
critical values for the usual significance levels.   This brings us to another
reason for using rank correlation.   You may remember that the distribution of r
itself, from which the critical values (e.g. those in TABLE 6) are determined,
is based on both variables in the data being normally distributed.   If such an
assumption cannot be made, then rank correlation is a distribution-free method
that can be used instead.   The data (in FRAME 26) on the amounts of chromium
and nickel in shale specimens will be used as an illustration.   Taking the
chromium amounts first, and assigning rank 1 to the lowest, 2 to the next
lowest, and so on, gives:

Specimen	A	B	C	D	E	F
Chromium	2	6	1	3	4	5

What are the corresponding ranks, found in this way, for the amounts of nickel?

****

	A	B	C	D	E	F
	2	6	1	4	3	5

FRAME 33

We could alternatively have assigned rank 1 to the highest, 2 to the next highest etc. - it doesn't matter, as long as the same procedure is adopted for both chromium and nickel.   If there is a "tie" as would, for example, be the case if D and E both had a chromium content of 230 p.p.m., the tied observations are given the mean of the ranks that they would otherwise take, i.e. D and E would each be given a rank of $(3 + 4)/2 = 3 \cdot 5$.   However, the derivation of (31.1) and of the sampling distribution of r_s are based on ties not occurring and the ensuing complications caused by ties will not be considered here.   No problem of this kind arises in the case of the data on shale specimens, so go ahead and calculate the value of r_s.

****

33A

$\Sigma d^2 = 2 \qquad r_s = 0 \cdot 943$

FRAME 34

Reference to a table of critical values for r_s shows that, for a sample size of 6, $0 \cdot 943$ is significant at the 5% level, but not at the 1%.   In this example, therefore, we have arrived at the same decision using r_s as was reached in answer frame 26A using r, but with much simpler calculations.   The two coefficients do not always lead to the same decision but it can be shown that r_s is 91% as effective as r in detecting a correlation which exists.

Even if the conditions for the use of r apply, the simpler calculations involved in r_s (as with other distribution-free methods) are in its favour as an alternative.   The same can be said of KENDALL'S RANK CORRELATION COEFFICIENT τ, named after M.G. Kendall who drew attention to it in 1938.   The method of calculating τ will not be given here but can be found in Siegel's Non-parametric Statistics (McGraw Hill).

FRAME 35

Miscellaneous Examples

In this frame a collection of miscellaneous examples is given for you to try. Answers are supplied in FRAME 36, together with such working as is considered helpful.

1. You have already seen that the value of a correlation coefficient is not affected by the units in which the two variables are measured.   Now, to investigate the effect of a change of origin, begin by subtracting, say, 200 from each of the chromium figures and 100 from each of the nickel figures in the data in FRAME 26.   Then find r for the new variables u and v, where u = x - 200 and v = y - 100, by writing down the values of $u - \bar{u}$ and $v - \bar{v}$ and hence calculating $\Sigma(u - \bar{u})^2$, $\Sigma(v - \bar{v})^2$ and $\Sigma(u - \bar{u})(v - \bar{v})$.   Then compare your working with that obtained in 26A and make a general conclusion about the effect of a change of origin.

FRAME 35   (continued)

2. The following data are taken from a study of the flow of traffic through a vehicular tunnel.   The figures are average values based on observations made during each of ten 5-minute intervals.

Density (vehicles/km)	43	55	40	52	39	33	50	33	44	21
Speed (km/h)	27·0	23·8	30·7	24·0	34·8	41·4	27·0	40·4	31·7	51·2

Draw a scatter diagram to represent the data.   The value of r in this case is one of the following: 0·968, -0·968, -0·198.   Which does the diagram suggest to you to be the correct one?   Check your answer by calculating r from the data.   Is there real evidence of an association between vehicle speed and density.

3. Eight drivers were given a written test to assess their knowledge on matters relevant to driving (meaning of road signs, etc.).   The table below shows the score each driver obtained in this test, together with the number of years of driving experience.

Number of years	2	5	4	9	23	15	30	16
Test score %	74	81	70	69	65	59	64	78

(i)   Calculate the value of the product moment correlation coefficient r given by this data and test it for significance.

(ii) Calculate the value of the rank correlation coefficient r_s obtained by first ranking the data.

4. In the 1975 finals of the BBC TV "Young Scientists of the Year" contest, the team from Aberdeen submitted a project in which possible links between drinking water and health were investigated.   Samples of tap water from major towns in the U.K. were obtained and analysed and, where available, data about deaths from various diseases in these towns were also collected. One aspect of the water that was considered was its acidity or alkalinity, as measured by its pH.   For 32 towns in England, the measurements (x) of pH gave, after making the change of origin $u = x - 7$ to reduce the size of numbers involved, $\Sigma u = 4·7$, $\Sigma u^2 = 3·63$.   For the same towns, standard mortality ratios were available for deaths from coronary disease. The standard mortality ratio takes into account not only the size of the population but also other factors such as the age structure and the proportion of males to females.   Denoting the values of this ratio for male and female coronary deaths by y and z respectively, then, with $v = y - 100$ and $w = z - 100$, the data gave $\Sigma v = 162$, $\Sigma v^2 = 6988$, $\Sigma w = 242$, $\Sigma w^2 = 12\ 258$, $\Sigma uv = -25·0$, $\Sigma uw = 3·3$, $\Sigma vw = 5290$.

Use the product moment correlation coefficient to decide whether there is evidence of an association between (i) male coronary deaths and pH, (ii) female coronary deaths and pH,   (iii) male and female coronary deaths.

At a later stage in this project, values of u, v and w for another 7 towns (Aberdeen, Belfast, Burnley, Dundee, Edinburgh, Glasgow and Londonderry) became available.   For these 7 towns, $\Sigma u = 0·4$, $\Sigma u^2 = 0·16$, $\Sigma v = 194$, $\Sigma v^2 = 5884$, $\Sigma w = 216$, $\Sigma w^2 = 8364$, $\Sigma uv = 7·1$, $\Sigma uw = 6·4$, $\Sigma vw = 6708$. If this data is now combined with that for the original 32 towns, what is the situation with regard to (i), (ii) and (iii) for all 39 towns?

5. In the project described in Qu. 4, the water samples were also analysed for Mg (magnesium) and K (potassium) content.   The data for the original 32 English towns give the following values of r: Between male coronary deaths and Mg, $-0 \cdot 149$; female coronary deaths and Mg, $-0 \cdot 141$; male coronary deaths and K, $-0 \cdot 240$;   female coronary deaths and K, $-0 \cdot 240$; pH and Mg, $0 \cdot 454$;   pH and K, $0 \cdot 514$;   Mg and K, $0 \cdot 621$.   Comment on the significance in each case.

6. In an investigation into a possible relationship between surface quality of an ingot and surface quality after being rolled into slabs, 12 ingots in a steel rolling mill were selected for inspection.   They were ranked for quality before and after rolling, with the following results:

Rank of ingot	1	2	3	4	5	6	7	8	9	10	11	12
Rank of slab	6	5	2	8	3	1	9	11	4	10	12	7

Find the rank correlation coefficient r_s.   The sample size here is large enough for the critical values of r to be used as an approximation for those of r_s.   Use this approximation to test the hypothesis of no correlation between the two surface qualities.

7.

x	1	2	2	2	3	4	4	5	5	6	7	7	7	8	8	9
y	9	16	15	17	21	24	25	25	26	24	21	19	22	16	15	9

The values of x and y represent, after coding, the age and the strength of grip, respectively, of 16 people.   Calculate r.   (The data is fictitious and has been devised to give simple arithmetic if (4.1) is used.) Then plot the points and explain why r shows no significant association between age and strength of grip.

8. FRAMES 14 - 19 gave some indication of how a value of r would be calculated from data given in the form of a bivariate frequency table.   The calculation of r for the data on heights and weights was not proceeded with at the time as the numbers involved would have been rather unwieldy.   Now that you have seen that neither a change of unit nor a change of origin affects the values of r , the calculations can be reduced to manageable proportions. Check the value $0 \cdot 627$, given for r in FRAME 19, by changing the variables to u and v, where $u = (x - 162)/5$ and $v = (y - 47 \cdot 95)/5$. Then use the equivalent of (13.1).   Don't forget that you will have to weight the various values of u, v, uv etc. by multiplying by the corresponding frequencies.   (If you can write computer programs you may find it a rewarding exercise to write one for calculating r from a bivariate frequency table and then test it with this data.)

9. If you have read "Nonparametric (Distribution-free) Tests" in Unit 2 you will be aware of the relative simplicity of the sampling distributions on which such methods are based.   The distribution of r_s is no exception.

For 3 pairs of observations the table shows all the possible ranks for an attribute B which could be paired with the ranks shown for an attribute A. If there is no correlation between A

A	Possible ranks for B					
1	1	1	2	2	3	3
2	2	3	3	1	1	2
3	3	2	1	3	2	1

FRAME 35   (continued)

and B, each set of pairs is as likely to occur as another.   For each of
the 6 possibilities calculate the value of r_s.   Hence obtain the

probability distribution of r_s.   The total number of possibilities here is

the number of ways of arranging 3 numbers and is therefore 3!.   How many
possibilities would have to be considered if the sample size was 4?

FRAME 36

Answers to Miscellaneous Examples

1.   r = 0·901.   The values of u − ū and v − v̄ are the same as those of
     x − x̄ and y − ȳ respectively.   Thus the change of origin does not affect
     the value of r.

2.   −0·968. Sig. at 0·1% level.

3.   (i) r = −0·542. Not sig. at 5% level, as |r| < 0·707.   A value of
     0·542, or less, for |r| could happen quite easily (the chance is more
     than 10%) if ρ = 0, so the data provides no real evidence of any general
     association between test score and driving experience. (ii) −0·524

4.   (i) −0·362. |r| > 0·349. Sig. at 5% level.   Note that this only indicates
     a tendency for coronary deaths to increase as pH decreases (i.e. the
     acidity is greater) and could suggest that it might be worthwhile following
     this up by medical research.   It does not in itself prove that low pH is
     a cause of coronary disease, but could support medical evidence that had
     been found for this.   (ii) −0·184. Not sig. at 5% level. (iii) 0·507.
     Sig. at 1% level.   The most likely explanation of this positive
     correlation is that factors contributing to coronary disease in men also
     contribute to it in women.   For all 39 towns: (i) −0·372, Sig. at 5%
     level, (ii) −0·230, Not sig. at 5% level,   (iii) 0·645, Sig. at 0·1%
     level.

5.   No real evidence of an association between coronary deaths and either Mg
     or K content as none of the values of r reaches the 5% sig. level.
     Both pH − Mg and pH − K correlation coefficients sig. at 1% level;
     this is what one would expect, as Mg and K are alkali metals and therefore
     the greater the quantity of them, the higher the pH.   Correlation between
     Mg and K sig. at 0·1% level;   also not surprising, as the concentration
     of both will be related to the solubility of rocks in the area.

6. r_s = 0·5 < 0·576.   Hypothesis not rejected at 5% level.   Note: The
     alternative hypothesis here covers either positive or negative correlation,
     i.e. the test is two-sided.   If the question had specified that you were to
     look only for evidence of agreement between the two rankings, the A.H. would
     be one of positive correlation and the test would be one-sided.   The 5%
     critical value given by TABLE 6 is then 0·497 and the exact value (given
     by a table of critical values of r_s) is 0·506, so you would still not
     have a good case for rejecting the N.H.

7.

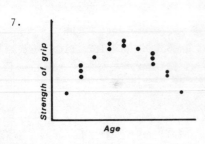

r = 0·029.   The reason why this does not show
an association is that r only measures <u>linear</u>
association.   Whilst strength of grip
increases with age at the beginning it declines
in later years.   The diagram suggests a
relationship between strength and age, but it
is not a linear one.

8. $r = \dfrac{50 \times 627 - 155 \times 177}{\sqrt{(50 \times 593 - 155^2)(50 \times 765 - 177^2)}} = 0·627$

9.   Values of r_s for 1st to 6th columns of B ranks:
1, 0·5, −0·5, 0·5, −0·5, −1.

r_s	−1	−0·5	0·5	1
Probability	1/6	1/3	1/3	1/6

4!,   i.e.   24.

APPENDIX

Derivation of the formula for Spearman's rank correlation coefficient

Two standard results from algebra that will be required are:

$$1 + 2 + 3 + \ldots + n = n(n + 1)/2 \tag{1}$$
$$1^2 + 2^2 + 3^2 + \ldots + n^2 = n(n + 1)(2n + 1)/6 \tag{2}$$

The formula for the product moment correlation coefficient is

$$r = \frac{\Sigma(x - \bar{x})(y - \bar{y})}{\sqrt{\Sigma(x - \bar{x})^2 \Sigma(y - \bar{y})^2}}$$

If the variables x and y are ranks, then they each take the values 1, 2, 3, ... n, in some order, n being the number of pairs of observations.

Hence, from (1), $\Sigma x = \Sigma y = n(n + 1)/2$ and $\bar{x} = \bar{y} = (n + 1)/2$
and from (2), $\Sigma x^2 = \Sigma y^2 = n(n + 1)(2n + 1)/6$

$$\therefore \quad \Sigma(x - \bar{x})^2 = \Sigma x^2 - n\bar{x}^2 = \frac{n(n + 1)(2n + 1)}{6} - \frac{n(n + 1)^2}{4} = \frac{n(n^2 - 1)}{12} \tag{3}$$

Similarly $\Sigma(y - \bar{y})^2 = n(n^2 - 1)/12$ \quad (4)

If the difference in ranks for a pair of observations is denoted by d,

$$d = x - y = (x - \bar{x}) - (y - \bar{y}), \text{ as } \bar{x} = \bar{y}$$
$$d^2 = (x - \bar{x})^2 - 2(x - \bar{x})(y - \bar{y}) + (y - \bar{y})^2$$
$$\Sigma d^2 = \Sigma(x - \bar{x})^2 - 2\Sigma(x - \bar{x})(y - \bar{y}) + \Sigma(y - \bar{y})^2$$
$$= \frac{n(n^2 - 1)}{12} - 2\Sigma(x - \bar{x})(y - \bar{y}) + \frac{n(n^2 - 1)}{12}$$

$$\Sigma(x - \bar{x})(y - \bar{y}) = \frac{n(n^2 - 1)}{12} - \frac{1}{2}\Sigma d^2 \tag{5}$$

Substituting (3), (4) and (5) in the formula for r leads to

$$r_s = \frac{\dfrac{n(n^2 - 1)}{12} - \dfrac{1}{2}\Sigma d^2}{\dfrac{n(n^2 - 1)}{12}} = 1 - \frac{6\Sigma d^2}{n(n^2 - 1)}$$

Regression

Introduction

The previous programme, on correlation, studied the question of whether an association between two variables exists, and if so, how closely they are interrelated and in which direction, i.e. whether the higher values of one variable tend to be associated with the higher or lower values of the other. In some situations this may be all that is required.   Take the case of a campaigner for the addition of fluoride to the water supply.   To make his point he may find it quite sufficient to establish a high negative correlation between the incidence of tooth decay among children and the fluoride concentration of their drinking water.   There are other situations, however, where it is not enough just to know that two variables are related but a knowledge of the relationship is required that can be used to estimate the value of one variable from a value of the other.   This would be useful if measurements of the property which is of interest either (i) involve a destructive test or (ii) are difficult to make.   As an example of (i), the direct measurement of the strength of a specimen of timber would result in its destruction but if, from previous tests on this type of timber, a relationship between strength and density has been derived, then the density of the specimen could be found and the strength estimated from it.   As an example of (ii), one property of a synthetic rubber that might be required is its resistance to abrasion. Measuring this by recording the loss in weight caused by abrasion, when subjected to a specified form of treatment, requires elaborate apparatus and is much more difficult than measuring hardness, which can be done quickly and easily.   A relationship between abrasion loss and hardness, if it can be found, would enable abrasion loss to be estimated from hardness.   In this programme we shall look at the relationship between two variables, where it exists, with a view to predicting values of one from values of the other.

Regression Lines

Diagrams (i) and (ii) in FRAME 2 on page 368 illustrate two possible forms of relationship.   In (ii) there is, in theory, a complete correlation between the two variables but observed values show deviations from this because of errors in measurement.   In such a situation let us make the assumption (a not unreasonable one) that one variable, x, can be measured with negligible error but that errors are unavoidable in the other variable, y.   If the measurement of y is without bias (i.e. no systematic error is involved) then, if you imagine an infinite number of measurements of y being recorded for a particular value of x, you will have a population whose mean is the true value of y for that x.   The plot of such means for various values of x will then represent the functional relationship between y and x.

The other diagram, (i), provides an illustration of some degree of correlation existing between two variables without their being functionally related. However, the idea of a mean value of y for each value of x is still applicable.   If y is the weight of a man of height x, for instance, and we look at the mean weight of all men of the same height x, for each of a number of values of x, the plot of these means will show the general tendency for tall men to weigh more than short ones.

FRAME 2   (continued)

The following diagrams may help to explain the idea being put forward in this
frame.   A little imagination on your part will be required in their
interpretation as it is not possible to show an infinite number of points for
each value of x.   The points with circles round them are the means.

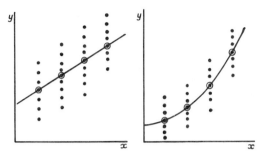

Where a functional relationship
exists between y and x, the
variation of the y-observations
about each mean would be caused
solely by measurement errors.
Where it does not, the presence of
other chance effects would also
contribute to this variation.

The simplest case occurs when, as
in the left-hand diagram, the
y-means lie on a straight line,
called the LINE OF REGRESSION OF
y ON x.   Obviously the true line can exist only in theory, as we will
never have an infinite number of observations at our disposal.   How the line
can best be estimated from a limited number of observations will now be
described.   (The situation depicted in the right-hand diagram, where the y-means
lie on a curve, will be dealt with later on.)

FRAME 3

Let us suppose that there are n pairs of observations (x_1, y_1), (x_2, y_2), ...
(x_n, y_n) in which the values of y are those of a random variable, whether
because of measurement error or other chance causes.   The equation of the line
of regression of y on x will be of the form $y = \alpha + \beta x$.   The coefficient β
is called the REGRESSION COEFFICIENT.   The problem is how the values of α
and β can best be estimated from the data.   In this course, the properties
desirable in an estimator have only been touched on, as, for example, when
discussing a requirement that a variance estimate be unbiased.   Suffice to say
that, in the present problem, estimators with good properties are provided by
the METHOD OF LEAST SQUARES.   You are, in fact, already familiar with an
estimator which satisfies the least squares criterion.   To see if you remember
this feature of it, can you state what value of a makes

$$\sum_{i=1}^{n} (x_i - a)^2, \quad \text{i.e.} \quad (x_1 - a)^2 + (x_2 - a)^2 + \dots + (x_n - a)^2 \qquad (3.1)$$

a minimum?

****

3A

*$a = \bar{x}$, where $\bar{x} = (x_1 + x_2 + \dots + x_n)/n$.   This property of the arithmetic
mean was shown in FRAMES 26 and 27 on page 16 of Unit 1.*

FRAME 4

Thus if x_1, x_2, ... x_n are the results of making n repeat measurements of a
quantity, we are, in using their mean $\bar{x}$ as an estimate of that quantity, using
a value for which the sum of the squares of the deviations of the observed
values from it is least.   In Unit 1 this property of $\bar{x}$ was derived

algebraically.   Its derivation using differentiation will now be a useful
exercise.   Denoting the sum (3.1) by S and then considering it varying as a
varies, its minimum value will occur when $\dfrac{dS}{da} = 0$.   Write down $\dfrac{dS}{da}$ and by
equating it to zero, deduce the value of a that makes S a minimum.

****

4A

$$\frac{dS}{da} = -2(x_1 - a) - 2(x_2 - a) - \ldots - 2(x_n - a)$$

$$\frac{dS}{da} = 0 \quad gives \quad (x_1 - a) + (x_2 - a) + \ldots + (x_n - a) = 0$$

$$i.e. \quad x_1 + x_2 + \ldots + x_n - na = 0$$

$$whence \quad a = \frac{x_1 + x_2 + \ldots + x_n}{n} = \bar{x}$$

Obviously it is possible to choose a so that S can be as large as you wish.
Thus $\dfrac{dS}{da} = 0$ evidently gives a minimum rather than a maximum.   This can also
be confirmed by showing $\dfrac{d^2S}{da^2}$ to be positive.

FRAME 5

In a similar way the method of least squares leads to estimates of α and β

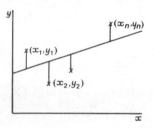

when the equation of the regression line is being
sought.   Here it involves minimising S, where S is
the sum of the squares of the deviations of the
observed y's from the corresponding y-estimates
given by the line.   These deviations are represented
by the vertical lines drawn from the points to the
line in the diagram.   For a line whose equation is
$y = a + bx$,   state the values of y given by the line
for $x = x_1, x_2, \ldots x_n$ respectively.   Deduce an
expression for S.

****

5A

$$a + bx_1, \quad a + bx_2, \quad \ldots, \quad a + bx_n$$

$S = (y_1 - a - bx_1)^2 + (y_2 - a - bx_2)^2 + \ldots + (y_n - a - bx_n)^2$, *which you*

could also have written as $\displaystyle\sum_{i=1}^{n} (y_i - a - bx_i)^2$.

FRAME 6

Different lines are represented by different values of a and/or b.   Varying a
moves the line bodily upwards or downwards and varying b alters the slope of the
line so that it effectively rotates.   The values of a and b that will be used
as estimates of α and β are those which make S a minimum.   In FRAME 4, where
the sum S to be minimised was a function of only one variable, a, the

FRAME 6   (continued)

necessary condition was $\frac{dS}{da} = 0$.   Now, with S a function of two variables, a

and b, the corresponding requirement is that $\frac{\partial S}{\partial a}$ and $\frac{\partial S}{\partial b}$ should both be zero.

As a first step, find $\frac{\partial S}{\partial a}$ and $\frac{\partial S}{\partial b}$.   (The partial differential coefficient $\frac{\partial S}{\partial a}$

is found by differentiating S with respect to a, treating b as constant.

Similarly $\frac{\partial S}{\partial b}$ is found by differentiating S with respect to b, treating a as

constant.)

****

6A

$\frac{\partial S}{\partial a} = -2(y_1 - a - bx_1) - 2(y_2 - a - bx_2) - \ldots - 2(y_n - a - bx_n)$

which you could also have written as $-2 \sum\limits_{i=1}^{n} (y_i - a - bx_i)$

$\frac{\partial S}{\partial b} = -2x_1(y_1 - a - bx_1) - 2x_2(y_2 - a - bx_2) - \ldots - 2x_n(y_n - a - bx_n)$

or $-2 \sum\limits_{i=1}^{n} x_i(y_i - a - bx_i)$

FRAME 7

Putting $\frac{\partial S}{\partial a} = 0$ gives $(y_1 - a - bx_1) + (y_2 - a - bx_2) + \ldots + (y_n - a - bx_n) = 0$

which may be rearranged as $(y_1 + y_2 + \ldots + y_n) - na - (x_1 + x_2 + \ldots + x_n)b = 0$

or $na + (x_1 + x_2 + \ldots + x_n)b = y_1 + y_2 + \ldots + y_n$

Using Σ notation, the more compact form of this is

$$na + \left(\sum_{i=1}^{n} x_i \right) b = \sum_{i=1}^{n} y_i \qquad (7.1)$$

Putting $\frac{\partial S}{\partial b} = 0$ gives

$$x_1(y_1 - a - bx_1) + x_2(y_2 - a - bx_2) + \ldots + x_n(y_n - a - bx_n) = 0$$

Check that, with the change to Σ notation and some rearrangement, this equation

becomes $\left(\sum_{i=1}^{n} x_i \right) a + \left(\sum_{i=1}^{n} x_i^2 \right) b = \sum_{i=1}^{n} x_i y_i \qquad (7.2)$

****

7A

$x_1 y_1 + x_2 y_2 + \ldots + x_n y_n - (x_1 + x_2 + \ldots + x_n)a - (x_1^2 + x_2^2 + \ldots + x_n^2)b = 0$

i.e. $(x_1 + x_2 + \ldots + x_n)a + (x_1^2 + x_2^2 + \ldots + x_n^2)b = x_1 y_1 + x_2 y_2 + \ldots + x_n y_n$

which, with the introduction of Σ notation, becomes (7.2).

(7.1) and (7.2) are two simultaneous equations in a and b, called the NORMAL
EQUATIONS.   The suffix notation is only necessary in order to define the sums
exactly and may be dropped, if you prefer, once it is understood what terms are
to be added.   The equations can then be written

$$na + (\Sigma x)b = \Sigma y \qquad (8.1)$$
$$(\Sigma x)a + (\Sigma x^2)b = \Sigma xy \qquad (8.2)$$

Solving for b gives $b = \dfrac{n\Sigma xy - \Sigma x \Sigma y}{n \Sigma x^2 - (\Sigma x)^2}$

$$= \frac{\Sigma xy - (\Sigma x \Sigma y)/n}{\Sigma x^2 - (\Sigma x)^2/n} \qquad (8.3)$$

Now from (12.1) on page 374 you know that the numerator is $\Sigma(x - \bar{x})(y - \bar{y})$
and you should, by this time, recognise the denominator as $\Sigma(x - \bar{x})^2$.

Thus (8.3) is, alternatively, $b = \dfrac{\Sigma(x - \bar{x})(y - \bar{y})}{\Sigma(x - \bar{x})^2}$ (8.4)

As these Σ's occur quite often in correlation and regression analysis, it is
convenient to use the abbreviated forms of notation:

$$S_{xx} = \Sigma(x - \bar{x})^2 \qquad \text{and} \qquad S_{xy} = \Sigma(x - \bar{x})(y - \bar{y})$$

Then (8.4) can be written as $b = \dfrac{S_{xy}}{S_{xx}}$ (8.5)

There is a certain logic behind this notation and you can probably guess what
will be used for $\Sigma(y - \bar{y})^2$ when it is required.

****

$S_{yy} = \Sigma(y - \bar{y})^2$

Dividing both sides of (8.1) by n gives $a + \dfrac{1}{n}(\Sigma x)b = \dfrac{1}{n}\Sigma y$

i.e. $a + b\bar{x} = \bar{y}$ (9.1)

where $\bar{x}$ and $\bar{y}$ are the means of the x- and y-observations respectively.

Thus $a = \bar{y} - b\bar{x}$ (9.2)

from which a can be calculated when b has been found.

Now look at (9.1).   It tells you that the line must pass through a particular
point.   What point is that?

****

$(\bar{x}, \bar{y})$

Substituting $\bar{y} - b\bar{x}$ for a in $y = a + bx$ gives the equation of the line as

$$y = \bar{y} - b\bar{x} + bx$$

i.e. $y - \bar{y} = b(x - \bar{x})$ (10.1)

If you are familiar with the forms of equation for a straight line you will
recognise this as that of a line with slope b, passing through the point
$(\bar{x}, \bar{y})$. The equation of the estimated line of regression of y on x is
sometimes more conveniently quoted in this form. It is, for instance,
pertinent to how the term "regression" came to be introduced by Sir Francis
Galton, a leading pioneer of statistical thought, in connection with the
inheritance of stature. Suppose that, in data on the heights of father and
son, x is the height of father and y the height of son, and that b, the
regression coefficient of y on x, is less than 1. Then consider fathers
who are, say, 5 cm taller than the average father. Will the mean height of
their sons be (i) 5 cm above the mean height $\bar{y}$ of all sons, (ii) more than 5 cm
above $\bar{y}$ or (iii) less than 5 cm above $\bar{y}$?

****

10A

$x - \bar{x} = 5$ *gives* $y - \bar{y} = 5b < 5$. *Hence (iii) is correct.*

*(The ordinary dictionary definition of "regression" is "backward movement or
reversion". The point made by Galton was that the line showing how height of
offspring tended to increase with height of parent had a slope less than 1.
Thus, on the whole, the offspring differed less from the norm than did their
parents and this he called 'a regression to mediocrity'.)*

FRAME 11

Having explained the basis on which the equation of a regression line is
estimated, we can now proceed to some numerical examples.

The amount of potassium bromide (KBr) that would dissolve in 100 g of water was
recorded for various temperatures, with the following results:

Temperature (°C)	0	10	20	30	40	50
Amount of KBr (g)	54	59	64	73	76	82

As you might guess from a quick glance at this data, the levels of temperature
were selected by the experimenter. With the temperature of the water
maintained at the selected level, the amount of KBr that would dissolve in it
was then determined. Under those circumstances, the values of temperature
could be considered relatively free from error but not so the KBr measurements.
Over the range of temperatures covered by the experiment, the relationship
between temperature and amount of KBr can be assumed linear. Thus, if y grams
is the amount of KBr that will dissolve at x°C, there is a straight line
relationship between y and x. We are going to form an estimate of that
relationship.

In this experiment, x is the controlled variable, free from error, and the
observations of y are subject to random variation caused by errors of
measurement. Therefore the regression line
of y on x, i.e. of amount of KBr on
temperature, is the line for which an estimate
is needed. To find values of a and b such
that $y = a + bx$ is the least squares estimate,
the sums Σx, Σy, Σx^2 and Σxy are needed.
The calculations are set out on the left. By
reference to (8.1) and (8.2), write down the
normal equations in a and b.

x	y	x^2	xy
0	54	0	0
10	59	100	590
20	64	400	1280
30	73	900	2190
40	76	1600	3040
50	82	2500	4100
150	408	5500	11200

****

$6a + 150b = 408, \qquad 150a + 5500b = 11\,200$

You can then either solve these equations for a and b, or, substituting in (8.3), get

$$b = \frac{11\,200 - 150 \times 408/6}{5500 - 150^2/6} = \frac{1000}{1750} = \frac{4}{7}$$

This represents the increase in the amount of KBr that will go into solution, per 1°C rise in temperature.

As $\bar{x} = 25$ and $\bar{y} = 68$, the estimated regression line is

$$y - 68 = \frac{4}{7}(x - 25)$$

$$\text{i.e.} \quad y = \frac{376}{7} + \frac{4}{7}x \tag{12.1}$$

Taking this as an estimate of the functional relationship between amount of KBr and temperature, how much KBr do you predict will dissolve in 100 g of water at 25°C?

****

Substituting $x = 25$ *in (12.1) gives* $y = 68$, *i.e.* *68 g of KBr.*

Note that 25°C is within the range of temperature over which the line is fitted.   There is no claim that (12.1) will predict amounts of KBr corresponding to any temperature and, in fact, solubility does not continue indefinitely to increase at a uniform rate as temperature increases.   The fact that a relationship can be taken as linear over a given range of values of the variables does not necessarily mean that it can be assumed linear over all values.   As a general rule it is unwise to extrapolate beyond the range for which data are available.

The data providing the next illustration resulted from recording the number of cars leaving a large town by a main road to the coast on each of 10 randomly chosen Sundays.   The observations were made at a checkpoint on the road during a fixed time interval and, to keep the numbers simple, are given here to the nearest 1000.   Also shown is the temperature recorded in the town earlier in the day.

Temperature (°C) at 8 a.m.	13	16	9	10	18	23	19	27	15	10
Number of cars (thousands)	18	19	9	12	21	25	26	30	24	14

This example has two features which were not present in the previous one. Firstly, with the KBr experiment, the values of one variable (temperature) were controlled and only the amount of KBr recorded was subject to random variation (ascribed to errors of measurement).   In the present case, neither variable has had its values chosen.   Nor is the variation mainly due to errors of

FRAME 14   (continued)
measurement.   The error in reading the temperature, for instance, would be negligible compared with the differences in temperature that occur from Sunday to Sunday.

Secondly, nobody would seriously entertain the idea of a functional relationship between the temperature and the number of cars.   It is, however, well known that as temperatures soar people tend to flock to the coast and, as you may like to check for yourself, a scatter diagram of the present data shows a clear tendency for traffic to increase with temperature.   If this trend is a linear one, the regression line of number of cars on temperature could be useful in making some prediction about the exodus of cars that may be expected when the temperature at 8 a.m. is known.   Denoting temperature by x and number of cars by y, find Σx, Σy, Σx^2, Σxy, S_{xx} and S_{xy}.   Hence estimate the line of regression of y on x.

****

14A

$\Sigma x = 160$ $\Sigma y = 198$ $\Sigma x^2 = 2874$ $\Sigma xy = 3496$ $S_{xx} = 314$ $S_{xy} = 328$

$$y - 19 \cdot 8 = \frac{328}{314} (x - 16 \cdot 0)   \quad i.e. \quad   y = 3 \cdot 09 + 1 \cdot 04x$$

FRAME 15

If the assumption of a linear trend is correct, the regression line that you have just estimated would give the mean number of cars leaving the town on Sundays when the temperature is $x^{\circ}C$ at 8 a.m.   Thus, although the lack of a complete functional relationship means that we cannot say, having read the temperature at 8 a.m., just how many cars will leave town, we can at least say what number may be expected on average.   By how many thousands of cars is this average outflux higher, for every $1^{\circ}C$ that the temperature at 8 a.m. is higher?   How do you explain the negative value for y when x = -3 is substituted?

****

15A

1·04, over the range of temperature for which the regression line is valid. That proviso is the key to the answer to the second question.   A negative y could hardly mean that people start rushing into the town when the temperature is low enough!   It just shows how unwise it can be to apply the regression line outside the range of values in the data on which it was based.

FRAME 16

The data now shown was obtained by recording the height and weight of each of 20 randomly chosen men.

Height (cm)	180	181	179	165	188	178	183	170	184	182
Weight (kg)	54·4	66·8	68·0	67·1	76·2	64·9	72·6	59·0	68·1	59·0

Height (cm)	168	169	175	173	163	168	181	187	180	166
Weight (kg)	67·1	49·0	65·3	68·0	57·2	63·5	69·9	78·0	76·2	53·7

If x denotes height and y weight, then $\Sigma x = 3520$ $\Sigma y = 1304 \cdot 0$
$\Sigma x^2 = 620\ 642$ $\Sigma y^2 = 86\ 192 \cdot 56$ $\Sigma xy = 230\ 193 \cdot 3$

Clearly, as in the previous example, neither variable took controlled values and
we are not dealing with variables that are functionally related.   However, as
has been said before, taller men tend to weigh more than shorter ones.   If this
trend is linear, the regression line of weight on height, i.e. of y on x,
would give the mean weight of men of height x.   Write down an expression (no
need to evaluate it) for b, the estimate of the regression coefficient.

****

16A

$$b = \frac{230\ 193 \cdot 3 - 3520 \times 1304/20}{620\ 642 - 3520^2/20} \quad \textit{(which simplifies to} \quad \frac{689 \cdot 3}{1122} \text{)}$$

FRAME 17

As $\bar{x} = 176$ and $\bar{y} = 65 \cdot 2$, the estimated regression line equation may be
written as $y - 65 \cdot 2 = \dfrac{689 \cdot 3}{1122} (x - 176)$ which simplifies to

$$y = -42 \cdot 93 + 0 \cdot 614x \qquad\qquad (17.1)$$

This predicts mean weight for men of given height.   If you look at the data in
the previous frame you will see that there were two men of height 180 cm.   For
each man, say whether, according to (17.1), he is above or below average weight
for his height.

****

17A

*(17.1) gives 67·6 kg as the average weight of men of height 180 cm.   Thus the
man weighing 54·4 kg is below average weight for his height and the other above.*

FRAME 18

Now we could also look at the relationship between weight and height from
another point of view.   Instead of considering how mean weight increases with
height, we could consider how mean height
increases with weight.   That would be given
by the line of regression of height on
weight, i.e. of x on y.   An estimate of
this line having been found, it could then
be used to predict the mean height of men of
given weight.

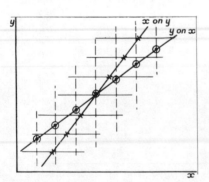

The diagram on the left may help you to
distinguish between what the two regression
lines represent.   Each circled point is the
mean of the y-distribution (depicted by a
vertical broken line) for that particular x.
Each cross is the mean of the x-distribution
(depicted by a horizontal line) for that
particular y.

Taking the equation of the line of regression of x on y to be of the form
$x = \alpha' + \beta'y$, least squares estimates a' and b' of α' and β' respectively
can be found by following a similar procedure to that used in FRAMES 5-10 to
obtain values for a and b.   It is just a matter of interchanging x and y in
the previous procedure.   Then it was the sum of the squares of the deviations
of the observed y's from the corresponding y-estimates given by the line, i.e.

$\sum_{i=1}^{n} (y_i - a - bx_i)^2$, that was minimised.   Now it will be the sum of the

squares of the deviations of the observed x's from the corresponding

x-estimates given by the line, i.e. $\sum_{i=1}^{n} (x_i - a' - b'y_i)^2$ that must be

minimised.   The diagrams may help to make this clear.

Sum of squares
of vertical
deviations
minimised to
give line of
regression of
y on x.

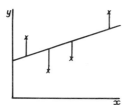

Sum of squares
of horizontal
deviations
minimised to
give line of
regression of
x on y.

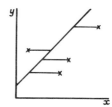

From (8.3), (8.4) and (8.5) you should be able to write down the corresponding
formulae for b' and, from (9.2), that for a'.   What equation now corresponds
to (9.1) and through what point does it tell you that the line $x = a' + b'y$
passes?

****

$b' = \dfrac{\Sigma xy - \Sigma x \Sigma y/n}{\Sigma y^2 - (\Sigma y)^2/n} = \dfrac{\Sigma (x - \bar{x})(y - \bar{y})}{\Sigma (y - \bar{y})^2} = \dfrac{S_{xy}}{S_{yy}}$

$a' = \bar{x} - b'\bar{y}$

$a' + b'\bar{y} = \bar{x}.$ *Hence the line passes through* $(\bar{x}, \bar{y}).$

The estimated regression line equation, in the form corresponding to (10.1), is
now readily seen to be $x - \bar{x} = b'(y - \bar{y})$ (20.1)

Note also that as both regression lines have been found to pass through $(\bar{x}, \bar{y})$,
this must be their point of intersection.

Now write down, without necessarily evaluating it, an expression for b' when
it is the estimate of the regression coefficient of height on weight obtained
from the data in FRAME 16.

****

$b' = \dfrac{230\ 193 \cdot 3 - 3520 \times 1304/20}{86\ 192 \cdot 56 - 1304^2/20}$ *(which simplifies to* $\dfrac{689 \cdot 3}{1171 \cdot 76}$)

For the regression line of height on weight, the estimated equation is

$$x - 176 = \frac{689 \cdot 3}{1171 \cdot 76} (y - 65 \cdot 2)$$

$$\text{i.e. } x = 137 \cdot 6 + 0 \cdot 588y \qquad\qquad (21.1)$$

Is this simply (17.1) re-expressed with x given in terms of y?

****

No. $y = -42 \cdot 93 + 0 \cdot 614x$ *would give* $x = 69 \cdot 9 + 1 \cdot 63y$

It is not surprising that (17.1) and (21.1) are two different lines as they are estimates of lines based on two different concepts and were obtained by minimising two different sums of squares.   (17.1) is an estimate of $y = \alpha + \beta x$, which gives the mean weight of men of height x whereas (21.1) is an estimate of $x = \alpha' + \beta'y$, which gives the mean height of men of weight y.

Now find (i) the line of regression of y on x, (ii) the line of regression of x on y, for the following set of values of x and y.

x	0	6	4	16	22	12	8	14	26
y	13	10	11	5	2	7	9	6	0

What do you notice about the two lines in this case?

****

(i) $y - 7 = \dfrac{-288}{576} (x - 12)$ *or* $y = 13 - 0 \cdot 5x$

(ii) $x - 12 = \dfrac{-288}{144} (y - 7)$ *or* $x = 26 - 2y$

The two lines are the same.

The pairs of values of x and y in the preceding frame are, though written down in different order, the same as those given at the end of FRAME 5 on page 370.   There you found that they gave a correlation coefficient of -1.   It was also noted that they were connected by a linear functional relationship, all points lying on the straight line $y = 13 - 0 \cdot 5x$. Thus, in this particular case, the two regression lines coincide with the line representing the relationship.   You would find the same thing to be true of the pairs of values of x and y given at the beginning of FRAME 5 on page 370 – you may care to check that both (10.1) and (20.1) give the line $y = x/2$ (it can be done quite quickly as the values of b and b' can be written down immediately from the calculations shown for the correlation).

Taking now the general regression lines (10.1) and (20.1), the latter can be written as $y - \overline{y} = \dfrac{1}{b'}(x - \overline{x})$.   This will be the same line as $y - \overline{y} = b(x - \overline{x})$ if $bb' = \ldots\ldots$ Can you fill the gap?

****

b = 1/b' gives bb' = 1.

As $b = \dfrac{\Sigma(x - \bar{x})(y - \bar{y})}{\Sigma(x - \bar{x})^2}$ and $b' = \dfrac{\Sigma(x - \bar{x})(y - \bar{y})}{\Sigma(y - \bar{y})^2}$, this condition can be

written as

$$\dfrac{\{\Sigma(x - \bar{x})(y - \bar{y})\}^2}{\Sigma(x - \bar{x})^2 \Sigma(y - \bar{y})^2} = 1$$

$$\text{i.e.} \qquad r^2 = 1$$

Thus as $r = \pm 1$ means a linear functional relationship, the two regression
lines will coincide when this type of relationship exists.

At the other extreme, you have seen in the programme on correlation that when
two variables are completely unrelated, the correlation coefficient is zero.
The pairs of values of x and y in (i) in FRAME 9 on page 372 gave $r = 0$.
Making use of the calculations already done there, find b and b' and hence
write down the equations of the two regression lines.

****

As $\Sigma(x - \bar{x})(y - \bar{y}) = 0$, $b = 0$ and $b' = 0$

Line of regression of y on x: $y - \bar{y} = 0$ i.e. $y = \bar{y}$
Line of regression of x on y: $x - \bar{x} = 0$ i.e. $x = \bar{x}$

The equations that you have just obtained could have been anticipated by
reasoning thus.   If y-values and x-values are quite unrelated, the y's for
one x will have the same mean as for any other x.   Hence the line of
regression of y on x, on which all these means lie, will be the line $y = \bar{y}$.
A similar argument leads to the equation $x = \bar{x}$ for the other regression line.
The following diagrams summarise the conclusions reached in the last few frames,
linking regression lines with linear correlation.

   (1) Line of regression   (2) Line of regression
       of y on x   of x on y

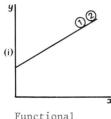
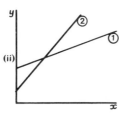
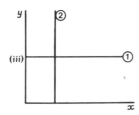

    Functional   Some degree of   No correlation
    relationship   correlation
    Complete correlation

State the coordinates of the point of intersection of the two regression lines
in (ii) and (iii).

****

In both (ii) and (iii) it is $(\overline{x}, \overline{y})$.

(Note that the line in (i) also passes through $(\overline{x}, \overline{y})$.)

Although the concept of two regression lines exists, it is usually only one that
can be used or is relevant in any particular problem.   In the case of the KBr
data in FRAME 11, where a functional relationship was involved, the values of
the temperature (x) had been carefully controlled and it was the amount (y) of
KBr that was subject to random variation (due to error).   Therefore the line
of regression of y on x was used to estimate the relationship.   Had it been
practicable to select different amounts of KBr and then observe the temperature
required for each to dissolve in 100 g of water, with y then the controlled
variable relatively free from error, the line of regression of x on y would
have been used.   In the case of the data on traffic leaving the town, a
functional relationship was not involved.   Neither variable took preselected
values and either regression line could have been estimated.   However, it is
obviously traffic density that is dependent on temperature, not the reverse,
and finding the line of regression of number of cars on temperature enables us
to make some predictions about the Sunday traffic flow when the temperature at
8 a.m. is known.   One cannot envisage a use for the other regression line –
who would want to estimate the temperature at 8 a.m. from traffic counts made
later in the day?

Underlying Assumptions and Model

In regression, as elsewhere in this course, due consideration must be given to
the risks involved in basing conclusions about a population on a sample taken
from it.   It may be necessary to test a hypothesis about the population or to
place confidence limits on an estimate.   To do this we shall need to be aware
of the model and assumptions on which the procedures used have been based and to
make further assumptions.   In considering the line of regression of y on x it
has been assumed that, for any given x_i, the corresponding y_i is a random

variable, the mean of whose distribution is $\alpha + \beta x_i$.   Thus we may write

$$y_i = \alpha + \beta x_i + e_i \qquad\qquad (27.1)$$

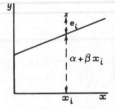

Where a functional relationship exists, e_i represents the
error in an observation;   in other cases it represents the
effects, apart from that due to x_i, that influence the
value of y_i.

For each x_i, what is the mean of the distribution of e_i,
i.e. what is the expected value of e_i?

****

As the mean of the y_i's is $\alpha + \beta x_i$, the mean of the e_i's must be zero.

In this text, to avoid complications, it is assumed that the variance of the distribution is the same for all x_i. This would mean, for instance, that the precision in measuring the amount of KBr that will dissolve in 100 g of water is the same for all temperatures at which observations were made. In the case of men's heights and weights, it would mean that the distribution of the weights of men of height 170 cm has the same variance as the distribution of the weights of men of height 180 cm. If $var(e_i) = \sigma^2$, what is $var(y_i)$?

****

28A

We are here considering the variation of y_i for a given x_i. Hence, in the present context, $y_i = constant + e_i$ and $var(y_i) = var(e_i) = \sigma^2$.

To proceed to finding confidence limits or making tests of significance, it will be necessary to know not only the mean and variance of the distribution of e_i but

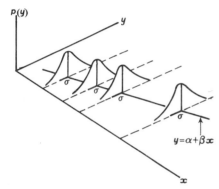

also the appropriate probability model. This will be assumed normal and therefore e_i will be $N(0, \sigma^2)$. The diagram attempts to portray the various distributions of y-observations that will correspond to different x_i's.

The linear regression model has been described here in terms of the regression of y on x. Obviously you will see that, with x and y interchanged, what has been said can be applied to the regression of x on y.

Analysis of Variance for Linear Regression

The model (27.1) takes account of two contributions to the variation in the y-values – the effect of the x-value and the residual variation that occurs for a given x-value. If x and y are not related at all, the first contribution is absent, i.e. $\beta = 0$, and the regression line of y on x is parallel to the x-axis. The only variation that then occurs is due to the second contribution, represented in (27.1) by e_i. Now, when the value of β is being estimated from a sample of, say, n data points, it is quite possible to get a non-zero value for the estimate b when, in the population from which the sample is taken, $\beta = 0$. That is, the data points may appear to suggest that x and y are related though, in fact, they aren't. You may care to refer back to FRAME 21 on page 377, where the diagrams illustrate the same problem that occurred in interpreting a value of r, it being possible to get a non-zero value for r when the sample is taken from a population in which $\rho = 0$. That showed how there could be a need for testing the hypothesis $\rho = 0$, just as

now there could be a need for testing the hypothesis $\beta = 0$.   This can be done
by analysing the variation in the y-values, along the lines now described.

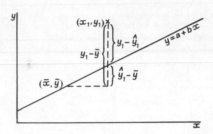

The diagram shows one of the data points,
(x_1, y_1) .   The notation $\hat{y}_1$ will be used
to denote the value of y, corresponding
to x = x_1 , given by the estimated
regression line.   Thus, $\hat{y}_1 - \overline{y} = b(?)$.
What expression should be contained in the
brackets?

****

30A

$x_1 - \overline{x},$ as $\hat{y}_1 - \overline{y} = b(x_1 - \overline{x})$ (30A.1)

Now, looking at the deviation of y_1 from the mean $\overline{y}$, it can be seen that it is
composed of two parts: $\hat{y}_1 - \overline{y}$, which is explained by the regression, and
$y_1 - \hat{y}_1$, which is the residual difference left unaccounted for by the
regression,

i.e. $y_1 - \overline{y}$ = $\hat{y}_1 - \overline{y}$ + $y_1 - \hat{y}_1$ (31.1)

TOTAL	DEVIATION	RESIDUAL
DEVIATION	FROM MEAN	DEVIATION
FROM MEAN	EXPLAINED BY	
	REGRESSION	

This may remind you of the partitioning of the deviation from a mean that
occurred in the "Analysis of Variance" programme.   The analysis of variance
approach is now going to be used here.   First, (31.1) can be rewritten

$y_1 - \hat{y}_1 = y_1 - \overline{y} - (\hat{y}_1 - \overline{y})$

and then, substituting from (30A.1), as

$y_1 - \hat{y}_1 = y_1 - \overline{y} - b(x_1 - \overline{x})$

Squaring both sides gives

$(y_1 - \hat{y}_1)^2 = (y_1 - \overline{y})^2 - 2b(x_1 - \overline{x})(y_1 - \overline{y}) + b^2(x_1 - \overline{x})^2$

Summing over all data points leads to

$$\sum_{i=1}^{n} (y_i - \hat{y}_i)^2 = \sum_{i=1}^{n} (y_i - \overline{y})^2 - 2b \sum_{i=1}^{n} (x_i - \overline{x})(y_i - \overline{y}) + b^2 \sum_{i=1}^{n} (x_i - \overline{x})^2$$

or, dropping suffixes,

$\Sigma(y - \hat{y})^2 = \Sigma(y - \overline{y})^2 - 2b\Sigma(x - \overline{x})(y - \overline{y}) + b^2\Sigma(x - \overline{x})^2$ (31.2)

Now, $\Sigma(x - \overline{x})(y - \overline{y})$ can be expressed in terms of b and $\Sigma(x - \overline{x})^2$.   Perhaps
you can do so straight away.   If not, refer back to (8.4).

****

$$\Sigma (x - \overline{x})(y - \overline{y}) = b\Sigma (x - \overline{x})^2$$

Substituting in (31.2) then leads to

$$\begin{aligned}
\Sigma (y - \hat{y})^2 &= \Sigma (y - \overline{y})^2 - 2b^2\Sigma (x - \overline{x})^2 + b^2\Sigma (x - \overline{x})^2 \\
&= \Sigma (y - \overline{y})^2 - b^2\Sigma (x - \overline{x})^2 \\
&= \Sigma (y - \overline{y})^2 - \Sigma (\hat{y} - \overline{y})^2 \quad \text{as a consequence of (30A.1)}
\end{aligned}$$

Rearranging, $\Sigma (y - \overline{y})^2 \quad = \qquad \Sigma (\hat{y} - \overline{y})^2 \qquad + \qquad \Sigma (y - \hat{y})^2$ (32.1)

TOTAL SUM	SUM OF SQUARES	RESIDUAL
OF SQUARES	DUE TO REGRESSION	SUM OF SQUARES

Thus the total variation in y, as represented by the sum of squares, can be divided into two parts, one attributable to the straight line regression and the other to deviations from this line.   The following questions will test your grasp of what these parts represent.

(i)   If all the data points lie exactly on a straight line as, for instance, was the case with the data given in FRAME 22, what will be the value of $\Sigma (y - \hat{y})^2$?

(ii)   If the line of regression of y on x has equation $y = \overline{y}$, as you found to be the case with the data referred to in FRAME 24, what is the value of $\Sigma (\hat{y} - \overline{y})^2$?

****

(i)   0   (Thus the regression explains the whole of the variation.)   (ii)   0

The residual sum of squares represents the variation of the observations about the regression line and this suggests it as a means of estimating σ^2.   It can be shown to provide an unbiased estimate of σ^2 when divided by the appropriate number of degrees of freedom.   There are n terms in the sum which, if

suffixes are retained, is more exactly given as $\sum_{i=1}^{n} (y_i - \hat{y}_i)^2$.   This may

also be expressed as $\sum_{i=1}^{n} (y_i - a - bx_i)^2$.   Now there are two parameters, a

and b, which have been fitted to the data.   Thus if we consider all the different ways in which a set of n data points could vary about the line, we see that there are two constraints imposed on the n points by the requirement that they should give these values of a and b.   Can you now state the number of degrees of freedom in the residual sum of squares?

****

n - 2   i.e. number of terms in sum - number of constraints to which terms are subject.

We are now well on the way to forming an analysis of variance table for the regression.   The degrees of freedom for the other sums of squares will be required.   Deciding the number of d.f. in the total sum of squares, i.e. in

$$\sum_{i=1}^{n} (y_i - \overline{y})^2,$$ is quite straightforward and you should be able to write it down.

****

34A

$n - 1$

FRAME 35

The numbers of degrees of freedom have the same additive property as in previous ANOVA tables.   For the regression the table is therefore:

Source of variation	Sum of squares	Degrees of freedom
Due to regression	$\Sigma(\hat{y} - \overline{y})^2$	1
About regression (residual)	$\Sigma(y - \hat{y})^2$	$n - 2$
Total	$\Sigma(y - \overline{y})^2$	$n - 1$

In this form the table shows clearly what the various sums of squares represent, but not how they would be calculated.   Obviously only two need to be calculated from the data, the other then following from (32.1).   The total sum of squares is an obvious choice for one of the two as it is simply S_{yy}.   You have already noted that, as a consequence of (30A.1), $\Sigma(\hat{y} - \overline{y})^2 = b^2\Sigma(x - \overline{x})^2$. Now express this sum in terms of S_{xx} and S_{xy} by substituting for b.

****

35A

$$\left(\frac{S_{xy}}{S_{xx}}\right)^2 \times S_{xx} = \frac{\left(S_{xy}\right)^2}{S_{xx}}$$

FRAME 36

Thus, once the three sums S_{xx}, S_{xy} and S_{yy} have been calculated, the table is easily completed.

Source of variation	Sum of squares	Degrees of freedom
Due to regression	$(S_{xy})^2/S_{xx}$	1
About regression (residual)	By subtraction	By subtraction
Total	S_{yy}	$n - 1$

For the KBr data in FRAME 11 calculations subsequently carried out gave
S_{xx} = 1750, S_{xy} = 1000.   Further calculations give S_{yy} = 578 and the sum of
squares due to regression is therefore $1000^2/1750$ = 4000/7 ≈ 571·43.   Now
complete the ANOVA table, as outlined above, for this regression.

****

36A

Source of variation	Sum of squares	Degrees of freedom
Due to regression	571·43	1
About regression (residual)	6·57	4
Total	578	5

FRAME 37

It is now a simple matter to test the hypothesis β = 0 against the alternative
β ≠ 0, i.e. to decide whether the regression is real or has merely appeared by
the chance fluctuations of sampling.   You have already noted that the mean
square (SS/d.f.) based on the residual sum of squares estimates σ^2.   If the
hypothesis is true, then the variation that appears to be due to the regression
can be attributed to chance and the mean square derived from the "due to
regression" sum of squares will also estimate σ^2.   If these variance estimates
are now included in the table we have:

Source of variation	Sum of squares	Degrees of freedom	Variance estimate (Mean square)
Due to regression	571·43	1	571·43
About regression (residual)	6·57	4	1·64
Total	578	5	

We now have to decide whether it is unlikely that 571·43 and 1·64 are both
estimates of the same variance σ^2.   This can be done by considering their
ratio 571·43/1·64 (= 348·4) in relation to an F-distribution.   Which one?

****

37A

That of F with 1 d.f. in the numerator and 4 d.f. in the denominator, i.e.
F_4^1.

FRAME 38

The alternative hypothesis β ≠ 0 would mean that there is more variation than
is measured by σ^2 so the F-test is one-sided, as in the similar tests which
you met in the "Analysis of Variance" programme.   As TABLE 4 shows that there
is only a 1% chance of a value of F_4^1 exceeding 21·2, it is clear that 571·43

is significantly greater than 1·64 at the 1% level.   (In fact, the 0·1%
critical value for F_4^1 is only 74·1, so the result is easily significant even
at that level.)   It is hardly surprising that the F-test reveals very strong
evidence of the existence of a linear regression, as the data points, when
plotted, follow very closely a sloping linear path.   Such a well-defined
relationship did not exist in the case of the traffic-temperature data in
FRAME 14, but some degree of relationship was apparent.   Confirm this by
forming an ANOVA table for the regression and then making the appropriate F-test.
(Not a great deal of fresh calculations are required, as you can make use of
those previously done and recorded in 14A.)

****

38A

Source of variation	Sum of squares	d.f.	Variance estimate	
Due to regression	342·62	1	342·62	$F_8^1 = 44·96 > 11·3$
About regression (residual)	60·98	8	7·62	Sig. at 1%
Total	403·6	9		

(The 0·1% critical value of F_8^1 is 25·4, so the result is also significant at
this level, but not as overwhelmingly as with the KBr data.)

It would now be easy for you to test the hypothesis β = 0 for the regression
line of weight on height, if you make use of the sums given in FRAME 16.

****

39A

Source of variation	Sum of squares	d.f.	Variance estimate	
Due to regression	423·47	1	423·47	$F_{18}^1 = 10·19 > 8·29$
About regression (residual)	748·29	18	41·57	Sig. at 1%
Total	1171·76	19		

(The 0·1% critical value of F_{18}^1 is 15·4, so the hypothesis would not be
rejected at that level.)

It has already been observed that in the case of a complete functional
relationship between the two variables, represented by all the points lying on a
line, the regression explains the whole of the variation.

i.e.   SS due to regression = Total SS   or $\dfrac{\text{SS due to regression}}{\text{Total SS}} = 1.$

FRAME 40   (continued)

At the other extreme, when there is no relationship at all between the two
variables, the whole of the variation is accounted for by the residual (e.g.
error) variation and none by a regression, i.e. $\dfrac{\text{SS due to regression}}{\text{Total SS}} = 0.$ In
between these two extremes, the ratio will have a value between 0 and 1.
Express the ratio in terms of S_{xx}, S_{xy} and S_{yy}, and hence in terms of r, the
product moment correlation coefficient.

****

<u>40A</u>

$$\frac{SS\ due\ to\ regression}{Total\ SS} = \frac{\left(S_{xy}\right)^2}{S_{xx}\ S_{yy}} = r^2$$

<u>FRAME 41</u>

The ANOVA table for the regression of y on x can therefore be given in the
form:

Source of variation	Sum of squares	Degrees of freedom
Due to regression	$r^2 S_{yy}$	1
About regression (residual)	$(1 - r^2)S_{yy}$	$n - 2$
Total	S_{yy}	$n - 1$

r^2 is called the COEFFICIENT OF DETERMINATION or, if expressed as a percentage,
the PERCENTAGE FIT.

In the KBr example, the % fit was $\dfrac{571 \cdot 43}{578} \times 100 = 98 \cdot 9$, i.e. $98 \cdot 9\%$ of the
total variation in the amount of KBr which would dissolve was explained by the
regression (i.e. relation with temperature).   What percentage of the total
variation was explained by the regression of (i) traffic flow on temperature
(analysis in 38A), (ii) weight on height (analysis in 39A)?

****

<u>41A</u>

(i) $\dfrac{342 \cdot 62}{403 \cdot 6} \times 100 \simeq 84 \cdot 9$ (ii) $\dfrac{423 \cdot 47}{1171 \cdot 76} \times 100 \simeq 36 \cdot 1$

<u>FRAME 42</u>

Confidence Intervals

Clearly, different samples of data points from a bivariate population will yield
different estimates of the required regression line.   This must be taken into
account in assessing how good the estimates a and b are of α and β
respectively, and how good are any predictions given by the estimated regression
line.   As you might expect, the extent to which estimates vary from sample to
sample will be related to the sample size.   It will also be influenced by how

much individual observations vary about the true regression line.   The more
scatter there is about the line, the less precisely can estimates be made.
This scatter is measured by σ^2 in the model.   From a sample of n pairs of
observations, an unbiased estimate of σ^2, denoted here by s^2 (sometimes, in

other texts, by $\hat{\sigma}^2$), can be obtained from $\sum\limits_{i=1}^{n} (y_i - \hat{y}_i)^2$.   State the formula

for s^2 in terms of this sum of squares.   (Refer back to FRAME 33 if in
difficulty.)

****

42A

$$s^2 = \frac{\sum\limits_{i=1}^{n} (y_i - \hat{y}_i)^2}{n - 2} \quad \textit{or, dropping suffixes,} \quad s^2 = \frac{\Sigma(y - \hat{y})^2}{n - 2}$$

FRAME 43

Turning our attention first to b as an estimate of the regression coefficient
β, it can be shown that the sampling distribution of b has mean β and

variance $\frac{\sigma^2}{\Sigma(x - \bar{x})^2}$, i.e. $\frac{\sigma^2}{S_{xx}}$, and is normal if the assumptions embodied in

the model depicted in FRAME 29 are made.   If you wish to see it, the derivation
of these results concerning the sampling distribution of b can be found in the

APPENDIX at the end of this programme.   Now, if b is $N\left(\beta, \frac{\sigma^2}{S_{xx}}\right)$, what can

be said of the distribution of $\dfrac{b - \beta}{\sigma/\sqrt{S_{xx}}}$?

****

43A

It is the standard normal distribution, i.e. $\dfrac{b - \beta}{\sigma/\sqrt{S_{xx}}}$ *is* $N(0, 1)$.

FRAME 44

It can therefore be said that, for instance, there is a 95% probability that
$|b - \beta| < 1 \cdot 96 \dfrac{\sigma}{\sqrt{S_{xx}}}$, from which, if σ were known, a 95% confidence

interval for β could be deduced.   What would the boundaries of this interval be?

****

44A

$b - 1 \cdot 96\sigma/\sqrt{S_{xx}}$ *and* $b + 1 \cdot 96\sigma/\sqrt{S_{xx}}$

If, however, σ has to be estimated from the sample, then, in the statement in
43A, s will replace σ and hence the standard normal distribution must be
replaced by the t-distribution with $n - 2$ d.f. ($n - 2$ being the number of
d.f. on which s^2 is based). In the 95% confidence limits for β, 1·96 would
then have to be replaced by the appropriate value of t. Complete the
statement below, supposing estimates to have been obtained from a sample of 6
pairs of observations.

There is a 95% probability that $\dfrac{|b - \beta|}{s/\sqrt{S_{xx}}} <$ ....

i.e. that $|b - \beta| <$ ....

and thus that $b -$ .... $< \beta < b +$ ....

****

$\dfrac{|b - \beta|}{s/\sqrt{S_{xx}}} < 2 \cdot 78$ *i.e.* $|b - \beta| < 2 \cdot 78 \dfrac{s}{\sqrt{S_{xx}}}$

The 95% confidence interval is then given by $b - 2 \cdot 78 \dfrac{s}{\sqrt{S_{xx}}} < \beta < b + 2 \cdot 78 \dfrac{s}{\sqrt{S_{xx}}}$

More generally, when the sample size is n, the $(100 - 2P)$% confidence limits
for β will be $b \pm t_c \dfrac{s}{\sqrt{S_{xx}}}$, where t_c is such that, for the t-distribution
with $n - 2$ d.f., there is a P% chance that $t > t_c$.

For a sample size of 6, you have already seen that, for 95% confidence limits,
the value of t_c is 2·78. What would it be for 99% confidence limits?

****

4·60

Taking the data on KBr and temperature, given in FRAME 11, as an example, we
have $n = 6$ and from subsequent calculations $S_{xx} = 1750$, $b = 4/7 \approx 0 \cdot 571$ and
$s^2 = 6 \cdot 57/4 \approx 1 \cdot 64$.

Thus 95% confidence limits for β are $0 \cdot 571 \pm 2 \cdot 78\sqrt{1 \cdot 64}/\sqrt{1750}$, i.e.
$0 \cdot 571 \pm 0 \cdot 085$ or $0 \cdot 49$ and $0 \cdot 66$. For 99% confidence limits, 4·60 would be
substituted for 2·78 in these calculations. With the close functional
relationship that exists between amount of KBr and temperature, there will be
comparatively little variation in the slope of the estimated regression line
from one set of 6 observations to another. With a less close relationship
between two variables, greater variation in slope estimates must be allowed for.

This implies poorer relative precision in the estimates, as will be evidenced
by your answers to the following.

Based on the sets of data in FRAMES 14 and 16, find the respective 95%
confidence intervals for (i) the slope of the line of regression of number of
cars on temperature, (ii) the increase in mean weight per unit increase in
height.

****

47A

(i) $1 \cdot 045 \pm \dfrac{2 \cdot 31 \sqrt{7 \cdot 62}}{\sqrt{314}}$ $i.e.$ $1 \cdot 045 \pm 0 \cdot 360$ or $0 \cdot 68$ and $1 \cdot 40$

(ii) $0 \cdot 614 \pm \dfrac{2 \cdot 10 \sqrt{41 \cdot 57}}{\sqrt{1122}}$ $i.e.$ $0 \cdot 614 \pm 0 \cdot 404$ or $0 \cdot 21$ and $1 \cdot 02$

FRAME 48

Turning our attention next to a as an estimate of α in the equation of the
regression line $y = \alpha + \beta x$, it can be shown that, with the usual assumptions,
the sampling distribution of a is normal with mean α and variance
$\dfrac{\sigma^2 \Sigma x^2}{n \Sigma (x - \bar{x})^2}$,   i.e. $\dfrac{\sigma^2 \Sigma x^2}{n S_{xx}}$.   Again you can find the derivation of these results
set out in the APPENDIX if you wish to see it.

Confidence limits for α can be obtained by developing a similar argument to
that which led to confidence limits for β.   You may care to verify for
yourself that, when this is done, the (100 - 2P)% confidence limits for α are

$a \pm t_c s \sqrt{\dfrac{\Sigma x^2}{n S_{xx}}}$ where t_c is such that, for the t-distribution with n - 2 d.f.,
there is a P% chance that $t > t_c$.   Find 95% confidence limits for α, based
on the data on KBr and temperature.

****

48A

$a = 376/7 \simeq 53 \cdot 71$, $t_c = 2 \cdot 78$, $s^2 = 1 \cdot 64$, $S_{xx} = 1750$, $\Sigma x^2 = 5500$, $n = 6$

$give$ $53 \cdot 71 \pm 2 \cdot 78 \sqrt{1 \cdot 64} \sqrt{\dfrac{5500}{6 \times 1750}}$ $i.e.$ $53 \cdot 71 \pm 2 \cdot 58$ or $51 \cdot 1$ and $56 \cdot 3$.

FRAME 49

The most common purpose of obtaining the regression line of y on x is to use
it to make predictions about the value of y for any given value of x - say
$x = x_0$.   Suppose we want to know the amount of KBr that will dissolve in 100 g
of water at x_0°C, or the mean number of cars leaving the town on Sundays when
the 8 a.m. temperature was x_0°C or the mean weight of men of height x_0 cm.
Then what we require is the value of $\alpha + \beta x_0$, which is the mean of the
y-distribution corresponding to $x = x_0$.   Where a functional relationship
exists (as in the KBr example) this will represent the true value, for $x = x_0$,
of what the y-observations are measuring.   The values of α and β being
unknown, $a + b x_0$ will be used to provide an estimate of $\alpha + \beta x_0$.   To give
a confidence interval, it will be necessary to take account of the sampling
distribution of $a + b x_0$.   In the APPENDIX at the end of this programme it is
shown that, with the usual assumptions, this distribution is normal, with mean

FRAME 49   (continued)

$\alpha + \beta x_0$ and variance $\sigma^2 \left\{ \dfrac{1}{n} + \dfrac{(x_0 - \overline{x})^2}{\Sigma(x - \overline{x})^2} \right\}$, i.e. $\sigma^2 \left\{ \dfrac{1}{n} + \dfrac{(x_0 - \overline{x})^2}{S_{xx}} \right\}$.

By similar arguments to those used for α and β, the $(100 - 2P)\%$ confidence limits for $\alpha + \beta x_0$ are found to be $a + bx_0 \pm t_c s \sqrt{\dfrac{1}{n} + \dfrac{(x_0 - \overline{x})^2}{S_{xx}}}$ where t_c has the same meaning as before. You will notice that the width of the confidence interval depends on the value of x_0. For what value of x_0 is it a minimum?

****

49A

$x_0 = \overline{x}$, which makes the term involving $(x_0 - \overline{x})^2$ zero. (As an estimate, the precision of $a + bx_0$ is therefore best when $x_0 = \overline{x}$. The further x_0 is from $\overline{x}$, the larger is the value of $(x_0 - \overline{x})^2$ and the poorer is the precision of the estimate.)

FRAME 50

Let us suppose that the 95% confidence interval is required for the mean weight of men of height 182 cm, based on the data in FRAME 16.

We have $a = -42 \cdot 93$, $b = 0 \cdot 614$, $x_0 = 182$, $t_c = 2 \cdot 10$, $s^2 = 41 \cdot 57$, $n = 20$, $\overline{x} = 176$ and $S_{xx} = 1122$. Thus the 95% confidence limits for $\alpha + \beta x_0$ are

$(-42 \cdot 93 + 0 \cdot 614 \times 182) \pm 2 \cdot 10 \sqrt{41 \cdot 57} \sqrt{\dfrac{1}{20} + \dfrac{6^2}{1122}}$ i.e. $68 \cdot 82 \pm 3 \cdot 88$ or $64 \cdot 9$ and $72 \cdot 7$ kg. What would be the 95% confidence interval for the mean weight of men of height 176 cm?

****

50A

$65 \cdot 13 \pm 2 \cdot 10 \sqrt{41 \cdot 57/20}$ i.e. $65 \cdot 13 \pm 3 \cdot 03$ or $62 \cdot 1$ and $68 \cdot 2$ kg. (Note that the limits are closer together here, where $x_0 = 176 = \overline{x}$, than they were for $x_0 = 182$.)

FRAME 51

Now suppose that we want to make a prediction about the weight of an <u>individual</u> man of height x_0 cm, rather than being concerned with the mean weight of all such men. Or, on a Sunday when the temperature is $x_0 {}^\circ C$ at 8 a.m., the traffic controllers want to know how great or how small the exodus of cars is likely to be later in the day. Or, an experimenter wants to know limits within which an individual observation (error and all) of the amount of KBr is likely to fall when the temperature of the water is $x_0 {}^\circ C$. In giving a confidence interval for a future individual observation, we shall have to take account of the variation, represented in the model by e_i (variance σ^2), of the individual y's around their mean. This variation is independent of the random sampling variation that affects the estimate $a + bx_0$; hence the sum of the two variances, σ^2 and $\sigma^2 \left\{ \dfrac{1}{n} + \dfrac{(x_0 - \overline{x})^2}{S_{xx}} \right\}$, gives the variance required for obtaining the prediction interval now being sought. With s^2 estimating σ^2, the (100 - 2P)% confidence limits for a predicted value of an individual

y-observation when $x = x_0$ are $a + bx_0 \pm t_c s \sqrt{1 + \dfrac{1}{n} + \dfrac{(x_0 - \bar{x})^2}{S_{xx}}}$.   Thus, if

a man of height 182 cm is to be selected at random, we can say that there is
a 95% probability that his weight will be within the limits

$(-42{\cdot}93 + 0{\cdot}614 \times 182) \pm 2{\cdot}10\sqrt{41{\cdot}57} \sqrt{1 + \dfrac{1}{20} + \dfrac{6^2}{1122}}$,   i.e. $68{\cdot}82 \pm 14{\cdot}08$ or

$54{\cdot}7$ and $82{\cdot}9$ kg.   This interval is, of course, wider than the 95%
confidence interval found in the preceding frame for the mean weight of men of
this height.

Now find the prediction interval within which you can say, with 95% confidence,
the weight of a randomly chosen man of height 176 cm will lie.

****

$65{\cdot}13 \pm 2{\cdot}10\sqrt{41{\cdot}57} \sqrt{1 + 1/20}$ i.e. $65{\cdot}13 \pm 13{\cdot}87$ or $51{\cdot}3$ and $79{\cdot}0$ kg.

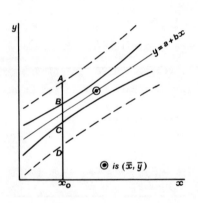

$\odot$ is $(\bar{x}, \bar{y})$

As with the confidence interval for $\alpha + \beta x_0$,
the width of the prediction interval for an
individual observation depends on x_0, and is
a minimum when $x_0 = \bar{x}$.   The diagram shows the
regression line estimated from a set of data
together with two confidence bands associated
with the same degree of confidence, say 95%.
The inner band shows the 95% confidence
interval for mean y for a given value of x,
e.g. BC when $x = x_0$.   The outer band
(represented by the broken curves) shows, for
each value of x, the limits between which it
is forecast that 95% of individual
observations will lie.   When $x = x_0$, this
interval is represented by AD.

Multiple and Curvilinear Regression

So far, in this programme, consideration has been restricted to simple linear
regression, where there is a linear relationship between the dependent (response)
variable and just one independent (regressor) variable.   You have seen that the
less the degree of correlation between the two variables, the poorer are the
estimates given by the regression.   The variation about the regression can be
explained by the presence of other variables whose values affect that of the
response variable - for instance, there are other factors besides height that
determine a man's weight.   Obviously closer estimates would be given by a
regression model that takes account of these other variables.   Here are a few
examples of regressor variables that might be used jointly for predicting a
response.

FRAME 53   (continued)

Dependent (response) variable	Regressor variables
Man's weight	Height, chest girth
Nitrogen oxide emission from internal combustion engines	Humidity, atmospheric pressure
Strength of ceramic coating	Humidity, iron content, kiln temperature
Rate of absorption of a branched-chain synthetic alcohol	Reactor temperature, % acetic acid catalyst in reactor, power input to reactor heater

FRAME 54

Once one has moved on to the consideration of more than one independent variable, i.e. to MULTIPLE REGRESSION, the principle involved is the same whether there are 2 or 20 of them, so, for simplicity, we shall work with just 2. Continuing with a linear model, this will mean introducing another term into (27.1), each y-observation now being represented by

$$y_i = \alpha + \beta x_i + \gamma z_i + e_i$$

The data will now be in groups of three, instead of pairs, i.e. of the form (x_1, z_1, y_1), (x_2, z_2, y_2), ..., (x_n, z_n, y_n).   In terms of a visual presentation, the extra term introduces another dimension.   Whereas in simple regression the data could be represented by points in a plane, now points in space would be required, and the regression equation $y = \alpha + \beta x + \gamma z$ would represent a plane instead of a line.   (With the introduction of more regressor variables we would run out of dimensions and a geometric form of representation would no longer be possible.)

In obtaining estimates of α, β and γ, which will be denoted by a, b and c respectively, the method of least squares is again used.   When $x = x_1$ and $z = z_1$, the observed value of y was y_1, the value given by the equation $y = a + bx + cz$ would be $a + bx_1 + cz_1$ and the difference between them $y_1 - a - bx_1 - cz_1$.   It will be the sum of the squares of all such differences that must be minimised.   Thus if we write

$$S = (y_1 - a - bx_1 - cz_1)^2 + (y_2 - a - bx_2 - cz_2)^2 + .. + (y_n - a - bx_n - cz_n)^2$$

or, more compactly,

$$S = \sum_{i=1}^{n} (y_i - a - bx_i - cz_i)^2$$

the problem is one of finding the values of a, b and c that make S a minimum.   This will occur when $\frac{\partial S}{\partial a}$, $\frac{\partial S}{\partial b}$ and $\frac{\partial S}{\partial c}$ are all zero.   You may like to put your knowledge of differentiation to the test and obtain these differential coefficients for yourself.   If not, just read straight on to the answer frame.

****

54A

$$\frac{\partial S}{\partial a} = -2(y_1 - a - bx_1 - cz_1) - 2(y_2 - a - bx_2 - cz_2) - .. - 2(y_n - a - bx_n - cz_n) \quad \text{which}$$

$$\text{you may have written as} \quad -2 \sum_{i=1}^{n} (y_i - a - bx_i - cz_i).$$

$$\frac{\partial S}{\partial b} = -2x_1(y_1 - a - bx_1 - cz_1) - 2x_2(y_2 - a - bx_2 - cz_2) - \ldots - 2x_n(y_n - a - bx_n - cz_n)$$

$$\text{or} \quad -2\sum_{i=1}^{n} x_i(y_i - a - bx_i - cz_i)$$

$$\frac{\partial S}{\partial c} = -2z_1(y_1 - a - bx_1 - cz_1) - 2z_2(y_2 - a - bx_2 - cz_2) - \ldots - 2z_n(y_n - a - bx_n - cz_n)$$

$$\text{or} \quad -2\sum_{i=1}^{n} z_i(y_i - a - bx_i - cz_i)$$

Putting $\dfrac{\partial S}{\partial a} = 0$ gives $\sum\limits_{i=1}^{n} y_i - na - b\sum\limits_{i=1}^{n} x_i - c\sum\limits_{i=1}^{n} z_i = 0$

$\dfrac{\partial S}{\partial b} = 0$ gives $\sum\limits_{i=1}^{n} x_i y_i - a\sum\limits_{i=1}^{n} x_i - b\sum\limits_{i=1}^{n} x_i^2 - c\sum\limits_{i=1}^{n} x_i z_i = 0$

and $\dfrac{\partial S}{\partial c} = 0$ gives $\sum\limits_{i=1}^{n} z_i y_i - a\sum\limits_{i=1}^{n} z_i - b\sum\limits_{i=1}^{n} z_i x_i - c\sum\limits_{i=1}^{n} z_i^2 = 0$

With the dropping of suffixes and some rearrangement of terms these three equations in a, b and c become

$$na + (\Sigma x)b + (\Sigma z)c = \Sigma y \qquad\qquad (55.1)$$
$$(\Sigma x)a + (\Sigma x^2)b + (\Sigma xz)c = \Sigma xy \qquad\qquad (55.2)$$
$$(\Sigma z)a + (\Sigma xz)b + (\Sigma z^2)c = \Sigma zy \qquad\qquad (55.3)$$

These are the normal equations which the least squares method gives rise to in the present situation.   They are comparable with the normal equations (8.1) and (8.2) obtained for simple regression.   Now in FRAME 9 you saw that from (8.1) a formula for a in terms of b, $\bar{x}$ and $\bar{y}$ could be derived.   See if you can, in a similar way, derive from (55.1) a formula for a in terms of b, c, $\bar{x}$, $\bar{z}$ and $\bar{y}$.

****

Dividing both sides of (55.1) by n gives $a + b\bar{x} + c\bar{z} = \bar{y}$

$$\text{i.e.} \quad a = \bar{y} - b\bar{x} - c\bar{z} \qquad\qquad (55A.1)$$

Substituting $a = \bar{y} - b\bar{x} - c\bar{z}$ in $y = a + bx + cz$ gives

$$y - \bar{y} = b(x - \bar{x}) + c(z - \bar{z})$$

This is the form of the estimated regression equation which is comparable with (10.1) in simple regression.   Notice that it shows, as does (55A.1), that the equation is satisfied by $x = \bar{x}$, $z = \bar{z}$, $y = \bar{y}$.   Eliminating a from (55.1) and (55.2) leads to

$$\{n\Sigma x^2 - (\Sigma x)^2\}b + (n\Sigma xz - \Sigma x\Sigma z)c = n\Sigma xy - \Sigma x\Sigma y \qquad\qquad (56.1)$$

and eliminating a from (55.1) and (55.3) leads to

FRAME 56   (continued)

$$(n\Sigma xz - \Sigma x\Sigma z)b + \{n\Sigma z^2 - (\Sigma z)^2\}c = n\Sigma zy - \Sigma z\Sigma y \qquad (56.2)$$

Now with the conventional notation that $S_{xx} = \Sigma(x - \bar{x})^2 = \Sigma x^2 - (\Sigma x)^2/n$, etc., (56.1) and (56.2) can be expressed in terms of S_{xx}, S_{xy}, S_{xz}, S_{zz}, S_{zy}, b and c. See if you can do this. (HINT: Begin by dividing both sides of each equation by n.)

****

56A

(56.1) becomes $S_{xx}b + S_{xz}c = S_{xy}$

(56.2) becomes $S_{xz}b + S_{zz}c = S_{zy}$

FRAME 57

These equations are easily solved for b and c giving, for the general case,

$$b = \frac{S_{xy}S_{zz} - S_{zy}S_{xz}}{S_{xx}S_{zz} - (S_{xz})^2} \qquad\qquad c = \frac{S_{xx}S_{zy} - S_{xz}S_{xy}}{S_{xx}S_{zz} - (S_{xz})^2}$$

and a can then be found from (55A.1)

The following data will provide an illustration. In the table y represents a particular physical property of forged alloy bars and x and z the percentages of alloying elements A and B respectively which were present. Four levels were chosen for x and four for z, giving 16 possible combinations, and a value of y was recorded experimentally for a bar of each type. (This is an example of what is known as a complete factorial design.)

x	5	5	5	5	10	10	10	10	15	15	15	15	20	20	20	20
z	1	2	3	4	1	2	3	4	1	2	3	4	1	2	3	4
y	28	30	48	74	29	50	57	42	20	24	31	47	9	18	22	31

Calculations give

$\Sigma x = 200$ $\qquad$ $\Sigma z = 40$ $\qquad$ $\Sigma y = 560$ $\qquad$ $\Sigma x^2 = 3000$

$\Sigma xz = 500$ $\qquad$ $\Sigma xy = 6110$ $\qquad$ $\Sigma z^2 = 120$ $\qquad$ $\Sigma zy = 1580$

You could now calculate S_{xx}, S_{xz} etc. and use the formulae already found for a, b and c. Alternatively you could write down and solve the normal equations (55.1), (55.2) and (55.3) which become respectively

$$16a + 200b + 40c = 560$$

$$200a + 3000b + 500c = 6110$$

$$40a + 500b + 120c = 1580$$

Either way leads to a = 34·75, b = -1·78, c = 9 and the estimated regression equation is therefore y = 34·75 - 1·78x + 9z. The linearity of the model means that there is a straight line relationship between y and x

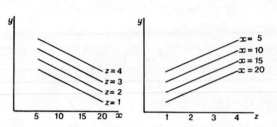

when z is fixed and between y and z when x is fixed. This is illustrated by the diagrams on the left.

Within the range of values investigated, what combination, according to the regression, gives the highest expectation for y and what is that expected value?

****

$\hat{y}$, the estimate given by the regression equation which we have just found, will be highest when x is lowest and z is highest, i.e. when x = 5 and z = 4. This combination gives $\hat{y}$ = 61·85.

In both the simple regression model, involving one independent variable, and the extension to a multiple regression model, involving two or more, we have considered only linear models.   A brief indication will now be given of how CURVILINEAR REGRESSION, an example of which was illustrated in the right-hand diagram in FRAME 2, can be dealt with.   Sometimes it may be possible to avoid the problem by transforming one or more of the variables involved.   Suppose, for instance, that the relationship between y and x is exponential in form, i.e. $y = \alpha e^{\beta x}$.   Then the transformation y' = log y (to any base) will result in a linear relationship between y' and x.   It must be remembered, however, that in working with the line of regression of y' on x, the assumptions made about y in our previous discussion of regression lines will now apply to y'.

Another possibility is that the regression can be described by a polynomial model.   In the case of one independent variable, this would mean including powers of x such as x^2, x^3 etc.   In the diagram in FRAME 2 the regression curve is a parabola whose equation can be expressed as $y = \alpha + \beta x + \gamma x^2$, i.e. a quadratic.   From given data, estimates a, b and c of α, β and γ respectively can again be obtained by the method of least squares.   This will require the values of a, b and c to be such that $\sum_{i=1}^{n} (y_i - a - bx_i - cx_i^2)^2$

is a minimum.   Now if you compare this sum with the S that you minimised in FRAME 54 you will see that it is S with z_i replaced by x_i^2.   It follows that all the partial differential coefficients of the present sum with respect to c will be those in 54A with x_i^2 replacing z_i.   Hence there is no need to repeat the procedure of finding the partial differential coefficients and equating them to zero - the result of this can be anticipated by substituting x^2 for z in (55.1), (55.2) and (55.3).   Try to write down the normal equations for the quadratic regression this way.

****

$$na + (\Sigma x)b + (\Sigma x^2)c = \Sigma y$$
$$(\Sigma x)a + (\Sigma x^2)b + (\Sigma x^3)c = \Sigma xy$$
$$(\Sigma x^2)a + (\Sigma x^3)b + (\Sigma x^4)c = \Sigma x^2 y$$

FRAME 59

These equations can then be solved for a, b and c to give the estimated regression curve equation as $y = a + bx + cx^2$. Had an x^3 term also been included in the model, there would be four coefficients to estimate and hence four normal equations to solve. Difficulties may arise with the use of the least squares method for higher degree polynomials because of a tendency for the normal equations to be ill-conditioned (an undesirable feature of some simultaneous equations that is described in "Numerical Methods for Engineers and Scientists".) If the values of the controlled variable are equally spaced, this difficulty can be avoided by the use of the method of orthogonal polynomials, which is not included in this course. Nor is it considered appropriate to give a detailed coverage of either curvilinear or multiple regression. Enough has been said to show you that the basic principles are the same as for simple linear regression but the inclusion of more variables or higher powers makes everything more complicated. As before, regression coefficients can be tested for significance, confidence intervals can be found and analysis of variance tables can be drawn up. Obviously, as the number of terms in the model increases, so also does the amount of computation and the number of normal equations which have to be solved. The approach adopted here was adequate for solving 2 or 3 such equations but would be impracticable if there were more. Computers are much used in regression calculations and programs are widely available. The solution of the normal equations is usually incorporated in the program, so that the user does not have to concern himself with this problem. However, no very advanced skills in computer programming or solving simultaneous equations would be required for you to write your own program to deal with simple linear regression. You could then go on to multiple regression with only 2 regressor variables, or to the quadratic form, using formulae for a, b and c along the lines adopted in this text.

FRAME 60

Miscellaneous Examples

In this frame a collection of miscellaneous examples is given for you to try. Answers are supplied in FRAME 61, together with such working as is considered helpful.

1. Six bearings were tested for wear, each bearing being run under a different operating temperature controlled by an oil bath. The test results were:

Operating temperature (in units of 100°C)	1	1·5	2	3	3·5	4
Amount of wear (in mg/100 h of operation)	3·3	5·0	5·5	9·4	11·4	12·8

The temperature values can be assumed to be without error and there are grounds for supposing wear and temperature to be connected by a linear functional relationship. Estimate its equation, giving your answer (i) for temperature in units of 100°C as in the data, (ii) for temperature in $^{\circ}$C. What estimate would then be obtained for the amount of wear when the operating temperature is 250°C? Comment on the estimated amount of wear given by the equation for an operating temperature of 0°C.

2. The following data resulted from an investigation seeking to relate the
percentage of waste solids removed in a filtration system with the flow
rate of the effluent being fed into the system.   The flow rate (shown here
in units of $10^2 \times cm^3 s^{-1}$,   to give you the simplest figures in your
working) was controlled at 7 different levels in turn, and at each level
the percentage of waste solids removed was measured and recorded.   It is
required to estimate the equation of a line that could be used to make
estimates about the percentage removal of waste solids for various flow
rates.   Obtain the normal equations and by solving them, or otherwise,
find the required straight line equation.   What would the equation be for
flow rate in $cm^3 s^{-1}$?

Flow rate	2	3	4	5	6	7	8
% waste solids removed	22·7	19·8	18·6	16·6	14·0	12·7	10·4

3. Based on the regression line equation that you obtained in 14A, find 90%
confidence limits for the mean number of cars leaving the town during the
fixed time interval, following an 8 a.m. Sunday temperature of 17°C.
Also find limits between which, on a Sunday when an 8 a.m. temperature of
17°C has been recorded, you can say that there is a 90% chance that the
number of cars will be.   For what temperature can the closest predictions
about traffic (i.e. with narrowest confidence interval) be made?

4.

u	0	1	-1	-15	8	-2	3	-10	4	2
v	-5·6	6·8	8·0	7·1	16·2	4·9	12·6	-1·0	8·1	-1·0

u	-12	-11	-5	-7	-17	-12	1	7	0	-14
v	7·1	-11·0	5·3	8·0	-2·8	3·5	9·9	18·0	16·2	-6·3

(i) From the above 20 pairs of observations estimate the equation of the
line of regression of v on u.   (ii) Then compare the table of values
given here with that for heights and weights in FRAME 16.   How are
(a) u and x,   (b) v and y, related?   (iii) From your answers to (i)
and (ii) deduce an estimate of the equation of the line of regression of
weight on height and compare with (17.1).

5. The method used in FRAMES 43-47 for obtaining confidence limits for β was
based on the distribution of $\dfrac{b - \beta}{s/\sqrt{S_{xx}}}$ being that of t with n - 2 d.f.

The hypothesis $\beta = 0$ could also be tested on this basis, by calculating
$\dfrac{b}{s/\sqrt{S_{xx}}}$ as the test statistic and referring to the appropriate critical
value of t in TABLE 3.   With $\beta \neq 0$ as the alternative hypothesis, try
this out on each of the three sets of data in FRAMES 11, 14 and 16
respectively.   Check that you reach the same conclusion in each case as
when following the analysis of variance procedure by an F-test.   Also,
compare the square of each t-value that you use with the corresponding
F-value used previously.   What do you notice?

6. The following table shows, for each of 8 command module pilots, the
post-flight change in maximal calf circumference as a percentage of the

pre-flight value, and the time, t, of his exposure to weightlessness
(which, for these crewmen, was the length of duration of the flight.)

t (hours)	260	147	241	192	194	295	266	301
y (% change)	-3·46	-1·02	-3·60	-3·04	-1·08	-2·28	-2·99	-4·05

Calculations give $\Sigma t = 1896$, $\Sigma y = -21\cdot52$, $S_{tt} = 20\ 820$, $S_{yy} = 9\cdot0322$,
$S_{ty} = -297\cdot09$.

(i) The possible existence of an equation showing how average % change
in calf circumference varies with duration of exposure to
weightlessness is to be investigated. A plot of the data points
suggests that the linear regression model might be appropriate.
Estimate the equation of the appropriate regression line. Use an
ANOVA table for the regression to test the hypothesis $\beta = 0$, where
β is the slope of the true regression line. Next, before making
any further calculations, say whether you think that zero will be
inside the 95% confidence interval for β. Then check your answer
by actually finding this confidence interval.

(ii) Find the value of r, the correlation coefficient, given by the data
and test the hypothesis $\rho = 0$. If this were done at the outset,
would one then go ahead with estimating the regression line?

(This example was suggested by the study of the effects of the space
environment made on crew members of the Apollo flights, when very similar
measurements were recorded.)

7. You have seen that, in linear regression problems where the relationship
between the two variables x and y is not a functional one, there are two
regression lines. The equation (10.1), i.e. $y - \bar{y} = b(x - \bar{x})$, estimates
the line of regression of y on x and is the one to use if estimates of y
are required for given values of x. On the other hand, the equation
(20.1), i.e. $x - \bar{x} = b'(y - \bar{y})$, estimates the line of regression of x
on y and would be used for estimating x from given y. However, you
have also seen that when the relationship is a functional one, the two
regression lines coincide. Then (10.1) and (20.1) both estimate the same
equation. Thus (10.1) could be used both for estimating y from x and x
from y, and the same goes for (20.1). An illustration of this occurs in
calibration problems, of which the following is an example.

There is a linear relationship between potassium concentration and the peak
height recorded on the print-out from the chart recorder of an atomic
absorption spectrophotometer. If this relationship can be determined, it
can then be used to convert a reading of peak height into a reading of
potassium concentration. To this end, standard solutions of 1, 2, 3, 4
and 5 ppm were made up and peak heights recorded as shown.

Potassium concentration (ppm)	1	2	3	4	5
Peak height (cm)	4·7	8·2	12·0	16·2	19·2

The values for the potassium concentrations in these standard solutions
can be assumed to be without error; it is the peak height observations
that are subject to random error and it is therefore appropriate to use the
regression of peak height on potassium concentration to estimate the
relationship between the two. Obtain this equation and use it to convert
a peak height of 9·1 cm into a value of potassium concentration.

(This problem was suggested by the technique used by the Aberdeen team, in
the 1975 finals of the BBC TV "Young Scientists of the Year" contest, for

determining the potassium concentration in drinking water samples from
different towns in the U.K.)

8. In the previous example, let potassium concentration and peak height be
    denoted by x and y respectively.   If values of concentration are coded
    using the formula $u = x - 3$, what does this give for Σu?   Obtain the
    normal equations that will lead to estimating the line of regression of y
    on u and hence write down the equation of this line.   Deduce the equation
    connecting y and x, and check that it is the same as obtained previously.

9. What coding formulae will transform $x = 5, 10, 15, 20$ into $u = -3, -1, 1,$
    3 respectively, and $z = 1, 2, 3, 4$ into $v = -3, -1, 1, 3$ respectively?
    Apply these formulae to the data in FRAME 57.   Hence obtain and solve the
    normal equations that will give the values of a, b and c in the estimated
    regression equation $y = a + bu + cv$.   Check that this leads to the same
    equation relating y, x and z as was arrived at in FRAME 57.

10. Prior knowledge about a relationship sometimes requires that a regression
    curve should pass through the origin.   The equation of the line of
    regression of y on x would then reduce to $y = \beta x$, and only the slope β
    has to be estimated from the data.   By writing down the expression for the
    appropriate S and putting $\frac{dS}{db} = 0$, use the method of least squares to
    obtain an estimate b of this slope, from the n pairs of observations
    $(x_1, y_1), (x_2, y_2), \ldots, (x_n, y_n)$.   Great caution should be exercised in
    the adoption of this simplified model, particularly when the data points
    are in a region away from the origin.   Whilst the regression may be
    adequately described by a straight line in that region, it is, as you know,
    unwise to assume that this state of affairs continues beyond.   However the
    model could, with reason, be applied to the following data, obtained in an
    experiment to determine the stiffness of a spring.   The extension of the
    spring (from its natural length) was measured under different loads.

Load (newtons)	2	4	6	8	10	12
Extension (mm)	10	19	29	40	48	56

    Obviously the extension is zero when the load is zero, the origin is not
    very distant from the region of the data points and extension is generally
    assumed to be directly proportional to load, thus justifying the use of
    $y = \beta x$.   On this basis, estimate the equation relating extension and load.
    (The values of load were controlled and may be taken to be without error.)

11. As a comparison, find the equation relating extension and load that would
    have been obtained from the data in the previous example, had the initial
    assumption $\alpha = 0$ not been made.   What would the 95% confidence interval
    for α then be?   Deduce whether the estimate of α differs significantly
    from zero, i.e. whether the hypothesis $\alpha = 0$, tested against the
    alternative $\alpha \neq 0$, should be rejected.

12. The remarks made in Ex.10 could also apply to non-linear regression.   If
    a quadratic model were being used, and the regression curve required to pass
    through the origin, then the equation of the curve would be $y = \beta x + \gamma x^2$.
    What would the normal equations in b and c, the estimates of β and γ,
    be in this case, for n pairs of observations
    $(x_1, y_1), (x_2, y_2), \ldots, (x_n, y_n)$?

13. The yield of a chemical process was measured at three temperatures, each with two concentrations of a particular reactant, as recorded below:

Temperature, $t^{\circ}C$	40	40	50	50	60	60
Concentration, x	0·2	0·4	0·2	0·4	0·2	0·4
Yield, y	38	42	41	46	46	49

Use the method of least squares to find the best values of the coefficients a, b, c in the equation $y = a + bt + cx$, and from your equation estimate the yield at $70^{\circ}C$ with concentration 0·5.   (L.U.)

(Hint: Coding values of temperature and concentration can simplify the normal equations, as in Examples 8 and 9.)

14. When a mass of x kg is suspended from each of a number of wires the proportion breaking is y. Experimental values of x and y are

x	28	29	30	31	32
y	0·16	0·34	0·58	0·79	0·92

Assuming the values of y to be cumulative areas for a normal distribution of x with mean μ and standard deviation σ, use the table of areas under the standard normal curve to find values of $(x - \mu)/\sigma$, with appropriate sign, corresponding to each value of x. By plotting values of $(x - \mu)/\sigma$ against x, or otherwise, estimate the values of μ and σ. Find the value of x for which $y = 0·75$.   (L.U.)

15. Tensile tests on a steel specimen yielded the following results:

Tensile force	x	1	2	3	4	5	6
Elongation	y	15	35	41	63	77	84

Assuming the regression of y on x to be linear, estimate the parameters of the regression line and determine 95% confidence limits for its slope.   (C.E.I.)

Answers to Miscellaneous Examples

1. (i) $y = -0·171 + 3·23x$, (ii) $y = -0·171 + 0·0323x'$, where y = amount of wear, x = temperature in units of $100^{\circ}C$, x' = temperature in $^{\circ}C$. 7·9 mg/100 h. Leaving aside the question of whether an operating temperature of $0^{\circ}C$ would be practicable, the amount of wear could not possibly be negative. This illustrates again what can happen if you extrapolate beyond the range of the data.

2. For $y = a + bx$, where y = % waste solids removed and x = flow rate in units of $10^2 \times cm^3s^{-1}$, normal equations are $7a + 35b = 114·8$, $35a + 203b = 518·3$. $y = 26·35 - 1·99x$ or $26·35 - 0·0199x'$ for x' in cm^3s^{-1}.

3. 19·2 and 22·5; 15·5 and 26·2 (all in thousands). $16^{\circ}C$.

4. (i) $v - 5·2 = \dfrac{689·3}{1122} (u + 4)$ leading to $v = 0·614u + 7·657$
   (ii) (a) $u = x - 180$ (b) $v = y - 60$ (iii) The two equations may differ slightly if round-off error has occurred in your working. Note that although the number of pairs of observations was only 20, the original

data on heights and weights in FRAME 16 gave rise to some quite large numbers in the calculations and these have been reduced by a temporary change of origin for both variables.

5.   KBr data: $b = \dfrac{4}{7}$ $s^2 = \dfrac{6 \cdot 57}{4}$ with 4 d.f. $S_{xx} = 1750$

$t = 18 \cdot 65 > 4 \cdot 60$ $\therefore$ Sig. at 1%   (Also $> 8 \cdot 61$, $\therefore$ sig. at $0 \cdot 1$%)

Traffic data: $t = 6 \cdot 71 > 3 \cdot 36$ $\therefore$ Sig. at 1%   (Also $> 5 \cdot 04$, $\therefore$ sig. at $0 \cdot 1$%)

Height/weight data: $t = 3 \cdot 19 > 2 \cdot 88$ $\therefore$ Sig. at 1%   (But $\not> 3 \cdot 92$ $\therefore$ not sig. at $0 \cdot 1$%)

The square of every t-value used is equal to the corresponding F-value, pointing to the distribution of F_ν^1 being that of the square of t with ν d.f. (A hint of this relationship occurred in Misc. Ex. 5 on page 365.)   Hence the same conclusion is reached, whether F-test or t-test is used.

6.   (i) $y + 2 \cdot 69 = \dfrac{-297 \cdot 09}{20\,820}\, (t - 237)$ i.e. $y = 0 \cdot 692 - 0 \cdot 0143t$

Source of variation	Sum of squares	d.f.	Variance estimate	
Due to regression	4·2393	1	4·2393	$F_6^1 = 5 \cdot 31$
Residual	4·7929	6	0·7988	$< 5 \cdot 99$
Total	9·0322	7		Not sig. at 5%

−0·0294 and 0·0009.   The interval contains zero, in agreement with our previous finding (based on F, which you now know to be equivalent to being based on t) that the hypothesis $\beta = 0$ could not be rejected at the 5% level.

(ii) $r = -0 \cdot 685$ $|r| < 0 \cdot 707$ Not sig. at 5%, i.e. hypothesis $\rho = 0$ would not be rejected at this level.   With this lack of evidence of any correlation between the two variables, there would be no point in proceeding to the estimation of a regression line (which, as you have seen, will only lead you to the same conclusion).   As a matter of interest, the data recorded on all the 24 Apollo crew men whose calf measurements were investigated did show a significant correlation but not a very high value of r.   This illustrates how a small sample (of only 8 in this case) can easily fail to reveal a low degree of correlation.

7. $y = 0 \cdot 96 + 3 \cdot 7x$, where x = potassium concentration and y = peak height. $y = 9 \cdot 1$ gives $x = 2 \cdot 2$, i.e. a potassium concentration of $2 \cdot 2$ ppm.   (It must be stressed that it is only when there is a functional relationship that the line of regression of y on x would be used for estimating x from y.)

8. $\Sigma u = 0$.   Normal equations are $5a = 60 \cdot 3$, $10b = 37 \cdot 0$ $y = 12 \cdot 06 + 3 \cdot 7u = 12 \cdot 06 + 3 \cdot 7(x - 3) = 0 \cdot 96 + 3 \cdot 7x$.

9. $u = \dfrac{x - 12 \cdot 5}{2 \cdot 5}$, $v = \dfrac{z - 2 \cdot 5}{0 \cdot 5}$ Note that then $\Sigma u = 0$, $\Sigma v = 0$, $\Sigma uv = 0$ and the normal equations are simply $16a = 560$, $80b = -356$, $80c = 360$.

$y = 35 - 4 \cdot 45u + 4 \cdot 5v$.   Changing back to x and z gives the same equation
as in FRAME 57.   Note that the symmetry about zero of the values after
coding, i.e. -3, -1, 1, 3 in this example and -2, -1, 0, 1, 2 in Ex.9,
leads to normal equations which can be solved immediately.

10. $\dfrac{dS}{db} = -2 \displaystyle\sum_{i=1}^{n} x_i (y_i - bx_i)$ $\dfrac{dS}{db} = 0$ gives $\displaystyle\sum_{i=1}^{n} x_i y_i - (\Sigma x_i^2)b = 0$ whence

$b = \dfrac{\displaystyle\sum_{i=1}^{n} x_i y_i}{\displaystyle\sum_{i=1}^{n} x_i^{2}}$ or more simply, $\dfrac{\Sigma xy}{\Sigma x^2}$

$y = 4 \cdot 79x$ where y = extension (in mm) and x = load (in N)

11. $y = 0 \cdot 867 + 4 \cdot 69x$. $-1 \cdot 85$ and $3 \cdot 59$.   As this interval contains zero,
the N.H., $\alpha = 0$ would not be rejected at the 5% level.

12. $(\Sigma x^2)b + (\Sigma x^3)c = \Sigma xy$ and $(\Sigma x^3)b + (\Sigma x^4)c = \Sigma x^2 y$

13. $u = \dfrac{t - 50}{10}$ gives -1, 0 and 1 for values of u. $v = \dfrac{x - 0 \cdot 3}{0 \cdot 1}$ gives -1
and 1 for values of v.   Regression equation is then found to be
$y = 43 \cdot 6 + 3 \cdot 75u + 2v$ i.e. $y = 18 \cdot 917 + 0 \cdot 375t + 20x$.   When $t = 70$
and $x = 0 \cdot 5$, $y = 55 \cdot 2$.

14. As values of y are only given to 2 d.p., values of u, where
$u = (x - \mu)/\sigma$, can only be given to 1 d.p.   They are, in order, $-1 \cdot 0$,
$-0 \cdot 4$, $0 \cdot 2$, $0 \cdot 8$, $1 \cdot 4$.   Relationship between u and x is of the form
$u = \alpha + \beta x$, where $\alpha = -\mu/\sigma$ and $\beta = 1/\sigma$.   Normal equations give
$a = -17 \cdot 8$, $b = 0 \cdot 6$, whence estimates of μ and σ are $29 \cdot 67$ and $1 \cdot 67$
respectively. $y = 0 \cdot 75$ gives $u = 0 \cdot 7$, whence $x = 30 \cdot 8$.

15. $y = 3 \cdot 2 + 14 \cdot 09x$ $11 \cdot 2^{\cdot}$ and $17 \cdot 0$

APPENDIX

When the regression line $y = \alpha + \beta x$ is estimated by $y = a + bx$, based on n pairs of observations, the relevant confidence intervals are based on the results given below.

Sampling Distribution of b

$$b = \frac{\Sigma(x - \bar{x})(y - \bar{y})}{\Sigma(x - \bar{x})^2}$$

Now
$$\begin{aligned}
\Sigma(x - \bar{x})(y - \bar{y}) &= \Sigma\{(x - \bar{x})y - x\bar{y} + \bar{x}\bar{y}\} \\
&= \Sigma(x - \bar{x})y - \bar{y}\Sigma x + n\bar{x}\bar{y} \\
&= \Sigma(x - \bar{x})y \quad \text{as} \quad n\bar{x} = \Sigma x
\end{aligned}$$

Hence $b = \dfrac{\Sigma(x - \bar{x})y}{\Sigma(x - \bar{x})^2} = \dfrac{1}{\Sigma(x - \bar{x})^2}\{(x_1 - \bar{x})y_1 + (x_2 - \bar{x})y_2 + \ldots + (x_n - \bar{x})y_n\}$

Now, in the regression of y on x, we are considering how y is subject to random variation for fixed values of x. Thus $\dfrac{x_1 - \bar{x}}{\Sigma(x - \bar{x})^2}, \dfrac{x_2 - \bar{x}}{\Sigma(x - \bar{x})^2}, \ldots$ $\dfrac{x_n - \bar{x}}{\Sigma(x - \bar{x})^2}$ are to be regarded as constants, which we will denote by $a_1, a_2, \ldots, a_n$ respectively. We then have $b = a_1 y_1 + a_2 y_2 + \ldots + a_n y_n$ where $y_1, y_2, \ldots y_n$ are independent random variables, and results (1) and (2) of FRAME 50 on page 142 apply.

$$\begin{aligned}
\text{mean}(b) &= a_1 \times \text{mean}(y_1) + a_2 \times \text{mean}(y_2) + \ldots + a_n \times \text{mean}(y_n) \\
&= a_1(\alpha + \beta x_1) + a_2(\alpha + \beta x_2) + \ldots + a_n(\alpha + \beta x_n) \\
&= (a_1 + a_2 + \ldots + a_n)\alpha + (a_1 x_1 + a_2 x_2 + \ldots + a_n x_n)\beta
\end{aligned}$$

Now $a_1 + a_2 + \ldots + a_n = \dfrac{(x_1 - \bar{x}) + (x_2 - \bar{x}) + \ldots + (x_n - \bar{x})}{\Sigma(x - \bar{x})^2} = 0$

and $a_1 x_1 + a_2 x_2 + \ldots + a_n x_n = \dfrac{(x_1 - \bar{x})x_1 + (x_2 - \bar{x})x_2 + \ldots + (x_n - \bar{x})x_n}{\Sigma(x - \bar{x})^2}$

$$= \frac{\Sigma x^2 - \bar{x}\Sigma x}{\Sigma(x - \bar{x})^2} = \frac{\Sigma(x - \bar{x})^2}{\Sigma(x - \bar{x})^2} = 1$$

$\therefore \quad \text{mean}(b) = \beta$

$$\begin{aligned}
\text{var}(b) &= a_1^2\,\text{var}(y_1) + a_2^2\,\text{var}(y_2) + \ldots + a_n^2\,\text{var}(y_n) \\
&= a_1^2\sigma^2 + a_2^2\sigma^2 + \ldots + a_n^2\sigma^2 \quad \text{where } \sigma^2 \text{ is the common variance} \\
&\qquad\qquad\qquad\qquad\qquad\qquad\qquad \text{assumed in the model} \\
&= \frac{\sigma^2}{\{\Sigma(x - \bar{x})^2\}^2}\left\{(x_1 - \bar{x})^2 + (x_2 - \bar{x})^2 + \ldots + (x_n - \bar{x})^2\right\} = \frac{\sigma^2}{\Sigma(x - \bar{x})^2}
\end{aligned}$$

As the model assumes normal distributions for $y_1, y_2, \ldots, y_n$, the distribution of b will also be normal.

Sampling Distribution of a

$$a = \bar{y} - b\bar{x}$$

Applying results (1) and (2) previously referred to,

$$\text{mean}(a) = \text{mean}(\overline{y}) - \overline{x} \times \text{mean}(b) = \alpha + \beta\overline{x} - \beta\overline{x} = \alpha$$

$$\text{var}(a) = \text{var}(\overline{y}) + \overline{x}^2 \text{var}(b)$$

$$= \frac{\sigma^2}{n} + \overline{x}^2 \frac{\sigma^2}{\Sigma(x - \overline{x})^2} = \sigma^2 \frac{\Sigma(x - \overline{x})^2 + n\overline{x}^2}{n\Sigma(x - \overline{x})^2}$$

$$= \frac{\sigma^2 \Sigma x^2}{n\Sigma(x - \overline{x})^2}$$

It follows from the assumptions of the model that the distributions of $\overline{y}$ and b are normal and hence that of a will also be normal.

Sampling Distribution of $a + bx_0$

Applying results (1) and (2) previously referred to,

$$\text{mean}(a + bx_0) = \text{mean}(a) + x_0 \times \text{mean}(b)$$

$$= \alpha + \beta x_0$$

As $a + bx_0 = \hat{y}_0 = \overline{y} + b(x_0 - \overline{x})$

$$\text{var}(a + bx_0) = \text{var}(\overline{y}) + (x_0 - \overline{x})^2 \text{var}(b)$$

$$= \frac{\sigma^2}{n} + (x_0 - \overline{x})^2 \frac{\sigma^2}{\Sigma(x - \overline{x})^2}$$

$$= \sigma^2 \left\{ \frac{1}{n} + \frac{(x_0 - \overline{x})^2}{\Sigma(x - \overline{x})^2} \right\}$$

The distribution of $a + bx_0$ is normal - this follows, as before, from the assumptions of the model.

Note that putting $x_0 = 0$ gives the results obtained above for the sampling distribution of a.

UNIT 3—Revision Examples

1. (i) Show that $\displaystyle\sum_{i=1}^{k}\sum_{j=1}^{n}(x_{ij} - \bar{x})^2$ can be expressed in the form

$$\sum_{i=1}^{k}\sum_{j=1}^{n}(x_{ij} - \bar{x}_i)^2 + \sum_{i=1}^{k}n(\bar{x}_i - \bar{x})^2 \quad \text{where} \quad \bar{x} = \frac{1}{nk}\sum_{i=1}^{k}\sum_{j=1}^{n}x_{ij}$$

and $\displaystyle \bar{x}_i = \frac{1}{n}\sum_{j=1}^{n}x_{ij}$.

   (ii) Samples of four makes of tyre were tested under identical conditions for braking distances, with the following results:

Trial	1	2	3	4
Brand A	27	30	25	26
Brand B	25	20	22	21
Brand C	27	31	30	32
Brand D	26	26	25	23

Test at a level of significance of 1% whether the differences between the mean braking distances obtained for the four makes of tyre are significant.   (C.E.I.)

(In (ii), we suggest that you calculate the sums of squares in the original form, as given in (i), instead of using the alternative versions usually adopted for computational purposes.   This will serve as a reminder of what the sums of squares actually represent.)

2. The animal feed sold by a firm contains a growth regulator.   It is important that, in the production process, mixing is thorough, so that the growth regulator is uniformly distributed.   As a check on this, after 30 minutes agitation in a ribbon blender, the blend was discharged into a drum.   Samples of the blend were taken, one from each of the top, middle and bottom of the drum.   Four analyses were made on each sample giving the results shown for percentage (by weight) of growth regulator.   Assuming that the analytical error variance was the same throughout, obtain an estimate of it and decide whether it offers a reasonable explanation of the differences between the estimates of the amount of regulator present in the different parts of the drum.

Top	Middle	Bottom
2·32	2·20	2·29
2·25	2·26	2·21
2·36	2·35	2·14
2·23	2·27	2·24

3. The table gives readings by four operators making hardness tests on each of five blocks of metal.

Operator	Blocks				
	a	b	c	d	e
A	733	735	739	732	730
B	731	731	736	732	738
C	732	732	734	732	734
D	736	736	736	735	739

Explain how to find the following sums of squares:

> sum of squares between operators = 36·55,
> sum of squares between blocks   = 37·30,
> total sum of squares = 138·55.

Complete the two-factor analysis of variance and comment on the results.

(L.U.)

4. Determinations of percentage paste strength were carried out on four different batches of a chemical paste product by three different laboratories (the customer's, the supplier's and an independent one), giving the following results:

Batch	Customer's	Laboratory Supplier's	Independent
1	62	60	63
2	60	58	61
3	59	64	65
4	57	58	65

Use an analysis of variance technique to find whether, at the 5% level of significance, there is (i) a significant difference between the laboratories in their determinations of paste strength, (ii) a significant difference between the paste strengths of the four batches.

5. Four workshops in the same factory are producing quantities of a machined article.   The numbers of finished articles that were rejected by an inspector are listed under the headings of workshops A, B, C, D and shifts a, b, c in the following table:

	A	B	C	D
a	20	24	28	30
b	21	25	27	31
c	19	22	16	32

Discuss the variability of these results with regard (i) to shifts, (ii) to workshops. (L.U.)

6. Before being appointed to their job, salesmen in a certain firm are subjected to psychological tests.   The eight men listed below all joined the firm at the same time and, after a year, the sales manager was asked to assess their value to the firm by ranking them in order of their selling ability.   This assessment is now compared with the ranking given by the tests, to see how good an indication these tests give of salesmanship potential.   Calculate Spearman's rank correlation coefficient for making this comparison.

Salesman	Rank given by sales manager	Rank given by psychological tests
T. Pearce	1	2
W. Brewer	2	1
J. Stewer	3	7
P. Gurney	4	4
P. Davey	5	8
D. Widdon	6	3
H. Hawke	7	5
T. Cobley	8	6

7. In a study of the effectiveness of a drug in lowering the heart rate in
    adults, observations were made on the reduction in heart rate (in beats
    per minute) following the administration of selected levels of dosage
    (in mg).   The results were as shown below.

Dose x	0·75	1·00	1·25	1·50	1·75	2·00	2·25	2·50	2·75	3·00	3·25
Reduction y	8	12	11	13	13	16	18	17	19	18	20

Display the data on a scatter diagram.   If $y = a + bu$ estimates the
equation of the regression line of y on u, where $u = 4(x - 2)$, obtain
and solve the normal equations in a and b.   Deduce the corresponding
equation relating y and x and draw, on the scatter diagram, the line that
it represents.   Comment on the result of substituting $x = 0$ in the
equation that you have obtained.

8. If $y = a + bx$ represents the equation of the regression line of y on x,
    and $x = a' + b'y$ that of x on y, estimated from a sample of n data
    points, what equation connects b, b' and r, where r is the value of the
    correlation coefficient given by the sample?   If $\bar{x}$ and $\bar{y}$ are the means
    of the x- and y-observations respectively, express (i) a in terms of b,
    $\bar{x}$ and $\bar{y}$, (ii) a' in terms of b', $\bar{x}$ and $\bar{y}$.

    The equation of the regression line of y on x is estimated from a sample
    to be $y = 14 - 0\cdot8x$ and that of x on y, from the same sample, to be
    $x = 7 - 0\cdot2y$.   What value of the correlation coefficient r is given by
    this sample and what are the values of $\bar{x}$ and $\bar{y}$?

9. The relation between breaking strength of yarn and humidity has, in the
    past, been influential in determining the location of centres of the
    textile industry.   The table shows 15 pairs of observations, y being
    yarn breaking strength (in appropriate units) and x percentage humidity.

y	104	100	105	115	97	100	96	106	120	114	122	103	110	111	117
x	76	69	52	63	57	45	44	58	65	63	82	46	52	56	72

With $x' = x - 60$ and $y' = y - 100$, calculations give $\Sigma x' = 0$,
$\Sigma y' = 120$, $\Sigma x'^2 = 1842$, $\Sigma y'^2 = 1926$, $\Sigma x'y' = 794$.

   (i)   Plot the points on a scatter diagram.

  (ii)   By calculating r, confirm that the data shows a significant linear
          correlation between yarn strength and humidity, at the 5% level.

 (iii)   Estimate the equations of (a) the line of regression of y on x,
          (b) the line of regression of x on y.   Check that you have
          obtained two different equations, i.e. one is not just a
          rearrangement of the other.   For what value of r would the two
          equations have been the same?   What is the point of intersection
          of the two lines whose equations you have found?   Draw both lines
          on the diagram in (i).   Which line do you think would be of
          interest in this particular situation?

10. u |1·9 3·0 3·5 2·0 4·6 3·0 5·0 4·1 3·6 3·7 3·1 4·7 4·3 4·0 3·5 3·6
     v |5·2 5·4 4·9 5·4 7·3 6·2 7·7 6·0 6·7 6·4 5·6 7·2 8·1 6·7 8·3 6·9

The table shows data recorded on the oxygen consumption per minute, v,
by 16 newborn infants in incubators, when heating methods were being
investigated.   To make allowance for the size of the infant, v is given
as volume of oxygen in ml/mass of infant in kg: u is the temperature
gradient (i.e. increase in temperature per unit distance) between foot

skin and incubator roof.   Calculations give $\Sigma u = 57\cdot6$, $\Sigma v = 104\cdot0$, $\Sigma(u - \bar{u})^2 = 11\cdot52$, $\Sigma(v - \bar{v})^2 = 16\cdot44$, $\Sigma(u - \bar{u})(v - \bar{v}) = 9\cdot43$.

   (i)   Calculate the value of r, the correlation coefficient, for this
         sample.   Does it provide evidence of a linear correlation between
         oxygen consumption and temperature gradient at (a) the 5%
         significance level, (b) the 1% significance level?

   (ii) If you required to know the mean oxygen consumption by infants
         when the temperature gradient is given, would this information be
         provided by (a) the regression curve of v on u, or (b) the
         regression curve of u on v?   Taking the regression to be linear,
         estimate the equation of whichever line you consider appropriate.
         Show, by setting up a variance analysis table, that the slope of
         the estimated line differs significantly from zero, i.e. that there
         is good evidence that the two variables are linearly related.   What
         is the percentage fit of the regression line, i.e. what percentage
         of the total variation (as measured by the sum of squares) in
         oxygen consumption is explained by the regression on temperature
         gradient?

   (iii) When the temperature gradient is such that $u = 3\cdot6$, find a 90%
         confidence interval for infants' mean oxygen consumption and also
         an interval within which there is a 90% chance that an individual
         infant's oxygen consumption will fall.   Would these intervals be
         wider, narrower or the same (a) if 95% were substituted for 90%,
         (b) if a different temperature gradient were being considered?

11.   The total time required by a driver to bring a vehicle to a halt from the
      moment when he is alerted consists of the reaction time (i.e. the time
      between recognising the need to stop and applying the brakes) plus braking
      time (i.e. the time between the brakes being applied and the vehicle
      coming to a halt).   The distance travelled during the whole of this time
      was observed for a car when its speed at the instant of the alert was each
      of 5 selected values.   The results were:

Speed V (ms^{-1})	10	15	20	25	30
Distance D (m)	18	30	46	68	98

      By using a coding formula that will transform values of V into
      $x = -2, -1, 0, 1, 2$, or otherwise, obtain estimates of the parameters
      α, β, γ in the regression equation $D = \alpha + \beta V + \gamma V^2$.

12.   The determination of the number of red cells in a blood sample by using a
      microscope is time consuming and subject to considerable error.   Similar
      problems do not arise, however, with measurement of what is called "the
      packed cell volume" of the blood.   It would therefore be convenient to
      estimate the red blood cell count from the packed cell volume if a
      relationship between the two could be established.   Both were recorded
      for blood samples taken from 10 dogs with the results as shown in the
      table.

Packed cell volume (mm^3)	35	58	40	39	45	42	48	56	42	45
Red blood cell count (millions)	5$\cdot$73	9$\cdot$32	6$\cdot$03	6$\cdot$38	6$\cdot$55	6$\cdot$82	7$\cdot$33	9$\cdot$35	6$\cdot$13	6$\cdot$36

      The data gives a clear indication that the two variables are linearly
      correlated.   Find the equation that could be used for estimating red
      blood cell count from packed cell volume.

13. A method used in the assay of samples of penicillin involves allowing the penicillin solution to diffuse into a bulk-inoculated nutrient medium and then, after a period of incubation, measuring the diameter of the circular zone in which the growth of organisms has been inhibited. There is a functional relationship between the diameter of the zone and the concentration of penicillin in the solution. Thus, if this relationship can be determined it can be used (as a calibration curve, in effect) to estimate concentration from observed circle diameter. The following data resulted from measuring the diameter y produced by each of six penicillin solutions of known, selected concentration c (from 1 to 32 units per ml).

Concentration of penicillin solution c | 1   2   4   8   16   32
Diameter of zone of inhibition y (mm) | 15·5 17·4 19·1 20·9 22·7 24·4

There is a linear relationship between y and the logarithm of c. It is convenient to choose base 2, so that then, with $x = \log_2 c$, the values of x corresponding to the selected values of c will be x = 0, 1, 2, 3, 4, 5. Obtain an estimate of the relationship between y and x. (The values of c can be assumed to be without error.)

14. The number of defective items, y, produced by a machine per unit of time, is thought to be linearly related to the speed x (in revolutions per unit time) at which the machine is being operated. In 8 one-hour periods selected at random the following observations were recorded:

x | 13·1   14·8   8·0   16·3   13·0   10·7   10·8   17·3
y | 9·4   12·2   6·0   11·5   9·6   7·5   5·9   12·3

Estimate the equation of the line of regression of y on x. By setting up an ANOVA table, and making an F-test, show that there is very strong evidence of the existence of a linear relationship. Find 95% confidence limits for the slope of the regression line.

ANSWERS

1. (i) See FRAMES 23-24 on pages 343-4 (where the overall mean was denoted by $\bar{\bar{x}}$, not by $\bar{x}$ as here). (ii) $F_{12}^3 = 11·3 > 5·95$. Sig. at 1%.

2. $0·0342/9 = 0·0038$. $F_9^2 = 1·37 < 4·26$. Not sig. at 5%. This error variance offers a reasonable explanation of the differences.

3. Operator effect: $F_{12}^3 \simeq 2·26 < 3·49$. Not sig. at 5%.

   Block effect: $F_{12}^4 \simeq 1·73 < 3·26$. Not sig. at 5%.

   Thus no significant difference is revealed either between blocks or between operators.

4. (i) $F_6^2 = 3·8 < 5·14$. Not sig. at 5%. (ii) $F_6^3 = 1·2 < 4·76$. Not sig. at 5%.

5. (i) $F_6^2 \simeq 1·55 < 5·14$. No sig. difference between shifts at 5% level.

   (ii) $F_6^3 \simeq 5·97 > 4·76$. Sig. difference between workshops at 5% level.

6. $r_s = 10/21 \simeq 0.476$.

7. $11a = 165$, $110b = 121$. $a = 15$, $b = 1.1$. $y = 6.2 + 4.4x$.   Substituting $x = 0$ gives $y = 6.2$, whereas obviously there would be no effect on heart rate if no drug were administered.   This illustrates the danger inherent in assuming the linear regression to extend beyond the range of the data on which it was based.

8. $bb' = r^2$ (i) $a = \bar{y} - b\bar{x}$ (ii) $a' = \bar{x} - b'\bar{y}$, $r = -0.4$, $\bar{x} = 5$, $\bar{y} = 10$.

9. (ii) $r = 0.595$.   Sig. at 5%, for 13 d.f.   (iii) (a) $y = 82.1 + 0.431x$ (b) $x = -28.8 + 0.822y$, $r = \pm 1$.   (60, 108)   (a), as one would want to see how yarn strength varies with humidity.   If the two variables are related, it is surely the yarn strength that is affected by the humidity and not the reverse.

10.   (i) $r = 0.685$ (a) Yes, as $|r| > 0.497$.   (b) Yes, as $|r| > 0.623$.
    (ii) (a). $v = 0.819u + 3.55$. $F_{14}^1 = 12.4 > 8.86$.   Sig. at 1% level.
       About 47%.
    (iii) 6.15 and 6.85, 5.07 and 7.93.   (a) Wider   (b) Wider

11. Estimated regression equation is $D = 14.8 - 0.84V + 0.12V^2$.

12. $y = -0.665 + 0.170x$, where $x =$ packed cell volume and $y =$ red blood cell count in millions.

13. $y = 15.56 + 1.777x$.   (This, representing a functional relationship, can then be used to estimate x, and hence c, from observed y.)

14. $y = -0.966 + 0.790x$. $F_6^1 = 43.8 > 13.7$.   Sig. at 1% level.
    0.50 and 1.08.

BIBLIOGRAPHY

Some books dealing with the application of statistical methods in specialised subject areas are:

Statistical Methods for Engineers, J.J. Leeming, Blackie 1963
Probability, Statistics and Decision for Civil Engineers, J.R. Benjamin and
C.A. Cornell, McGraw-Hill 1970
Statistical Models in Engineering, G.J. Hahn and S.S. Shapiro, John Wiley 1967
Reliability - a Mathematical Approach, A. Kaufmann, Transworld Publishers 1972
An Introduction to Reliability Engineering, R. Lewis, McGraw-Hill 1970
Statistical Methods for Quality Control, A.K.S. Jardine, J.D. Macfarlane and
C.S. Greensted, Heinemann 1975
I.C.I. Monograph No. 3 Cumulative Sum Techniques, R.H. Woodward and
P.L. Goldsmith, Oliver and Boyd 1964
Statistical Methods in Research and Production (4th edition), ed. O.L. Davies
and P.L. Goldsmith, Oliver and Boyd 1972
Statistical Methods for the Process Industries, M.H. Belz, Macmillan 1973
Statistical Methods for Textile Technologists, T. Murphy, K.P. Norris and
L.H.C. Tippett, Textile Institute 1963
An Outline of Statistical Methods for use in the Textile Industry, A. Brearley
and D.R. Cox, Wira 1974
An Introduction to Statistical Models in Geology, W.C. Krumbein and
F.A. Graybill, McGraw-Hill 1965
Statistics and Data Analysis in Geology, J.C. Davis, John Wiley 1973
Introductory Statistics for Biology, R.E. Parker, Edward Arnold 1973
Biostatistics, A. Goldstein, Macmillan 1964
Statistics for Biology, O.N. Bishop, Longman 1971
Biostatistics: A Foundation for Analysis in the Health Sciences, W.W. Daniel,
John Wiley 1974
Statistical Methods in Medical Research, P. Armitage, Blackwell 1971
Interpretation and Uses of Medical Statistics, G.J. Bourke and J. McGilvray,
Blackwell 1975
Elements of Medical Statistics, J.V. Smart, Staples Press 1970

Some collections of statistical tables which are available are:

Tables for Statisticians, J. White, A. Yeats, G. Skipworth, Stanley Thornes
Statistical Tables for Science, Engineering, Management and Business Studies,
J. Murdoch and J.A. Barnes, Macmillan
Biometrika Tables for Statisticians, ed. E.S. Pearson and H.O. Hartley,
Cambridge University Press
Statistical Tables for biological, agricultural and medical research,
R.A. Fisher and F. Yates, Oliver and Boyd

TABLE 1

THE NORMAL PROBABILITY INTEGRAL

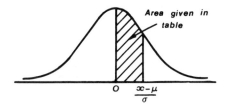

$\frac{x-\mu}{\sigma}$	0	1	2	3	4	5	6	7	8	9
0·0	0000	0040	0080	0120	0160	0199	0239	0279	0319	0359
0·1	0398	0438	0478	0517	0557	0596	0636	0675	0714	0753
0·2	0793	0832	0871	0910	0948	0987	1026	1064	1103	1141
0·3	1179	1217	1255	1293	1331	1368	1406	1443	1480	1517
0·4	1554	1591	1628	1664	1700	1736	1772	1808	1844	1879
0·5	1915	1950	1985	2019	2054	2088	2123	2157	2190	2224
0·6	2257	2291	2324	2357	2389	2422	2454	2486	2517	2549
0·7	2580	2611	2642	2673	2704	2734	2764	2794	2823	2852
0·8	2881	2910	2939	2967	2995	3023	3051	3078	3106	3133
0·9	3159	3186	3212	3238	3264	3289	3315	3340	3365	3389
1·0	3413	3438	3461	3485	3508	3531	3554	3577	3599	3621
1·1	3643	3665	3686	3708	3729	3749	3770	3790	3810	3830
1·2	3849	3869	3888	3907	3925	3944	3962	3980	3997	4015
1·3	4032	4049	4066	4082	4099	4115	4131	4147	4162	4177
1·4	4192	4207	4222	4236	4251	4265	4279	4292	4306	4319
1·5	4332	4345	4357	4370	4382	4394	4406	4418	4429	4441
1·6	4452	4463	4474	4484	4495	4505	4515	4525	4535	4545
1·7	4554	4564	4573	4582	4591	4599	4608	4616	4625	4633
1·8	4641	4649	4656	4664	4671	4678	4686	4693	4699	4706
1·9	4713	4719	4726	4732	4738	4744	4750	4756	4761	4767
2·0	4772	4778	4783	4788	4793	4798	4803	4808	4812	4817
2·1	4821	4826	4830	4834	4838	4842	4846	4850	4854	4857
2·2	4861	4864	4868	4871	4875	4878	4881	4884	4887	4890
2·3	4893	4896	4898	4901	4904	4906	4909	4911	4913	4916
2·4	4918	4920	4922	4925	4927	4929	4931	4932	4934	4936
2·5	4938	4940	4941	4943	4945	4946	4948	4949	4951	4952
2·6	4953	4955	4956	4957	4959	4960	4961	4962	4963	4964
2·7	4965	4966	4967	4968	4969	4970	4971	4972	4973	4974
2·8	4974	4975	4976	4977	4977	4978	4979	4979	4980	4981
2·9	4981	4982	4982	4983	4984	4984	4985	4985	4986	4986

$\frac{x-\mu}{\sigma}$	3·0	3·1	3·2	3·3	3·4	3·5	3·6	3·7	3·8	3·9
	4987	4990	4993	4995	4997	4998	4998	4999	4999	5000

The decimal point preceding each entry has been omitted.

TABLE 2

PERCENTAGE POINTS OF THE STANDARD NORMAL DISTRIBUTION

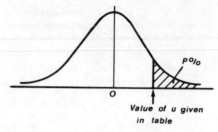

Value of u given in table

P	50	25	20	15	10	5
(2P)	(100)	(50)	(40)	(30)	(20)	(10)
u	0·00	0·67	0·84	1·04	1·28	1·64

P	2·5	2	1	0·5	0·1	0·05
(2P)	(5)	(4)	(2)	(1)	(0·2)	(0·1)
u	1·96	2·05	2·33	2·58	3·09	3·29

The values of 2P correspond to the area under two tails.

For example, taking P = 2·5, there is a

       2·5% probability that u > 1·96
         5% probability that |u| > 1·96
      95% probability that −1·96 < u < 1·96

The same applies to TABLE 3 on the opposite page.

For example, taking P = 2·5, for the t-distribution with 9 degrees of freedom there is a

       2·5% probability that t > 2·26
         5% probability that |t| > 2·26
      95% probability that −2·26 < t < 2·26

TABLE 3

PERCENTAGE POINTS OF THE t-DISTRIBUTION

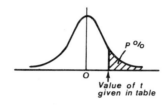

Value of t given in table

P (2P)	10 (20)	5 (10)	2·5 (5)	1 (2)	0·5 (1)	0·1 (0·2)	0·05 (0·1)
1	3·08	6·31	12·7	31·8	63·7	318	637
2	1·89	2·92	4·30	6·96	9·92	22·3	31·6
3	1·64	2·35	3·18	4·54	5·84	10·2	12·9
4	1·53	2·13	2·78	3·75	4·60	7·17	8·61
5	1·48	2·02	2·57	3·36	4·03	5·89	6·87
6	1·44	1·94	2·45	3·14	3·71	5·21	5·96
7	1·41	1·89	2·36	3·00	3·50	4·78	5·41
8	1·40	1·86	2·31	2·90	3·36	4·50	5·04
9	1·38	1·83	2·26	2·82	3·25	4·30	4·78
10	1·37	1·81	2·23	2·76	3·17	4·14	4·59
11	1·36	1·80	2·20	2·72	3·11	4·02	4·44
12	1·36	1·78	2·18	2·68	3·05	3·93	4·32
13	1·35	1·77	2·16	2·65	3·01	3·85	4·22
14	1·34	1·76	2·14	2·62	2·98	3·79	4·14
15	1·34	1·75	2·13	2·60	2·95	3·73	4·07
16	1·34	1·75	2·12	2·58	2·92	3·69	4·02
17	1·33	1·74	2·11	2·57	2·90	3·65	3·96
18	1·33	1·73	2·10	2·55	2·88	3·61	3·92
19	1·33	1·73	2·09	2·54	2·86	3·58	3·88
20	1·33	1·72	2·09	2·53	2·85	3·55	3·85
21	1·32	1·72	2·08	2·52	2·83	3·53	3·82
22	1·32	1·72	2·07	2·51	2·82	3·50	3·79
23	1·32	1·71	2·07	2·50	2·81	3·48	3·77
24	1·32	1·71	2·06	2·49	2·80	3·47	3·74
25	1·32	1·71	2·06	2·49	2·79	3·45	3·72
26	1·32	1·71	2·06	2·48	2·78	3·44	3·71
27	1·31	1·70	2·05	2·47	2·77	3·42	3·69
28	1·31	1·70	2·05	2·47	2·76	3·41	3·67
29	1·31	1·70	2·05	2·46	2·76	3·40	3·66
30	1·31	1·70	2·04	2·46	2·75	3·38	3·65
40	1·30	1·68	2·02	2·42	2·70	3·31	3·55
60	1·30	1·67	2·00	2·39	2·66	3·23	3·46
120	1·29	1·66	1·98	2·36	2·62	3·16	3·37
∞	1·28	1·64	1·96	2·33	2·58	3·09	3·29

Degrees of Freedom ν

TABLE 4

PERCENTAGE POINTS OF THE F-DISTRIBUTION

The three values of F given for each combination of ν_1, ν_2 correspond to

$$P = \begin{cases} 5 \\ 2 \cdot 5 \\ 1 \end{cases}$$

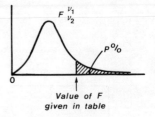

Value of F
given in table

ν_2 \ ν_1	1	2	3	4	5	6	7	8	10	12	24	∞
	Degrees of freedom for numerator											
1	161	200	216	225	230	234	237	239	242	244	249	254
	648	800	864	900	922	937	948	957	969	977	997	1018
	4052	5000	5403	5625	5764	5859	5928	5981	6056	6106	6235	6366
2	18·5	19·0	19·2	19·2	19·3	19·3	19·4	19·4	19·4	19·4	19·5	19·5
	38·5	39·0	39·2	39·2	39·3	39·3	39·4	39·4	39·4	39·4	39·5	39·5
	98·5	99·0	99·2	99·2	99·3	99·3	99·4	99·4	99·4	99·4	99·5	99·5
3	10·1	9·55	9·28	9·12	9·01	8·94	8·89	8·85	8·79	8·74	8·64	8·53
	17·4	16·0	15·4	15·1	14·9	14·7	14·6	14·5	14·4	14·3	14·1	13·9
	34·1	30·8	29·5	28·7	28·2	27·9	27·7	27·5	27·2	27·1	26·6	26·1
4	7·71	6·94	6·59	6·39	6·26	6·16	6·09	6·04	5·96	5·91	5·77	5·63
	12·2	10·6	9·98	9·60	9·36	9·20	9·07	8·98	8·84	8·75	8·51	8·26
	21·2	18·0	16·7	16·0	15·5	15·2	15·0	14·8	14·5	14·4	13·9	13·5
5	6·61	5·79	5·41	5·19	5·05	4·95	4·88	4·82	4·74	4·68	4·53	4·36
	10·0	8·43	7·76	7·39	7·15	6·98	6·85	6·76	6·62	6·52	6·28	6·02
	16·3	13·3	12·1	11·4	11·0	10·7	10·5	10·3	10·1	9·89	9·47	9·02
6	5·99	5·14	4·76	4·53	4·39	4·28	4·21	4·15	4·06	4·00	3·84	3·67
	8·81	7·26	6·60	6·23	5·99	5·82	5·70	5·60	5·46	5·37	5·12	4·85
	13·7	10·9	9·78	9·15	8·75	8·47	8·26	8·10	7·87	7·72	7·31	6·88
7	5·59	4·74	4·35	4·12	3·97	3·87	3·79	3·73	3·64	3·57	3·41	3·23
	8·07	6·54	5·89	5·52	5·29	5·12	4·99	4·90	4·76	4·67	4·42	4·14
	12·2	9·55	8·45	7·85	7·46	7·19	6·99	6·84	6·62	6·47	6·07	5·65
8	5·32	4·46	4·07	3·84	3·69	3·58	3·50	3·44	3·35	3·28	3·12	2·93
	7·57	6·06	5·42	5·05	4·82	4·65	4·53	4·43	4·30	4·20	3·95	3·67
	11·3	8·65	7·59	7·01	6·63	6·37	6·18	6·03	5·81	5·67	5·28	4·86
9	5·12	4·26	3·86	3·63	3·48	3·37	3·29	3·23	3·14	3·07	2·90	2·71
	7·21	5·71	5·08	4·72	4·48	4·32	4·20	4·10	3·96	3·87	3·61	3·33
	10·6	8·02	6·99	6·42	6·06	5·80	5·61	5·47	5·26	5·11	4·73	4·31

Degrees of freedom for denominator

ν_2 \ ν_1	Degrees of freedom for numerator											
	1	2	3	4	5	6	7	8	10	12	24	∞
10	4·96	4·10	3·71	3·48	3·33	3·22	3·14	3·07	2·98	2·91	2·74	2·54
	6·94	5·46	4·83	4·47	4·24	4·07	3·95	3·85	3·72	3·62	3·37	3·08
	10·0	7·56	6·55	5·99	5·64	5·39	5·20	5·06	4·85	4·71	4·33	3·91
11	4·84	3·98	3·59	3·36	3·20	3·09	3·01	2·95	2·85	2·79	2·61	2·40
	6·72	5·26	4·63	4·28	4·04	3·88	3·76	3·66	3·53	3·43	3·17	2·88
	9·65	7·21	6·22	5·67	5·32	5·07	4·89	4·74	4·54	4·40	4·02	3·60
12	4·75	3·89	3·49	3·26	3·11	3·00	2·91	2·85	2·75	2·69	2·51	2·30
	6·55	5·10	4·47	4·12	3·89	3·73	3·61	3·51	3·37	3·28	3·02	2·72
	9·33	6·93	5·95	5·41	5·06	4·82	4·64	4·50	4·30	4·16	3·78	3·36
14	4·60	3·74	3·34	3·11	2·96	2·85	2·76	2·70	2·60	2·53	2·35	2·13
	6·30	4·86	4·24	3·89	3·66	3·50	3·38	3·29	3·15	3·05	2·79	2·49
	8·86	6·51	5·56	5·04	4·70	4·46	4·28	4·14	3·94	3·80	3·43	3·00
16	4·49	3·63	3·24	3·01	2·85	2·74	2·66	2·59	2·49	2·42	2·24	2·01
	6·12	4·69	4·08	3·73	3·50	3·34	3·22	3·12	2·99	2·89	2·63	2·32
	8·53	6·23	5·29	4·77	4·44	4·20	4·03	3·89	3·69	3·55	3·18	2·75
18	4·41	3·55	3·16	2·93	2·77	2·66	2·58	2·51	2·41	2·34	2·15	1·92
	5·98	4·56	3·95	3·61	3·38	3·22	3·10	3·01	2·87	2·77	2·50	2·19
	8·29	6·01	5·09	4·58	4·25	4·01	3·84	3·71	3·51	3·37	3·00	2·57
20	4·35	3·49	3·10	2·87	2·71	2·60	2·51	2·45	2·35	2·28	2·08	1·84
	5·87	4·46	3·86	3·51	3·29	3·13	3·01	2·91	2·77	2·68	2·41	2·09
	8·10	5·85	4·94	4·43	4·10	3·87	3·70	3·56	3·37	3·23	2·86	2·42
24	4·26	3·40	3·01	2·78	2·62	2·51	2·42	2·36	2·25	2·18	1·98	1·73
	5·72	4·32	3·72	3·38	3·15	2·99	2·87	2·78	2·64	2·54	2·27	1·94
	7·82	5·61	4·72	4·22	3·90	3·67	3·50	3·36	3·17	3·03	2·66	2·21
30	4·17	3·32	2·92	2·69	2·53	2·42	2·33	2·27	2·16	2·09	1·89	1·62
	5·57	4·18	3·59	3·25	3·03	2·87	2·75	2·65	2·51	2·41	2·14	1·79
	7·56	5·39	4·51	4·02	3·70	3·47	3·30	3·17	2·98	2·84	2·47	2·01
40	4·08	3·23	2·84	2·61	2·45	2·34	2·25	2·18	2·08	2·00	1·79	1·51
	5·42	4·05	3·46	3·13	2·90	2·74	2·62	2·53	2·39	2·29	2·01	1·64
	7·31	5·18	4·31	3·83	3·51	3·29	3·12	2·99	2·80	2·66	2·29	1·80
60	4·00	3·15	2·76	2·53	2·37	2·25	2·17	2·10	1·99	1·92	1·70	1·39
	5·29	3·93	3·34	3·01	2·79	2·63	2·51	2·41	2·27	2·17	1·88	1·48
	7·08	4·98	4·13	3·65	3·34	3·12	2·95	2·82	2·63	2·50	2·12	1·60
120	3·92	3·07	2·68	2·45	2·29	2·18	2·09	2·02	1·91	1·83	1·61	1·25
	5·15	3·80	3·23	2·89	2·67	2·52	2·39	2·30	2·16	2·05	1·76	1·31
	6·85	4·79	3·95	3·48	3·17	2·96	2·79	2·66	2·47	2·34	1·95	1·38
∞	3·84	3·00	2·60	2·37	2·21	2·10	2·01	1·94	1·83	1·75	1·52	1·00
	5·02	3·69	3·12	2·79	2·57	2·41	2·29	2·19	2·05	1·94	1·64	1·00
	6·63	4·61	3·78	3·32	3·02	2·80	2·64	2·51	2·32	2·18	1·79	1·00

Degrees of freedom for denominator

440

TABLE 5

PERCENTAGE POINTS OF THE χ^2-DISTRIBUTION

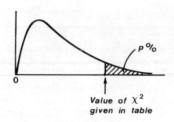

Value of χ^2
given in table

P ν	99·5	99	97·5	95	90	10	5	2·5	1	0·5	0·1
1	0·00	0·00	0·00	0·00	0·02	2·71	3·84	5·02	6·63	7·88	10·83
2	0·01	0·02	0·05	0·10	0·21	4·61	5·99	7·38	9·21	10·60	13·82
3	0·07	0·11	0·22	0·35	0·58	6·25	7·81	9·35	11·34	12·84	16·27
4	0·21	0·30	0·48	0·71	1·06	7·78	9·49	11·14	13·28	14·86	18·47
5	0·41	0·55	0·83	1·15	1·61	9·24	11·07	12·83	15·09	16·75	20·52
6	0·68	0·87	1·24	1·64	2·20	10·64	12·59	14·45	16·81	18·55	22·46
7	0·99	1·24	1·69	2·17	2·83	12·02	14·07	16·01	18·48	20·28	24·32
8	1·34	1·65	2·18	2·73	3·49	13·36	15·51	17·53	20·09	21·96	26·12
9	1·73	2·09	2·70	3·33	4·17	14·68	16·92	19·02	21·67	23·59	27·88
10	2·16	2·56	3·25	3·94	4·87	15·99	18·31	20·48	23·21	25·19	29·59
11	2·60	3·05	3·82	4·57	5·58	17·28	19·68	21·92	24·72	26·76	31·26
12	3·07	3·57	4·40	5·23	6·30	18·55	21·03	23·34	26·22	28·30	32·91
13	3·57	4·11	5·01	5·89	7·04	19·81	22·36	24·74	27·69	29·82	34·53
14	4·07	4·66	5·63	6·57	7·79	21·06	23·68	26·12	29·14	31·32	36·12
15	4·60	5·23	6·26	7·26	8·55	22·31	25·00	27·49	30·58	32·80	37·70
16	5·14	5·81	6·91	7·96	9·31	23·54	26·30	28·85	32·00	34·27	39·25
17	5·70	6·41	7·56	8·67	10·09	24·77	27·59	30·19	33·41	35·72	40·79
18	6·26	7·01	8·23	9·39	10·86	25·99	28·87	31·53	34·81	37·16	42·31
19	6·84	7·63	8·91	10·12	11·65	27·20	30·14	32·85	36·19	38·58	43·82
20	7·43	8·26	9·59	10·85	12·44	28·41	31·41	34·17	37·57	40·00	45·32
21	8·03	8·90	10·28	11·59	13·24	29·62	32·67	35·48	38·93	41·40	46·80
22	8·64	9·54	10·98	12·34	14·04	30·81	33·92	36·78	40·29	42·80	48·27
23	9·26	10·20	11·69	13·09	14·85	32·01	35·17	38·08	41·64	44·18	49·73
24	9·89	10·86	12·40	13·85	15·66	33·20	36·42	39·36	42·98	45·56	51·18
25	10·52	11·52	13·12	14·61	16·47	34·38	37·65	40·65	44·31	46·93	52·62
26	11·16	12·20	13·84	15·38	17·29	35·56	38·89	41·92	45·64	48·29	54·05
27	11·81	12·88	14·57	16·15	18·11	36·74	40·11	43·19	46·96	49·64	55·48
28	12·46	13·56	15·31	16·93	18·94	37·92	41·34	44·46	48·28	50·99	56·89
29	13·12	14·26	16·05	17·71	19·77	39·09	42·56	45·72	49·59	52·34	58·30
30	13·79	14·95	16·79	18·49	20·60	40·26	43·77	46·98	50·89	53·67	59·70
40	20·71	22·16	24·43	26·51	29·05	51·81	55·76	59·34	63·69	66·77	73·40
50	27·99	29·71	32·36	34·76	37·69	63·17	67·50	71·42	76·15	79·49	86·66
60	35·53	37·48	40·48	43·19	46·46	74·40	79·08	83·30	88·38	91·95	99·61
70	43·28	45·44	48·76	51·74	55·33	85·53	90·53	95·02	100·4	104·2	112·3
80	51·17	53·54	57·15	60·39	64·28	96·58	101·9	106·6	112·3	116·3	124·8
90	59·20	61·75	65·65	69·13	73·29	107·6	113·1	118·1	124·1	128·3	137·2
100	67·33	70·06	74·22	77·93	82·36	118·5	124·3	129·6	135·8	140·2	149·4

TABLE 6

THE CORRELATION COEFFICIENT

Percentage points of the distribution of the sample value (r) when the population value (ρ) is zero

2P / ν	10	5	1	0·1
1	·988	·997	1·00	1·00
2	·900	·950	·990	·999
3	·805	·878	·959	·991
4	·729	·811	·917	·974
5	·669	·754	·875	·951
6	·621	·707	·834	·925
7	·582	·666	·798	·898
8	·549	·632	·765	·872
9	·521	·602	·735	·847
10	·497	·576	·708	·823
11	·476	·553	·684	·801
12	·457	·532	·661	·780
13	·441	·514	·641	·760
14	·426	·497	·623	·742
15	·412	·482	·606	·725
16	·400	·468	·590	·708
17	·389	·456	·575	·693
18	·378	·444	·561	·679
19	·369	·433	·549	·665
20	·360	·423	·537	·652
25	·323	·381	·487	·597
30	·296	·349	·449	·554
35	·275	·325	·418	·519
40	·257	·304	·393	·490
45	·243	·288	·372	·465
50	·231	·273	·354	·443
60	·211	·250	·325	·408
70	·195	·232	·302	·380
80	·183	·217	·283	·357
90	·173	·205	·267	·338
100	·164	·195	·254	·321

ν = number of degrees of freedom = n − 2 if n = number of pairs of observations.
When ρ = 0, the probability of |r| exceeding the value in the table is 2P%.
For example, if r is based on a sample of 8 pairs of observations, there is

$$a \ 2 \cdot 5\% \ \text{probability that} \quad r < -0 \cdot 707$$
$$a \ 2 \cdot 5\% \ \text{probability that} \quad r > +0 \cdot 707$$
$$\text{and a} \quad 5\% \ \text{probability that} \quad |r| > 0 \cdot 707$$

442

INDEX

The two figures following each entry are respectively the page number and frame number.